AQA A

advanced Geography

AQA A

advanced Geography

Amanda Barker
David Redfern
Malcolm Skinner

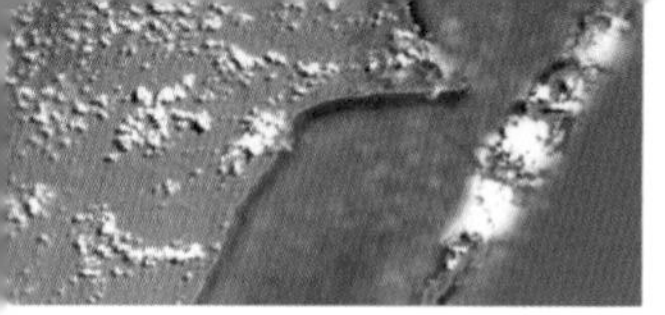

To Mike, from Amanda
To my sons, Michael and Andrew, from David
To my family, and to John Carter — 'where it all began', from Malcolm

Philip Allan Updates
Market Place, Deddington, Oxfordshire, OX15 0SE

Orders
Bookpoint Ltd, 130 Milton Park, Abingdon, Oxfordshire, OX14 4SB
tel: 01235 827720
fax: 01235 400454
e-mail: uk.orders@bookpoint.co.uk
Lines are open 9.00 a.m.–5.00 p.m., Monday to Saturday, with a 24-hour message answering service. You can also order through the Philip Allan Updates website: www.philipallan.co.uk

ISBN-13: 978-1-84489-426-0
ISBN-10: 1-84489-426-6

Front cover photographs reproduced by permission of TopFoto, Grahame Austin/Kitchenham.

Printed in Great Britain by CPI Bath.

Philip Allan Updates' policy is to use papers that are natural, renewable and recyclable products and made from wood grown in sustainable forests. The logging and manufacturing processes are expected to conform to the environmental regulations of the country of origin.

P00920

Contents

Assessment exercises

AS Module 3 Geographical skills

Chapter 7 Geographical skills

Assessment exercises

A2 Module 4 Challenge and change in the natural environment

Chapter 8 Coast processes and problems

Chapter 9 Geomorphological processes and hazards

Chapter 10 Cold environments and human activity

Assessment exercises

A2 Module 5 Challenge and change in the human environment

Introduction

This textbook provides a resource specifically for AQA specification A in AS and A2 geography. It covers the subject content of the specification, module by module, as it is laid out in the specification document, and forms a backbone for studies of AQA (A) geography. However, it should be supplemented by reference to topical sources of information including newspapers, television, periodicals aimed at post-16 geography students and the internet.

The following are key features of the content:

- concepts are clearly and concisely explained, and related issues are explored and analysed
- relevant, up-to-date and detailed case studies are provided
- a variety of stimulus material is provided, including full-colour maps, graphs, diagrams and photographs
- sample examination questions are included at the end of each module.
- the skills required for the modules that assess practical abilities are covered in depth

The sample questions included can be used for formal or informal assessment. Further advice and guidance can be found in the Unit Guides for AQA (A) Modules 1, 2 and 4, also published by Philip Allan Updates.

An overview of AQA (A) geography

This specification enables students to follow a thematic people–environment approach to geography throughout the course. It has a developmental structure designed to facilitate progression. Concepts covered at AS are revisited and further developed, but not repeated, at A2.

All students study a range of themes, places and environments at different scales and in different contexts, including **the UK and countries that are in various states of development**. At AS, it is important that students deal with at least one case study for each of the specification sub-sections. At A2, appropriate examples and case studies should be applied throughout the subject content.

The trend towards **global interdependence** is highlighted and it is important that students appreciate that this has economic, social and environmental dimensions, as well as political.

At appropriate points during the course, students have to analyse different **values and attitudes** (including their own), regarding a range of issues.

In order to satisfy the requirement for synoptic assessment, it is essential that students have an overview of the subject content as a whole, even though they may have chosen to concentrate detailed study on certain topics. The synoptic elements of Modules 4 and 5 require candidates to demonstrate this holistic overview.

Assessment Objectives

Like other geography specifications, AQA (A) has four Assessment Objectives. Candidates should:

- show knowledge of the specified content
- show critical understanding of the specified content
- apply knowledge and critical understanding to unfamiliar contexts
- select and use a variety of skills and techniques, including communication skills, appropriate to geographical studies

In addition to these, A2 candidates are required to develop:

- a deeper understanding of the connections between different aspects of geography represented in this specification
- a greater ability to synthesise geographical information in various forms and from various sources

Scheme of assessment

The scheme of assessment is modular. AS and A2 each consist of three modules and make up 50% of the total award.

AS

Unit 1 is based on Module 1. The exam lasts 1 hour, and consists of three structured physical geography questions, based on each of the sub-sections making up the module:

- Water on the land
- Climatic hazards and change
- Energy and life

All three questions are compulsory.

Unit 2 is based on Module 2. The exam lasts 1 hour and consists of three structured human geography questions, based on each of the sub-sections making up the module:

- Population dynamics
- Settlement processes and patterns
- Economic activity

All three questions are compulsory.

Unit 3 is based on the content of Modules 1 and 2. The exam lasts 1 hour. Students answer one of two questions, the choice being between a question on physical geography or one on human geography. The paper concerns geographical skills (Chapter 7). It is based on a topic given to centres well in advance and involves pre-release material.

A2

Units 4 and 5 have the same structure. In each case, the exam lasts 1 hour 30 minutes and consists of two sections.

Section A consists of three resource-based questions of which candidates have to answer two.

Section B consists of three essays from which the candidate must choose one. Answers are synoptically assessed.

Unit 4 is based on Module 4. One question in each section is based on each of the three sub-sections in the module, namely:

- Coast processes and problems
- Geomorphological processes and hazards
- Cold environments and human activity

Unit 5 is based on Module 5. One question in each section is based on each of the three sub-sections in the module, namely:

- Population pressure and resource management
- Managing cities: challenges and issues
- Recreation and tourism

Unit 6 is a fieldwork investigation at a local small scale. The report should consist of approximately 4,000 words. This is externally assessed.

Unit 7 is a written alternative to Unit 6. The exam lasts 2 hours and consists of a fieldwork enquiry tested under examination conditions and based on a pre-release information pack. All questions are compulsory. The topic for Unit 7 is released 2 years in advance of the examination and may be selected from the content of Modules 1, 2, 4 or 5.

Command words used in the examinations

One of the major challenges in any examination is interpreting the demands of the questions. Thorough revision is essential, but an awareness of what is expected in the examination itself is also required. Too often candidates attempt to answer the question they think is there rather than the one that is actually set. Answering an examination question is challenging enough, without the self-inflicted handicap of misreading the question.

Correct interpretation of the **command words** of a question is therefore very important. In AQA (A) geography examination papers, a variety of command words are used. Some demand more of the candidate than others; some require a simple task to be performed; others require greater intellectual thought and a longer response.

The notes below offer advice on the main command words that are used in both AS and A2 examinations.

Identify..., What...? Name..., State..., Give...

These words ask for brief answers to a simple task, such as:

- identifying a landform from a photograph
- giving a named example of a feature

Do not answer using a single word. It is always better to write a short sentence.

Define..., Explain the meaning of..., What is meant by...? Outline...

These words require a relatively short answer, usually two or three sentences, giving the precise meaning of a term. Use of an example is often helpful. The size of the mark allocation indicates the length of answer required.

Describe...

This is one of the most widely used command words. A factual decription is required, with no attempt to explain. Usually the question will give some clue about exactly what is to be described. Some examples are given below.

Describe the characteristics of...

In the case of a landform, for example, the following sub-questions can be useful in writing the answer:

- What does it look like?
- What is it made of?
- How big is it?
- Where is it in relation to other features?

Describe the changes in...

This command often relates to a graph or a table. Good use of accurate adverbs is required here — words such as rapidly, steeply, gently, slightly, greatly.

Describe the differences between...

Here only differences between two sets of data will be credited. It is better if these are presented as a series of separate sentences, each identifying one difference. Writing a paragraph on one data set, followed by a paragraph on the other, forces the examiner to complete the task on your behalf.

Describe the relationship between...

Here only the links between two sets of data will be credited. It is important, therefore, that you establish the relationship and state the link clearly. In most cases the relationship will either be positive (direct) or negative (inverse).

Describe the distribution of...

This is usually used in conjunction with a map or set of maps. A description of the location of high concentrations of a variable is required, together with a similar description of those areas with a lower concentration. Better answers will also tend to identify anomalous areas or areas which go against an overall trend in the distribution, for example a spot of high concentration in an area of predominantly low concentration.

Compare...

This requires a point by point account of the similarities and differences between two sets of information or two areas. Two separate accounts do not make up a comparison, and candidates will be penalised if they present two such accounts and expect the examiner to do the comparison on their behalf. A good technique is to use comparative adjectives, for example larger than, smaller than, more steep than, less gentle than. Note that 'compare' refers to similarities and differences, whereas the command word 'contrast' just asks for differences.

Explain..., Suggest reasons for..., How might...? Why...?

These commands ask for a statement about why something occurs. The command word tests your ability to know or understand why or how something happens. Such questions tend to carry a large number of marks, and expect candidates to write a relatively long piece of extended prose. It is important that this presents a logical account which is both relevant and well organised.

Using only an annotated diagram..., With the aid of a diagram....

Here the candidate must draw a diagram, and in the first case provide only a diagram. Annotations are labels which provide additional description or explanation of the main features of the diagram. For example, in the case of a hydrograph, the identification of 'a rising limb' would constitute a label, whereas 'a steep rising limb caused by an impermeable ground surface' would be an annotation.

Analyse...

This requires a candidate to break down the content of a topic into its constituent parts, and to give an in-depth account. As stated above, such questions tend to carry a large number of marks, and candidates will be expected to write a relatively long piece of prose. It is important that candidates present a logical account that is both relevant and well-organised.

Discuss...

This is one of the most common higher-level command words, and is used most often in questions which carry a large number of marks and require a lengthy piece of prose. Candidates are expected to build up an argument about an issue, presenting more than one side of the argument. They should present arguments for and against, making good use of evidence and appropriate examples, and express an opinion about the merits of each side. In other words, they should construct a verbal debate.

In any discussion there are likely to be both positive and negative aspects — some people are likely to benefit (the winners), and others are likely not to benefit (the losers). Candidates are invited to weigh up the evidence from both points of view, and may be asked to indicate where their sympathies lie.

Sometimes, additional help is provided in the wording of the question, as shown below.

Discuss the extent to which...
Here a judgement about the validity of the evidence or the outcome of an issue is clearly requested.

Discuss the varying attitudes to...
Here the question states that a variety of views exists, and candidates are required to debate them. There is often a range of people involved in an issue, including those responsible for the decision to go ahead with an idea or policy (the decision makers), and those who will be affected, directly or indirectly, by the decision. Each of these individuals or groups will have a different set of priorities, and a different viewpoint on the outcome.

Evaluate..., Assess...

These command words require more than the discussion described above. In both cases an indication of the candidate's viewpoint, having considered all the evidence, is required. 'Assess' asks for a statement of the overall quality or value of the feature or issue being considered, and 'evaluate' asks the candidate to give an overall statement of value. The candidate's own judgement is requested, together with a justification for that judgement.

The use of 'critically' often occurs in such questions, for example 'Critically evaluate...'. In this case the candidate is being asked to look at an issue or problem from the point of view of a critic. There may be weaknesses in the argument and the evidence should not be taken at face value. The candidate should question not only the evidence itself but also where it came from, and how it was collected. The answer should comment on the strengths of the evidence as well as its weaknesses.

Justify...

This is one of the most demanding command words. At its most simplistic, a response to this command must include a strong piece of writing in favour of the chosen option(s) in a decision-making exercise, and an explanation of why the other options were rejected.

However, decision making is not straightforward. All the options in a decision-making scenario have positive and negative aspects. The options that are rejected will have some good elements, and equally, the chosen option will not be perfect in all respects. The key to good decision making is to balance the pros and cons of each option and to opt for the most appropriate based on the evidence available.

A good answer to the command 'justify' should therefore provide the following:

- for each of the options that are rejected: an outline of their positive and negative points, but with an overall statement of why the negatives outweigh the positives
- for the chosen option: an outline of the negative and the positive points, but with an overall statement of why the positives outweigh the negatives

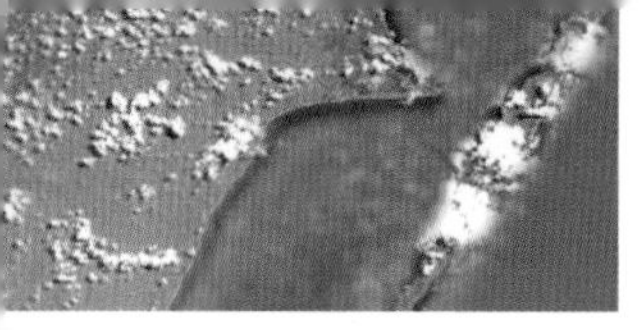

Developing extended prose and essay-writing skills

For many students essay writing is one of the most difficult parts of the exam. But it is also an opportunity to demonstrate your strengths. Before starting to write a piece of extended prose or an essay you must have a plan of what you are going to write, either in your head or on paper. All such pieces of writing must have a beginning (introduction), a middle (argument) and an end (conclusion).

The introduction

This does not have to be too long — a few sentences should suffice. It may define the terms in the question, set the scene for the argument to follow, or provide a brief statement of the idea, concept or viewpoint you are going to develop in the main body of your answer.

The argument

This is the main body of the answer. It should consist of a series of paragraphs, each developing one point only and following on logically from the previous one. Try to avoid paragraphs that list information without any depth, but do not write down all you know about a particular topic without any link to the question set. Make good use of examples, naming real places (which could be local to you). Make your examples count by giving accurate detail specific to those locations.

The conclusion

In an extended prose answer the conclusion should not be too long. Make sure it reiterates the main points stated in the introduction, but now supported by the evidence and facts given in the argument.

Should you produce plans in the examination?

If you produce an essay plan at all, it must be brief, taking only 2 or 3 minutes to write on a piece of scrap paper. The plan must reflect the above formula — make sure you stick to it. Be logical, and only give an outline — retain the examples in your head, and include them at the most appropriate point in your answer.

Other important points

Always keep an eye on the time. Make sure you write clearly and concisely. Do not provide confused answers, endlessly long sentences, or pages of prose with no paragraphs.

Above all: *read the question and answer the question set.*

How are questions marked?

Examination questions for AQA (A) are marked according to levels based on certain criteria. The following general criteria relate to knowledge, understanding and critical application, and the quality of written communication:

Level 1

A Level 1 answer is likely to:

- display a basic understanding of the topic
- make one or two points without the support of appropriate exemplification or application of principle
- demonstrate a simplistic style of writing, perhaps lacking close relation to the terms of the question and unlikely to communicate complexity of subject matter
- lack organisation, relevance and specialist vocabulary
- demonstrate deficiencies in legibility, spelling, grammar and punctuation, which detract from the clarity of meaning

Level 2

A Level 2 answer is likely to:

- display a clear understanding of the topic
- make one or two points with the support of appropriate exemplification and/or application of principle
- demonstrate a clear style of writing, which addresses the terms of the question
- demonstrate a degree of organisation and use of specialised terms
- demonstrate sufficient legibility and quality of spelling, grammar and punctuation to communicate meaning clearly

Level 3

A Level 3 (the highest level) answer is likely to:

- display a detailed understanding of the topic
- make several points with the support of appropriate exemplification and/or application of principle
- demonstrate a sophisticated style of writing, incorporating measured and qualified explanation and comment as required by the question and reflecting awareness of the complexity of subject matter
- demonstrate a clear sense of purpose so that the responses are seen to closely relate to the requirements of the question, with confident use of specialist vocabulary
- demonstrate legibility of text, and qualities of spelling, grammar and punctuation, which contribute to a complete clarity of meaning

AS
Module 1

Core concepts in physical geography

Chapter 1

Water on the land

Drainage basin systems

The drainage basin is the catchment area from which a river system obtains its water. An imaginary line called the **watershed** delimits one drainage basin from another. The watershed generally follows a ridge of high land; any rain falling on the other side of the ridge will eventually flow into another river in the adjacent drainage basin.

The drainage basin hydrological cycle is an open system with inputs and outputs — water and energy from the sun are introduced into the drainage basin from outside and water can be lost from the drainage basin in a number of ways (Figures 1.1 and 1.2).

The drainage basin hydrological cycle can be studied using a systems approach:

- **Inputs** into the drainage basin include:
  - energy from the sun for evaporation
  - precipitation (rain, snow)

Figure 1.1 The drainage basin hydrological cycle

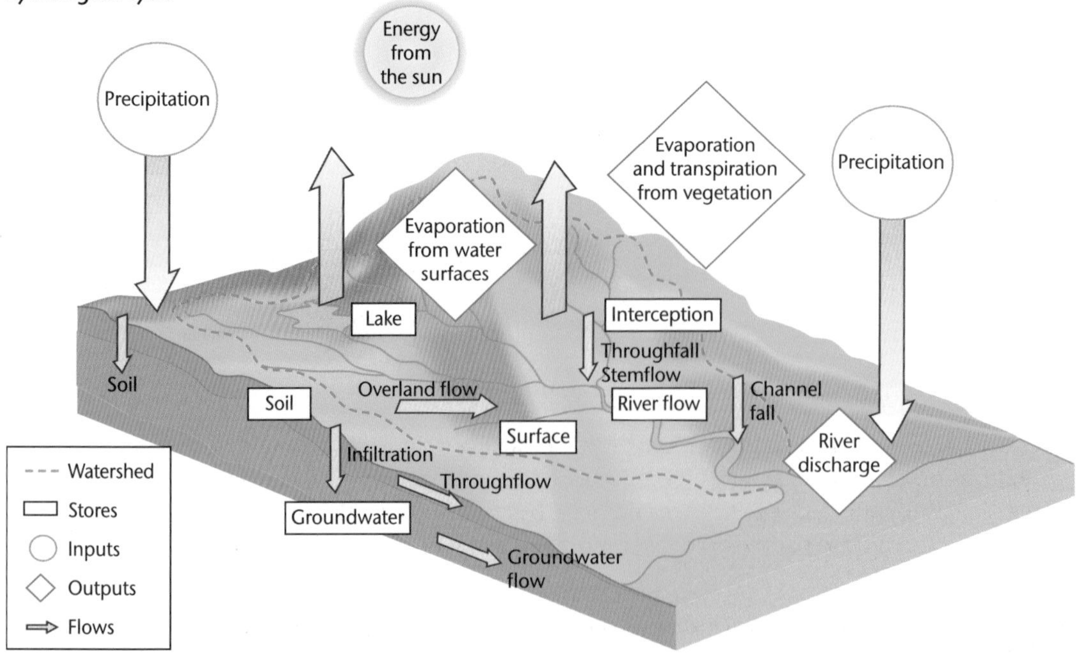

- **Outputs** move moisture out of the drainage basin and include:
  - evaporation and transpiration from plants (collectively called evapotranspiration)
  - runoff into the sea
  - water percolating deep into underground stores where it can be effectively lost from the system
- Many **stores of water** within the drainage basin (such as glaciers, rivers, lakes and puddles) occur on the surface. Other stores are less obvious. For example, vegetation stores water by interception and plants also contain a significant amount of water taken up from the soil through their roots. The soil itself holds water and groundwater is stored in permeable rocks.
- **Transfers** and **flows** move water through the system and enable inputs of water to be processed from one store to another. Transfers include throughfall, stemflow, infiltration, throughflow and groundwater flow.

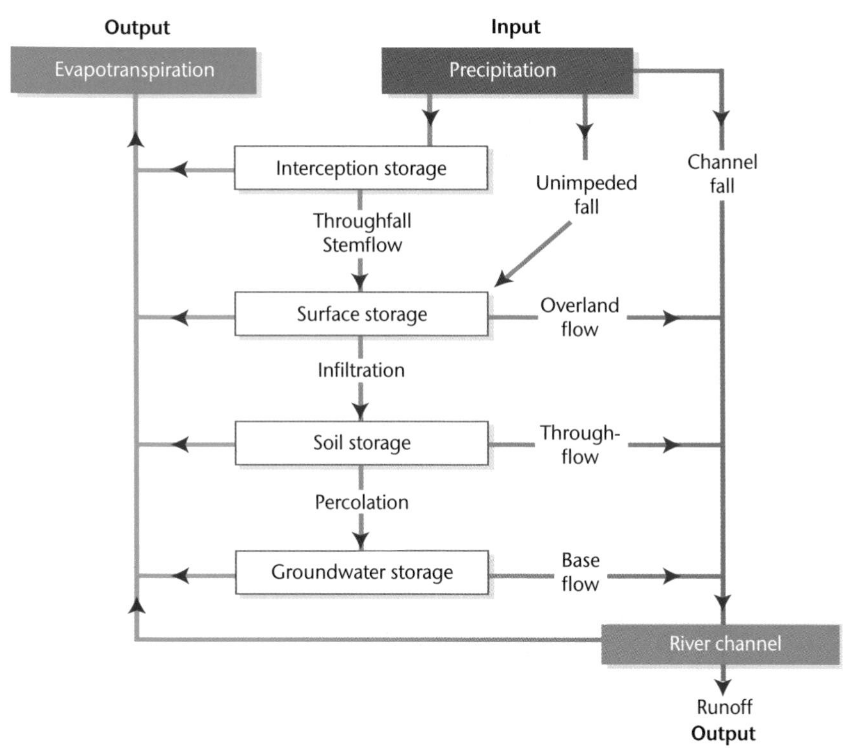

Figure 1.2 A flow diagram of drainage basin hydrology

The factors influencing river discharge

River discharge is defined as the volume of water passing a measuring point or gauging station in a river in a given time. It is measured in cubic metres per second (cumecs). The overall discharge from the drainage basin depends on the relationship between precipitation, evapotranspiration and storage factors and can be summarised as follows:

drainage basin discharge = precipitation − evapotranspiration ± changes in storage

Discharge can be illustrated using **hydrographs**. These can show annual patterns of flow (the river regime) in response to climate. Short-term variations in discharge are shown using a flood or storm hydrograph.

The storm hydrograph

The storm hydrograph (Figure 1.3) shows variations in a river's discharge over a short period of time, usually during a rainstorm. The starting and finishing level show the **base flow** of the river. As storm water enters the drainage basin the discharge rises, shown by the **rising limb**, to reach the **peak discharge** which indicates the highest flow in the channel. The **receding limb** shows the fall in the discharge back to the base level. The time delay between maximum rainfall amount and peak discharge is the **lag time**.

Figure 1.3
A storm hydrograph

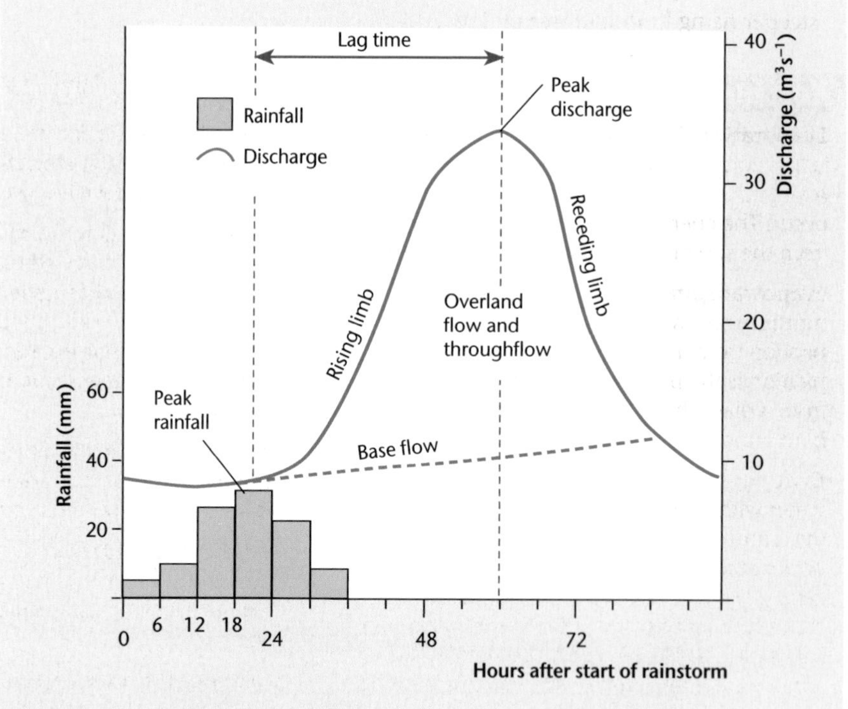

The shape of the hydrograph is influenced by a number of factors:

- The intensity and duration of the storm — if both are high they produce a steep rising limb as the infiltration capacity of the soil is exceeded.
- The antecedent rainfall — heavy rain falling on a soil which is saturated from a previous period of wet weather will produce a steep rising limb.
- Snow — heavy snowfall may not initially show on a hydrograph since the water is being 'stored' in snow on the ground. Indeed, water levels in a river may fall during a prolonged period of snowfall and cold weather. When temperatures rise and melting occurs, massive amounts of water are released, greatly increasing discharge. This water may reach the river channel even quicker if the ground remains frozen and restricts infiltration.

- Porous soil types and/or permeable rock types, such as limestone — these produce less steep (or less flashy) hydrographs because water is regulated more slowly through the natural systems.
- Impermeable rock types such as granite and clay — these tend to have higher densities of surface streams (higher drainage densities). The higher the density the faster the water reaches the main river channel, causing rapid increases in discharge.
- Size of drainage basin — a small drainage basin tends to respond more rapidly to a storm than a larger one, so the lag time is shorter.
- Shape of drainage basin — rainfall reaches the river more quickly from a round basin than from an elongated basin.
- Slope angle — in steep-sided upland river basins the water reaches the channels much more quickly than in gently-sloping lowland river basins, producing a steeper rising limb and shorter lag times.

Key terms

Evaporation The process by which liquid water is transformed into water vapour, which is a gas. A large amount of energy is required for this to occur. The energy is usually provided by heat from the sun or by the movement of air (wind).

Evapotranspiration The total amount of moisture removed by evaporation and transpiration from a vegetated land surface. Transpiration is the process by which water is lost from a plant through stomata (very small pores) in its leaves.

Groundwater flow The slowest transfer of water within the drainage basin. It provides the main input of water into a river during drought or dry seasons. Groundwater flows at a slow but steady rate through bands of sedimentary rock. It can take thousands of years for moisture that seeps into permeable rocks deep under the surface to be returned to the drainage basin hydrological cycle as groundwater flow.

Infiltration The passage of water into the soil. Infiltration takes place relatively quickly at the beginning of a storm, but as the soil becomes saturated the infiltration rate falls rapidly. Infiltration rates are affected by the nature of the soil itself. Sandy soils let more water pass through than clay soils.

Interception The process by which raindrops are prevented from directly reaching the soil surface. Leaves, stems and branches on trees, and herbaceous plants and grasses growing close to the surface, intercept water. Evaporation removes some of this moisture from the system and it does not reach the river as runoff.

Percolation The downward movement of water within the rock under the soil surface. The rate of percolation depends on the nature of the rock. Some rocks, particularly those of an igneous or metamorphic nature, are impermeable so there is no percolation or groundwater flow.

Precipitation Water in any form that falls from the atmosphere to the surface of the Earth. It includes rain, snow, sleet and hail.

Runoff All the water that enters a river and eventually flows out of the drainage basin. It can be quantified by measuring the discharge of a river.

Stemflow The water that runs down the stems and branches of plants and trees during and after rain to reach the ground. It takes place after interception has occurred.

Throughfall The water that drips off leaves during a rainstorm. It occurs when the amount of water falling onto the interception layer of the tree canopy has exceeded the capacity of the trees to hold water.

Throughflow The water that moves downslope through the subsoil, pulled by gravity. It is particularly effective when underlying impermeable rock prevents percolation.

- Temperature — high temperatures increase the rate of evapotranspiration, thereby reducing discharge. Cold temperatures may freeze the ground, restrict infiltration, increase overland flow and increase river discharge.
- Vegetation — this varies with the season. In summer there are more leaves on deciduous trees, so interception is higher and peak discharge lower. Plantations of conifers have a less variable effect.
- Land use — water runs more quickly over impermeable surfaces such as caravan parks or agricultural land which has been trampled by cattle. Lag time is reduced and peak discharge increased.

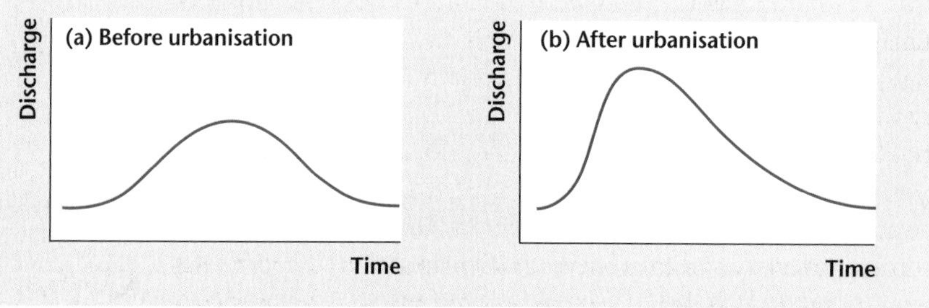

Figure 1.4 The shape of the storm hydrograph before and after urbanisation

- Urbanisation — this is the main human impact on a storm hydrograph. The following processes combine to alter the shape of the hydrograph by reducing the lag time and increasing peak discharge (Figure 1.4):
  - removal of topsoil and compaction of the ground with earth-moving machinery during building work
  - building of roads which increase the impermeable surface area
  - building of drains and sewers that transport water rapidly to river channels, reducing the lag time
  - straightening of river channels and lining with concrete. This also leads to the faster delivery of water downstream of the urban area and increases the risk of flooding in downstream areas

  Less water reaches the channel by throughflow and base flow, and more gets there by overland flow. Local authorities and water companies may need to respond to these changes to prevent damaging flooding in their areas.

Channel processes and landforms

Processes of erosion, transport and deposition

The work of a river involves three main processes — **erosion, transportation** and **deposition**. At any one time the dominant process operating within the river depends on the amount of energy available. This is governed by the velocity of the flow and the amount of water flowing within the channel (discharge).

Erosion

Rivers erode because they possess energy. Their total energy depends on:

- the weight of the water — the greater the mass of the water the more energy it will possess due to the influence of gravity on its movement
- the height of the river above its base level (usually sea level) — this gives it a source of potential energy, and the higher the source of the river the more such energy it has
- the steepness of the channel — this controls the speed of the river which determines how much kinetic energy it has

Much of this energy is lost through friction, either internally through turbulence within the flow of the river, or externally through contact with the bed and banks of the river channel. Energy loss through friction can be great in all parts of a river, but it is perhaps easier to understand in the context of an upland river channel. Here, the channel often has a rocky bed with many large boulders. The rough shape of the channel means that the **wetted perimeter** — the overall length of the bed and banks that the river is in contact with — is large. More energy is thus lost through friction, and the river's velocity, and therefore its energy level, is reduced. Hence, in normal conditions, the river is unable to perform much erosion. However, when the river contains large quantities of water, following heavy rain or snowmelt, it does possess the energy to perform great amounts of erosion.

Key terms

Deposition The laying down of solid material, in the form of sediment, on the bed of a river or on the sea floor.

Erosion The break up of rocks by the action of rock particles being moved over the Earth's surface by water, wind and ice.

Transportation The movement of particles from the place they were eroded to the place where they are deposited.

There are four main processes of river erosion:

- **Abrasion** (corrasion) is the scraping, scouring and rubbing action of materials carried along by a river (the **load**). Rivers carry rock fragments in the flow of the water or drag them along the bed, and in doing so wear away the banks and bed of the river channel. Abrasion is most effective in short turbulent periods when the river is at bankfull or in flood. During times when river levels are low, the load consists of small particles, such as sand grains, and these tend to smooth the surface of the river channel.
- **Hydraulic action** is caused by the sheer power of moving water. It is the movement of loose unconsolidated material due to the frictional drag of the moving water on sediment lying on the channel bed. As velocity increases, turbulent flow lifts a larger number of grains, particularly sand-sized particles, from the floor of the channel. Hydraulic action is particularly effective at removing loose material in the banks of meanders, which can lead to undercutting and collapse. It can be locally strong within rapids or below waterfalls where it may cause the rocks to fragment along joints and bedding planes or other lines of weakness.
- **Corrosion** is most active on rocks that contain carbonates, such as limestone and chalk. The minerals in the rock are dissolved by weak acids in the river water and carried away in solution.
- **Attrition** is the reduction in the size of fragments and particles within a river due to the processes described above. The fragments strike one another as well as the river bed. They therefore become smoother, smaller and more rounded as they move along the river channel. Consequently larger, more angular

fragments tend to be found upstream while smaller, more rounded fragments are found downstream.

In the upper reaches of a river, where the land lies high above sea level, river erosion is predominantly vertical. **Vertical erosion** dominates because the river is attempting to cut down to its base level, which is usually sea level. In times of spate, when the river level and velocity are high, the river cuts down into its valley mainly by abrasion and hydraulic action. Such rivers often produce steep-sided valleys.

Lateral erosion occurs more frequently in the middle and lower stretches of the river, where the valley floor lies closer to sea level. Here the river possesses a great deal of energy, particularly when close to bankfull. However, this energy is used laterally to widen the valley as the river meanders. The strongest current is found on the outside of the bend and hydraulic action causes the bank to be undermined and to collapse.

Transport

River energy not used for erosion or not lost through friction can be used to transport the river's load. A river obtains its load from two main sources:

- material that has been washed, or has fallen, into the river from the valley sides
- material that has been eroded by the river itself from the bed or banks

A river transports its load in four main ways:

- **Traction** — large stones and boulders are rolled along the river bed by water moving downstream. This process only operates at times of high discharge (and consequently high energy levels). During the Boscastle flood of August 2004, when the River Valency burst its banks, large boulders transported from further upstream contributed significantly to the damage to the town.
- **Saltation** — small stones bounce or leap-frog along the channel bed. This process is associated with relatively high energy conditions. Small particles may be thrust up from the bed of the river only to fall back to the bottom again further downstream. As these particles land they in turn dislodge other particles upwards, causing more such bouncing movements to take place.
- **Suspension** — very small particles of sand and silt are carried along by the flow of the river. Such material is not only carried but is also picked up, mainly through the turbulence that exists within the water. Suspension normally contributes the largest proportion of sediment to the load of the river. The suspended load is the main cause of the brown appearance of many rivers and streams.
- **Solution** — dissolved minerals are transported within the mass of the moving water.

Two other terms are often used in the context of river transport — capacity and competence. Both of these are influenced by the velocity, and therefore the discharge, of the river.

The **capacity** of a river is a measure of the amount of material it can carry, that is, the total volume of the load. Research has found that a river's capacity increases according to the third power of its velocity. For example, if a river's velocity doubles, then its capacity increases by eight times (2^3).

The **competence** of a river is the diameter of the largest particle that it can carry for a given velocity. Again, research has shown that a river's competence increases according to the sixth power of its velocity. For example, if a river's velocity doubles, then its competence increases by 64 times (2^6). This is because fast-flowing rivers have greater turbulence and are therefore better able to lift particles from the river bed.

Deposition

A river **deposits** when, owing to a decrease in its level of energy, it is no longer competent to transport its load. Deposition usually occurs when:

- there is a reduction in the gradient of the river, for example when it enters a lake
- the discharge is reduced, such as during and after a dry spell of weather
- there is shallow water, for example on the inside of a meander
- there is an increase in the calibre (size) of the load. This may be due to a tributary bringing in larger particles, to increased erosion along the river's course, or to a landslide into the river
- the river floods and overtops its banks, resulting in a reduced velocity on the floodplain outside the main channel

In general, the largest fragments are the first to be deposited, followed by successively smaller particles, although the finest particles may never be deposited (Figure 1.5). This pattern of deposition is reflected in the sediments found along the course of a river. The channels of upland rivers are often filled with large boulders. Gravels, sands and silts can be carried further and are often deposited further downstream. Sands and silts are deposited on the flat floodplains either side of the river in its lower course.

Photograph 1.1 The River Eea in Cumbria. (a) Upper course, (b) middle course

How are erosion, transport and deposition related to changes in discharge?

Figure 1.5
Hjulström's curve

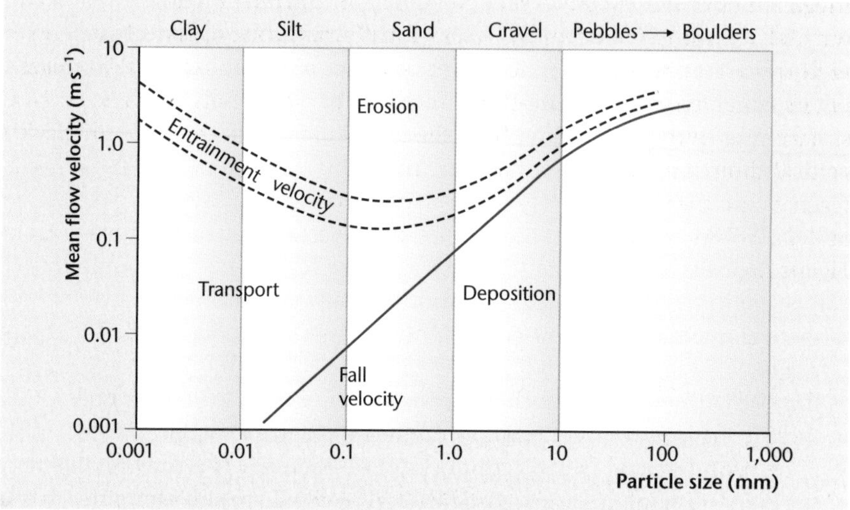

The Hjulström graph (Figure 1.5) shows the relationship between the velocity of a river and the size of particles that can be eroded, transported or deposited. Velocity increases as discharge rises and generally this enables a river to pick up larger particles from the bed or banks of the channel. Similarly, as velocity and discharge reduce, then particles are generally deposited according to their size, largest first. However, Hjulström's research showed three interesting relationships:

- Sand particles are moved by lower pick up or critical erosion velocities than *smaller* silts and clays or *larger* gravels. The small clay and silt particles are difficult to pick up (entrain) because they tend to stick together. They lie on the river bed and offer less resistance to water flow than larger particles. Much more powerful flows of water are required to lift them into the water.
- Once entrained (picked up), particles can be carried at lower velocities than those required to pick them up. However, for larger particles there is only a small difference between the critical erosion velocity and the settling velocity. Such particles will be deposited soon after they have been entrained.
- The smallest particles, clays and silts, are only deposited at very low velocities. Indeed, some clay particles may never be deposited on the river bed and can be carried almost indefinitely. This explains why such deposits occur in river estuaries. Here the fresh water of the river meets the salt water of the sea, causing chemical settling of the clays and silts to occur and creating extensive areas of mudflats. This process is called **flocculation**. This coagulation (clustering) of the clay and silt particles causes them to sink more rapidly.

Long profile and channel cross-sections

The long profile of a river

The long profile of a river illustrates the changes in the altitude of the course of the river from its source, along the entire length of its channel, to the river-mouth.

In general, the long profile is smoothly concave, with the gradient being steeper in the upper course and becoming progressively gentler towards the mouth. Irregularities in the gradient frequently occur and may be represented by rapids, waterfalls or lakes. There may also be marked breaks or changes in slope, known as **knick points**, which are generally the product of rejuvenation. Rejuvenation occurs either when the sea level (in relation to the land) falls or when the land surface rises. Either situation allows the river to revive its erosion activity in a vertical direction. The river adjusts to the new base level, at first in its lowest reaches, and then progressively inland. The processes of erosion, transportation and deposition along the long profile of a typical river are summarised in Figure 1.6.

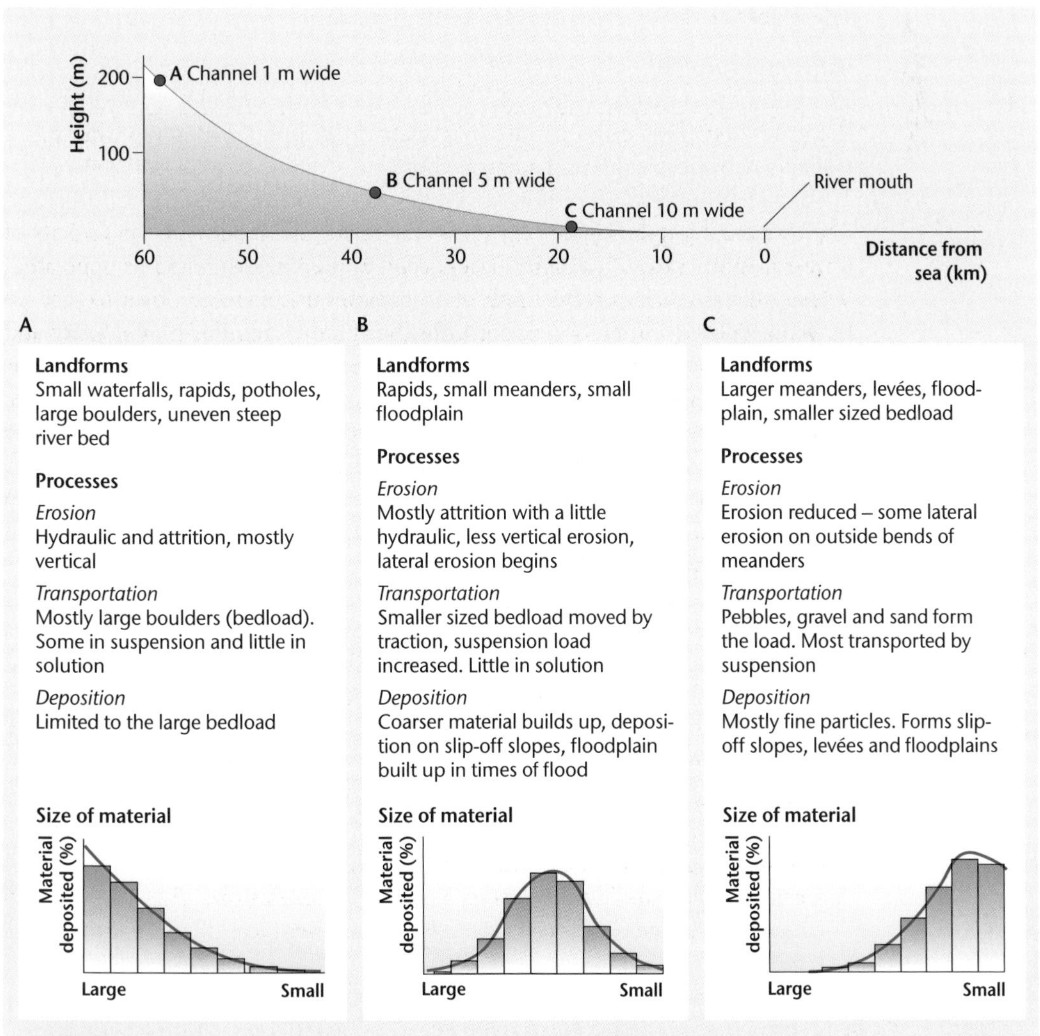

Figure 1.6 Summary of river landforms, processes and size of depositional material, from a river's source to its mouth

Channel cross sections

The channel cross section (or profile) is a view of the river bed and banks from one side to the other at any one point on its course. As a river flows from its source to its mouth, a number of typical changes take place in the channel morphology. In the upper course, the channel is narrow and uneven, because of the presence of deposited boulders. Where both banks are being eroded channels tend to be broadly rectangular in shape. As the river enters its middle course and starts to meander, the channel becomes asymmetrical on the river bends but mainly smooth and symmetrical on the straight stretches. In the lower course, the river widens and deepens further, but banks of deposition and **eyots** (islands of deposition) can disrupt the shape of the channel cross-section, leading to a braided channel. Sometimes embankments called **levées** can be seen on either side of the channel. Levées can also be man-made.

Valley cross profile

The valley cross profile is the view of the valley from one side to another. For example, the valley cross profile of a river in an upland area typically has a V-shape, with steep sides and a narrow bottom.

Variations in the cross profile can be described and explained as follows (and as illustrated in Figure 1.7):

- in the upper course — a narrow steep-sided valley where the river occupies all of the valley floor. This is the result of dominant vertical erosion by the river
- in the middle course — a wider valley with distinct valley bluffs, and a flat floodplain. This is the result of lateral erosion, which widens the valley floor
- in the lower course — a very wide, flat floodplain in which the valley sides are difficult to locate. Here there is a lack of erosion, and reduced competence of the river, which results in large-scale deposition

The shape of the channel influences the velocity of the river. In the upper course, where the channel is narrow and uneven, due to the presence of large boulders, there is a large **wetted perimeter**. The wetted perimeter is the total length of the river bed and banks in cross section that are in contact with the water in the channel. River levels only rise after heavy rain or snowmelt and in the upper course the river is relatively shallow. When there is a large wetted perimeter in relation to the amount of water in the river, there is more friction. Friction results in energy loss and, consequently, the velocity of the river is slowed. As channels become larger and smoother, in the middle and lower courses of the river, they tend to be more efficient. The wetted perimeter is proportionately smaller than the volume of water flowing in the channel. Therefore, there is less friction to reduce velocity. Channel shape is described by the **hydraulic radius**. This is calculated using the formula:

$$\text{hydraulic radius} = \frac{\text{cross-sectional area of the channel}}{\text{wetted perimeter}}$$

A high hydraulic radius means that the river is efficient. This is because the moving water loses proportionately less energy in overcoming friction than when the ratio between the cross-sectional area and the wetted perimeter is low

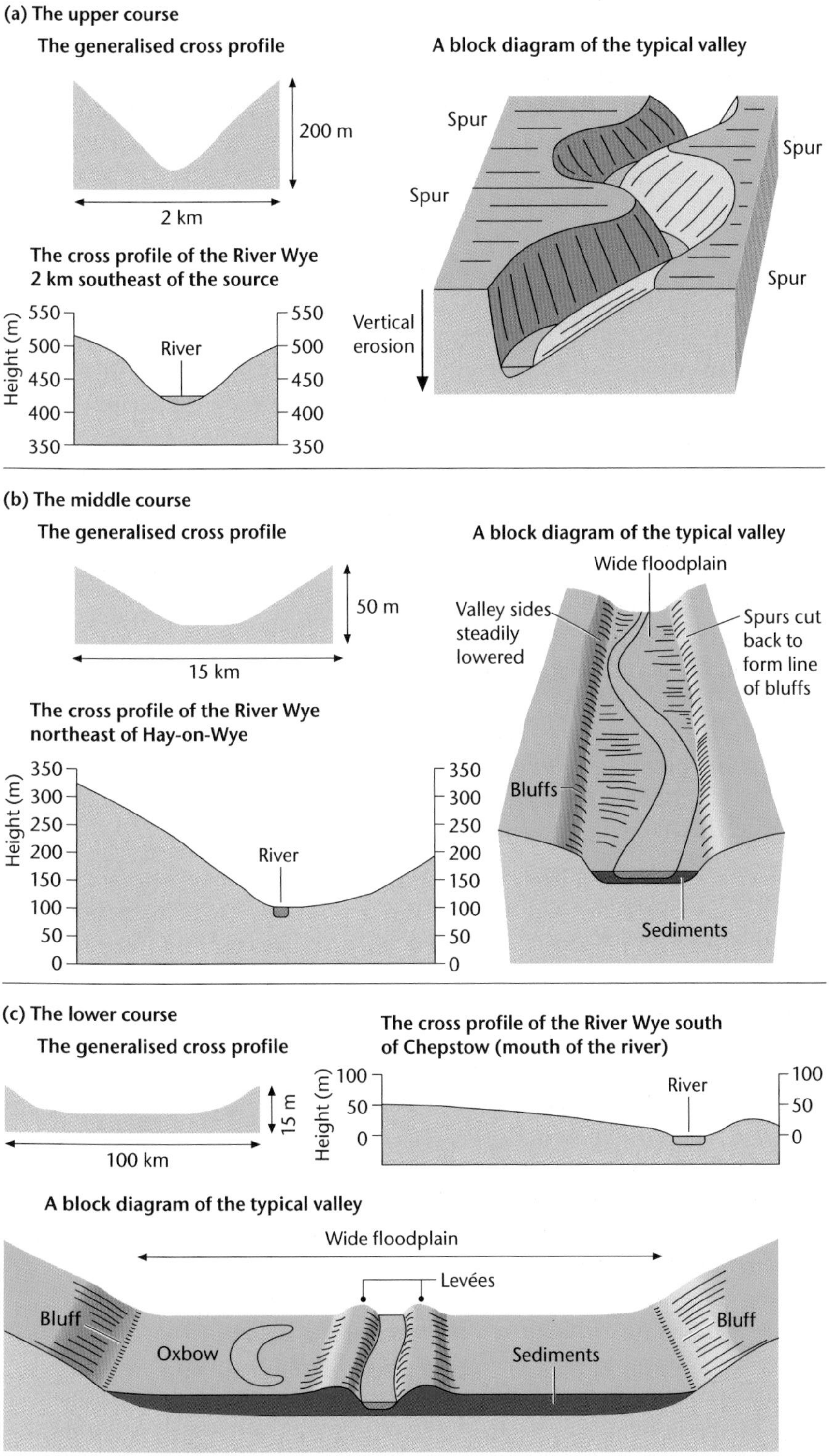

Figure 1.7
Valley cross profile characteristics

(a) The upper course

The generalised cross profile

200 m
2 km

The cross profile of the River Wye 2 km southeast of the source

Height (m)
550 500 450 400 350
River

A block diagram of the typical valley

Spur
Spur
Spur
Spur
Vertical erosion

(b) The middle course

The generalised cross profile

50 m
15 km

The cross profile of the River Wye northeast of Hay-on-Wye

Height (m)
350 300 250 200 150 100 50 0
River

A block diagram of the typical valley

Wide floodplain
Valley sides steadily lowered
Spurs cut back to form line of bluffs
Bluffs
Sediments

(c) The lower course

The generalised cross profile

15 m
100 km

The cross profile of the River Wye south of Chepstow (mouth of the river)

Height (m)
100 50 0
River

A block diagram of the typical valley

Wide floodplain
Levées
Bluff
Oxbow
Sediments
Bluff

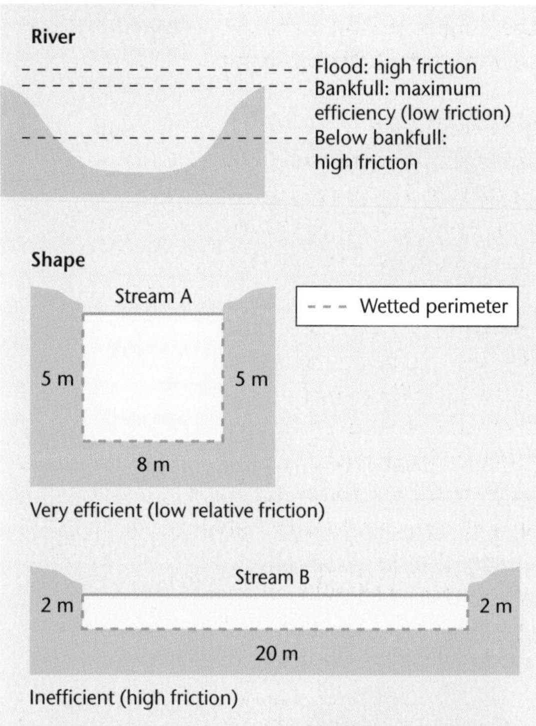

Wetted perimeters	Hydraulic radius
Stream A: 5 + 5 + 8 = 18 m	Stream A: 40/18 = 2.22 m
Stream B: 2 + 2 + 20 = 24 m	Stream B: 40/24 = 1.66 m

Figure 1.8 Channel shape efficiency

Type of load	Particle diameter (mm)
Boulders and cobbles	> 100
Pebbles	10–99.99
Gravel	1.0–9.99
Sand	0.1–0.99
Silt	0.01–0.099
Clay	< 0.01

Table 1.1 River load categorised by size

(Figure 1.8). Larger channels tend to be more efficient; area increases to a greater degree than wetted perimeter. For example, at bankfull, a channel that is 10 m wide and 2 m deep has a hydraulic radius of 20/14 = 1.43. A channel that is 20 m wide and 4 m deep has a hydraulic radius of 80/28 = 2.86.

Types, sources and spatial variations in river load

The type, source and character of the load of the river depend upon the nature of the drainage basin, its location and, increasingly, on human activity. The Hjulström graph (Figure 1.5) categorises the type of river load by size. These data are also given in Table 1.1. **Dissolved load** consists of soluble materials carried as chemical ions, so there are no measurable particles.

Large particles only form part of the load of a river during and immediately after extreme events that lead to significant increases in stream discharge. Such temporal changes occur following prolonged heavy rainfall (particularly if the ground is also saturated), after flash floods or after significant snowmelt. In these circumstances, the competence of the river increases and allows larger particles to be carried. Boulders and cobbles form part of the load in the upper course because rivers seldom have the capacity to transport these particles great distances.

In general, the further downstream the river travels, the smaller the particles making up the load. This is partly the result of attrition — when particles are rounded and smoothed by this process they are also broken down into smaller pieces.

Total sediment yields tend to increase with distance downstream, due mainly to increases in both average discharge and velocity in the lower reaches of the river. Here, the river possesses a greater competence, so it is able to transport more material.

Spatial variations in load can be seen when comparing rivers located in different parts of the world. The Mississippi River has a vast drainage basin, roughly one-third the size of the entire USA. On average every year, it transports some 136 million tonnes of load in solution, 340 million tonnes in suspension and 40 million tonnes by saltation. Other major sediment-bearing rivers are located in Asia and South America, for example the Yangtze in China and the Amazon in Brazil. In other parts of the world, for example in Australia, sediment yields are much smaller.

Spatial variations in load are influenced by the following factors:

- **Size of the drainage basin** — large drainage basins with many tributaries have a greater potential for transporting sediment, particularly in their lower courses, than do small drainage basins. In the UK, a relatively small country, the largest drainage basin — that of the River Severn — covers a much smaller area than the largest continental drainage basins.
- **Rock type** — in drainage basins where the underlying geology consists of relatively soft (and easily eroded) sandstones and clays, the sediment transported consists mainly of sand or clay particles. Where the rock is limestone, more material will be transported as dissolved load because this rock type is soluble. Moving water does not easily erode resistant igneous rocks, such as granite and basalt. Therefore, the total sediment yield in river basins of igneous rock may be low whereas in drainage basins where the underlying rock is softer, sediment yield may be high.
- **Relief** — in drainage basins with low relief, where there is a small difference in altitude between the source and base level, the energy available for erosion and transport is limited. Such rivers have low loads compared with rivers that have upper reaches in areas of high relief.
- **Precipitation** — low loads are generally found in drainage basins with low rates of precipitation. In such areas, less water is available as runoff compared with drainage basins with high precipitation. Seasonal differences in sediment yield occur in some drainage basins, particularly those in areas where the climate has wet and dry seasons and where snowmelt in the spring adds to normal runoff from precipitation.
- **Human activity** — this can both increase and decrease sediment yield. In areas of the world where deforestation is occurring rapidly, there have been marked increases in the load carried by rivers. This is mainly caused by increased soil erosion, which occurs because the vegetation that protected the soil from the actions of moving water on its surface has been removed. There is also reduced water uptake by trees and other plants in deforested areas. The result is that soil is washed into the river and adds to the suspended load.

  Many farmers use nitrates and phosphates as chemical fertilisers. These substances can enter rivers by throughflow and overland flow and are then transported in solution.

  Major dams have been constructed on some rivers, for example the Aswan dam on the River Nile and the Hoover dam on the Colorado River. Such dams trap sediment, significantly lowering downstream sediment yields.

The effects of channel load on landforms

A fast-flowing river, at bankfull, has the competence to carry a large load. The particles erode the river bed and banks by abrasion, creating distinctive features such as potholes, waterfalls and gorges.

If the volume of water in the river falls quickly, the load is deposited because of a fall in competence. When this occurs, depositional features such as levées, floodplains and deltas are created.

In some sections of the river, both erosion and deposition occur. This is particularly noticeable on a meander bend, where suspended load carried by the river erodes the outside edge of the bend by abrasion and load is deposited on the inside of the bend to form a point bar.

Erosional and depositional landforms

As a river flows from its source to its mouth a number of changes take place in its morphology. These changes affect the shape and size of the channel and result in distinctive landforms along its course. Some of these landforms are the result of erosion, some are the result of deposition and some are a consequence of both.

Waterfalls and rapids

Waterfalls and rapids occur when there is a sudden change in the gradient of the river as it flows downstream. Waterfalls are more dramatic features than rapids and may be the result of:

- a resistant band of rock occurring across the course of the river
- the edge of a plateau
- the rejuvenation of the area, giving the river renewed erosional power as sea level falls

The river falls over a rock edge into a deep plunge pool at the foot of the fall, where the layers of weak rock are excavated more quickly than the overlying resistant rock. The force of the swirling water around the rocks and boulders enlarges and deepens the plunge pool by hydraulic action and abrasion. This undercuts the resistant (cap) rock above. Eventually the overhanging cap rock collapses and the waterfall retreats upstream, leaving a gorge ahead of it (Figure 1.9).

Figure 1.9
A waterfall

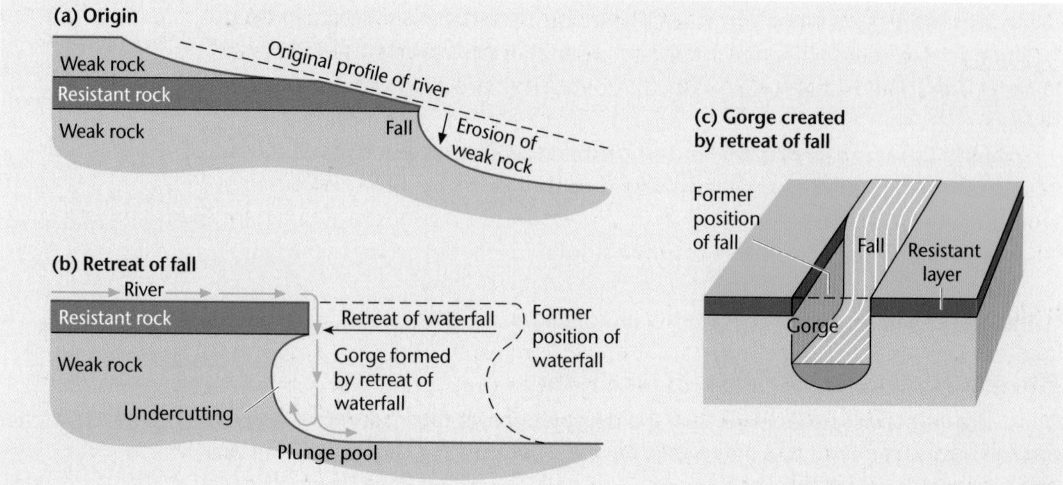

Case study High Force in upper Teesdale

In upper Teesdale an outcrop of an igneous rock called the Whin Sill causes the formation of the High Force waterfall. The Whin Sill is the resistant cap rock which overlies softer sandstone, limestone, shales and coal seams. These are eroded more quickly, leaving the overhang of High Force. The waterfall created is 22 m high — the tallest in England. Ahead of it lies a gorge stretching over 500 m downstream.

John Pallister

Photograph 1.2 High Force waterfall

Potholes

Potholes are cylindrical holes drilled into the rocky bed of a river by turbulent high-velocity water loaded with pebbles. The pebbles become trapped in slight hollows and vertical eddies in the water are strong enough to allow the sediment to grind a hole into the rock by abrasion (corrasion). Attrition rounds and smooths the pebbles caught in the hole and helps to reduce the size of the bed-load.

Potholes can vary in width from a few centimetres to several metres. They are generally found in the upper or early-middle course of a river. This is where the valley lies well above base level, giving more potential for downcutting, and where the river bed is more likely to be rocky in nature.

Braided channels

Braiding occurs when the river is forced to split into several channels separated by islands. It is a feature of rivers that are supplied with large loads of sand and gravel. It is most likely to occur when a river has variable discharges. The banks formed from sand and gravel are generally unstable and easily eroded. As a consequence, the channel becomes very wide in relation to its depth. The river can

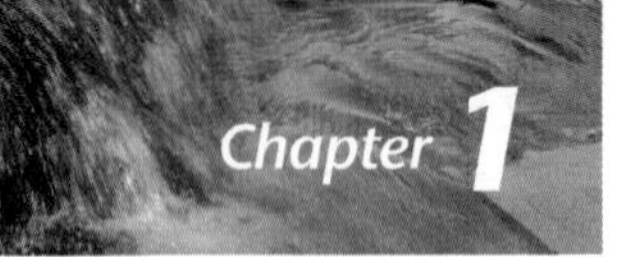

become choked, with several sandbars and channels that are constantly changing their locations.

Braiding also occurs in environments in which there are rapidly fluctuating discharges:

- semi-arid areas of low relief that receive rivers from mountainous areas
- glacial streams with variable annual discharge. In spring, meltwater causes river discharge and competence to increase, therefore the river can transport more particles. As the temperature drops and the river level falls, the load is deposited as islands of deposition in the channel

Meanders and oxbow lakes

Meanders

Meanders are sinuous bends in a river. Explaining the formation of meanders in a river has caused some problems for geographers. In low flow conditions straight channels are seen to have alternating bars of sediment on their beds and the moving water is forced to weave around these bars. This creates alternating shallow sections (riffles) and deeper sections (pools). The swing of the flow that has been induced by the riffles directs the maximum velocity towards one of the banks, and results in erosion by undercutting on that side. An outer concave bank is therefore created. Deposition takes place on the inside of the bend, the convex bank. Consequently, although the river does not get any wider, its sinuosity increases.

The cross-section of a meander is asymmetrical (Figure 1.10). The outer bank forms a river cliff or bluff with a deep pool close to the bank. This bank is undercut by erosion, particularly abrasion and hydraulic action. The inner bank is a gently sloping deposit of sand and gravel, called a **point bar**.

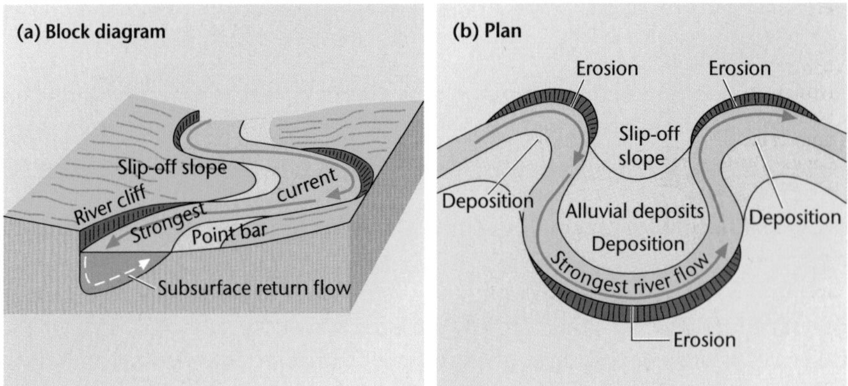

Figure 1.10 A meander

Once they have been created, meanders are perpetuated by a surface flow of water across to the concave outer bank with a compensatory subsurface return flow back to the convex inner bank. This corkscrew-like movement of water is called **helicoidal flow**. In this way, eroded material from the outer bank is transported away and deposited on the inner bank. Modern research suggests that the flow is rarely strong enough for the river to transport material across to the point bar on the opposite bank. Point bars are most likely to be maintained by sediment from erosion at the bluff of the meander upstream on the same side of the channel.

The zone of greatest erosion is downstream of the midpoint in the meander bend, because the flow of the strongest current does not exactly match the shape of the meander. As erosion continues on the outer bank, the whole feature begins to migrate slowly, both laterally and downstream. Imprints of former channels can be seen on the floodplain. These are particularly clear on aerial photographs.

Photograph 1.3 A meander on the River Hodder

Oxbow lakes

Oxbow lakes are features of both erosion and deposition. An oxbow lake is a horseshoe-shaped lake separated from an adjacent river. The water is stagnant, and in time the lake gradually silts up, becoming a crescent-shaped stretch of marsh called a **meander scar**. An oxbow lake is formed by the increasing sinuosity of a river meander. Erosion is greatest on the outer bank, and with deposition on the inner bank, the neck of the meander becomes progressively narrower. During times of high discharge, such as floods, the river cuts through this neck, and the new cut eventually becomes the main channel. The former channel is sealed off by deposition (Figure 1.11).

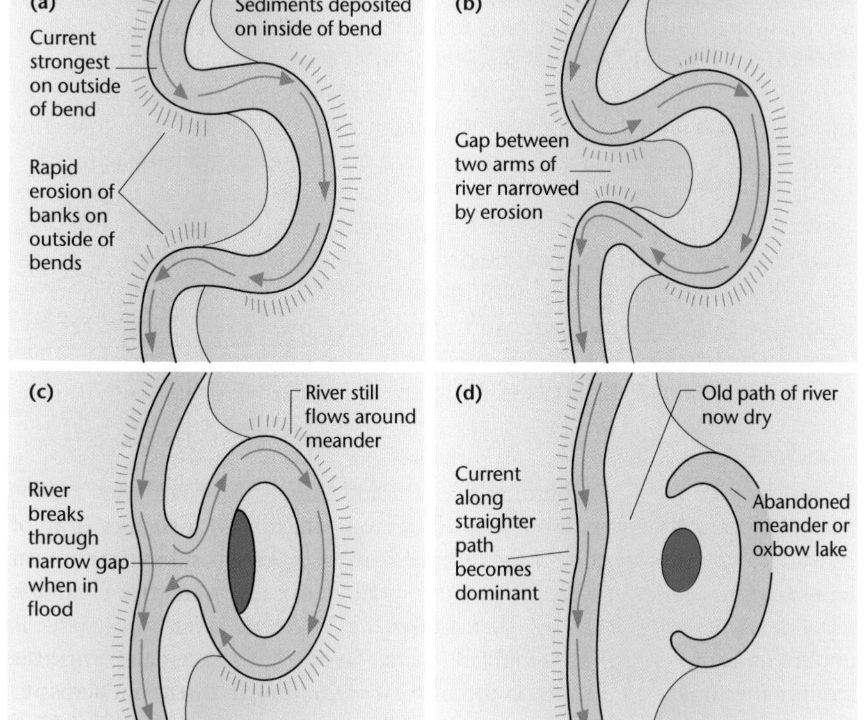

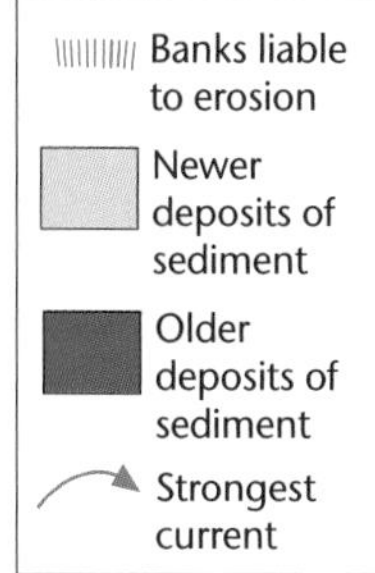

Figure 1.11 The development of an oxbow lake

Photograph 1.4 Meanders on the River Avon in Hampshire

Levées

In its middle and lower courses, a river is at risk from flooding during times of high discharge. If it floods, the velocity of the water falls as it overflows the banks. This results in deposition, because the competence of the river is suddenly reduced. It is usual for the coarsest material to be deposited first, forming small raised banks (**levées**) along the sides of the channel. Subsequent floods increase the size of these banks and further deposition on the bed of the river also occurs. This means that the river, with channel sediment build-up, now flows at a higher level than the floodplain. For this reason, the authorities sometimes strengthen levées and increase their heights. On the Mississippi River (USA), for example, levée strengthening began in 1699. By the 1990s, the length of engineered levées was 3,200 km.

Floodplains

Floodplains are the most common depositional feature of a river. They are the relatively flat areas of land either side of the river, which form the valley floor in the middle and lower courses of the river. They are composed of alluvium — river-deposited silts and clays. Over time, a floodplain becomes wider and the depth of sediment accretions increases. The width of the floodplain is determined by the amount of meander migration and lateral erosion that has taken place, while the depth of the alluvium depends on the amount of flooding in the past. Over time, point bars and old meander scars become incorporated into the floodplain. They become stabilised by vegetation as the meanders migrate and abandon their former courses.

Studies in the USA suggest that point-bar deposits account for around 80% of the volume of sediment contained within a floodplain. In Britain, a large proportion of the accumulated sediment in floodplain deposits was laid down by post-glacial streams, following the last ice age.

Deltas

A **delta** is a feature of deposition, located at the mouth of a river as it enters a sea or lake. Deposition occurs as the velocity and sediment-carrying capacity of the river decrease on entering the lake or sea, and bed-load and suspended material are dumped. Flocculation occurs as fresh water mixes with seawater and clay particles coagulate due to chemical reaction. The clay settles on the river bed.

Deltas only form when the rate of deposition exceeds the rate of sediment removal. In order for a delta to form the following conditions are likely to be met:

- The sediment load of the river is very large, as in the Mississippi and Nile rivers.
- The coastal area into which the river empties its load has a small tidal range and weak currents. This means that there is limited wave action and, therefore, little transportation of sediment after deposition has taken place. This is a feature of the Gulf of Mexico and the Mediterranean Sea.

(a) Structure of a simple delta

Sea or lake
Turbidity current
Topset beds
Foreset beds
Bottomset beds

(b) Cuspate delta

(c) Arcuate delta

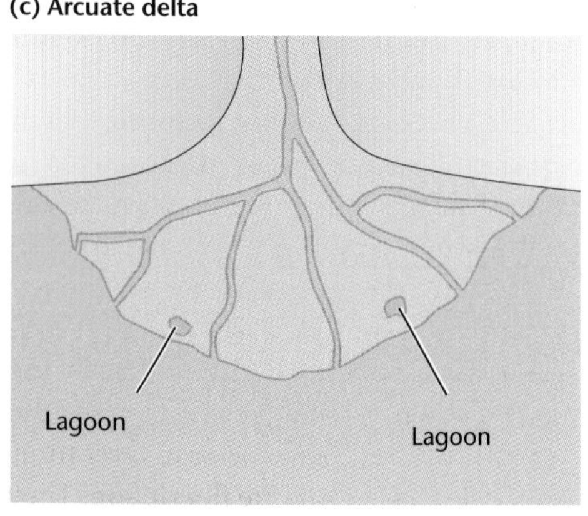

(d) Bird's foot delta

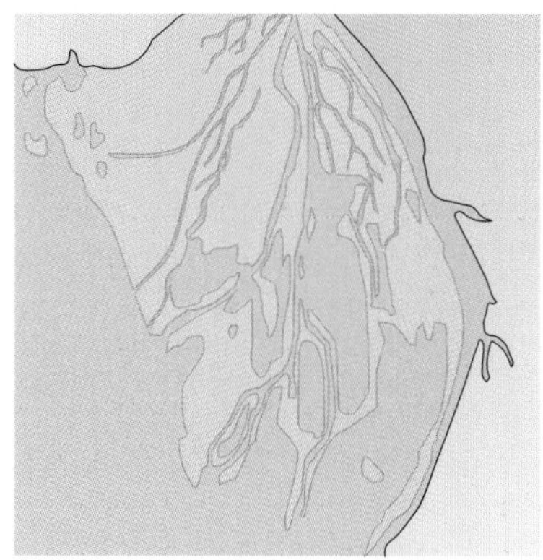

Figure 1.12 Deltas

Deltas are usually composed of three types of deposit:

- The larger and heavier particles are the first to be deposited as the river loses its energy. These form the **topset beds**.
- Medium graded particles travel a little further before they are deposited as steep-angled wedges of sediment, forming the **foreset beds**.
- The very finest particles travel furthest into the lake before deposition and form the **bottomset beds**.

Deltas can be described according to their shape. The most commonly recognised is the characteristic **arcuate delta**, for example the Nile delta, which has a curving shoreline and a dendritic pattern of drainage. Many distributaries break away from the main channel as deposition within the channel itself occurs, causing the river to braid. Longshore drift keeps the seaward edge of the delta relatively smooth in shape. The Mississippi has a **bird's foot delta**. Fingers of deposition build out into the sea along the distributaries' channels, giving the appearance, from the air, of a bird's claw. A **cuspate** delta is pointed like a cup or tooth and is shaped by gentle, regular, but opposing, sea currents or longshore drift.

Flooding and its management

The physical causes of flooding

Flooding occurs when a river's discharge exceeds the capacity of its channel to carry that discharge. The river overflows its banks. Flooding may be caused by a number of natural causes or physical factors:

- Excessive levels of precipitation occurring over a prolonged period of time. This eventually leads to saturation of the soil. When the water table reaches the ground surface, there is increased overland flow or runoff.
- Intensive precipitation over a short period of time, particularly when the ground surface is baked hard after a long period without rainfall. In such circumstances the infiltration capacity is such that the ground cannot soak up the rainfall quickly enough, so more water reaches the river than would normally be the case.
- The melting of snow, particularly when the subsoil is still frozen, so that infiltration capacity is reduced.
- Climatic hazards such as cyclones in Bangladesh, hurricanes in the Gulf of Mexico or deep low-pressure weather systems in mid-latitudes bring abnormally large amounts of precipitation.

The nature of the drainage basin has an influence on the likelihood of flooding. Some drainage basins are more likely to flood than others. Relief, vegetation, soil type and geology all have a part to play. In areas of the world vegetated by dense forest, interception and uptake by plants reduce the risk of flooding during times of heavy rainfall.

Key terms

Hazard A natural event that threatens life and property. A disaster is the realisation of the hazard. Flooding is an example of a natural hazard.

River management River basins are subject to strategies designed to prevent flooding and to ensure that there is an adequate supply of water.

Case study Boscastle floods, Cornwall, August 2004

By midday on 16 August 2004, heavy, thundery downpours had developed across southwest England as a result of an intensive low-pressure weather system that encouraged the uplift of warm, moist air. Some 200 mm of rain fell in 24 hours, most of it between midday and 5.00 p.m. The rainfall was particularly intensive between 3 p.m. and 4 p.m., when it exceeded 100 mm h^{-1} for short periods of time.

This rainfall was, however, very localised. The weather system appeared to stall over the hills above Boscastle. Rainfall was heaviest to the east of Boscastle on high ground. Indeed, the high land encouraged precipitation in the form of orographic rainfall. The ground was already saturated, due to previous wet weather, so infiltration of water into the ground was limited. The topography of the area also contributed to the scale of the flooding. The village of Boscastle lies in a deep valley just downstream of the confluence of the rivers Valency and Jordan.

Runoff into the river was rapid on that day and flooding in the town was first reported at 4.00 p.m. The situation developed swiftly from this point onwards and 60 or so properties were submerged under floodwater. Not all of these were in the town itself; some were in the catchment of the tributary River Jordan and were flooded as surface water cascaded down the hillsides. Around 70–80 cars were swept away in Boscastle and 100 people were airlifted to safety by the emergency services. There was significant damage to property, roads, bridges and services but, mercifully, no loss of life.

TopFoto

Photograph 1.5 Boscastle the day after the devastating floods

The impact of human activities on flooding

Urbanisation

Flooding is a natural event. However, in recent times its effects have been exacerbated by human activity. Over the last two centuries urbanisation has resulted in an ever-increasing proportion of the world's population living in towns and cities. This first occurred in Europe and other developed countries, such as the USA. Since the middle of the twentieth century, urbanisation has been an important feature in many less developed countries.

Coupled with natural population growth, urbanisation has led to an increasing demand for space to build housing and for other urban land uses. Floodplains were an obvious choice — their flat land is suitable to build on and good communications are relatively easy to establish. However, floodplains, by their very nature, are susceptible to flooding.

Human activity on the flat land surrounding the river has added to the risk of flooding. Concrete and tarmac are used in urban areas for roads and pavement. Such surfaces are impermeable, so precipitation is unable to infiltrate slowly into the soil, as it would in a vegetated area. In addition to this, there is less interception from trees and uptake from plants is reduced. Overall, a higher proportion of the original rainfall makes its way into a river in a town or city.

To add to the flood risk, surface water is channelled directly into drains and sewers in an urban area, so precipitation reaches the river quickly. This leads to a reduced lag time between peak rainfall and peak discharge.

Natural river channels may become constricted by bridges, which can slow down discharge and reduce the carrying capacity of the river. In times of spate, debris can be deposited directly behind the supports holding up a bridge and exaggerate the effects of a flood. During the Boscastle floods in August 2004, huge amounts of debris blocked culverts upstream of the town, which had been constructed to allow water to drain quickly through the town.

Deforestation

In some (mainly less developed) countries rapid deforestation has taken place over recent decades. The rainforests of South America, Africa and Asia have been at particular risk as new land has been opened up for farming, settlement and other uses. Other countries, for example Nepal in the Himalayas, have also suffered from deforestation — timber is a valuable resource, used for building and firewood.

Once trees have been removed there is a greater risk of soil erosion and sediment finds its way into rivers, obstructing them and adding to the flood risk. Trees intercept water and take it up through their roots, so in deforested areas more water reaches the channel as runoff.

Flood damage is greatest near the mouth of a river because wide, flat floodplains are most susceptible to damage. Here, the volume of water is at its greatest because many tributaries have joined the river.

Bangladesh lies downstream from Nepal and most of the land is low-lying floodplain that is less than 1 m above sea level, forming the delta of the rivers Brahmaputra, Meghna and Ganges. During the spring snowmelt occurs and once the heavy monsoon rains start in early summer there is a natural rise in the volume of water in the rivers. In recent years, it has been claimed that flooding in Bangladesh has been more severe, partly as a consequence of deforestation in Nepal.

River management

The main aim of river management is to reduce the likelihood of flooding. However, in some circumstances it can actually increase the risk:

- In Bangladesh, embankments have been built along the river channels in some places. These are designed to increase river capacity, but at times have prevented floodwater draining back into the rivers.
- The Farakka dam lies on the upper reaches of the River Ganges in northern India. In 1988, the Indian government allowed the floodgates of the dam to be opened during the rainy season, because the reservoir behind the dam was at risk of flooding. This saved the land surrounding the dam but downstream in Bangladesh it was a different matter. The extra discharge in the river coincided with the normal floods expected at that time of year and greatly increased their severity.
- The Mississippi River in the southern states of the USA is one of the most managed rivers in the world. Artificial embankments (levées) have been built along the lower reaches of the channel to protect the heavily settled floodplain. The city of New Orleans lies below sea level on the banks of the Mississippi and is at particular risk of flooding but is protected by levées and diversion channels, built by the government. In August 2005, devastating floods occurred, submerging the city as the levées were breached. A storm surge, brought about by Hurricane Katrina, gushed up the river from the coast. This, coupled with the heavy rainfall brought by the storm, caused the river to rise dramatically. Major damage to the embankments resulted as they were breached in several places (see case study, page 52).
- Some rivers in urban areas have been channelised. This involves lining the river channel with concrete and straightening it. Channelisation enables water to be directed through the urban area more rapidly. It may protect the immediate surrounding area, but there is a greater flood risk downstream. This is because water is delivered to downstream areas more rapidly than usual and the unmanaged river channel in these stretches is unable to cope with the rapid increase in discharge.

Climate change

In recent years, global warming has been blamed for what some claim is an increasing frequency of flooding. There is evidence that average sea temperatures have risen and this rise has been blamed for the increasing frequency and severity of tropical revolving storms in the Caribbean. Such storms bring heavy rainfall and storm surges along the coastlines of countries lying in their path. In spring 2005, scientists reported that average sea temperatures were 3°C above normal and predicted that the 2005 hurricane season in the Caribbean and southern states of the USA would be particularly savage. This proved to be the case. Notable hurricanes included Katrina, which led to the Mississippi River breaching its levées and flooding the entire city of New Orleans.

It is predicted that global warming will result in reduced rainfall in some areas, but in others, such as western Europe, rainfall totals might increase. Higher temperatures will result in increased evaporation over the seas and oceans, leading to greater precipitation. Such an increase will inevitably cause more rivers to flood, particularly since most floodplains have become heavily urbanised over the last two centuries.

Global warming has also been linked to an increased frequency of El Niño events. El Niño is caused by a reversal in ocean currents in the Pacific Ocean. Normally, a cold current flows off the coast of Peru, encouraging high-pressure weather conditions. In an El Niño year, low-pressure weather dominates, bringing increased rainfall and flooding to the west coast of South America.

Global warming could lead to the melting of the polar ice caps. One major consequence of this would be a rise in sea level, so floodplains lying close to present sea levels would be at risk from flooding. The major deltas of the world, such as those of the Nile, the Mississippi and the Ganges–Brahmaputra, would be at particular risk.

The impact of flooding as a hazard

Flooding is a natural hazard. In sparsely populated areas, such as the Amazon rainforest, a flood will greatly affect the natural environment. Ecological damage occurs if animal habitats are destroyed and it takes time for ecosystems to recover.

In urban areas the main impacts are social and economic. Some of the most densely populated parts of the world are located on the floodplains of major rivers, for example the Nile in northern Africa, the Ganges in India, the Yangtze in China and the Rhine in Europe. Flooding in such areas can cause great human suffering and economic loss.

Photograph 1.6* *In MEDCs the infrastructure exists to plan for flooding events

The level of economic development within a country has an important influence on the impacts of a major flood. In more economically developed countries (MEDCs) the impacts are likely to be predominantly economic, because there is a thriving economy, greater wealth and more possessions among the population. Although homes and businesses are damaged during a major flood, there is limited loss of life because wealthy societies have the infrastructure and services to cope with such events. Most people can afford to insure their homes and busi-nesses against such an eventuality, so the insurance companies face the economic costs.

In less economically developed countries (LEDCs), people are more likely to depend on the land for a living. Subsistence farming remains the main occupation in many such countries, for example Bangladesh, and the effects of flooding can be catastrophic. Homes in LEDCs may be less valuable and people have few possessions, but they may lose everything in a flood. The value of the damage caused in economic terms is low, but human suffering is extreme. Loss of life is also likely to be greater in LEDCs.

The responses to flooding

How well a flood hazard is dealt with largely depends upon:

- the level of preparedness at the location of the expected hazard
- the amount of warning there has been
- the level of economic development, which influences such factors as emergency service provision, infrastructure and the ability to repair and rebuild

Flood management

Flood management seeks to reduce the frequency and magnitude of flooding and, therefore, to limit the damage that floods cause.

Flood protection can be achieved by the following hard-engineering methods:

- The banks and/or channel can be modified to enable the river to carry a larger volume of water. Artificially raised and strengthened banks form a significant part of this strategy. In some cases, parallel lines of flood banks act as a double form of protection — if the river overtops the first barrier, then it has difficulty rising over the second bank some distance behind. The removal of large boulders from the bed of the river reduces roughness, therefore increasing the velocity of flow.
- Dams and weirs can be built to regulate the rate at which water passes down a river.
- Diversion channels can be constructed to divert rivers away from areas vulnerable to flooding.
- Dredging can be used to create a deeper channel so that greater volumes of water can pass through.
- The height of the floodplain can be increased by dumping material on it.
- Retention basins and balancing lakes can be constructed into which water is drained at times of high discharge.

Softer approaches are mainly concerned with flood abatement, which can be achieved by:

- afforestation in the drainage basin, which slows down the rate at which water reaches a river and reduces the amount that reaches the channel
- contour ploughing and strip farming in semi-arid areas, which reduce the amount of surface runoff and, therefore, reduce the liability to flooding
- floodplain zoning, which allows certain areas of the floodplain to flood naturally — land uses are limited to grazing and recreation in such areas. This method protects other, more economically valuable, areas

Comparing the impact and responses to a major flood in an MEDC and an LEDC

Case study MEDC: Shrewsbury, UK, 2000

During the autumn of 2000 the River Severn flooded several times, causing severe problems for the Shropshire town of Shrewsbury.

The source of the Severn is in upland Wales, on the western side of the UK. This area receives above average rainfall from the constant stream of depressions carried in from the Atlantic on the westerly winds. The precipitation feeds the River Severn and its tributaries. The town of Shrewsbury, with some 70,000 inhabitants, lies within the drainage basin of the River Severn, to the east of the Welsh mountains.

Flooding has historically been a problem in Shrewsbury, but in the past most of the built-up area was on higher ground, above the level of the floodplain, so the impact of flooding on the town was not catastrophic. In recent decades low-lying land has been used for both industrial and residential development, so the risk to properties has increased significantly.

A major flood causing significant damage is expected, on average, every 10 years in Shrewsbury, but between 1960 and the mid 1990s large-scale floods did not occur.

During the early 1990s the National Rivers Authority set out plans for a major flood defence scheme in the town. These included the construction of flood embankments along the riverside in the areas of the town that are most at risk. There were objections to the plans from many people living in Shrewsbury. Memories were short and people thought the threat had reduced. They believed that reservoirs constructed upstream in the years since the last major flood would allow the Severn's flow to be successfully regulated. The flood defences were

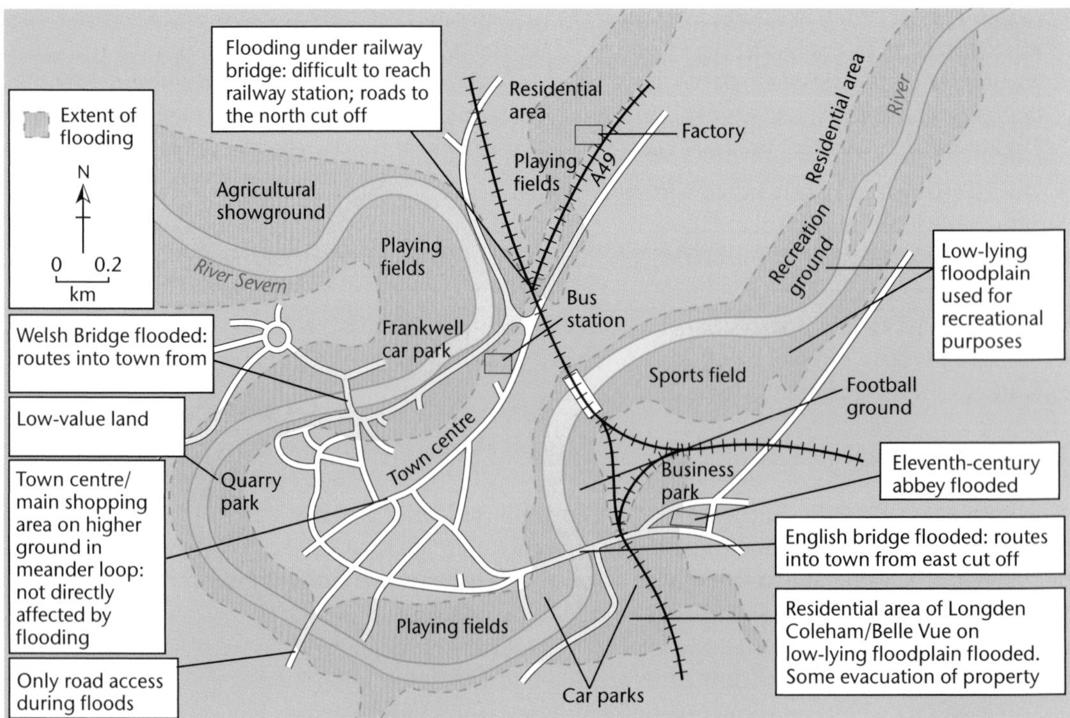

Figure 1.13 The Shrewsbury floods in autumn 2000

deemed unsightly and unnecessary, so the plans were shelved.

Between October and December 2000 the town of Shrewsbury experienced three major floods as the River Severn overflowed its banks.

Impacts

- Communications were severely disrupted and the town centre was effectively cut off, because access into the centre is over the Welsh Bridge from the west and the English Bridge from the east, both of which were flooded. Flooding also affected the main railway line into the town, hampering access by rail.
- Although most of the main shopping area was not flooded, being situated on higher land, many of the town's car parks were submerged under the flood-waters, so trade was severely affected. Since the flooding occurred when people traditionally do their Christmas shopping, sales figures were much lower than would normally be expected. The number of shoppers declined by roughly 60% during this period. Marks and Spencer estimated a loss of £975,000 in revenue, including £30,000 on food, which had to be thrown away.
- Around 400 properties were flooded, some more than once. Residents in the Abbey Gate and Frankwell areas of the town were evacuated.

Short-term responses

Warnings of flooding were issued by the Environment Agency via local flood wardens and automatic voice messaging. Local radio and television news also kept people up to date with the situation as it unfolded. The emergency services were on hand to assist with evacuation of people from homes at risk from flooding and to assist farmers to move livestock onto higher ground. The fire service assisted with the control of water and several thousand sandbags were issued to shopkeepers and householders. Boardwalks were constructed above the flood water to allow access to the town centre for pedestrians. Punts were also used to ferry people to and from places that were flooded.

Long-term responses

The Environment Agency is working on the Severn Catchment Flood Management Plan and the Fluvial Severn Strategy. This is a whole river approach involving many different organisations. It will enable a long-term strategic approach to be taken, looking at possible solutions along the full length of the River Severn. Wider issues, such as changes in land use, farming practice, development control and urban drainage will be considered to help reduce the risk from flooding.

Case study LEDC: Bangladesh, 2004

Bangladesh is a low-lying country most of which lies on the delta land of three major rivers, the Ganges, Brahmaputra and Meghna. The sources of these rivers are in the Himalayas, so snowmelt adds to their discharge during spring.

This part of south Asia has a monsoon climate and experiences a wet season between May and September, when low pressure and winds blowing from the southwest bring heavy rain to coastal regions.

At times during the rainy season, Bangladesh suffers from tropical revolving storms (cyclones) that bring exceptional winds, intense precipitation and storm surges. Such conditions severely affect the discharge of the three rivers and their distributaries, and cause regular floods.

Human factors have played an increasing role in the severity of the floods in recent decades. As in MEDCs, urbanisation has occurred and the capital city Dhaka now has a population of more than 1 million. In addition to this, rapid deforestation in the Himalayas has had a negative effect on the rates of interception and evapotranspiration, resulting in more water reaching the rivers.

River management is difficult to implement in LEDCs like Bangladesh. The country is one of the poorest in the world, with the average gross domestic product per capita standing at around $300. Most of the population rely on subsistence agriculture to survive, growing rice on rented plots of land. This means taxation revenue is limited and Bangladesh relies heavily on foreign aid to finance large-scale development projects which might help prevent floods. In 2004, the monsoon season brought more rainfall than usual. From late June through to September the three main rivers burst their banks, resulting in widespread flooding.

Impacts

- During July and August 2004, approximately 38% of the total land area of the country was flooded, including 800,000 hectares of agricultural land and the capital city, Dhaka.
- Nationwide, 36 million people (from a total population of 125 million) were made homeless.
- By mid-September, the death toll had risen to 800. Many people died as a result of disease because they had no access to clean water.
- The flood also caused serious damage to the country's infrastructure, including roads, bridges and embankments, railway lines and irrigation systems. Boats were afloat on the main runway at Sylhet airport and all domestic and internal flights had to be suspended during July. Road and rail links into Dhaka were also severely affected.
- The value of the damage was assessed as being in the region of $2.2 billion or 4% of the total GDP for 2004.
- Although the flood affected both poor and wealthy households, the poor were generally less able to withstand its impacts. Landless labourers and small farmers were the most severely affected in rural areas. In the urban areas, it was typically the slum dwellers, squatting on poorly drained land, that suffered the most.
- The floods caused four environmental impacts: riverbank erosion, especially on embankment areas close to the main channels; soil erosion; water-logging, particularly in urban areas; and water-contamination, with its associated health risks.

Photograph 1.7 Flooding near Dhaka

TopFoto

Short-term responses

The government, working with non-governmental organisations (NGOs) provided emergency relief in the form of rice, clothing, medicines, blankets and towels. In July, the UN activated a disaster management team to coordinate the activities of the various UN agencies. They supplied critical emergency supplies and conducted a 'damage and needs assessment' in the affected areas. Bilateral aid from individual countries was directed to the UN team. People in Bangladesh are resilient, and self-help schemes, in which local people work together to rebuild their properties and lives, are common.

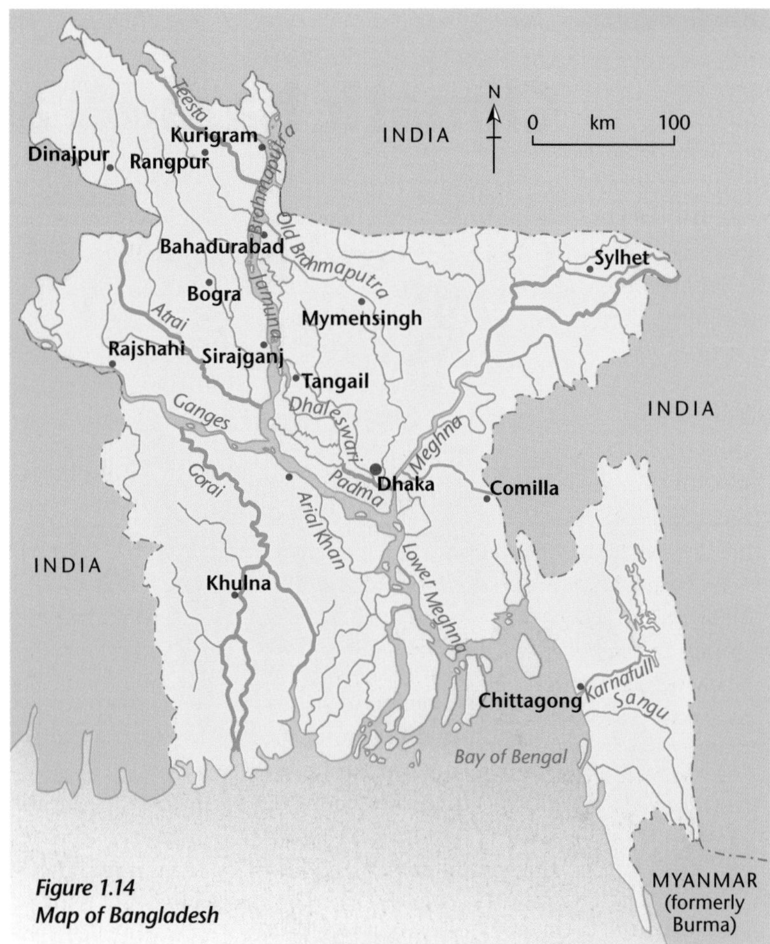

Figure 1.14
Map of Bangladesh

Long-term responses

For an LEDC such as Bangladesh, long-term responses to major floods are largely dependent on foreign aid from both official and unofficial sources. In the past, river management schemes implemented by foreigners and funded by aid have proved to be inadequate. Such schemes paid little attention to local knowledge of rivers and many attempts at river management failed. More recently, small-scale community-based projects have resulted in lives being saved. Flood shelters and early-warning systems have been successfully put in place.

Following the 2004 floods, additional financial aid was granted for a period of 5 years. This was mainly in the form of a loan from the World Bank, to pay for, in the first instance, repairs to infrastructure, water resource management and education.

Disaster-preparedness is a key priority for the future. This includes flood management and improved water resources. It is also planned that, in future, flood-resistant designs should be used in all social and economic infrastructure projects.

Chapter 2

Climatic hazards and change

Costs and benefits of weather and climate

Controls over climate

The climate is the mean atmospheric conditions of an area, measured over a substantial period of time. Different parts of the world have recognisable climatic characteristics with distinctive seasonal patterns, and these are largely determined by a number of controls including solar energy, pressure and winds.

Solar energy

The sun provides the Earth with energy that is vital for the survival of life on the planet. This energy also controls the climate and weather. The amount of energy available in different locations varies for a number of reasons including latitude, altitude and distance from the sea.

The energy budget of the Earth depends on the balance between incoming **solar radiation (insolation)** and outgoing radiation from the planet (Figure 2.1). Geological records show that, on average, the energy budget has remained constant over the last few thousand years. This means that the incoming and outgoing energies must be equal. However, there is evidence to suggest that global warming has occurred over recent decades.

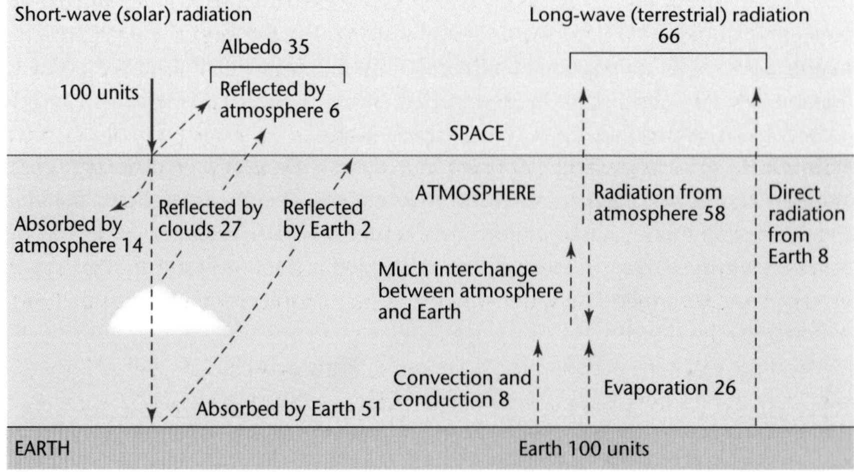

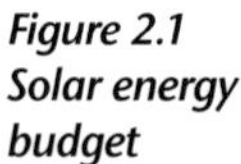
Figure 2.1 Solar energy budget

The Earth receives energy from the sun as incoming radiation. Some of this is lost on passing through the atmosphere but overall the surface has a net *gain* of energy. The only places where there is a deficit are the polar regions. Only about 24% of the incoming solar radiation reaches the surface of the Earth, because of absorption, reflection and scattering.

The atmosphere, in contrast, has a net *deficit* of energy. To compensate for this difference, heat is transferred from the surface of the Earth to the atmosphere by radiation, conduction and by the release of latent heat.

There are variations in energy and heat between different latitudes. Low latitudes have a net surplus of energy, due mainly to their relative proximity to the sun. The high latitudes (polewards 40°N and 40°S) have a net deficit. Theoretically, this differential heating should result in the equatorial regions being much hotter and the poles much colder than they are. Since the poles are not becoming colder, and the equatorial regions are not becoming hotter, heat must be being transferred between the two. This occurs by means of air movement (winds), and water movement (ocean currents).

Key terms

Cool temperate western maritime climate (CTWM) The seasonal pattern of the weather experienced in the mid-latitudes (between 45° and 60°) on the western side of continental land masses.

General atmospheric circulation The pattern of wind and pressure belts within the atmosphere. The circulation is complex but there are certain movements that occur regularly enough for us to recognise patterns of air pressure, distribution and winds.

Pressure

Atmospheric pressure is the pressure exerted by the atmosphere at the surface of the Earth. It is due to the weight of the air. The atmosphere consists of a mixture of gases. It is prevented from escaping from the Earth by the force of gravity.

The layers of the atmosphere closest to the ground surface have the greatest weight acting upon them, so pressure is greatest here. Consequently, air pressure decreases with altitude. At the top of the highest mountains it is very low. Climbers need to take similar precautions to surfacing divers to guard against falling air pressure. Air passengers are protected from low air pressure in the upper atmosphere by pressurised cabins.

Atmospheric pressure also varies horizontally, because it is a direct function of temperature. When the temperature rises, air expands and rises by convection, and pressure decreases. Conversely, when the temperature falls, air contracts and becomes denser, causing an increase in pressure.

High pressure occurs where air is descending and is associated with dry weather. This is because air warms as it descends, leading to the evaporation of most water vapour.

Low pressure occurs where air is rising. It is generally linked to precipitation and windy conditions. As it ascends air cools, and as a consequence it cannot hold as much water vapour. The water condenses into droplets, which become clouds at condensation level.

Atmospheric pressure is measured using a barometer. The unit of atmospheric pressure is the **millibar** (mb); the average sea-level value is 1,013 mb. Points of equal atmospheric pressure are shown on a weather map by lines called **isobars** (see Figure 2.8).

Winds

Winds result from differences in air pressure. These differences occur because of variations in temperature. When the air temperature of a place increases, the air in that area expands and rises, thus reducing air pressure. Conversely, when the temperature falls, the air becomes denser. It sinks and air pressure increases. The gradual change in air pressure over an area, seen in the pattern of isobars on a weather map, is called the **pressure gradient**. This gives rise to the movement of air from an area of relatively high pressure to an area of relatively low pressure. The movement of air on the Earth's surface from areas of high to low pressure is called **wind**.

The general atmospheric circulation system

The differential heating of the Earth's surface is sufficient to create a pattern of pressure cells. The movement of air within each cell is generally circular and, overall, is responsible for the transfer of surplus energy from equatorial regions to other parts of the Earth. Three cells form in each hemisphere, resulting in major areas of high and low pressure at the surface. High pressure forms where the air is falling and low pressure where it is rising.

The three cells in each hemisphere are known as the Hadley cell, the Ferrel cell and the Polar cell (Figure 2.2).

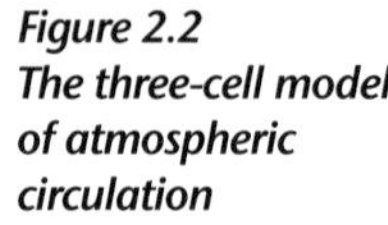

Figure 2.2 The three-cell model of atmospheric circulation

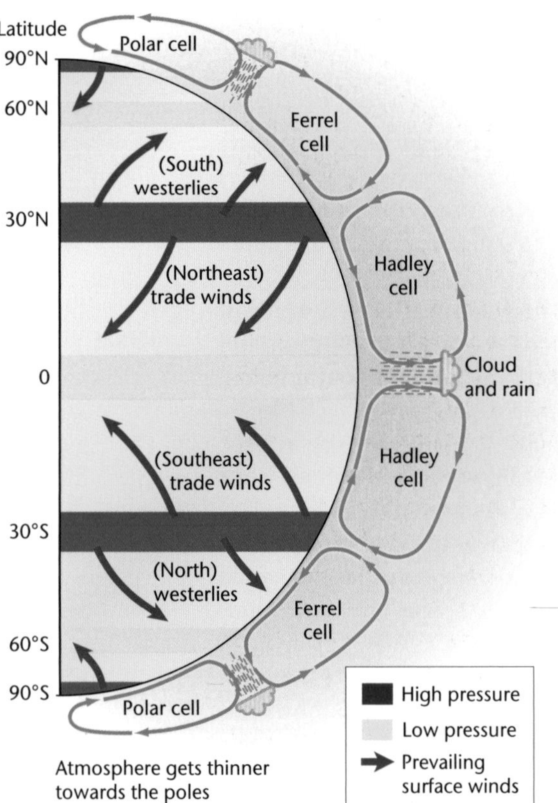

The Hadley cells

The two Hadley cells, one in each hemisphere, form the basis of tropical air circulation as shown in Figure 2.3, and are responsible for the seasonal changes in climate of those regions that experience a wet and dry climate. Note that the tropopause is the upper limit of the lower part of the atmosphere (known as the troposphere). It is about 16 km above the equator and 8 km above the poles.

Each Hadley cell can be divided into four components:

- Between the two cells there is an area of low pressure in equatorial latitudes which is known as the **inter-tropical convergence zone** or ITCZ. As the sun is always high in the sky, the ground heats rapidly by day and there is much surface evaporation. As the hot air rises in convection currents, an area of low pressure develops. This rising air cools and the water vapour eventually condenses, giving heavy rainfall.
- At high altitudes the air moves polewards. This air usually circulates as upper westerly winds around the planet due to the deflection

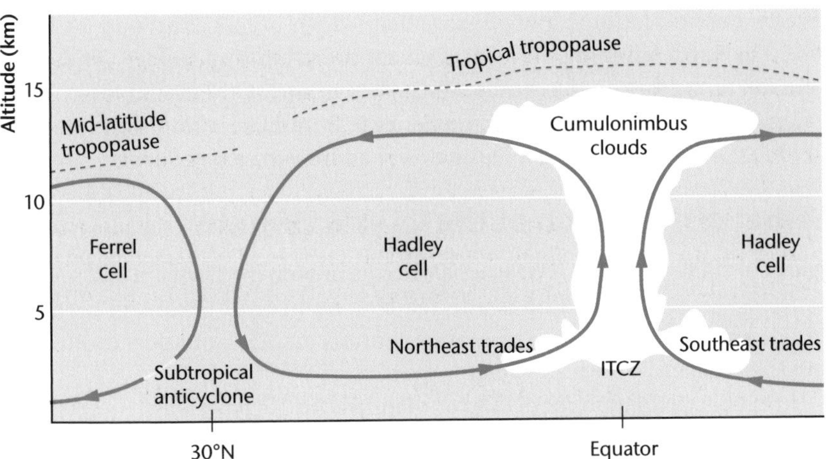

Figure 2.3 The circulation of the Hadley cells

effect of the rotation of the Earth, known as the **Coriolis effect**. The net effect, though, is for the air still to move polewards.

- Around 30°N and 30°S the colder air at higher altitudes begins to sink, or subside, back to the Earth's surface. As this air descends, it warms and any residual moisture evaporates. At the surface, high pressure is created, with cloudless skies. These areas are known as the **subtropical anticyclones**.
- On reaching the ground, some of the air returns towards equatorial areas as consistent winds known as the **trade winds**. These air movements are also subject to the Coriolis effect and are deflected to the right in the northern hemisphere and to the left in the south. As a result they blow from a north-easterly direction in the northern hemisphere and from the southeast in the southern hemisphere. The two trade wind systems move air towards the equator where it forms the ITCZ.

The Ferrel and Polar cells

A second cell called the Ferrel cell occurs at higher latitudes (between 30° and 60°N and 30° and 60°S). This is responsible for the climate types occurring in the mid-latitudes. As Figure 2.2 shows, air on the surface is pulled toward the poles, forming the warm southwesterly winds in the northern hemisphere and the north-westerlies in the southern hemisphere. These winds pick up moisture as they travel over the oceans. At around 60°N and 60°S, they meet cold air, which has drifted from the poles. The warmer air from the tropics is lighter than the dense, cold polar air and so it rises as the two air masses meet. This uplift of air causes low pressure at the surface and the resulting unstable conditions result in the mid-latitude depressions, characteristically experienced in the cool temperate western maritime (CTWM) climate.

On reaching the troposphere, some of this rising air eventually returns to the tropics as part of the Ferrel cell circulation; some is diverted polewards, as part of the Polar cell.

On the surface at the north and south poles, descending air from the Polar cell results in high pressure. Winds always blow from areas of high pressure to areas of low pressure. In both the northern and southern hemispheres they are pulled towards the mid-latitude low-pressure belt, which occurs at around 60°N and 60°S. The Earth spinning on its axis causes the prevailing surface winds to be deflected to the west in the southern hemisphere and to the east in the northern hemisphere. Thus cold air is transported away from high latitudes and warm air is brought in by the Polar cell. This helps to address the energy deficit.

Global distribution of the CTWM climate

Figure 2.4 shows that the CTWM climate occurs in both the northern and southern hemispheres. Its distribution is affected by a number of factors, in particular, latitude and proximity to the sea. Marine controls modify latitudinal controls and tend to overshadow them in winter.

- The global circulation model shows that this climate type, which occurs in the mid-latitudes between 40° and 60°N and 40° and 60°S, lies within the Ferrel cell. As such, the prevailing winds blow from the southwest in the northern hemisphere and from the northwest in the southern hemisphere. They transfer heat from the tropics, noticeably elevating temperatures during the winter months.
- The CTWM climate is heavily influenced by its proximity to the oceans. In summer, locations close to the sea experience lower temperatures than might be expected for the latitude. The sea warms up more slowly than the land because it has a lower specific heat capacity. As a result, onshore winds are relatively cool, so places close to the sea experience a chilling effect during the summer. The opposite effect occurs during the winter.
- All locations with a CTWM climate are located on the western side of continents. Warm ocean currents travel along the coastlines, transferring heat from the tropics towards the poles. These movements of water contribute to the global transfer of surplus energy and help to moderate temperatures. Ocean currents are largely set in motion by the prevailing surface winds associated

***Figure 2.4* Distribution of the CTWM climate**

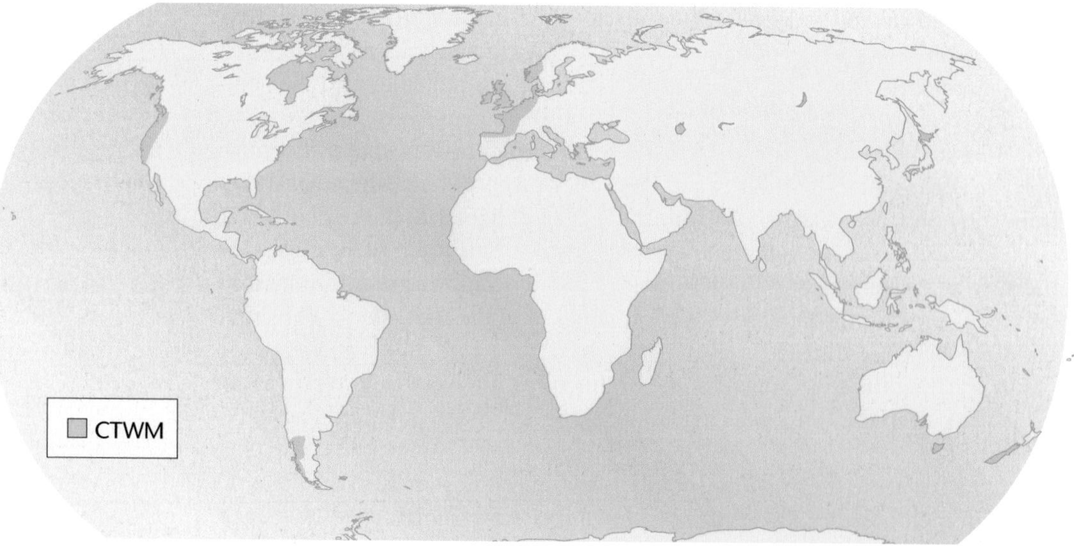

with the general atmospheric circulation. The influence of the North Atlantic drift on western Europe is a good example.

- Subtropical and subpolar air meet in these latitudes and this gives rise to low-pressure weather systems or depressions. On average, over 100 depressions cross the British Isles every year. They produce unsettled, stormy weather. Occasionally, high pressure takes over. Dry continental air becomes established and blocks out low-pressure systems, producing fine, settled weather.
- Rain-bearing winds blow onshore, bringing precipitation throughout the year to CTWM areas. The total annual rainfall is relatively high, usually over 500 mm. In mountainous areas, totals can be five times greater. Most of the rainfall is cyclonic and orographic, but in the summer convection storms can also occur.

Characteristics of the CTWM climate

Climate graphs present a view of the average conditions over at least 30 years. However, one of the most striking features of the CTWM climate is its unpredictability. The weather experienced within this climate zone is noted for its changeability on a day-to-day basis, which is partly due to the overall dominance of low-pressure weather systems.

Figures 2.5 and 2.6 are climate graphs for locations in Australia and the UK respectively. In summer, mean temperatures are lower than average for the latitude and although the daily maximum temperature can reach 30°C, average monthly values seldom exceed 20°C. In winter, the average temperatures are generally above freezing. In some coastal locations, such as Cornwall in England and Pembrokeshire in Wales, average values remain above 6°C. This minimum temperature, influenced by the warming effect of the sea, ensures a year-round growing season. The annual range of temperature within the CTWM is relatively small, but increases with distance away from the west coast. Cambridge in East Anglia has an annual temperature range of 14°C, compared with 10°C for Plymouth in Devon.

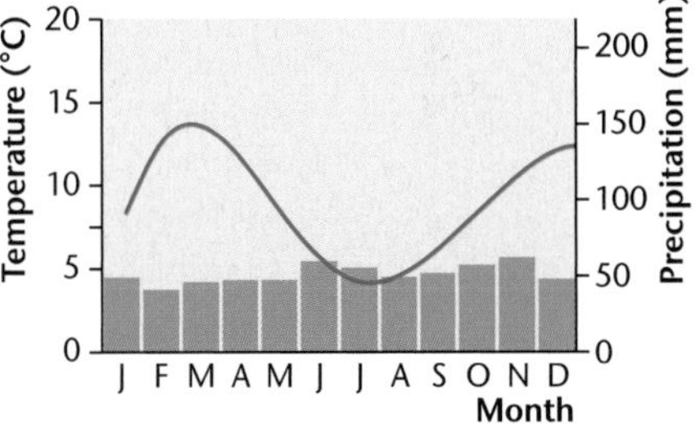

Figure 2.5
Climate graph for Hobart, Tasmania

Generally, rainfall is experienced throughout the year. However, within the climate zone it tends to vary with relief. In upland areas, particularly those close to western coasts, rainfall totals can exceed 2,500 mm. A short distance further east, on lowland in the shadow of the mountains, annual totals can be as little as 500 mm. Most of the rainfall experienced is brought in by frontal systems, which travel from west to east, disposing with moisture as they cross the land. In general, the summer tends to be the driest season, followed by winter, because the depressions during these seasons can track further north or south. High-pressure weather systems (anticyclones) are more likely to become established during these seasons and they block the approaching fronts, deflecting them away to the north or south.

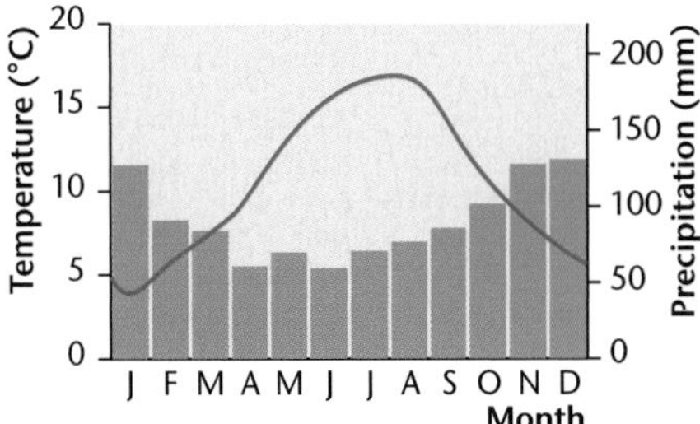

Figure 2.6
Climate graph for Falmouth, Cornwall

Atmospheric processes responsible for the CTWM climate

Air masses

Several different air masses may approach western Europe. Each brings with it a range of weather conditions:

- **Arctic** — from the north, brings extremely cold temperatures and snow in winter and early spring.
- **Polar maritime** — from the northwest Atlantic, is accompanied by cold, moist weather.
- **Polar continental** — from the east, brings bitterly cold temperatures in winter and possibly snow to eastern England.
- **Tropical maritime** — from the southwest, causes the weather to be mild and wet in winter but cool and moist in summer.
- **Tropical continental** (in summer only) — from the southeast, brings hot, dry, heat-wave conditions.

The weather associated with an air mass is related closely to the source region. A frontal system develops when two contrasting air masses meet.

Depressions

Depressions are low-pressure weather systems. They have the following characteristics:

- they are areas of relatively low atmospheric pressure, often below 1,000 mb
- they are represented on a weather map by a system of closed isobars with pressures decreasing towards the centre
- they usually move rapidly from west to east across the British Isles
- isobars are usually close together, producing a steep pressure gradient from the outer edges to the centre
- winds are often strong and blow inwards towards the centre of the low, anticlockwise in the northern hemisphere and clockwise in the southern hemisphere
- a place in the southern part of the British Isles will often experience changes of wind direction from south to southwest to west to northwest as the depression moves across from west to east — the wind is said to **veer**
- a place in the northern part of the British Isles will often experience a change of wind direction from southeast to east to northeast to east — the wind is said to **back**

Formation of a depression

A depression affecting the British Isles originates in the North Atlantic where two different **air masses** meet along the polar front (see Figure 2.7). The two air masses involved here are:

- polar maritime air from the northwest Atlantic which is cold, dense and moist
- tropical maritime air from the southwest which is warmer, less dense and also moist

As these two bodies of air move towards each other the warmer, less dense air from the south rises above the colder, dense air from the north. The rising air is removed

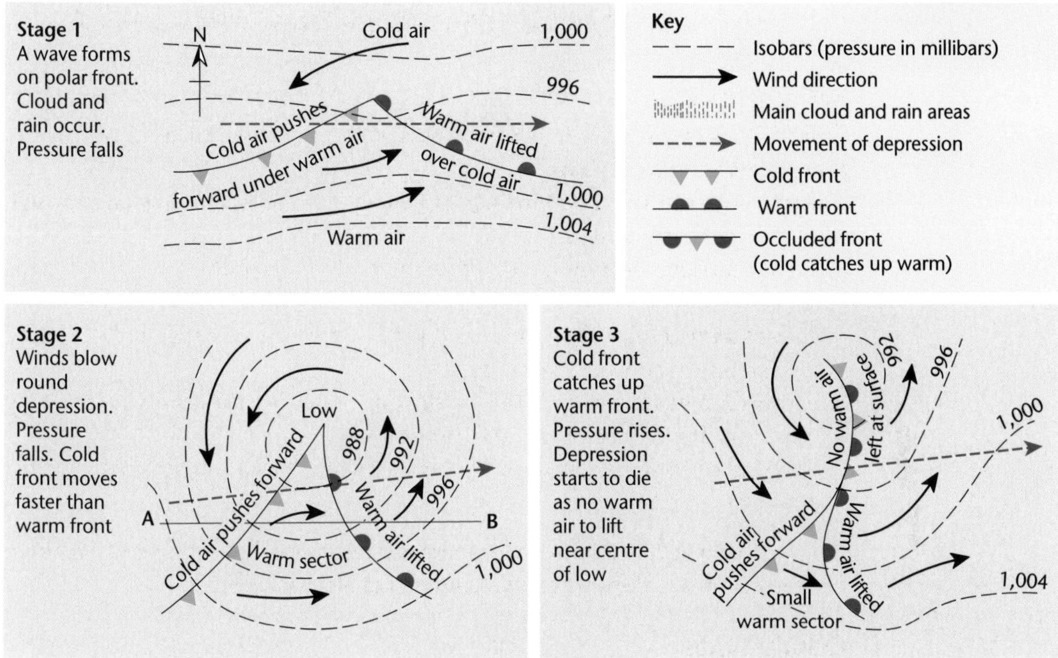

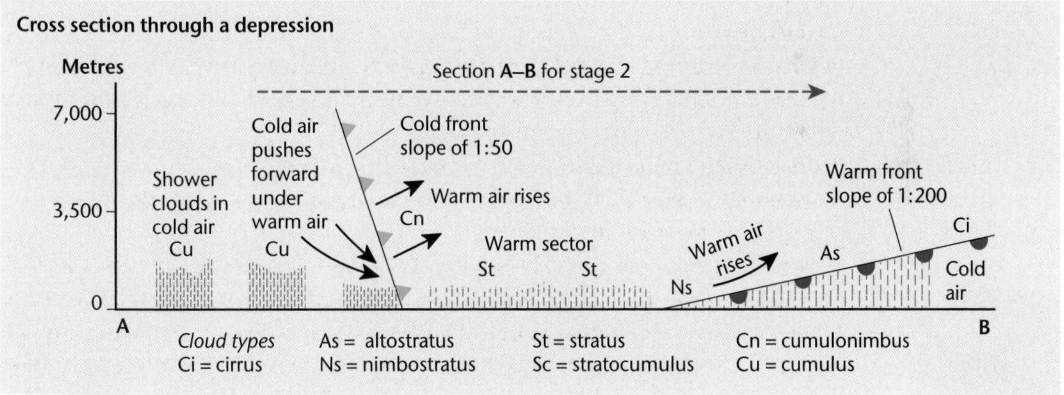

Figure 2.7* *The stages of a depression

by strong upper atmosphere winds (known as a **jet stream**), but as it rises the Earth's rotational spin causes it to twist. This twisting vortex produces a wave at ground level in the polar front, which increases in size to become a depression.

Two separate parts of the original front have now developed (stage 2 in Figure 2.7):

- the **warm front** at the leading edge of the depression where warm, less dense air rises over the colder air ahead
- the **cold front** at the rear of the depression where colder dense air pushes against the warmer air ahead

In between these two fronts lies the **warm sector** — an area of warm and moist air. As the depression moves eastwards, the cold front gradually overtakes the warm front to form an **occlusion** in which the warmer air is lifted off the ground.

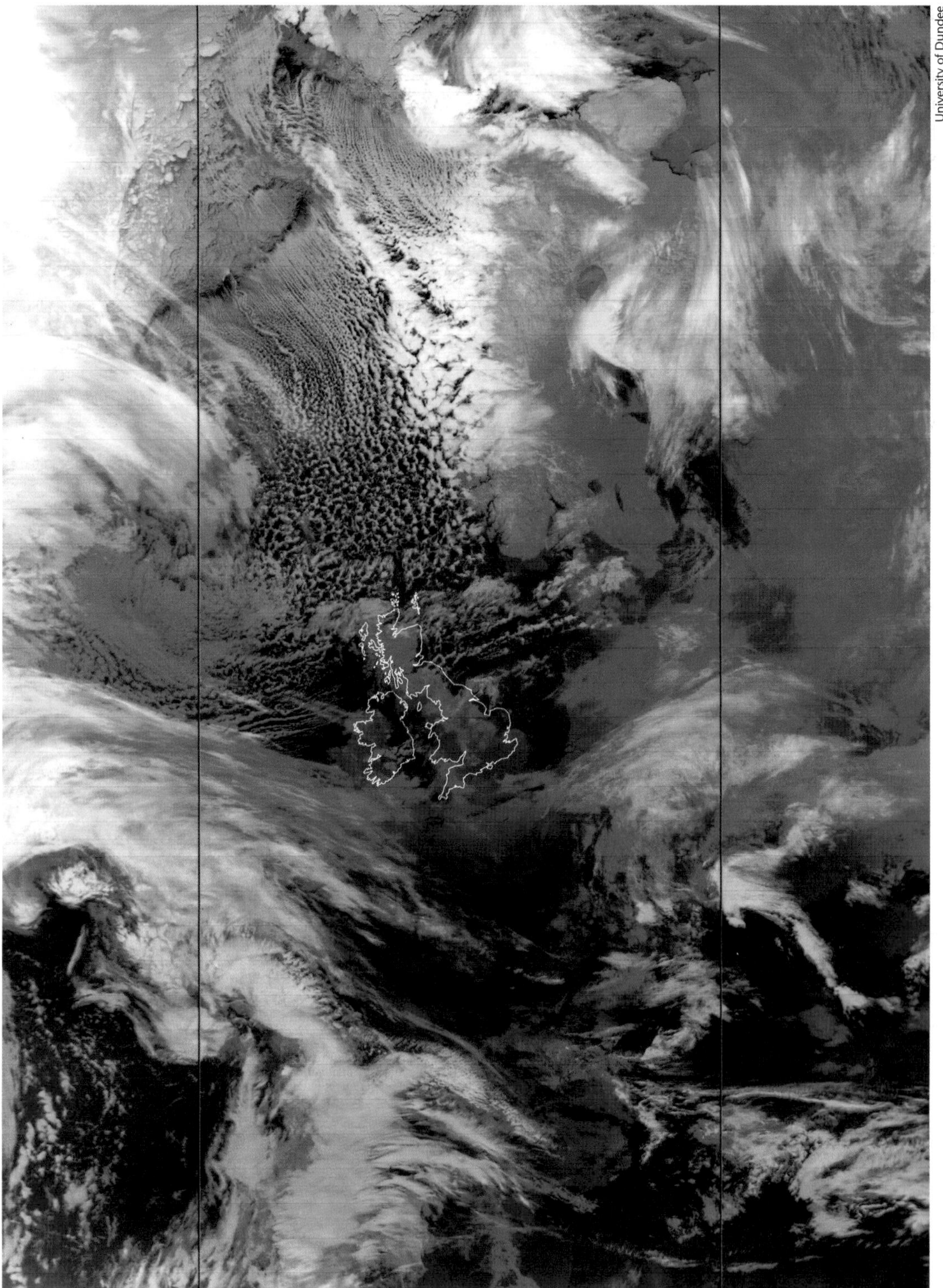
University of Dundee

Photograph 2.1 Satellite photograph showing a depression to the west of the British Isles

Weather conditions

The weather conditions associated with a depression therefore depend on whether the area in question has polar maritime air or tropical maritime air over it. Polar maritime air brings average temperatures for the season in winter (5–8°C in January) but noticeably cooler temperatures for the season in summer (16–18°C in July). Showers of rain are common in both seasons, with the possibility of sleet in winter.

Tropical maritime air brings humid and mild weather in winter, with temperatures well above the seasonal norm at 12–14°C in January. Low stratus cloud and fog are also common. In summer it may cause advection fog in western coastal areas, but elsewhere temperatures will be warm — 25°C in July. There will be the threat of showers and possibly thunderstorms due to the combination of high humidity levels and low pressure.

Table 2.1 summarises the main weather changes associated with the passage of a depression over an area in the British Isles. It should be used in conjunction with the cross section through a depression shown in Figure 2.7.

Table 2.1 Weather changes associated with the passing of a depression

Weather element	**Cold front**			**Warm front**		
	In the rear	*At passage*	*Ahead*	*In the rear*	*At passage*	*Ahead*
Pressure	Continuous steady rise	Sudden rise	Steady or slight fall	Steady or slight fall	Fall stops	Continuous fall
Wind	Veering to northwest, decreasing speed	Sudden veer, southwest to west. Increase in speed, with squalls	Southwest, but increasing in speed	Steady southwest, constant	Sudden veer from south to southwest	Slight backing ahead of front. Increase in speed
Temperature	Little change	Significant drop	Slight fall, especially if raining	Little change	Marked rise	Steady, little change
Humidity	Variable in showers, but usually low	Decreases sharply	Steady	Little change	Rapid rise, often to near saturation	Gradual increase
Visibility	Very good	Poor in rain, but quickly improves	Often poor	Little change	Poor, often fog/mist	Good at first but rapidly deteriorating
Clouds	Shower clouds, clear skies and cumulus clouds	Heavy cumulo-nimbus	Low stratus and stratocumulus	Overcast, stratus and stratocumulus	Low nimbostratus	Becoming increasingly overcast, cirrus to altostratus to nimbostratus
Precipitation	Bright intervals and scattered showers	Heavy rain, hail and thunder-storms	Light rain, drizzle	Light rain, drizzle	Rain stops or reverts to drizzle	Light rain, becoming more continuous and heavy

Anticyclones

Anticyclones have the following characteristics:

- they are areas of relatively high atmospheric pressure
- they are represented on a weather map by a system of closed isobars with pressures increasing towards the centre (see Figure 2.8)
- anticyclones move slowly and may remain stationary over an area for several days or even weeks
- the air in an anticyclone **subsides** (falls from above), warming as it falls. This produces a decrease in its relative humidity which leads to a lack of cloud development, and dry conditions
- isobars are usually far apart, and therefore there is little pressure difference between the centre and edges of the anticyclone
- winds are weak, and flow gently outwards
- in the northern hemisphere the winds flow clockwise around the centre of the anticyclone
- in the southern hemisphere the winds flow anticlockwise

Figure 2.8 An anticyclone over Scotland

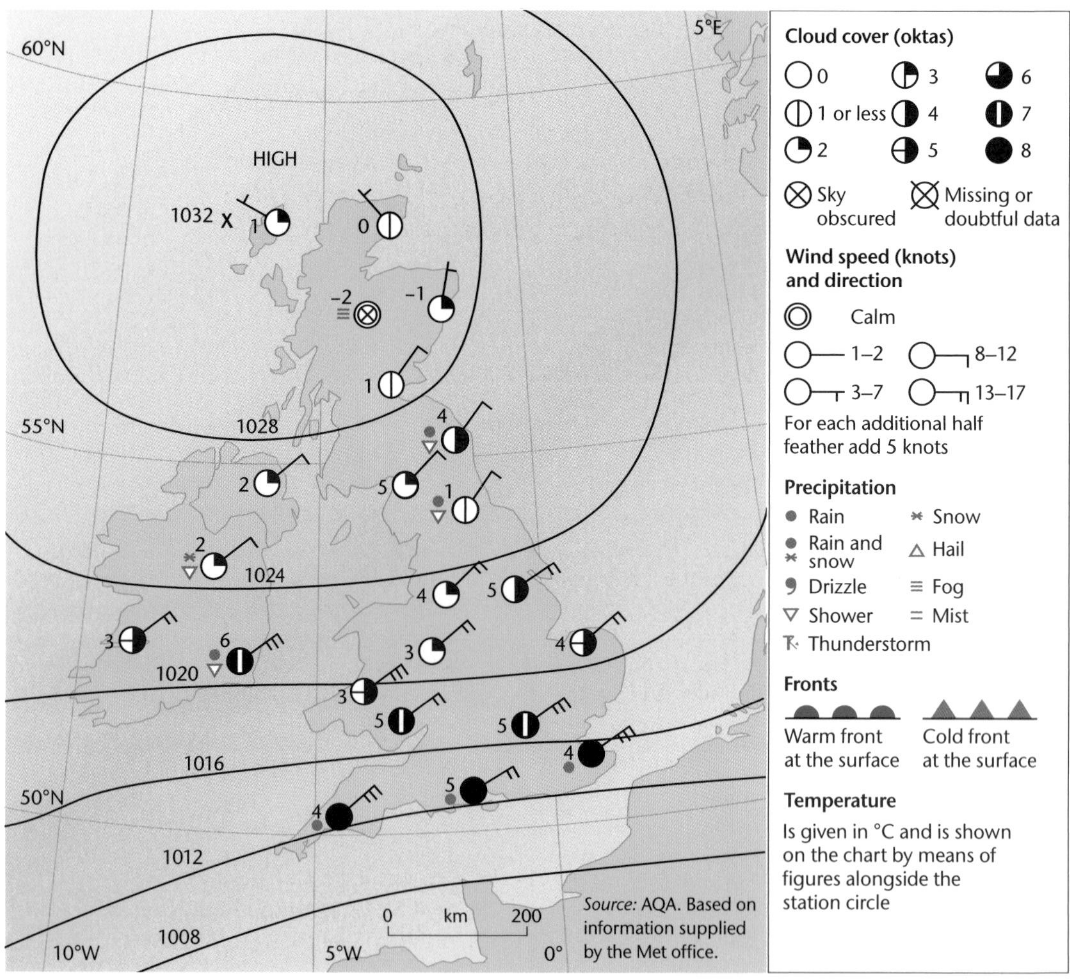

Jane Buckett

Photograph 2.2 A winter anticyclone traps pollution in the air over Burnley. The polluted air can be seen as a brown haze over the town

Weather conditions

In winter, anticyclones result in:

- cold daytime temperatures — from below freezing to a maximum of 5°C
- very cold night-time temperatures — below freezing with frosts
- generally clear skies by day and night. Low-level cloud may linger and **radiation fogs** (caused by rapid heat loss at night) may remain in low-lying areas
- high levels of atmospheric pollution in urban areas, caused by a combination of subsiding air and lack of wind. Pollutants are trapped by a **temperature inversion** (when the air at altitude is marginally warmer than air at lower levels, see Photograph 2.2)

In summer, anticyclones mean:

- hot daytime temperatures — over 25°C
- warm night-time temperatures — may not fall below 15°C
- generally clear skies by day and night
- hazy sunshine in some areas
- early morning mists which disperse rapidly
- heavy dew on the ground in the morning
- the east coast of Britain may have sea **frets** or **haars** caused by onshore winds
- thunderstorms may occur when the air has high relative humidity

Anticyclones which establish themselves over Britain and northwest Europe and remain stationary for many days are described as **blocking** anticyclones. Depressions which would normally travel across the British Isles on a westerly airstream are steered around the upper edge of the high, and away from the area. Extreme weather conditions are then produced — dry and freezing weather in winter, and heat waves in summer.

Fogs

Fogs are common features of anticyclonic conditions. Fog is cloud at ground level which restricts visibility to less than 1 km. It consists of tiny water droplets suspended in the atmosphere. There are two main types of fog — radiation fog and advection fog.

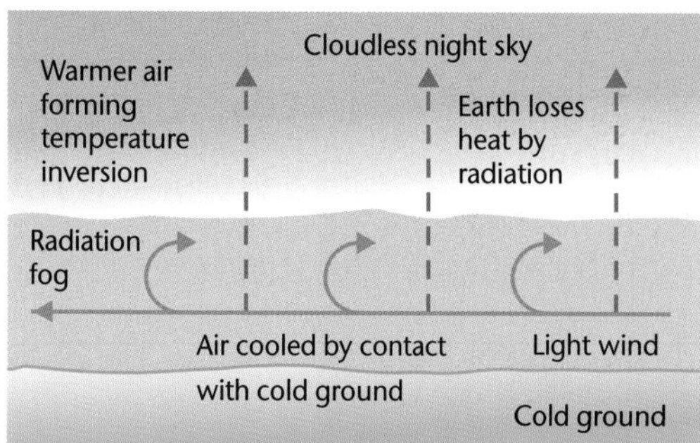

Figure 2.9 How radiation fog forms

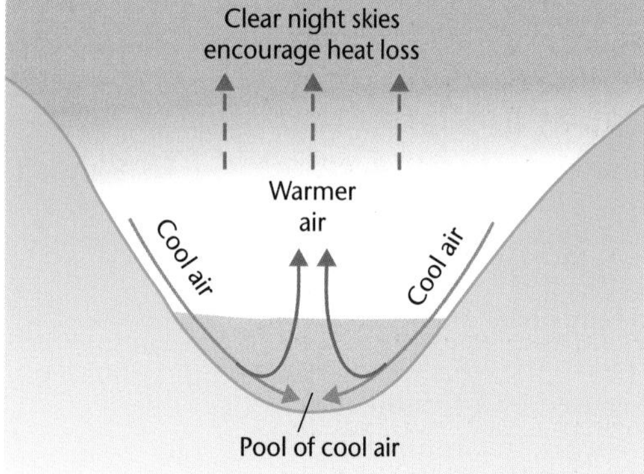

Figure 2.10 Fog formation under a temperature inversion in a valley

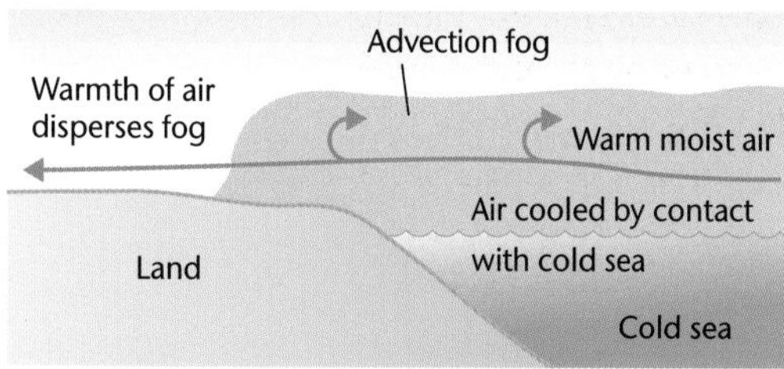

Figure 2.11 Advection fog

Radiation fog

Radiation fog forms under clear night skies when a moist atmosphere cools through the radiation of heat from the ground surface. The cooling extends some distance above the ground surface and is encouraged by light winds that allow slight mixing of the air. The air is cooled to its **dew point**, at which condensation occurs (Figure 2.9).

This type of fog is common in winter, when long hours of darkness allow maximum cooling. In such cases, the fog may persist all day. It disperses either through an increase in wind speed or through a warming of the air (and subsequent evaporation).

Radiation fog is common under temperature inversions, which often occur in valleys (Figure 2.10). In the evening, with clear skies and high humidity, the air on the upper slopes chills quicker than that in the valley bottom. Cooling increases the density of the air, and it begins to move downslope. The cooler air accumulates in the valley bottom, pushing the warmer air upwards. The cold air now in the valley bottom will cool to its dew point, and create a dense fog that can last all day, and cause a severe frost.

Advection fog

Advection fog forms when a mass of relatively warm air moves horizontally across a cooler surface. The air is cooled to its dew point, and condensation occurs. This type of fog is most common around coasts and over the sea in summer. In such areas it is sometimes called a **fret** or a **haar**. As the fog moves inland, it is warmed and evaporates (Figure 2.11).

The opportunities and constraints of the CTWM climate for human activity

Opportunities

The CTWM climate provides a relatively long growing season, with average temperatures above 6°C for most of the year and sufficient moisture to support plant growth. In lowland areas, arable farming is a productive and profitable activity and cereals, vegetables and fruit are grown. Those areas on the extreme western edges of Europe, such as Cornwall in the UK and Brittany in France experience year-long growing conditions and have become well known for early vegetable production.

Rainfall is abundant in upland areas, particularly those on the western side of the British Isles, such as Snowdonia and the Lake District. Both natural and artificially created lakes can be used to store water. For example, Lake Vrynwy in north Wales and Thirlmere in the Lake District supply water to the cities of Liverpool and Manchester respectively. Hydroelectric power can be generated using fast-flowing water from upland rivers.

Exposed areas on the west coast of the British Isles experience regular strong winds and gales from the Atlantic Ocean and the Irish Sea. They are ideal sites for wind farms, another renewable source of energy.

In an age of dwindling supplies of oil and concern about pollution from burning fossil fuels, both hydroelectric and wind power have potential for further development.

Constraints

Intense low-pressure weather systems cross the British Isles relentlessly from autumn through to spring. It is usually the areas on the western extremities that bear the brunt of the storms accompanying these depressions. Low pressure can bring gale-force winds and heavy rainfall, both of which present severe problems.

If, over a period of time, the rainfall associated with low-pressure weather systems is above that which is normally expected, the ground may become saturated. This is particularly true during winter, when deciduous trees are bare (so little water is intercepted) and little water is used by plants for growth. Under such circumstances more water reaches rivers as runoff.

This was the case in October 1998, when the River Severn experienced severe flooding. This was due in part to precipitation associated with a succession of low-pressure weather systems that crossed the drainage basin. The month of October 1998 was one of the wettest on record with over 135 mm of rain (almost 20% of normal annual rainfall). The topography of the Severn valley was also responsible for the rapid rise in the discharge of the river, but it was the excess rainfall that caused river levels to rise. Impacts were severe. In Shrewsbury, flooding damaged approximately 400 residential and commercial properties. In autumn 2000, the worst flooding for over 50 years occurred in the Severn valley. It was once more partly due to excessively high rainfall brought by intense low-pressure weather systems.

Anticyclonic weather conditions can lead to drought, particularly when rainfall levels are below average during spring and summer, and demand for water is high. In the summer of 2003 severe drought occurred across western Europe and temperatures reached record highs in Paris. It was necessary to implement emergency measures to restrict water use. Farmers faced controls on irrigation; householders had restrictions on car washing, watering lawns and filling swimming pools.

In urban areas, particularly those located inland, long periods of anticyclonic weather during summer can encourage the development of photochemical smog. This hazard tends to develop in cities where traffic discharges a high level of exhaust gases. Photochemical smog is produced when these pollutants react in the presence of sunlight. A combination of descending air and lack of wind prevents the smog dispersing. Photochemical smog endangers health — it causes respiratory problems and has been linked with increased occurrence of asthma in children.

In winter, high-pressure weather brings its own set of problems. Thick freezing fog can last for days because the sunlight is too weak to disperse it. Fog causes major disruption on the roads, and airports may be forced to cancel or divert flights. In the past, smog was a serious hazard in many of our cities during winter. However, the effects of the great smog in London in 1952 led to controls over the discharge of smoke into the atmosphere. Smog is the result of minute particles of carbon, from the burning of coal or wood, mixing with fog. It is still a problem in parts of the world where these fuels are used in large amounts.

Climatic hazards

The atmospheric processes responsible for severe gales

In the mid-latitudes, severe gales are generally associated with low-pressure weather systems and occur where there is a steep pressure gradient. Surface winds always blow from high to low pressure. Strong winds, and a steep pressure gradient, can be recognised on a weather chart by isobars that are close together. Severe gales occur when the air pressure drops to a very low level. For example, in 'the storm of the century' that hit southern England in 1987, the centre of the low-pressure area measured 964 mb (the average sea-level value for air pressure is 1,013 mb). The atmospheric processes that lead to strong winds are the same as those that cause any wind (see page 34), but they occur at a more rapid rate than normal.

The Beaufort scale is used to categorise wind strength:

- A moderate gale (Beaufort scale 7) has wind speeds of 50–60 km h^{-1} and can set whole trees in motion.
- A fresh gale (Beaufort scale 8) has wind speeds of 61–73 km h^{-1} and can break twigs from trees.
- A strong gale (Beaufort scale 9) has wind speeds of 74–86 km h^{-1} and can cause slight damage to buildings, particularly roofs.
- A whole gale (Beaufort scale 10) has wind speeds of 87–100 km h^{-1} and can uproot trees and cause considerable structural damage to buildings.
- Winds in excess of 100 km h^{-1} are classed as storms (Beaufort scale 11) and above 120 km h^{-1} as hurricanes (Beaufort scale 12).

The atmospheric processes responsible for tropical revolving storms

Tropical revolving storms are intense low-pressure weather systems that can develop in the tropics. These violent storms are usually 200–700 km in diameter. They begin with an area of low pressure, caused by surface heating, into which warm air is drawn in a spiralling manner. Such small-scale disturbances enlarge into tropical depressions with rotating wind systems and these may continue to grow into a much more intense and rapidly rotating system — the tropical revolving storm. It is not entirely clear why tropical storms are triggered into becoming tropical revolving storms, but there are several conditions that need to be present:

- an oceanic location with sea temperatures over 27°C — this provides a continuous source of heat to maintain rising air currents
- an ocean depth of at least 70 m — this moisture provides the latent heat, released by condensation, which drives the system
- a location at least 5° north or south of the equator in order that the Coriolis force can bring about the maximum rotation of air (the Coriolis force is weak at the equator and will stop a circular air flow from developing)
- low-level convergence of air in the lower atmospheric circulation system — winds have to come together near the centre of the low-pressure zone
- rapid outflow of air in the upper atmospheric circulation — this pushes away the warm air that has risen close to the centre of the storm

Key terms

Climatic hazard A natural event brought about by the weather or climate that threatens life and property.

Tornado A small-scale violent and destructive weather system. Tornadoes are characterised by extremely high wind speeds over a short period of time and tend to be unpredictable.

Tropical revolving storm A term that covers hurricanes, tropical cyclones, typhoons and willy-willies. These intense low-pressure weather systems are associated with catastrophic wind speeds and torrential rainfall.

The tropical revolving storm exists while there is a supply of latent heat and moisture to provide energy and low frictional drag on the ocean surface. Once the system reaches maturity, a central eye develops. This is an area 10–50 km in diameter in which there are calm conditions, clear skies, higher temperatures and descending air. Wind speeds of over 300 km h^{-1} have been observed around the eye. Figure 2.12 shows the structure of a typical mature tropical revolving storm. Once the system reaches land or the colder waters polewards, it will decline as the source of heat and moisture is removed.

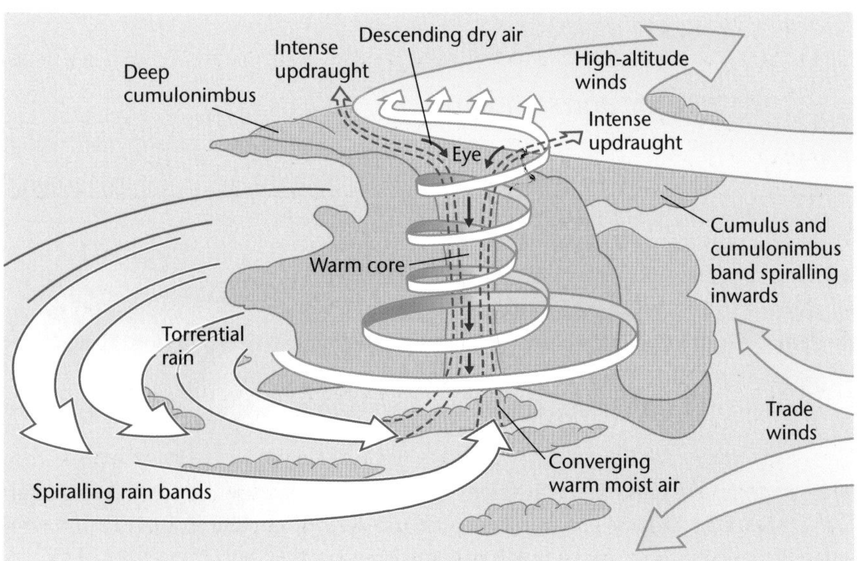

Figure 2.12 The structure of a tropical revolving storm

Distribution

Tropical revolving storms occur between latitudes 5° and 20° north or south of the equator (Figure 2.13). Once generated they tend to move westwards and are at their most destructive:

- in the Caribbean Sea/Gulf of Mexico area where they are known as **hurricanes** (11% of all tropical cyclones)
- on the western side of central America (east Pacific) (17%)
- in the Arabian Seà/Bay of Bengal area where they are known as **cyclones** (8%)
- off southeast Asia where they are known as **typhoons** (main area, with one third of all revolving storms)
- off Madagascar (southeast Africa) (11%)
- in northwestern Australia, where they are known as **willy-willies**, and the southwestern Pacific (20%)

Figure 2.13 Global distribution and seasons of tropical revolving storms

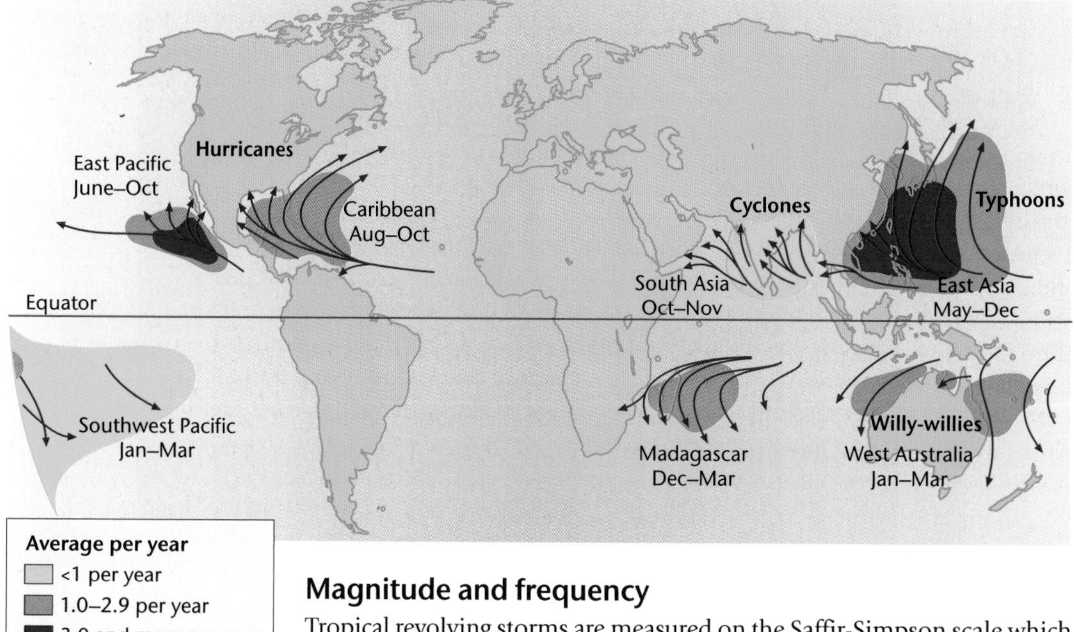

Magnitude and frequency

Tropical revolving storms are measured on the Saffir-Simpson scale which has five levels based upon central pressure, wind speed, storm surge and damage potential. Scale 5, for example, has:

- central pressure at 920 mb or below
- wind speed at 69 m s^{-1} (250 km h^{-1}) or greater
- storm surge at 5.5 m or greater
- damage potential that refers to 'complete roof failure of many buildings with major damage to lower floors of all structures lower than 3 m above sea level. Evacuation of all residential buildings on low ground within 16–24 km of coast is likely'

The average lifespan of a tropical storm is 7–14 days. Every year about 70–75 tropical storms develop around the world, of which around 50 will intensify to become tropical revolving storms.

The atmospheric processes responsible for tornadoes

A tornado is an extremely violent and destructive weather system characterised by powerful swirling winds, with speeds up to 300 km h^{-1}, that rotate towards the intense low pressure at its centre. Winds revolve in an anti-clockwise direction in the northern hemisphere and clockwise south of the equator. Tornadoes are small-scale weather systems compared with depressions and tropical revolving storms — the diameter of the storm centre may be less than 100 m. A tornado may last in an area for only a few minutes and the entire cycle of a single tornado may be only a couple of hours.

Tornadoes are the result of extreme instability in the atmosphere, convergence and vigorous updraughts in the air. They are common events during spring and summer in 'tornado alley', in the Great Plains area of midwestern USA, the Gulf Coast and the Mississippi basin. The USA experiences more tornadoes than anywhere else in the world. They generally travel from the southwest towards the northeast.

Tornadoes usually form over hot land surfaces (above 24°C), where vigorous uplift of air causes low pressure. In the USA, this uplift of air is often associated with a front that develops between two contrasting air masses. Cold, dry polar continental air flowing south from Canada and the Arctic meets warm moist tropical maritime air travelling north from the Gulf of Mexico. Powerful updraughts of warm air sometimes break through the cold, dry air forming huge cumulonimbus clouds. The jet stream, travelling in an easterly direction at speeds of up to 400 km h^{-1} in the upper atmosphere, catches this rapidly rising air and causes it to spin.

The Fujita scale is used to categorise the damage caused by tornadoes. (The precise speeds used in this scale have never been scientifically verified.) As with the Saffir–Simpson scale, there are five levels:

- At scale F0, the wind speeds are estimated to be less than 120 km h^{-1}. Therefore, the tornado would cause only light damage, for example branches could be broken off trees.
- At scale F3, the wind speeds are estimated at 250–330 km h^{-1}. The tornado would be likely to cause severe damage. For example, cars could be lifted off the ground and most trees in the path of the tornado would be uprooted.
- At scale F5, wind speeds are estimated to be in excess of 400 km h^{-1}. The tornado would cause extensive damage. It would be capable of lifting entire strong-frame buildings from the ground and car-sized missiles would be picked up and carried up to 100 m.

Figure 2.14 A tornado

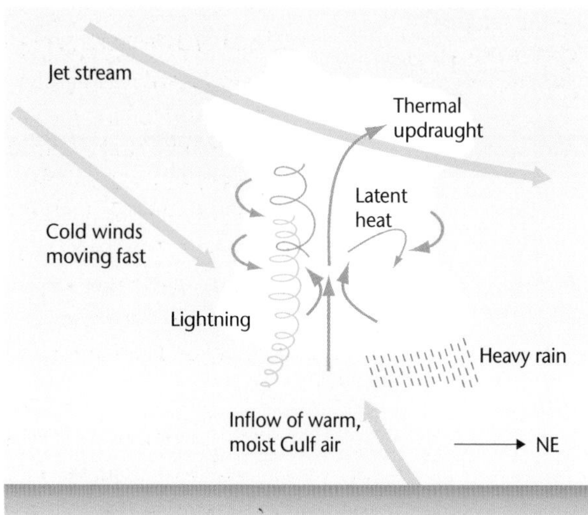

Human impacts and responses

Effects of severe gales

Gales are a common feature of the CTWM climate. They are generally at their worst during the autumn when the sea is still warm enough to fuel powerful low-pressure cells. Sometimes, during this season, the relics of tropical storms from the Caribbean wind their way across the Atlantic. However, by the time they reach the European coast much of their energy has been lost due to lower sea temperatures. Every year storms are expected to result in short-term disruption to transport and power supplies, but the damage caused is usually minor in comparison with that caused by tropical revolving storms and tornadoes.

In October 1987, the 'storm of the century' occurred over southern England. Meteorologists incorrectly predicted that this low-pressure weather system would sweep over France and Spain. However, it veered northwards instead and hit southern England. By midnight on 15 October gusts exceeding 150 km h^{-1} (normally classed as hurricane strength) were recorded over exposed coastal areas. The emergency services were stretched to their limits throughout the night, dealing with accidents, power cuts and fallen trees.

If the storm had occurred 8 hours later, during the rush hour, the impacts would undoubtedly have been much worse. The immediate effects were 19 people dead, colossal damage to property and power cuts to hundreds of thousands of homes. Train and ferry services were cancelled, caravan parks wrecked and many boats broke from their moorings and were washed ashore. Insurance claims were estimated to be over £1.5 billion. The clear-up took many months, particularly where structural damage to buildings had occurred. One of the most significant long-term impacts of this storm was the destruction of some 15 million trees, uprooted by the hurricane-strength winds.

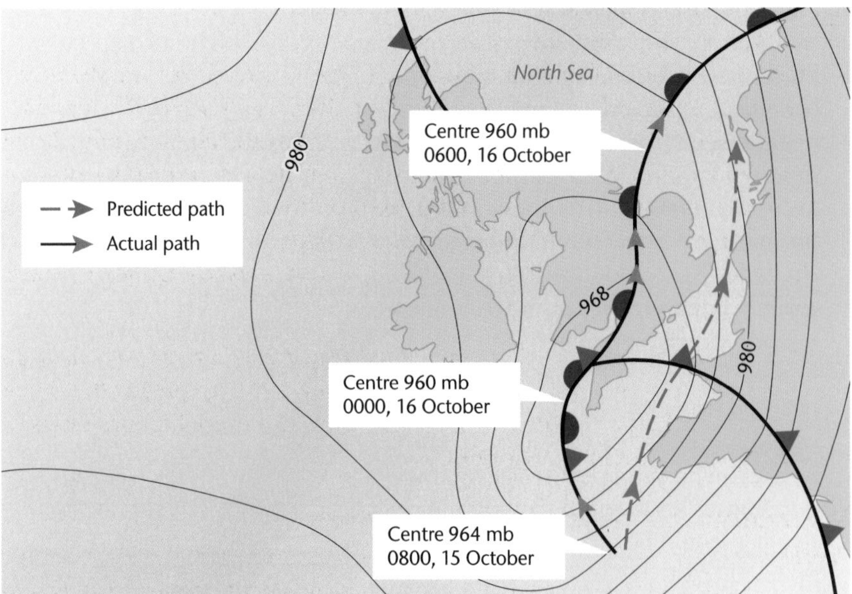

Figure 2.15 Predicted and actual paths of the great storm in southeast England, 1987

Storms of this nature are rare in the mid-latitudes, but when they do occur the scale of the damage is significant. However, the magnitude of the event can never equal that of a category 5 hurricane. This is because in the mid-latitudes the air pressure at the centre of an intense depression does not fall to such an extremely low level as it does in the tropics. Consequently, the wind speed caused by the steep pressure gradient in a tropical revolving storm is never quite matched.

Effects of tropical revolving storms

People's vulnerability to this hazard depends upon a whole range of factors, both physical and human. The main physical factors that determine the impact of a tropical revolving storm include:

- intensity of the storm (Saffir-Simpson scale 1–5)
- speed of movement, i.e. length of time over an area
- distance from the sea
- physical geography of the coastal area — width of coastal plain/size of delta, location of any mountain ranges relative to the coast

The human factors concern the preparations a community has made to resist the effects of a tropical revolving storm, and these are considered below in the section on management.

There are several ways in which tropical revolving storms pose a hazard to people and the built environment:

- **Winds** often exceed 150 km h^{-1} and have reached over 300 km h^{-1}. Such winds can bring about the collapse of buildings, cause structural damage to roads and bridges, bring down transmission lines and devastate agricultural areas. They can also hurl large pieces of debris around and this may cause deaths.
- **Heavy rainfall**, often over 100 mm per day, causes severe **flooding** and **landslides** (very common in Hong Kong). High relief can exaggerate already high rainfall figures and totals in excess of 500–700 mm per day have been recorded in some areas of the world.
- **Storm surges** result from the piling up of wind-driven waves and the ocean heaving up under reduced pressure. These can flood low-lying coastal areas and, in flat areas such as the Ganges delta, flooding may extend far inland. Storm surges cause most of the deaths that result from tropical revolving storms. A hurricane in 1970 that affected Bangladesh on the Ganges delta produced a storm surge of 6 m that killed more than 300,000 people. Agriculture in areas affected by such flooding often takes a long time to recover as the soil becomes contaminated with salt.

In 2005, the storm surge which accompanied Hurricane Katrina broke through the levées on the banks of the Mississippi that were meant to protect the city of New Orleans. Billions of dollars worth of damage was caused to thousands of commercial and residential properties.

Management of tropical revolving storms

Prediction

The prediction of tropical revolving storms depends upon the monitoring and warning systems available. Weather bureaus such as the National Hurricane Center in Florida (USA) are able to access data from geostationary satellites and from both land and sea-based recording centres. The USA also maintains round-the-clock surveillance by weather aircraft of tropical storms that have the potential to become hurricanes and affect the Caribbean/Gulf of Mexico area. Such information is compared with computer models to predict a path for the storm and warn people to evacuate the area.

It is essential that such warnings are accurate, as there is a high economic cost associated with evacuation, and false alarms can cause people to become complacent and refuse future advice. It has been estimated that the cost of evacuating coastal areas in the USA is roughly $1 million per kilometre of coastline due to losses in business and tourism and the provision of protection. As tropical revolving storms tend to follow an erratic path, it is not always possible to give more than 12–18 hours warning. LEDCs, where communications are not as developed as those in MEDCs, may not be as well prepared and this can lead to a higher death toll. Some coastal areas of LEDCs, however, including the Bay of Bengal and some Central American coasts, do have adequate warning systems. In 1997 a tropical cyclone warning in the Cox's Bazaar area of Bangladesh allowed the evacuation of 300,000 people, resulting in fewer than 100 deaths. Some progress is therefore being made in warning systems in LEDCs.

Prevention

Like other natural hazards, tropical revolving storms cannot really be prevented, but there has been research into the effect of cloud seeding to cause more precipitation before the storm hits land. The theory is that if the storm can be forced to release more water over the sea, this will result in a weakening of the system as it approaches land. There has been some concern over the effect of this on the global energy system. Because of this, research has not continued.

Case study MEDC: Hurricane Katrina, USA, 2005

In 2005, Hurricane Katrina was the eleventh named tropical storm, fourth hurricane and first category 5 hurricane in what was to become one of the most active hurricane seasons ever recorded in the Atlantic area. The storm first developed on 23 August over the southeastern Bahamas. It was upgraded and named Katrina the next day.

On 28 August Katrina was upgraded to category 4 and it became clear that it was heading for the coasts of Mississippi and Louisiana. It continued to intensify on that day, rapidly becoming a category 5 hurricane, with sustained wind speeds of 280 km h^{-1}, gusts of up to 345 km h^{-1} and a central pressure of 902 mb, making it the fifth most intense Atlantic Basin hurricane on record.

Advance warnings were in force by 26 August and the possibility of 'unprecedented cataclysm' was already being considered. On 27 August, 2 days before the hurricane was expected to make landfall, President Bush declared a state of emergency in Louisiana, Alabama and Mississippi.

Risk assessments conducted in preparation for such an event had been published, for example the *National Geographic* magazine had run an article less than 12 months before the storm occurred. However, when it actually happened, the authorities found it difficult to respond to the sheer scale of the disaster. At a news conference on 28 August, shortly after Katrina had been upgraded to a category 5 storm, the mayor of New Orleans ordered that the city be evacuated.

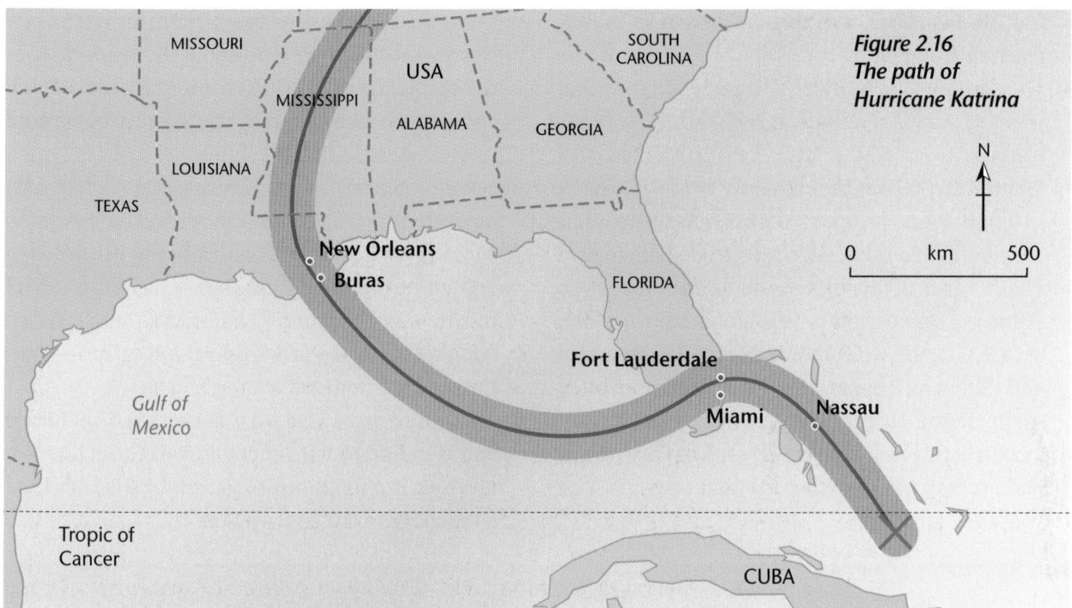

Figure 2.16 The path of Hurricane Katrina

Most of the population managed to leave in private cars and on school buses, but some 150,000 people remained in the city, mostly by choice. As a last resort, people who had been 'left behind' were encouraged to seek protection in the massive Louisiana Superdome. Basic supplies of food and water were delivered to support 150,000 people for 3 days.

When Katrina hit Louisiana on the morning of 29 August, it was accompanied by a massive storm surge, up to 10 m high in places. Although it had weakened to a category 3 storm as it reached the border of Louisiana and Mississippi, the storm was so intense that its powerful winds and storm surge smashed the entire Mississippi Gulf Coast as it passed through.

The main effects of the storm were:

- Initially, power and water supplies were disrupted. Almost 233,000 km^2 was declared a disaster zone — an area nearly as large as the UK. This left an estimated 5 million people without power and it took almost 2 months for the entire area affected to be re-connected.
- Over 1 million people were displaced from their homes and became refugees. One month after the storm, refugees were registered in all 50 states. About 75% of the evacuees stayed within 400 km of their origin, but tens of thousands located more than 1,000 km away.
- In New Orleans, a city situated mostly below sea level, the complex system of flood defences, including levées, was breached and 80% of the city was deluged by floodwater, several metres deep.
- Reports at the time claimed that those most affected by the hurricane were the black and coloured American urban dwellers, arguably the poorest and most disadvantaged members of society. It was alleged that the authorities would have responded differently if those suffering were of white European origin and many criticised President Bush for being slow to visit the disaster area.
- There were numerous incidents involving looters, who ran riot through the abandoned homes and shops in New Orleans. This resulted in the deployment of the Mississippi National Guard, which was given orders to treat looters ruthlessly.
- The financial cost of the storm broke all records in the USA, with damage estimated to be in the region of $200 billion.
- Many oil rigs and refineries in the Gulf area were damaged by Katrina. An immediate effect of this was that the price of oil shot-up to record levels (over $60 per barrel) affecting people worldwide.

For the first time, the price of petrol in the UK reached £1 per litre.

- The famous New Orleans' French Quarter was severely damaged, which will affect tourism revenue.
- Of the 180,000 houses in the city of New Orleans, 110,000 were flooded; 55,000 of these were considered too badly damaged to be repaired.
- The number of fatalities resulting from the storm — some 1,263 people — was far below initial estimates. Of these, 1,035 were recorded in Louisiana and 228 in Mississippi. Very few died in the aftermath of the storm, because the USA had the infrastructure and services to ensure that people had access to clean water, medical care and food supplies.
- Many businesses were affected by storm damage. However, most were adequately insured. As a consequence of Katrina, some major insurance companies were forced to declare profit warnings to their shareholders.
- Government aid was rapidly assigned to help with recovery. The US Senate authorised a bill assigning $10.5 billion in aid for victims in the first week of September and on 7 September another $51.8 billion was allocated from Federal funds. Other countries also responded to the disaster — even Afghanistan donated aid to the USA.
- The public were also very generous; $1.8 billion was donated to the American Red Cross alone — more than the amounts raised for 9/11 and the Indian Ocean tsunami appeal.

Photograph 2.3 National Guard troops patrolling flooded downtown New Orleans

TopFoto

Case study LEDC: Hurricane Mitch, Central America, 1998

Hurricane Mitch began as a tropical storm on around 22 October 1998 in the southern Caribbean Sea. In its early days it moved slowly westwards, on an unpredictable track, typical of many such disturbances in the region. Wind speeds built, however, and as the system deepened through the last days of the month, it became classified as a hurricane, building into one of the most severe to hit this part of the world, a category 5.

After following its predicted westward track, Mitch suddenly turned southward to hit the north Honduras

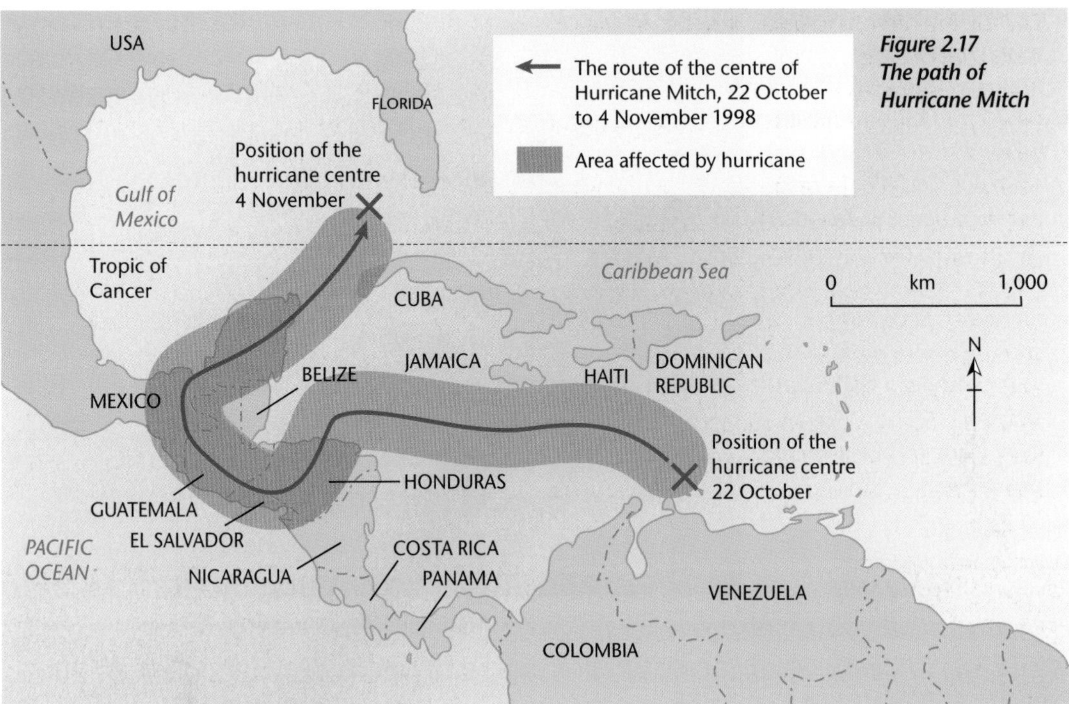

Figure 2.17 The path of Hurricane Mitch

coast, moving through that country and then Nicaragua before departing through El Salvador and Guatemala (Figure 2.17). What made Hurricane Mitch so devastating was not the winds, although they did reach 300 km h^{-1}, but the fact that the system was slow moving and produced torrential rain. It has been estimated that, in some places, the hurricane produced over 1,000 mm of rainfall in 5 days — as much as the region normally receives in a year. This led to severe flooding, as rivers burst their banks. The main effects of the hurricane were:

- more than 19,000 people dead or missing
- many settlements were completely wiped out, particularly on the northern coast of Honduras
- transport links were obliterated — in Nicaragua, 50 main bridges were destroyed, along with countless minor ones, including all those on the roads leading to the capital, Managua
- 2.7 million people were made homeless — in Honduras it is estimated that 20% of the population lost their homes (Photograph 2.4)
- the centre of the capital city of Honduras, Tegucigalpa, was turned into a vast lake as the Rio Choluteca overflowed
- in Nicaragua the crater lake in the dormant volcano Casita burst through the crater walls, sending a 6-m high wall of mud and water onto the villages that surrounded it and killing 1,500 people
- land worked by many farmers was covered by a deep layer of mud which baked hard after the hurricane had passed
- food supplies were destroyed, leading to serious shortages — food prices increased rapidly
- 70% of the Honduran economic output was lost, mainly in agriculture, where the coffee and banana plantations were severely affected. Even where crops could be harvested, the lack of communications meant that produce could not be marketed. Agricultural losses for 1998 and 1999 were put at $1.5 billion
- the limited export base in Nicaragua and Honduras, mainly agricultural, was severely cut, and this had implications for servicing large foreign debt commitments
- Honduras and Nicaragua, the two countries most affected, were already among the poorest in the Americas with GDPs, at the time, of under $700 per head

- crime vastly increased as abandoned homes and businesses were looted
- power transmission systems were destroyed and fuel sources quickly became depleted (immediately after the disaster, the Honduran Air Force had only 5 days' fuel left, important in a country where most of the roads had been left impassable)
- large amounts of aid had to be supplied

TopFoto

Photograph 2.4 Devastation in Honduras following Hurricane Mitch

Case study The Central Oklahoma tornado outbreak, USA, 1999

A slow-moving low-pressure storm brought several days of tornado activity to many of the southern states of the USA from 3 to 6 May 1999. There were reports of more than 70 'twisters' during this period.

The deadliest and most intense tornadoes for decades ripped across Oklahoma late on 3 May, killing 44 people, injuring hundreds and demolishing entire neighbourhoods. The tornado that hit Oklahoma city was classed as F5 on the Fujita scale, with winds in excess of 400 km h^{-1}. On the same day, tornadoes in Wichita, Kansas killed four people. On the following day in Texas, there was one fatality and when the storm hit Tennessee on 5 May, four more people died. The damage to residential and commercial properties caused by the outbreak was estimated to be in the region of $1.2 billion.

Warnings of possible tornado activity were issued at least 2 hours before the first tornado touched down. The National Weather Service put out alarm calls on local radio stations and community sirens and police gave out warnings, advising people to take shelter. The USA's warning system for severe weather in 'tornado alley' is considered by many to be the best in the world. It incorporates highly sophisticated radar technology, improved data analysis by forecasters, a vast network of specially trained spotters with eyes to the skies, close cooperation with the media and state civil-defence systems that utilise community sirens. The sophisticated technology has resulted in accurate tornado warnings some 15 minutes before touchdown — a huge improvement in just 20 years.

Some homes and all public buildings in urban areas have specially installed tornado shelters; older homes in rural areas often have storm cellars. Schools take part in 'tornado week', during which children practise hiding under desks or finding other shelter.

These advances in understanding and technology mean that the human cost of a severe outbreak of tornadoes, such as the one in May 1999, is much reduced. In 1925, 695 people died during the notorious 'tri-state tornado', largely because they did not know it was coming until it was already upon them.

Effects of tornadoes

Tornadoes, although intensely powerful, occur on a small scale and last for a much shorter time than severe gales and tropical revolving storms. They are not experienced exclusively in the USA — during the summer of 2005 there were reports of tornado damage to the cities of Birmingham and Peterborough in the UK.

Tornadoes can result in an immense amount of damage along their storm path, owing to their high wind speeds and the fall in air pressure. This fall can cause such rapid pressure changes that buildings explode and debris is thrown around the system. The strong up-draughts can uproot trees and lift people, cars and even railway engines.

The USA experiences more tornado damage than anywhere else. On average there are 100 deaths per year and damage runs into millions of dollars.

Climatic change at the micro scale

Urban microclimate

Urban climate is a good example of the impact of human activity on the atmosphere. Cities create their own climate and weather. Some geographers refer to this as the 'climatic dome' within which the weather is different from that of surrounding rural areas in terms of temperature, relative humidity, precipitation, visibility and wind speed (Table 2.2). For a large city, the dome may extend upwards to 250–300 metres and its influence may well continue for tens of kilometres downwind (Figure 2.18).

Within the urban dome, two levels can be recognised. Below roof level there is an urban canopy where processes act in the spaces between buildings (sometimes referred to as 'canyons'). Above this is the urban boundary layer, whose characteristics are governed by the nature of the urban surface. The dome extends downwind as a plume into the surrounding rural areas. Figure 2.18 shows that this phenomenon occurs at height. The effects of the plume are absent at ground level.

Table 2.2 The effects of urban areas on local climate

Element of climate	Effect of urban area (compared to nearby rural areas)
Temperature	
Annual mean	0.5–0.8°C increase
Winter minimum	1.0–1.5°C increase
Precipitation	
Quantity	5–10% increase
Days with less than 5 mm	10% increase
Relative humidity	
Annual mean	6% decrease
Winter	2% decrease
Summer	8% decrease
Visibility	
Fog in winter	100% increase
Fog in summer	30% increase
Wind speed	
Annual mean	20–30% decrease
Calms	5–20% increase
Extreme gusts	10–20% decrease
Radiation	
Ultraviolet in winter	30% lower
Ultraviolet in summer	5% lower
Total on horizontal surface	15–20% lower
Pollution	
Dust particles	1,000% increase

The urban heat island effect

An urban area can be identified as a warm spot in the 'sea' of surrounding cooler rural air. This is the **urban heat island**. Cities tend to be warmer than the surrounding rural areas for the following reasons:

- Building materials such as concrete, bricks and tarmac act like bare rock surfaces in that they absorb large quantities of heat which are slowly

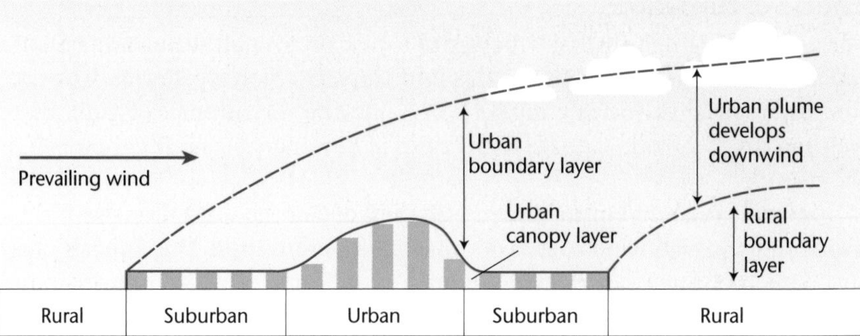

Figure 2.18 The urban climate dome

released at night. Some of these surfaces also have a high reflective capacity and multistorey buildings tend to concentrate the heating effect in the surrounding streets by reflecting energy downwards.

- Heat comes from industries, buildings and vehicles which all burn fuel (anthropogenic heat, i.e. caused by human activities) as well as from the large numbers of people present. Air conditioning units release heat into the atmosphere.
- Air pollution from industries and vehicles increases cloud cover and creates a 'pollution dome' which allows in the short-wave radiation but absorbs a large amount of the outgoing radiation as well as reflecting it back to the surface.
- In urban areas, water falling on to the surface is disposed of as quickly as possible. This changes the urban moisture and heat budget — reduced evapotranspiration means that more energy goes into heating the atmosphere.

Key terms

Convection When the lower air in the atmosphere is heated by the ground it expands and rises. This leads to instability within the atmosphere and formation of cumulonimbus clouds.

Microclimate The small-scale variations in temperature, precipitation, humidity, wind speed and evaporation which can occur within an environment.

Photochemical smog A form of air pollution that occurs mainly in cities and can be dangerous to health. Exhaust fumes become trapped by temperature inversions and in the presence of sunlight low-level ozone forms. Associated with high-pressure weather systems.

Temperature inversion An atmospheric condition in which temperature increases with height rather than the more usual decrease. As inversions are extremely stable conditions and do not allow convection, they trap pollution in the lower layer of the atmosphere.

Urban heat island The zone around and above an urban area which has higher temperatures than the surrounding rural areas.

Changes over time

The heat island effect develops best under certain meteorological conditions. The contrast between urban and rural areas is greatest under calm, high-pressure conditions, particularly with a temperature inversion in the boundary layer. Heat islands are also better developed in winter when there is a bigger impact from city heating systems. Urban– rural contrasts are much more distinct at night when the impact of insolation is absent and surfaces which absorbed heat by day slowly release it back into the atmosphere. Heat islands are not constant — they vary both seasonally and diurnally.

Changes over space

The heat island effect is also spatially variable. The edge of the island is usually well defined and temperatures change abruptly at the rural–urban boundary. Some climatologists have likened the effect to a 'cliff' in temperatures. From this point

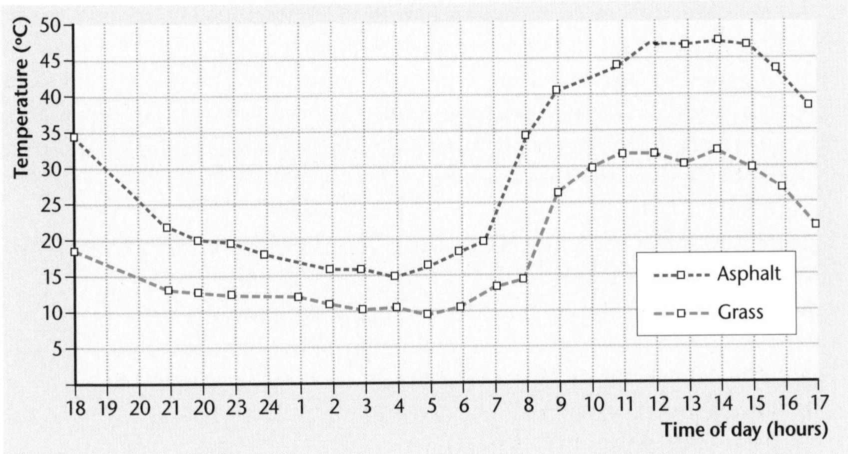

Figure 2.19 Summer temperatures of different surfaces in a European city

temperature rises steadily to a peak in the city centre where building densities are highest. The rise tends to be gentle, at an average of 2–4°C per kilometre.

After the cliff of the city edge, this steady rise has often been referred to as a 'plateau'. Within the plateau, though, there are variations that reflect the distribution of industries, power stations, water areas and open spaces. Figure 2.19 shows the temperatures of different surfaces in a city over a 24-hour period and indicates that at the middle of the day there can be a 15°C difference or more between the temperatures of roads and parks.

Albedo is the amount of insolation reflected by the Earth's surface and atmosphere. Figure 2.20 shows the albedo for various surfaces in the city. Highly reflective surfaces absorb very little insolation. They can reflect it back out into the atmosphere and keep urban areas cool, or reflect it

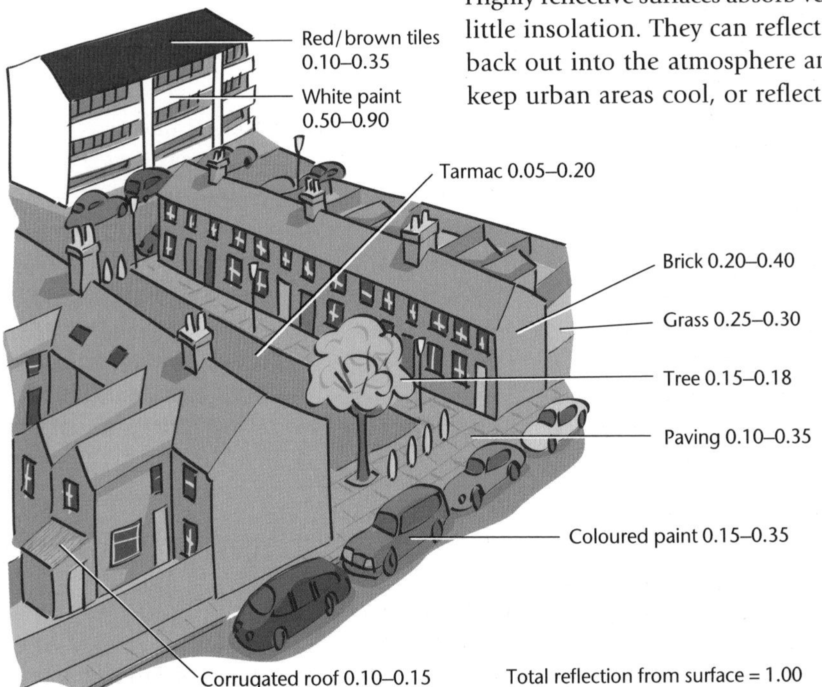

Figure 2.20 Various urban albedos

so that it focuses into a small area which heats up. Darker surfaces tend to absorb insolation much better and then re-radiate it as long-wave energy that heats up the urban area. Surfaces in the city tend to be much less reflective than those in rural areas — lots of tarmac but not a great deal of grass. In winter, rural areas keep snow for a much longer period and therefore have a greater albedo. Rural surface albedos include snow (0.86–0.95), sand (0.37), deciduous forest (0.17) and pine forest (0.14).

Figure 2.21 shows the temperature distribution over Montreal in Canada. The following can be clearly seen:

- the lower temperatures on the side of the prevailing wind
- the plateau-like temperature zone running from the city edge towards the city centre, which has the highest temperatures
- the correlation between the highest density of building (city centre) and the highest temperatures
- the fall in temperature over the park area which is an open, vegetated space

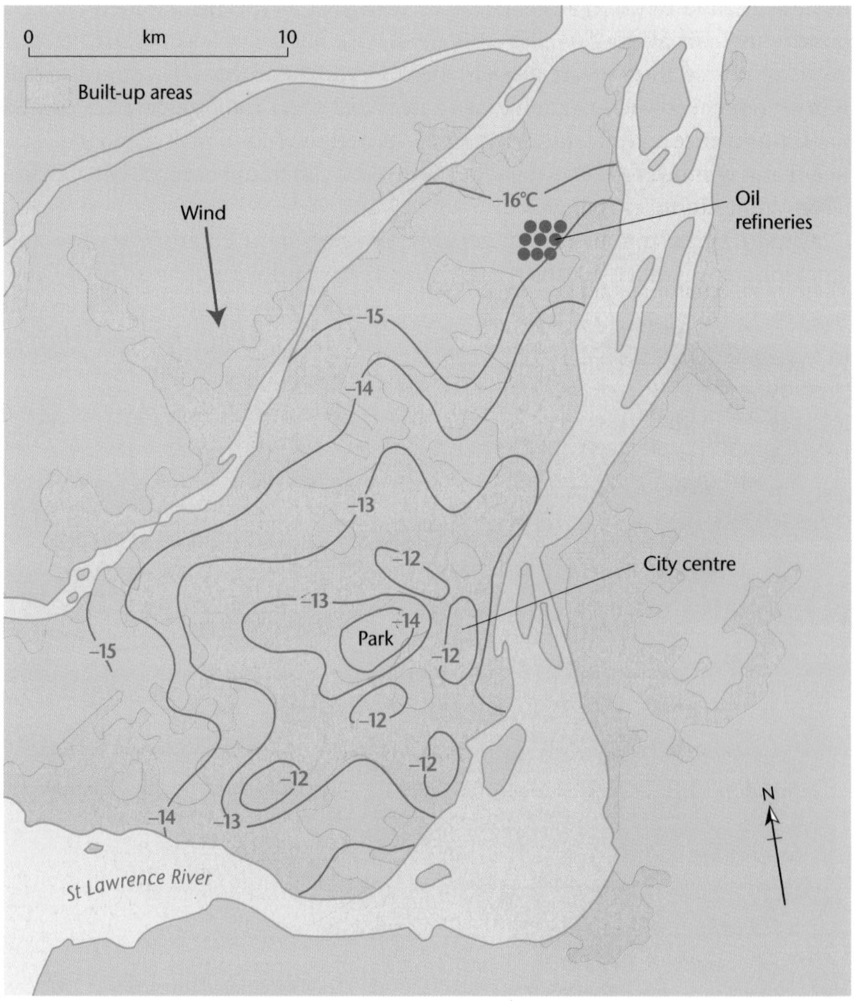

Figure 2.21 Temperature distribution over Montreal, 7 March, 7.00 a.m., with winds from the north at 0.5 m s^{-1}

Humidity

Overall, relative humidity is lower in cities than in surrounding rural areas. The amount of moisture available is reduced because:

- there are fewer areas of water, such as ponds and lakes, in cities
- cities have sparser vegetation cover, resulting in lower rates of evapotranspiration
- in the city, surface water from precipitation is channelled directly into drains and onwards into rivers

At night, the urban area maintains its humidity. In rural areas the air cools more rapidly and moisture is lost to dewfall. This can result in fog at night, particularly under anticyclonic weather conditions.

Precipitation

There is some evidence that rainfall, particularly that from summer thunderstorms, can be higher over urban than over rural areas. Convective storms tend to be heavier and more frequent, as does the incidence of thunder. There are several possible reasons for this:

- the urban heat island generates convection
- the presence of high-rise buildings and a mixture of building heights induces air turbulence and promotes increased vertical motion
- cities may produce large amounts of water vapour from industrial sources and power stations, as well as various pollutants that act as hygroscopic (water attracting) nuclei and assist in raindrop formation

There is also some evidence that cities increase precipitation downwind. Recent research by the University of Salford has shown that the building of tower blocks in the city in the 1970s brought more rain to parts of Greater Manchester. The prevailing wind tends to be westerly, and rainfall in areas downwind of Salford, such as Stockport, has increased by as much as 7% over the past few decades. With the effect of the urban heat island, though, it is not surprising that snow is less common in cities, and that which falls melts faster.

Figure 2.22
The effect of terrain on wind speeds

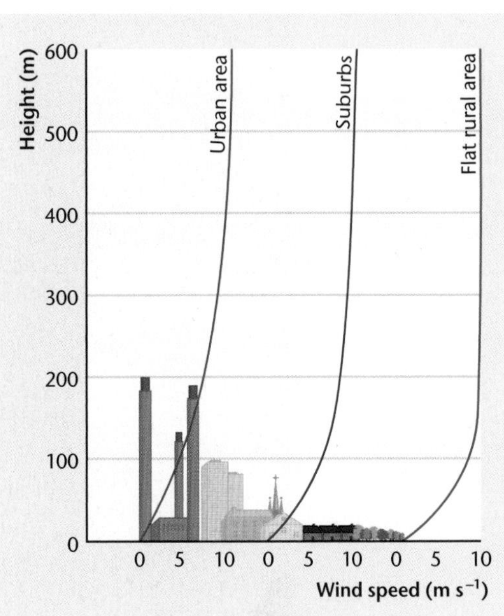

Winds

Urban areas have three main types of effects on winds:

- The surface area of cities is uneven due to the varying height of the buildings. Buildings, in general, exert a powerful frictional drag on air moving over and around them (Figure 2.22). This creates turbulence, giving rapid and abrupt changes in both wind direction and speed. Average wind speeds are lower in cities than in the surrounding areas and they are also lower in city centres than in suburbs.

- High-rise buildings may slow down air movement but they also channel air into the 'canyons' between them. Winds in such places can be so powerful that they make buildings sway and knock pedestrians off their feet.
- On calm and clear nights when the urban heat island effect is at its greatest, there is a surface inflow from the cooler areas outside the city to the warmer areas in the city centre. Such breezes transport pollution from the outer parts of an urban area to the city centre, accentuating the pollution problem during periods of photochemical smogs.

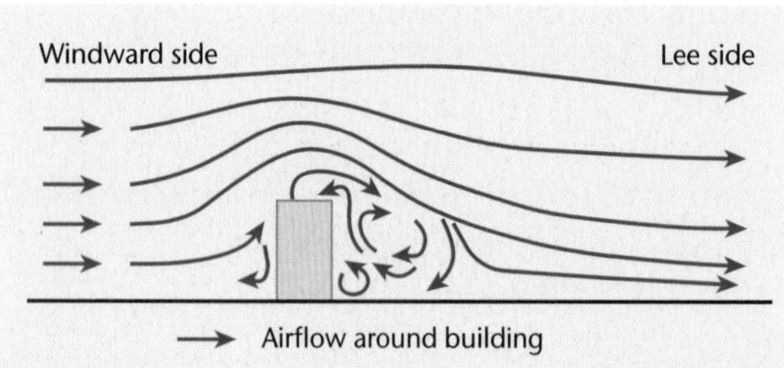

Figure 2.23 Airflow modified by a single building

Winds are therefore affected by the size and shape of buildings. Figure 2.23 shows how a single building can modify an airflow passing over it. Air is displaced upwards and around the sides of the building and is also pushed downwards in the lee of the structure.

Figure 2.24 shows the windward side of a building in more detail. The air will push against the wall on this side with relatively high pressures. As the air flows around the sides of the building it becomes separated from the walls and roof and sets up suction in these areas. On the windward side the overpressure, which increases with height, causes a descending flow which forms a vortex when it reaches the ground and sweeps around the windward corners. This vortex is considerably increased if there is a small building to windward.

In the lee of the building there is a zone of lower pressure, causing vortices behind it. If two separate buildings allow airflow between them, then the movement may be subject to the **Venturi effect** in which the pressure within the gap causes the wind to pick up speed and reach high velocities. Some buildings have gaps in them, or are built on stilts, to avoid this problem, but a reasonable flow of air at street level is essential to remove harmful pollution.

Figure 2.24 The effects of large urban buildings on winds

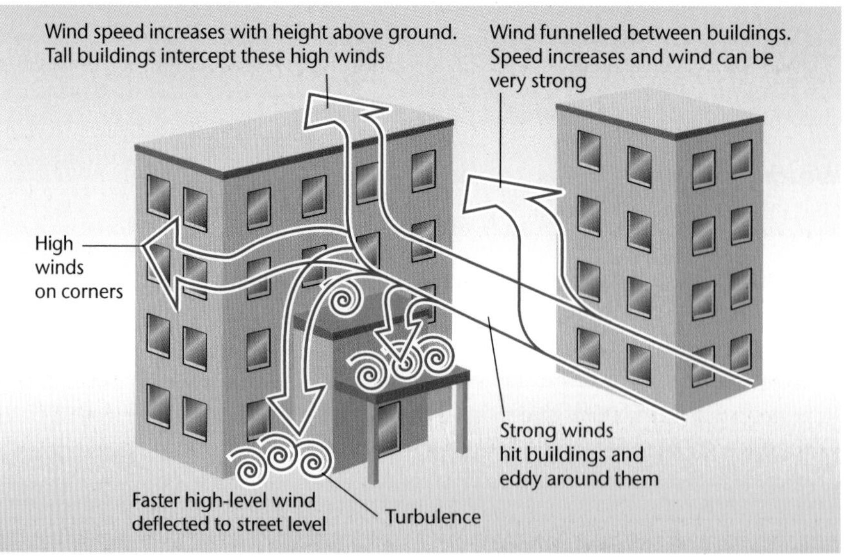

Usually buildings are part of a group and the disturbance to the airflow depends upon the height of the buildings and the spacing between them. If they are widely spaced, each building acts as an isolated block, but if they are closer, the wake of each building interferes with the airflow around the next structure and this produces a very complex pattern of airflow (Figure 2.25).

When buildings are designed it is important that pollution emitters (chimneys) are high enough to ensure that pollutants are released into the undisturbed flow above the building and not into the lee eddy or the downward-flowing air near the walls.

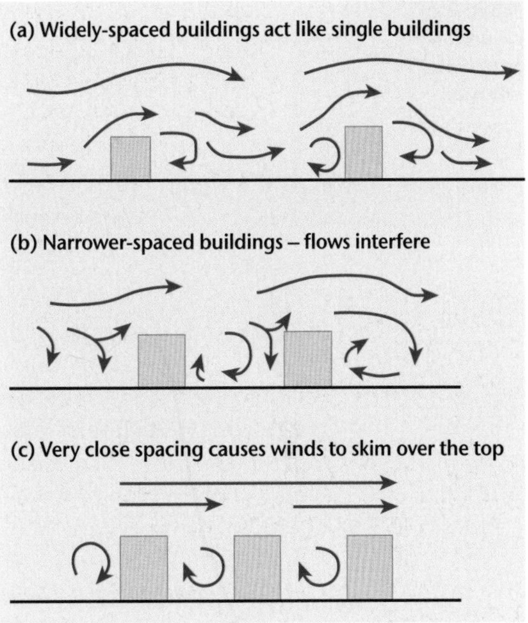

(a) Widely-spaced buildings act like single buildings

(b) Narrower-spaced buildings – flows interfere

(c) Very close spacing causes winds to skim over the top

Figure 2.25 Airflow in urban areas modified by more than one building

Air quality

Air quality in urban areas is often poorer than that in rural areas. The major pollutants of urban areas, and some of their consequences, are:

- **Suspended particulate matter** — the solid matter in the urban atmosphere which derives mainly from power stations and vehicle exhausts (particularly from burning diesel fuel). Such particles are usually less than 25 µm in diameter and are responsible for fog/smog, respiratory problems, soiling of buildings and may contain carcinogens. Other particulates in the atmosphere include cement dust, tobacco smoke, ash, coal dust and pollen. Coastal cities also have a vast number of sea salt particulates. Particulates are sometimes referred to as **PM10s**, as the bulk of particles have a diameter of less than 10 µm.
- **Sulphur dioxide** produces haze, acid rain, respiratory problems (including asthma), damage to lichens and plants and corrosion of buildings.
- **Oxides of nitrogen** cause accelerated weathering of buildings, photochemical reactions, respiratory problems, acid rain and haze.
- **Carbon monoxide** is associated with heart problems, headaches and fatigue.
- **Photochemical oxidants** (ozone and peroxyacetyl nitrate [PAN]) are associated with smog, damage to plants and a range of discomforts to people including headaches, eye irritation, coughs and chest pains.

Air pollution varies with the time of year and with the air pressure conditions. Concentration of pollutants may increase five to six times in winter because of temperature inversions trapping them over the city (Figure 2.26).

The mixture of fog and smoke particulates produces **smog**. This was a common occurrence in European cities through the nineteenth and first half of the twentieth centuries, because of the high incidence of coal burning, particularly on domestic fires. Britain suffered particularly badly, many of the smogs being so thick that they were known as 'pea-soupers'. In December 1952, a smog in London lasted for several days and was claimed to be responsible for over 4,000 deaths

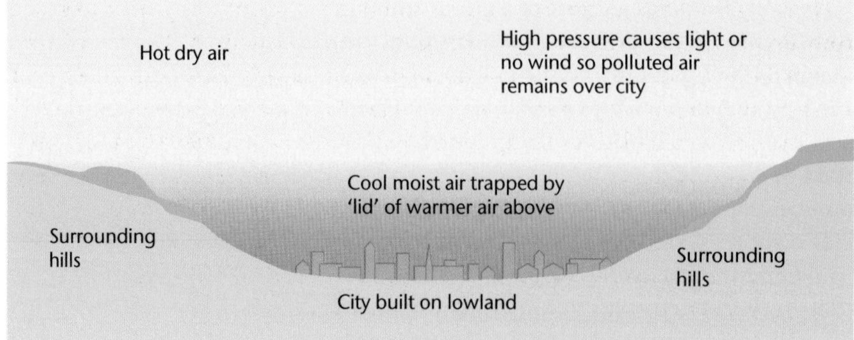

Figure 2.26 An urban temperature inversion

(Photograph 2.5). This event persuaded the British government of the time that legislation needed to be introduced to control coal burning.

More recently, there has been an increase in **photochemical smog**. The action of sunlight on the nitrogen oxides and hydrocarbons in vehicle exhaust gases leads to the production of ozone. (Do not confuse this low-level ozone with the high-level ozone in the atmosphere which protects the Earth from damaging ultraviolet radiation.) Los Angeles has a serious problem with photochemical smog because of its high density of vehicles, frequent sunshine and the favourable topography that traps the high concentration of photooxidant gases at low levels.

Photochemical smog is a particular hazard during anticyclonic conditions because once the air has descended it is relatively static due to the absence of wind. Additionally, such weather systems tend to be relatively stable and can persist for weeks at a time during the summer months. Many cities are located in river basins, so the relief provides a sheltered location, perfect for the establishment of photochemical smog.

Photograph 2.5 Smog on the Embankment, London, December 1952

TopFoto

High levels of ozone can have serious consequences, causing people to suffer from eye irritation, respiratory complaints and headaches. Ozone is also potentially toxic to many species of trees and other plants. European cities have seen a growth in photochemical smog in the last 50 years. Athens is often quoted as the worst affected place in Europe, but conditions can be equally bad in British cities, particularly those located inland, such as Oxford and Bath. A recent study found that concentrations of nitrogen oxides in the air in Oxford were equivalent to those in Mexico City, one of the most polluted places in the world. In London, high levels of nitrogen dioxide occur at certain times of the day. These come from vehicle exhaust emissions during peak travel times.

Strategies to reduce pollution in cities

There are a number of ways in which governments and other organisations have tried to reduce atmospheric pollution in cities.

Clean Air Acts

After the London pea-souper of 1952, the government decided legislation was needed to prevent so much smoke entering the atmosphere. The act of 1956 introduced smoke-free zones into the UK's urban areas and this policy slowly began to clean up the air. The 1956 act was reinforced by later legislation. In the 1990s, for example, very tough regulations were imposed on levels of airborne pollution, particularly on the level of PM10s in the atmosphere. Local councils in the UK are now required to monitor pollution in their areas and establish **Air Quality Management Areas** where levels are likely to be exceeded. Some have planted more vegetation to **capture particulates** on leaves.

Vehicle control in inner urban areas

A number of cities have looked at ways of controlling pollution by trying to reduce the number of vehicles that come into central urban areas. In Athens, for example, the city declared an area of about 2.5 km^2 in the centre **traffic free**. Many British towns and cities have **pedestrianised** their CBDs. In London, attempts to control vehicle numbers have included introducing a **congestion charge** (in effect, a road toll) which means vehicle owners have to pay if they wish to drive into the centre. In Mexico City, the city council passed **driving restriction** legislation known as the *Hoy no Circula* (don't drive today). This bans all vehicles from being driven in the city on one weekday per week, the vehicle's registration number determining the day. If conditions worsen, the legislation allows for a ban of two weekdays and one weekend day.

More public transport

Attempts have been made to persuade people to use public transport instead of cars. Such schemes have included Manchester's development of a **tram system** (Metrolink), the development of **bus-only lanes** into city centres, the growth of **park-and-ride** schemes in many British cities and the encouragement of **car-sharing** schemes.

Zoning of industry

Industry has been placed downwind in cities if at all possible and planning legislation has forced companies to build higher factory chimneys to emit pollutants above the inversion layer.

Vehicle emissions legislation

Motor vehicle manufacturers have been made to develop more efficient fuel-burning engines and to introduce **catalytic converters** which remove some of the polluting gases from exhaust fumes. The switch to **lead-free petrol** has also reduced pollution.

There is no doubt that all this legislation has worked, although it has not eliminated the problem. Reduction in coal burning has certainly produced cleaner air over British cities. In his book *The Skeptical Environmentalist*, Bjørn Lomborg states that 'London air has not been as clean as it is today since the Middle Ages. Almost all the modern period has been more polluted with smoke than it is today.'

There is still a great problem with pollution from vehicle exhausts but in many cities those levels are falling too. In Los Angeles, for example, despite large increases in both population and number of motor vehicles since 1970, peak ozone levels have declined markedly and the area subject to high ozone concentrations has shrunk in size. It is too early to say whether the policies introduced to deal with the problem of air quality in cities around the world have started to work. Inevitably there have been changes for the better in some cities. London is a more pleasant place to walk around today than it was before the congestion charge was introduced.

Climatic change at the global scale

Possible causes of climatic change

The climate of the British Isles has changed significantly since the Pleistocene ice age which ended around 10 or 11,000 years ago. At the end of the Pleistocene, in the period known as the pre-Boreal, the climate began to warm up and that trend has continued ever since. There have, however, been some fluctuations during which the climate has cooled, the best known being the 'little ice age' from the mid-sixteenth century to around 1800. During this period of global cooling the Thames regularly froze over and fairs were held on the ice. Table 2.3 shows the main climatic periods in the British Isles since the Pleistocene.

Several theories have been put forward to explain climatic change. Suggestions have included the following:

> ***Key terms***
>
> **Climatic change** Evidence shows that change has always been a feature of the Earth's climate. Apart from the Pleistocene ice age, recent research has revealed a whole series of climatic trends of a variety of timescales.
>
> **Global warming** The recent gradual warming of the Earth's atmosphere due largely to human activity.

Table 2.3 Climatic periods since the Pleistocene ice age

Climatic period	Time before present (years)	Climatic conditions
Sub-Atlantic to present day	2,500	Temperatures fluctuate; cooler than the present day A cool coastal climate with cooler summers and increased rainfall A marked cool period between AD 1300 and AD 1800 — the little ice age A period of warming in the last 200 years
Sub-Boreal	5,000	Temperatures falling but rainfall relatively low at the beginning of this period, increasing later Period known as the neoglacial in Europe, with evidence of ice advance in alpine areas Warm summers and colder winters
Atlantic	7,500	Temperatures reach the optimum for many trees and shrubs — 'the climatic optimum' A warm 'west coast' type of climate, with higher rainfall
Boreal	9,000	Climate becoming warmer and drier A continental-type climate
Pre-Boreal	10,300	Mainly cold and wet, but becoming warmer and drier Changing from tundra/sub-arctic to more continental

- variations in solar energy (sunspot activity)
- changes in the Earth's orbit and axial tilt (which will affect the amount of solar radiation reaching the surface)
- meteorite impact
- volcanic activity (increasing dust in the atmosphere)
- plate movement (redistribution of land masses)
- changes in oceanic circulation
- changes in atmospheric composition, particularly the build-up of carbon dioxide and other greenhouse gases

Long-term evidence for climatic change

Evidence for climatic change is taken from a variety of sources which can be used to reconstruct past climates. Most of the evidence is indirect — climatic changes are inferred from changes in indicators that reflect climate, such as vegetation.

Pollen analysis

Species have particular climatic requirements which influence their geographical distributions. Each plant species has a distinctively shaped pollen grain and if these fall into oxygen-free environments, such as peat bogs, they resist decay.

Changes in the pollen found in different levels of the bog indicate, by implication, changes in climate.

One limitation of this method is the fact that pollen can be transported considerable distances by wind or sometimes wildlife.

Dendrochronology

This is the analysis of tree rings from core samples. Each year, the growth of a tree is shown in its trunk by a single ring made up of two bands: a band reflecting rapid spring growth when the cells are larger; and a narrower band of growth during the cooler autumn. The width of the ring depends on the conditions of that particular year. A wide band indicates a warm and wet year, a narrower one cooler and drier conditions. The change in width from one ring to another is of greater significance than the actual width, as bigger growth rings tend to be produced in the early life of the tree, irrespective of the conditions.

Recent investigations, however, have shown that trees respond more to levels of moisture than to temperature. Dendrochronology has a limitation in that few trees exist that are older than about 4,000 years. It has been possible to extend surveys further back using remains of vegetation preserved in non-oxygen conditions.

Ice-core analysis

Glacial ice can be studied by drilling cores from areas such as Antarctica and Greenland. The carbon dioxide trapped within the ice is a climate indicator — levels tend to be lower during cooler periods and higher when it is warmer. Another method is to look at oxygen isotope levels (see below).

Sea-floor analysis

Core samples from the ocean floor reveal shifts in animal and plant populations which indicate climatic change. The ratio of the isotopes oxygen-18 to oxygen-16 in calcareous ooze can also be measured. This is linked to the ice-core analysis described above. During colder phases, when water evaporated from the oceans and precipitated onto the land eventually forms glacial ice, water containing lighter oxygen-16 is more easily evaporated than that containing heavier oxygen-18. As a result, the oceans have a higher concentration of oxygen-18, while the ice sheets and glaciers contain more of the lighter oxygen-16. During warmer periods, the oxygen-16 held in the ice is released and returns to the oceans, balancing out the ratio. Studies of isotope curves showing the ratio of oxygen-16 to oxygen-18 therefore give a picture of climatic change.

Recent investigations have suggested that isotope variations are an indication of changes in the volume of ice rather than water temperature, but as ice volume itself reflects climatic conditions, such studies have tended to confirm earlier findings.

Radiocarbon dating

Carbon-14 is a radioactive isotope of carbon (normally carbon-12). Carbon is taken in by plants during photosynthesis. As carbon-14 decays at a known rate and carbon-12 does not decay, comparison of the levels of the two isotopes present in plant remains will indicate the age at which a plant died (with an error of up to 5%). The type of vegetation present at any particular time is an indicator of the climate of that period. This method can accurately date organic matter up to 50,000 years old.

Coleoptera

Remains of Coleoptera (beetles) are common in freshwater and land sediments. Different species of beetles tend to be found under different climatic conditions. Knowledge of the present climatic range of the different species, and the age of the sediments in which remains are found, allows past climatic conditions to be worked out.

Changing sea levels

The presence of rias and fjords indicates rising (eustatic) sea levels flooding glacial and river valleys. Changes in sea levels are indicators of climate change — the volume of the sea water changes as it warms/cools.

Glacial deposits

These show records of ice advance during colder periods and retreat during warmer times.

Historical records

Historical records include cave paintings, depth of grave digging in Greenland, diaries, documentary evidence of events (such as 'frost fairs' on the Thames) and evidence of areas of vine cultivation. Since 1873 daily weather reports have been documented, and the Royal Society has encouraged the collection of data since the seventeenth century. Parish records are often a good source of climate data.

Recent global warming

Figure 2.27 shows how average world temperature has risen since records were first kept in 1860. Although the overall rise seems small, the top ten hottest years have all occurred since 1980, and the 1990s was the hottest recorded decade. The years 2001 and 2004 continued that trend: 2001 was the second hottest after 1998; and 2004 was the fourth hottest on record, with heatwaves across southern Europe bringing some of the highest temperatures ever recorded in Spain and Portugal.

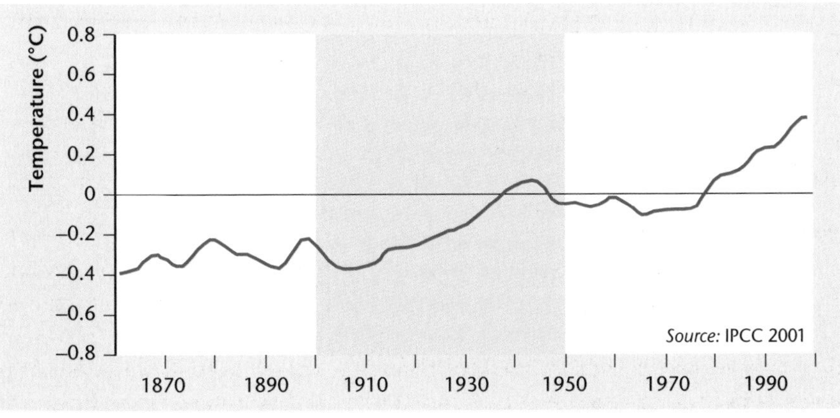

***Figure 2.27** Average variation in Earth-surface temperature from the mean since 1860*

The global mean surface temperature in 2004 was 14°C, which is 0.44°C above the average for the period 1961–90. Global warming is probably the major environmental issue of our time, and although scientists have often been slow to commit themselves about cause and effect, there is no doubt that the planet is heating up.

Climatic changes have happened in the past, but present evidence seems to suggest that the recent increase in temperature has been brought about by pollution of the atmosphere, in particular the release of huge amounts of carbon dioxide from fires, power stations, motor vehicles and factories.

Why global warming happens

The troposphere allows incoming short-wave radiation from the sun to pass through and warm the Earth. Some of this radiation is reflected back from the Earth's surface into space at a longer wavelength. Greenhouse gases in the troposphere such as carbon dioxide absorb some of this long-wave radiation and radiate it back again towards the Earth's surface. This trapping of heat is known as the greenhouse effect and is part of the natural process of heat balance in the atmosphere. In fact it is essential for life on Earth — without the greenhouse effect the planet would be about 30°C colder.

Figure 2.28 The greenhouse effect

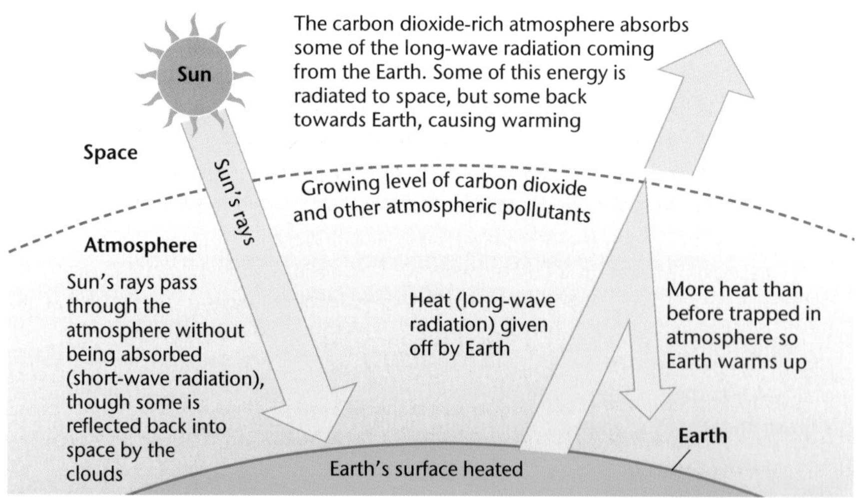

Figure 2.29 Where greenhouse gases come from

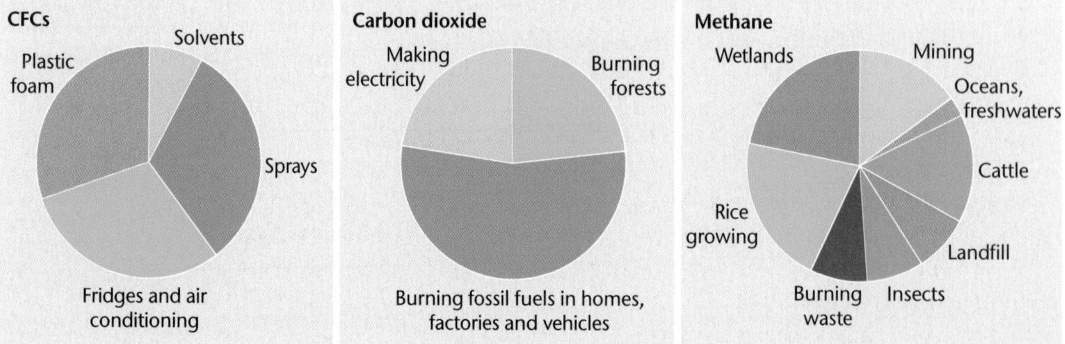

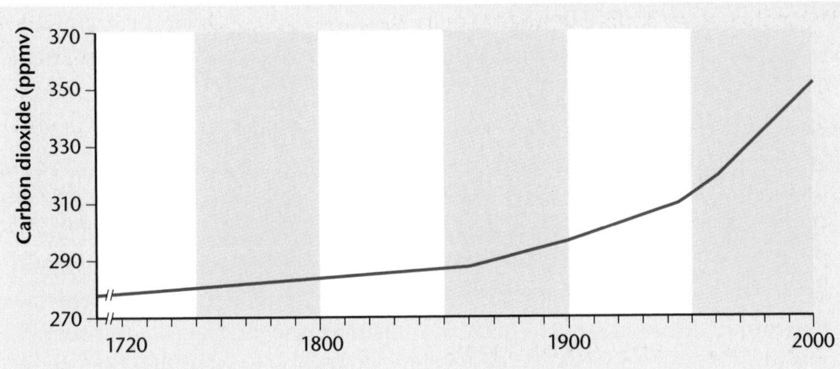

Figure 2.30 Changes in the concentration of carbon dioxide in the atmosphere, 1720–2000

The greenhouse gases responsible for trapping heat include carbon dioxide, chlorofluorocarbons (CFCs), methane, nitrous oxide and ozone.

Provided the amount of carbon dioxide and water vapour in the atmosphere stay the same and the amount of solar radiation is unchanged, then the temperature of the Earth remains in balance. This natural balance, however, has been influenced by human activity. The atmospheric concentration of carbon dioxide has increased by about 15% in the last 100 years and the current rate of increase is estimated to be 0.4% per year (Figure 2.30). This, together with increases in levels of other greenhouse gases such as methane and nitrous oxide, has upset the natural balance and led to global warming.

It is generally agreed that these continuing atmospheric changes will lead to a further rise in temperature, but it is difficult to predict the extent or speed of change. If carbon dioxide levels double, then temperatures could rise by a further 2–3 °C, with greater rises at higher latitudes, perhaps in the order of 7–8 °C. It is believed that this warming will cause sea levels to rise.

One of the main reasons for the increase in carbon dioxide in the atmosphere has been the burning of fossil fuels, such as coal, oil and natural gas, by the industrialised nations of the world. Fossil fuels contain hydrocarbons which means carbon dioxide is released when they are burnt. As LEDCs develop (and some, for example China, are well along the road), they too need to generate energy as cheaply as possible. At present this means consuming huge quantities of fossil fuels, thereby adding to the problem.

Deforestation has also been linked to global warming. Rainforests act as a 'carbon sink' because trees are a major store of carbon. The more vegetation there is, the more carbon dioxide that is taken in by trees and other plants and used in photosynthesis. The economic development of countries such as Brazil, has created a demand for space and resources, which has resulted in the loss of tropical rainforests. Deforestation contributes to the build-up of carbon dioxide in the atmosphere.

Large-scale pastoral farming, in which huge herds of domestic cattle are reared for meat in areas of cleared forest, leads to an increase in emissions of methane.

Where rainforests have been flooded to create reservoirs for the production of hydroelectric power, decaying vegetation within the lakes also adds to carbon dioxide levels, as the flooded vegetation decomposes.

Effects of global warming

Global warming has serious implications for sea levels, climate patterns and economic activity. Some of the likely effects are described below.

Rising sea levels

The sea level rise in the twentieth century has been estimated as 1.5 cm, but in the twenty-first century levels could rise between 5 and 10 cm per decade. This will be sufficient to cause serious flooding in coastal areas and increased erosion in others. For low-lying countries such as the Netherlands and Bangladesh, and for many Pacific and Indian Ocean islands, rising sea levels will have catastrophic consequences. There will also be the huge cost of providing substantial flood defences. Many British estuaries may need defences similar to the Thames Barrier.

Climatic change

Many places will experience warmer summers. One estimate for the UK suggests that, by 2030, average temperatures could rise by over 2°C. Continental areas could have reduced rainfall, producing desert-like conditions in places that were previously good for agriculture.

Some climatologists believe that, if global warming leads to changes in the pattern of ocean currents, the UK could experience a much *colder* climate. It is possible that the Gulf Stream and North Atlantic drift could be diverted and, without the warming effects of these currents, the UK would have a climate similar to that of Siberia.

Such climatic changes would have widespread effects on vegetation, wildlife and agriculture. The ability of some regions to provide food for the population would diminish, leading to mass migrations as people searched for new areas in which to grow crops. Some areas, though, could benefit. There might be more land suitable for agriculture in countries such as Russia and Canada.

Table 2.4 Predicted sea-level rises due to global warming

Year	Sea-level rise (cm) Best estimate	Worst estimate
2020	5	8
2040	12	20
2060	25	40
2080	35	60
2100	48	85

Watch out for the alligators in 'Everglades' Britain

Drought and floods 'may become a way of life'

London will be as hot as Loire valley in 25 years

GLOBAL WARMING IS 'DRIVING FISH NORTH'

'Global warming threat' to 40% of Britain's birds

Figure 2.31 Possible effects of global warming in the UK

Extreme events

Heatwaves, floods, droughts and storms will all last longer and show an increasing intensity. With higher temperature there will be increased evaporation over the oceans, leading to greater global precipitation.

Figure 2.31 shows a selection of newspaper headlines highlighting some of the possible effects of global warming in the UK.

Case study Global warming and the British Isles

As a result of global warming, the UK could experience warmer summers, longer hot spells, droughts and increased storm activity. In contrast, some climatologists believe that changes in the pattern of ocean currents could result in much colder conditions.

Coastal regions

Increases in mean sea levels and in the frequency and magnitude of storms, storm surges and waves would lead to more coastal flooding. Sea levels around Britain are predicted to rise by between 12 and 37 cm by 2050, which would make a number of low-lying areas vulnerable, particularly the coasts of East Anglia, Lancashire, the Humber estuary, the Essex mudflats, the Thames estuary, parts of the north Wales coast, the Clyde/Forth estuaries and Belfast Lough. Flooding would lead to disruption in transport, manufacturing and the housing sector. In addition, there would be longer-term damage to agricultural land and coastal power stations, and water supplies could be contaminated by salt infiltration.

Agriculture

Climate changes are likely to have a substantial effect on plant growth and, by extension, plant productivity. Higher temperatures could result in:

- a decrease in yields of cereal crops
- an increase in yields of sugar beet and potatoes
- an increase in the length of the growing season for grasses and trees, bringing a higher productivity

Photograph 2.6 Flooding in Sheerness, 1953, following a storm surge which flooded much of the east coast of England. Climate change could lead to an increase in such events

TopFoto

- the introduction of new crops and species – the UK could even become a major wine-producing region
- an increase in some pests, such as the Colorado beetle which causes serious damage to potatoes

Flora, fauna and landscape

A sustained rise in temperatures could have the following effects:

- a significant movement of species northwards and to higher elevations
- the extinction of some native species which are unable to adapt to the increasing temperatures
- the loss of species which occur in isolated damp, cool or coastal habitats
- the invasion and spread of alien weeds, pests, diseases and viruses
- an increased number of foreign species of invertebrates, birds and mammals which may outcompete native species
- the disappearance of snow from the tops of the highest mountains

Soils

Higher temperatures could reduce the water-holding capacity of some soils, increasing the likelihood of soil moisture deficits. The stability of building foundations and other structures, especially in central, eastern and southern England where clay soils with large shrink–swell potential are abundant, would be affected if summers became drier and winters wetter. There could be a loss of organic matter, which would affect the stability of certain soil structures. Soil structure could also be affected if the water table rose with rising sea levels.

Water resources

Water resources would benefit from wetter winters, but warmer summers with increased evaporation could have the opposite effect.

Energy use

Higher temperatures could decrease the need for heating, but a growing demand for air conditioning would increase electricity consumption.

What can be done about global warming?

Carbon dioxide has an effective lifetime in the atmosphere of about 100 years, so its concentration responds slowly to changes in emissions. At the 1992 Earth Summit in Rio de Janeiro the developed countries agreed to stabilise carbon dioxide emissions. This will slow down the rate of climatic change, but to prevent carbon dioxide concentrations from rising we will need to reduce current global emissions by about 60%.

In 1997, at a follow-up meeting in Kyoto, Japan, a Climate Change Protocol was signed by over 100 governments. This set more specific targets for pollution mitigation and proposed schemes to enable governments to reach these targets. Most governments agreed that by 2010 they should have reduced their atmospheric pollution levels to those of 1990. There are three things to note about this:

- Some countries are already polluting at levels significantly above those of 1990. The USA, for example, releases 15% more carbon dioxide at the start of the twenty-first century than it did 10 years ago. Despite this, President Bush refused to ratify the Kyoto proposals, claiming that 'the agreement was fatally flawed' and that the emission targets were unattainable and potentially damaging to the US economy.
- Some countries are disproportionately responsible for releasing greenhouse gases. In 1996, the USA released 21% of global carbon dioxide even though it only had 4% of the world's population.

- Some countries, particularly the least developed countries, which have little industry and few vehicles, release very low levels of greenhouse gases into the atmosphere.

Carbon credits

Following the Kyoto meeting, a system of global carbon credits was introduced, under which each country has an annual carbon dioxide pollution limit. Major polluters can buy 'carbon credits' from less polluting countries which are not using up their own quotas. If polluting countries still go over their limit, a number of options might be forced upon them:

- a fine
- investment in ways to reduce domestic carbon dioxide emissions (e.g. wind or solar power)
- paying for improved technologies in other countries or for other countries to plant trees (in February 2000 the Japanese paid the government of New South Wales in Australia £50 million to plant over 40,000 hectares of trees in the next 20 years)

Critics argue that this system is flawed because it serves the interests of the developed countries which are the major polluters, and enables them to go on polluting. Such people believe the mass industrialisation and consumerism which underpin the economies of the developed world are unsustainable. It is unlikely, though, that the citizens of the developed world will be willing to give up their current lifestyles. The monitoring systems have also been criticised — countries are expected to monitor themselves, leaving much room for cheating and 'massaging' of the figures.

One result of the carbon credit system in the UK has been the introduction of a Climate Change Levy — a tax on energy used by industry, commerce and the public sector. This came into effect in April 2001. It is designed to help meet the target agreed in the Kyoto Protocol which commits the UK to a 12.5% reduction in emissions of six greenhouse gases by 2010. Many people now believe the carbon credit system is the best way to reduce, if not entirely eradicate, atmospheric pollution in the twenty-first century.

Local responses to global warming

Sustainable development has become a key concept in the twenty-first century. In order to maintain current standards of living and to slow down the predicted impacts of global warming, societies need to use their resources more wisely. At the regional scale, many local governments have developed initiatives to respond to environmental problems. Some city councils are planning to follow London's lead and impose a congestion charge in order to limit traffic in their centres. Other initiatives introduced in cities to help reduce problems of urban pollution, for example trams and park-and-ride schemes, will also curb the rise in carbon emissions.

In recent years, many communities within the UK have been faced with increased risk of flooding. This is likely to continue, so people should begin to 'think globally and act locally'.

It is widely accepted that much energy is wasted in the home. Increased understanding of energy conservation and recycling is needed. If people become more aware of the ways in which the problems can be tackled, everyone can play a part. Education has a vital role to play in this, but individuals can respond to global warming at the local level by:

- Ensuring that their homes are **insulated** — many local councils promote and assist with the cost of cavity-wall insulation and loft-lagging of older houses. New housing is governed by regulations to ensure that it is properly insulated. Double-glazing also helps to retain heat, and this is generally a feature of new housing.
- **Recycling** — most local councils have targets for recycling and encourage householders to sort waste. In many places, garden waste is collected separately from household waste, and paper and cardboard, aluminium cans, plastic bottles and glass can be separated for recycling. Many local authorities provide recycling bins or boxes and recyclable refuse is collected kerbside.
- **Using energy wisely** — households can cut their energy bills significantly by adopting practices such as turning off lights in unoccupied rooms, turning down the central heating thermostat, not leaving televisions and computers on standby and using energy-efficient light bulbs.
- **Reducing car travel** — using public transport and joining car-sharing schemes or walking to work or school. Many primary schools have introduced 'walk-to-school' schemes. These have been promoted in local newspapers and on television.

Chapter 3

Energy and life

Systems, flows and processes

Biomes and ecosystems

Biomes

Comparing maps of the world's climate (Figure 3.1) and vegetation (Figure 3.2) zones (biomes) reveals marked similarities. A third map showing zonal soil distribution at the same scale would also bear comparison. Indeed within any ecosystem, the three main components — climate, vegetation and soils — are closely linked together in equilibrium.

In the tropical rainforest biome, because of the constant high temperature and rainfall, the vegetation grows more quickly than anywhere else on Earth. This produces the greatest amount of organic matter, referred to as net primary productivity. The units are g m^{-2} $year^{-1}$. (When calculating net primary productivity, the organic matter has to be dry.)

Tropical rainforest and deciduous woodland are both high-energy biomes. Each has its own distinctive vegetation. Each biome type, no matter on which continent it occurs, shows similarities in climate, soils, plants and animal

Figure 3.1 Climate zones of the world

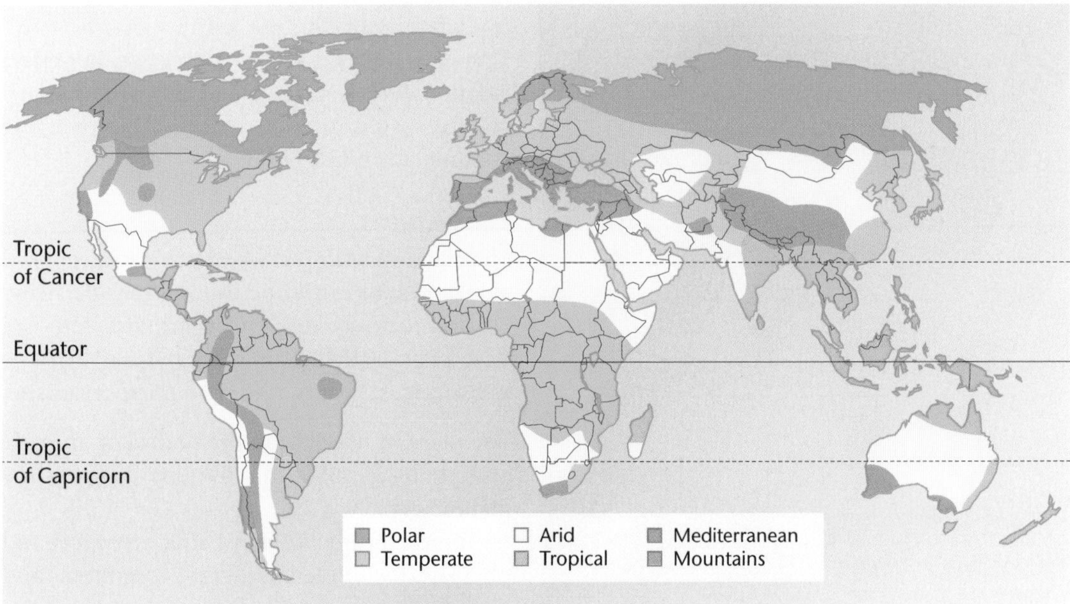

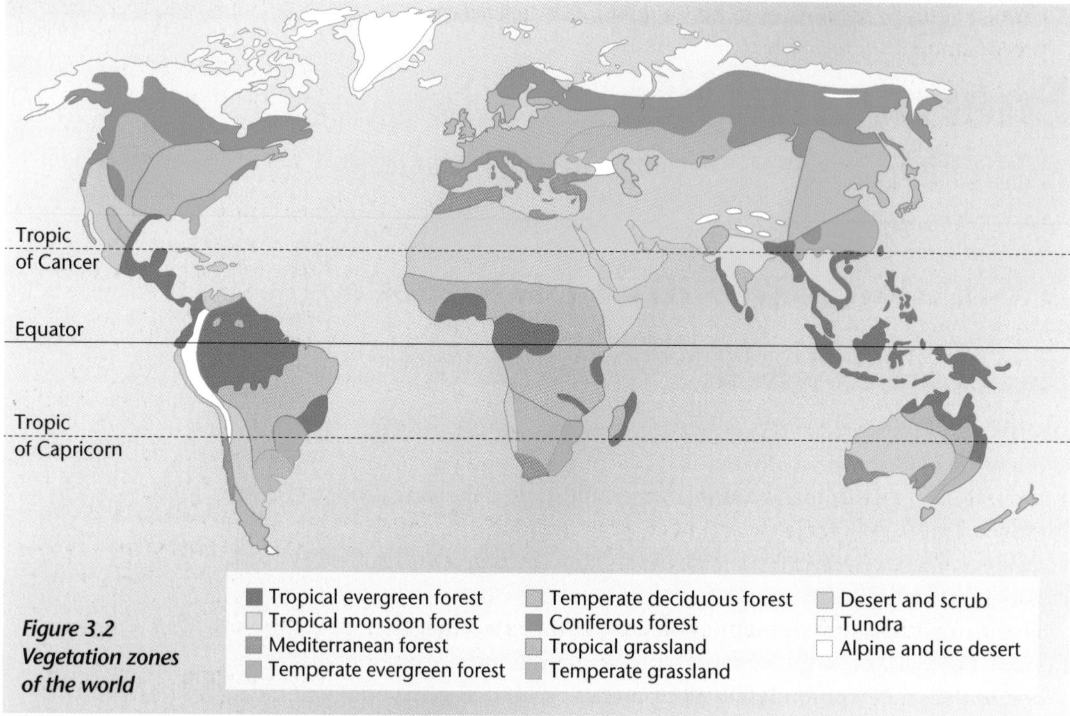

Figure 3.2 Vegetation zones of the world

Photograph 3.1 Hot desert is a low-energy biome, with little vegetation

life. Low-energy biomes are the tundra in the high latitudes and the hot deserts in the low latitudes. Here, the vegetation is scant and net primary productivity is low.

In a natural state a biome is considered to be in dynamic equilibrium with its environment. This means that the vegetation exists in perfect balance with the climate and soils and that any change would alter the balance between the components of the biome.

Ecosystems

The components of an ecosystem are categorised as either **biotic** or **abiotic**. Biotic means the living environment, so components include:

- vegetation (living and decomposing)
- mammals, insects, birds and microorganisms

The mass of material in the bodies of animals and plants is called the **biomass**. It is mainly plant tissue.

Abiotic means the non-living, chemical and physical components of the ecosystem and includes:

- climate — in particular the seasonal pattern of temperature and precipitation
- soil characteristics
- underlying parent rock
- relief of the land
- drainage characteristics

As with any system there are inputs, outputs, stores and flows. Ecosystems are open systems because energy and living matter can both enter and leave the system.

- **Inputs** — the most important input is energy (particularly light) from the sun, which drives photosynthesis and so enables plants to grow. Other inputs include animals that arrive from elsewhere, and water, transported into the ecosystem by precipitation or rivers.
- **Outputs** — nutrients are transferred out of the system in a number of ways. Animals can physically move; water can move out of the ecosystem in rivers and by evapotranspiration, throughflow and groundwater flow.
- **Flows** — within an ecosystem nutrients can be transferred from one store to another, for example from the soil to the vegetation through capillary uptake by plant roots.
- **Stores** — the three main stores of nutrients are in the vegetation, plant litter and soils.

Key terms

Biome Ecosystem at a continental scale covering a large area, with vegetation characteristics that are predominantly influenced by the climate. A biome can also be judged by the speed at which the vegetation grows.

Ecosystem A dynamic, stable system characterised by the interaction of plants and animals with each other and with the non-living components of the environment. An ecosystem can be considered at any scale from a small area, such as a pond or hedge, up to an area as large as the Earth itself.

Environment All the conditions in which an organism lives.

Energy flows and nutrient cycling

Energy from the sun provides warmth to both the abiotic and biotic components of an ecosystem and allows them to grow. Sunlight is extremely important because the green pigment chlorophyll, present in plants, captures light energy and converts it into chemical energy by manufacturing carbohydrates. This process of photosynthesis is the way in which plants grow and increase their biomass.

Within all ecosystems, nutrients are constantly required for plant growth and are recycled from one store to another. For example, leaves fall from trees and as they decompose nutrients are returned to the soil. The commonly accepted way of demonstrating the cycling of nutrients within the main stores of a biome is by a **Gersmehl diagram** (Figure 3.3). The stores are drawn as circles of proportionate size to

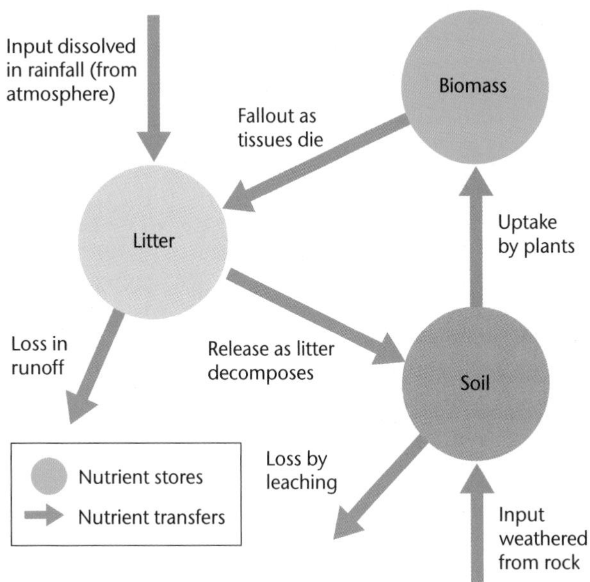

Figure 3.3 A model of the mineral nutrient cycle

represent the stores of nutrients within the biomass, litter and soil. Nutrient transfers, inputs and outputs are represented by arrows of varying thickness, depending on the relative rates of transfer between the stores.

- **Inputs** include nutrients such as carbon and nitrogen dissolved in precipitation and minerals from weathered parent rock.
- **Outputs** include loss of nutrients from the system through the soil by leaching and by surface runoff.
- **Flows** or **transfers** include leaf fall from the biomass to the litter, decomposition of litter, transferring nutrients to the soil, and uptake of nutrients from the soil by trees and other plants.

Trophic levels, food chains and webs

Energy transfer within an ecosystem can be illustrated using a pyramid diagram showing the four main trophic levels (Figure 3.4). At each trophic level, some of the energy contained is available as food for the next level in the hierarchy. The size of each layer in the pyramid decreases going up the hierarchy because around 90% of the energy contained within each level is lost through life processes, particularly respiration, movement and excretion. Only 10% is available for the next level as food, so the number of living organisms within an ecosystem decreases as the trophic level increases.

- **Producers** or autotrophs are the first and lowest layer in the pyramid. They are green plants and produce their own food through photosynthesis using energy from sunlight.
- **Primary consumers** or herbivores occupy the second trophic level. These insects, fish, birds and mammals eat the producers.
- **Secondary consumers** or carnivores are meat-eaters and survive primarily by consuming the herbivores.
- **Tertiary consumers** are at the top of the trophic pyramid. They are the top predators and eat the secondary consumers. They may be omnivores.
- **Detritivores** and **decomposers** operate at each trophic level. A detritivore is an animal that feeds on dead material or waste products; a decomposer is an organism that breaks down dead plants, animals and waste matter. Fungi and bacteria are decomposers.

Trophic pyramids can be illustrated by examining simple food chains that exist within a particular ecosystem. A food chain also shows the flow of energy through an ecosystem. There are usually four links in a food chain, as there are four levels

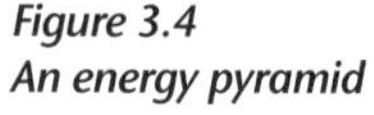
Figure 3.4
An energy pyramid

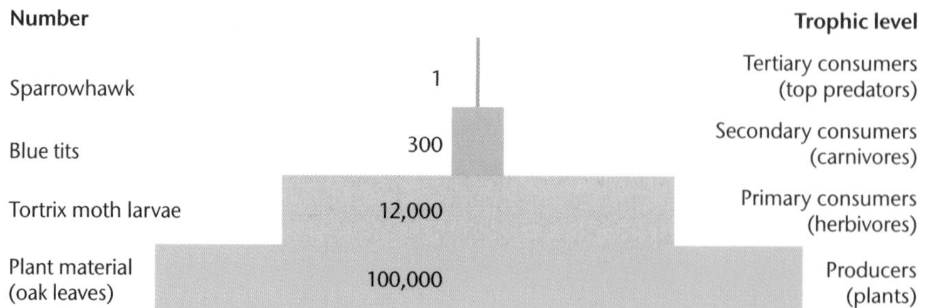

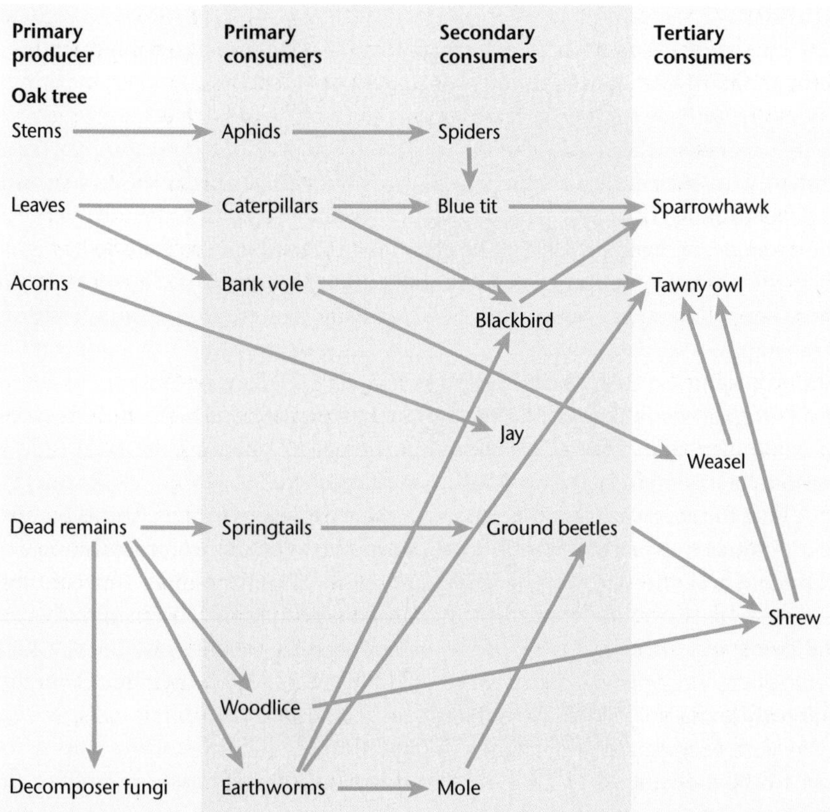

Figure 3.5
A food web

in a trophic pyramid. Each link in the chain feeds on and obtains energy from the preceding link and in turn is consumed by and provides energy for the following link. Examples of simple food chains include:

rose leaf → aphid → blue tit → sparrow hawk
phytoplankton → zooplankton → cod → human
corn → field mouse → weasel → fox

In reality, a large number of individual food chains operate within a single ecosystem. The overall picture can be shown using a food web (Figure 3.5). Many animals have a varied diet and any one species of animal or plant is likely to be the food for a number of different consumers. As a result, there are complex feeding interactions within an ecosystem. Humans, as omnivores, operate at several trophic levels.

The tropical rainforest: a high-energy biome

Tropical rainforest is the biome that circles the Earth, mainly between latitudes 10°N and 10°S of the equator. It occurs in the Amazon basin in South America, the Democratic Republic of Congo and the Guinea coast of Africa, parts of southeast Asia, Indonesia and north Australia.

Climate

The equatorial climate has little seasonal variation. Temperatures remain high throughout the year: mean monthly values seldom fall below 25°C and maximum values are unlikely to rise above 28°C.

In locations further away from the equator a dual peak of temperature can occur annually. In such locations the sun is directly overhead twice every year as it appears to move from the Tropic of Cancer to the Tropic of Capricorn between the summer and winter solstices. The daily range of temperature tends to be higher than the annual range of monthly averages. During sunny spells, often in the morning or late afternoon when the skies have cleared after a thunderstorm, temperatures can rise above 30°C. At night, if the sky is cloud free, temperatures can drop quite rapidly, sometimes to below 20°C. This is because there are no insulating clouds to keep the heat in. Annual precipitation is high, often in excess of 2,000 mm. Rain falls all year round at the equator because the ITCZ (a low-pressure belt) dominates atmospheric conditions here.

A little further away from the equator, a short dry season occurs. This is because of the annual movement of the ITCZ as it travels between the Tropics of Cancer and Capricorn and affects atmospheric pressure. In the months of May, June and July there is a dry season in the southern hemisphere because the ITCZ is directly over the Tropic of Cancer, pulling with it wet low-pressure weather into the northern hemisphere. The opposite occurs at the end of the year in late November, December and early January.

As with temperature, the pattern of rainfall in the rainforest varies during the day. In the morning, skies are generally clear. Evapotranspiration is rapid as the sun beats down on the humid forest and the low-pressure conditions allow this air to be rapidly uplifted. As the air rises it cools and water vapour condenses into clouds. These clouds continue to build up until the early afternoon. By this time they are of the towering cumulonimbus variety and their dense grey colour indicates that a heavy storm is soon to follow. In the middle of the afternoon, heavy rain, often accompanied by thunder and lightning, returns the previously uplifted moisture back to ground level. The cycle begins again and the day ends as it started with clear skies.

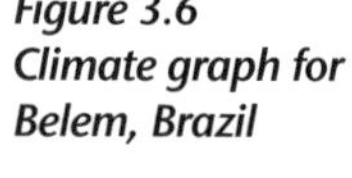
Figure 3.6 Climate graph for Belem, Brazil

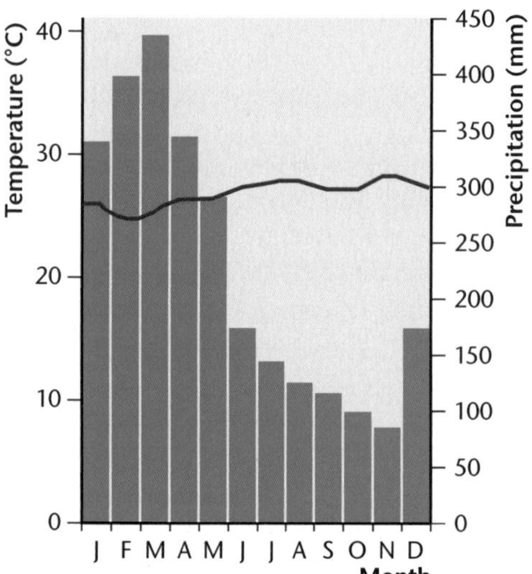

Humidity is high throughout the year — indeed the rainforest has been likened to a natural greenhouse. Continuous evapotranspiration adds water vapour to the air.

Day and night are the same length at the equator. Dawn arrives at around 6 a.m. and night falls quickly at 6 p.m. There is little twilight. Twelve hours of sunlight every day allow photosynthesis to take place all year.

On the forest floor there is little breeze. On the equator there is a distinct lack of wind because this is where the trade winds converge.

Vegetation

The rainforest is the most diverse and productive biome in the world but it is also the most fragile. Those remote parts of the forest untouched by modern society have developed over thousands of years and are said to be in a state of dynamic equilibrium. The vegetation is in harmony with its environment and is described as climatic climax vegetation, where the dominant species are the hardwood trees. This balance can be easily disturbed by human activity.

- The net primary productivity of the rainforest is 2,200 g m^{-2} $year^{-1}$. This means that energy from sunlight fixed by the producers produces 2,200 g of living matter to every square metre of land each year. This figure is so high because the growing season lasts all year and the litter is rapidly decomposed, replacing nutrients taken up by the vegetation.
- The forest has an evergreen appearance because, although most of the trees are deciduous, individual species lose their leaves at different times of the year. There are always some trees in full leaf.
- There can be up to 300 species of tree in every square kilometre. Species include mahogany, teak, rosewood, rubber, balsa and brazil nut.
- The forest has a layered appearance, with the tallest trees (**emergents**), standing up to 45 m tall, above the **canopy** (Figure 3.8). The canopy absorbs most of the sunlight and intercepts most of the precipitation.
- Many of the plants within the forest anchor their roots on the trees, rather than in the ground. This is because away from the riverbanks the forest floor is very dark. Such plants are called **epiphytes**. An epiphyte has a symbiotic relationship with the tree being used as the host. The tree is not damaged, as it would be by a parasite. **Lianas** are examples of epiphytes.
- When a tree dies naturally it brings down some others as it falls, creating a small clearing in the forest. New trees grow quickly, taking advantage of the light. The felled trees decompose rapidly, assisted by the detritivores and the hot, humid conditions, which accelerate the process.
- Fungi are saprophytes. They grow on trees and other plants and inhabit the forest floor. They have an important role in decomposition of the litter.

Figure 3.7 ***A nutrient cycle for tropical rainforest***

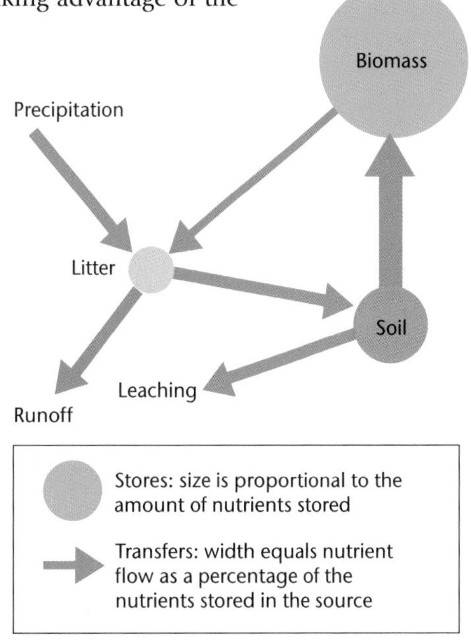

The vegetation has developed and adapted to the physical conditions of the rainforest in a number of ways:

- The trees grow rapidly upwards towards the light and their trunks are slender with few branches. Leaves at the tops of the trees absorb sunlight and photosynthesise. The bark is thin because the trees do not need protection from harsh winter temperatures. The tallest trees have flexible trunks that allow a good degree of movement. At 50 m above ground level the winds can be quite strong, so this allows the trees to sway without breaking.

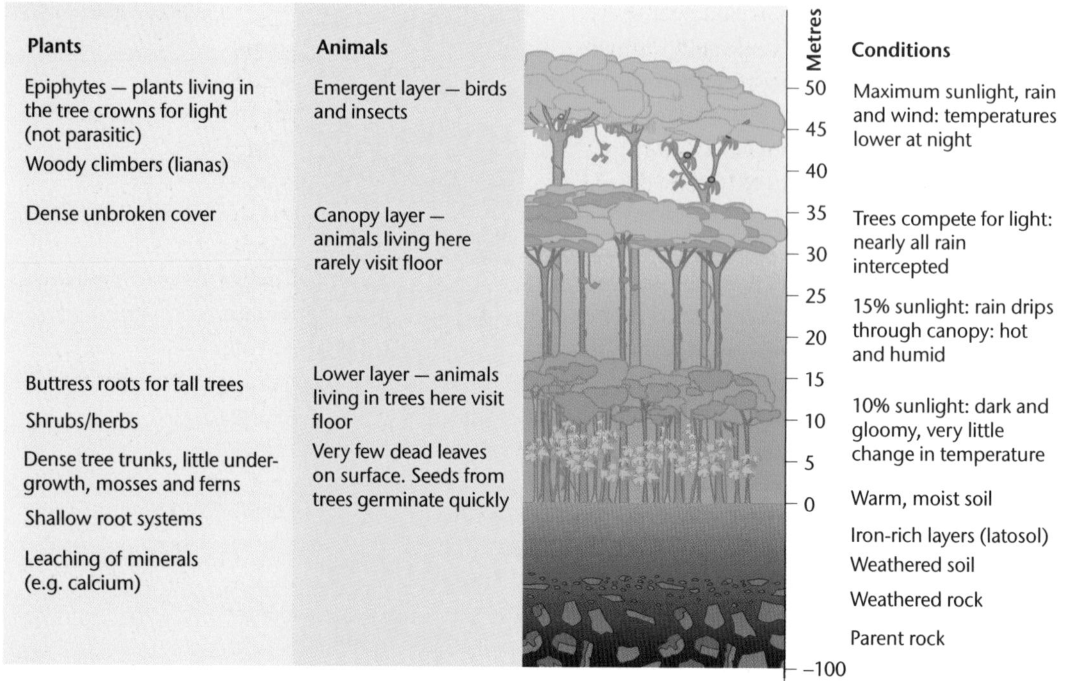

Figure 3.8 The layered structure of tropical rainforest

- Since the minerals that the trees need are only found in the top layer of the soil and there is an abundant supply of water, the roots of the trees do not penetrate the soil to any great depth. They tend to spread out on the forest floor. **Buttress roots**, emerging up to 3 m above the ground, help to stabilise the tallest trees.
- The leaves have adapted to the climate, in particular the regular heavy rainfall, by developing drip-tips. These allow excess water to be easily shed. In addition, some leaves are thick and leathery to withstand the strong sunlight and prevent too much loss of water from the plant.

Soils

In any undisturbed biome the underlying soil will have developed naturally over a long period of time and be in balance with its environment. Such a soil is known as a **zonal soil**. This is a mature soil and its characteristics strongly reflect the climate and vegetation. The zonal soil type associated with the tropical rainforest is **latosol**.

Characteristic features

A latosol can be more than 40 m deep. The constant hot wet climate of the rainforest provides perfect conditions for chemical weathering of the bedrock and there is a constant supply of minerals from the parent rock to the soil. **Ferrallitisation** is the name for the process by which the bedrock is broken down by chemical weathering into clay minerals and sesquioxides (hydrated oxides of iron and aluminium).

The red colour of the soil is partly the result of the precipitation of iron and aluminium minerals. As there is a moisture surplus in the equatorial climate (because rainfall exceeds evapotranspiration), there is downward movement of water through the soil. Silica minerals are washed out of the A horizon and transported downwards by this water in a process known as **leaching** or **eluviation**. Iron and aluminium compounds are less soluble and are left behind. The iron compounds give the soil its rich red colour.

The latosol is nutrient poor. Plant uptake of nutrients is roughly equal to the input from decomposed litter. Although there is a constant supply of organic matter from falling leaves and decaying vegetation, the year-round growing season ensures that, as soon as litter is broken down into humus, it is absorbed by the growing vegetation.

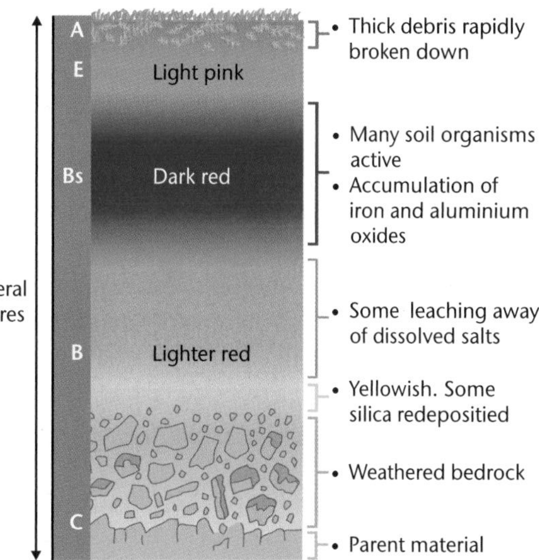

Figure 3.9
Profile of a latosol

The time factor

Succession and climatic climax

As exemplified by tropical rainforest, the vegetation of an ecosystem depends closely on interaction with climate and soils and is in equilibrium with its environment. Plant populations vary from one area to another and tropical rainforest is just one example of a climax community.

People can disturb and alter a climatic climax community in many ways, either by accident or by design. One major activity that has disturbed forest ecosystems is deforestation, which is covered in more detail later (pages 89–92).

All areas of the world in which plant communities grow undergo a series of changes, becoming more complex as time passes. This series of changes is called a vegetation **succession**. If allowed to continue undisturbed succession will reach its **climatic climax**, in which the plant species are living in perfect balance with the current environmental conditions. Although climate is the major influence on vegetation at a global scale, on a local scale other factors such as drainage, geology and relief affect plant growth. There are two basic types of succession:

- **Primary succession** occurs on surfaces that have had no previous vegetation. These include lava flows, bare rock and sand dunes. There are several types of primary succession:
  - those formed on land (**xeroseres**) — **lithoseres** on bare rock and **psammoseres** on sand dunes
  - those formed in water (**hydroseres**) — **haloseres** in salt water and **hydroseres** in fresh water

Key terms

Climatic climax The final stage of a plant succession, in which the vegetation is in balance with the environmental conditions (soil and climate). As long as the environmental conditions remain unchanged there will be no change in the vegetation once this stage is reached.

Deforestation The deliberate clearance of forest from land by cutting or burning.

Plagioclimax The plant community that exists when human interference prevents the climatic climax being reached.

Secondary succession Succession taking place on land that was formerly vegetated but has undergone loss of that vegetation.

Succession A series of changes that take place in a plant community over time.

- **Secondary succession** follows the destruction or modification of an existing plant community. This can occur naturally, perhaps after a landslide or a fire caused by lightning. It can also occur through human activity, such as deforestation to provide farmland.

Development of a succession

As a succession develops it passes through a series of stages called **seres**. Here the processes of invasion, colonisation, competition, domination and decline operate to influence the composition of the vegetation.

When plants first invade bare ground (through the processes of dispersal and migration), groups of a particular species, or colonies of two or more species, become established. These **pioneer species** are extremely hardy plants, adapted to survive in harsh conditions. Long-rooted salt-tolerant marram grass growing on a sand dune is an example of a pioneer plant. Pioneers compete for available space, light, water and nutrients and, as they die, they help to modify the habitat, adding organic matter to the developing soil. They can affect the microclimate of the area (wind speed at ground level, shelter, temperature and humidity) and soil conditions (organic content, nutrient recycling, acidity and water retention). The roots of the pioneer plants help to break up and weather the surface and so aid soil formation.

As the ground is improved by the creation of an immature soil, other plants are able to colonise and change the existing balance of species. Each stage of the colonisation provides better conditions for plant growth than the previous one, so an increasing number of species is found. The addition of organic matter (from decaying vegetation) to the developing soil improves its structure and water-retention qualities. This allows the growth of taller and more aggressive plants that are more demanding of water, nutrients and anchorage. Taller plants also provide shelter from the sun and wind, which in turn allows other plants to become established. In each stage of a plant succession, there are dominant plants. These are the tallest plants and cover the most ground.

In time, sometimes even thousands of years, a period of relative stability is reached in which the vegetation has reached its climax, with dominants excluding rivals less suited to the current environmental conditions. Once the major dominants are in place the number of species begins to decline. Climax is usually dominated by the tallest species that can grow in the given conditions. At this stage the community becomes 'closed' — saturation point has been reached with all potential niches occupied. This is known as the **climatic climax community**, the natural vegetation having reached a stable balance with the climate and soils of the area.

An example of a primary succession: a lithosere

A lithosere is a succession that begins life on a newly exposed rock surface. This surface might typically have been created by the eruption of a volcano, leaving a new, bare lava surface, as happened when Surtsey erupted in Iceland in 1963.

Another example of a lithosere is a raised beach, created either by falling sea levels or by the isostatic uplift of land from the sea. Raised beaches can be seen

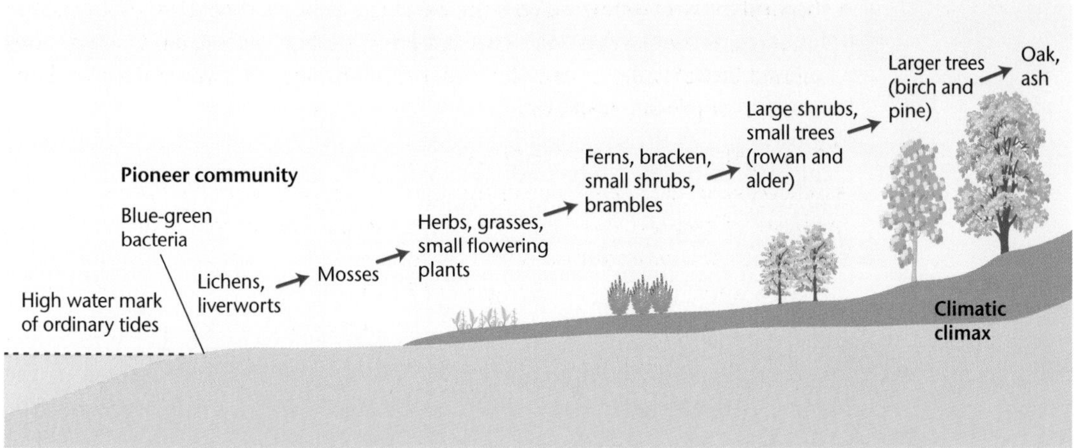

***Figure 3.10* The development of a lithosere on a raised beach**

on the west coast of Scotland. In the UK, a lithosere on a raised beach develops as follows:

- The bare rock surface is initially colonised by **bacteria and algae**, which can survive where there are few nutrients. Bare rock tends to be very dry and there is rapid surface runoff.
- The pioneers begin to colonise, starting with **lichens** which can withstand the acute water shortage. They begin to break down the rock and assist water retention.
- As water retention improves, **mosses** begin to grow. These also improve water retention and weathering to produce the beginnings of a soil in which more advanced plants can grow.
- **Grasses, ferns, herbs** and **flowering plants** appear. As these die back, bacteria convert their remains into humus, which helps to recycle nutrients and further improve soil fertility.
- **Shrubs** start to grow, shading out the grasses and herbs.
- Pioneer trees become established. These are mainly fast-growing species such as **willow, birch** and **rowan**.
- Slower-growing tree species begin to develop, such as **ash** and **oak**. Initially they are in the shade of shrubs, so they only appear in the later stages of the succession. They are the dominants of the climatic climax community — temperate deciduous woodland.

Arresting factors leading to secondary succession and plagioclimax

Successions can be stopped from reaching the climatic climax, or deflected towards a different climax, by human interference. The resulting vegetation is known as a **plagioclimax**. Examples of human activity that creates plagioclimaxes are:

- deforestation or afforestation
- animal grazing or trampling
- fire clearance

A good example of a plagioclimax in the UK is **heather moorland**. Many of the uplands in Britain were once covered by a climax vegetation of deciduous woodland, particularly oak forest. Heather (*Calluna vulgaris*) would have featured, but only in small amounts. Gradually the forests were removed, for a variety of purposes, and as the soils deteriorated without the deciduous vegetation, hardy plants such as heather came to dominate the uplands. Sheep grazing became the major form of agriculture and the sheep prevented the regeneration of climax woodland by destroying young saplings.

Many of these uplands have been controlled by managed burning to encourage new heather shoots. Burning has eliminated the less fire-resistant species, leading to the dominance of heather. When heather is burnt, one of the aims is to ensure that as much as possible of the available nutrient fund is conserved in the ecosystem. In many areas, heather is burnt on average every 15 years. If a longer time elapses there is too much woody tissue, the fires burn too hot, and nutrients are lost in the smoke.

Figure 3.11 shows the cycle associated with the heather system. If the burning was not continued, the heather moorland would degenerate, eventually allowing the entry of trees and a succession to woodland. Much of the present vegetation of the UK is a plagioclimax, largely as a result of clearance from the Roman and Anglo-Saxon periods through to the eleventh century. By this time only about 10% of the original woodland remained in England and Wales.

Figure 3.11 The heather nutrient cycle

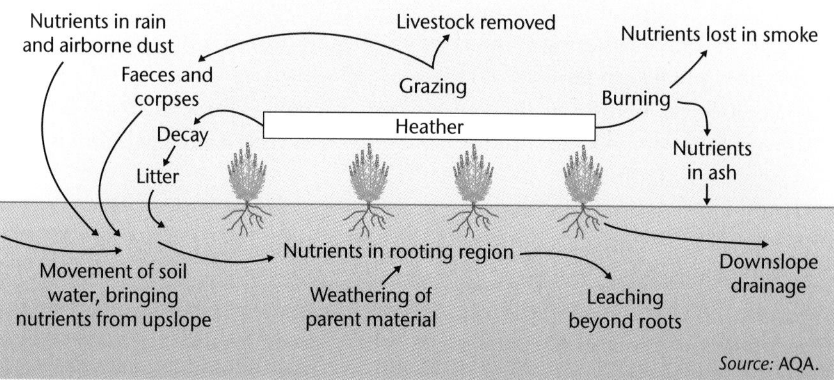

A secondary succession is a succession that develops on land that has previously been vegetated. For example, some areas might have been cleared for farming, but later abandoned. This abandoned land becomes colonised in a secondary succession. The stages of secondary succession may be more rapid than those of primary succession because organic matter is already present in the soil. The pioneer stage may be very short or absent altogether. The overall journey to climatic climax might occur in a much shorter time than if the succession had started on a new surface.

Secondary succession can also follow natural events such as a change in climate, a disease, a mudflow, a volcanic eruption or a spontaneous fire, which can be the result of lightning.

Deforestation and its impact on tropical rainforest

Deforestation is the deliberate clearing of woodland by cutting, burning or the application of a defoliant, such as that used during the 1960s by American troops to clear the jungle in Vietnam. In recent decades, it has become a major environmental concern in some LEDCs and newly industrialising countries (NICs) where tropical rainforests, such as those in the Amazon basin in South America and in Indonesia and Malaysia in the far east, are being destroyed at an alarming rate. It is claimed by some that half of the world's original rainforests have already been cleared, with an area the size of the UK being removed each year. By 2010, if the present rate of destruction continues, Brazil and the Democratic Republic of Congo will be the only countries with a significant area of rainforest remaining.

Climatic climax vegetation has been destroyed and this has led to both secondary succession and plagioclimax. The vegetation that eventually grows to replace the original rainforest tends to be smaller in height and less diverse, with a reduction in the overall biomass.

Figure 3.12 The extent of tropical rainforest and deforestation

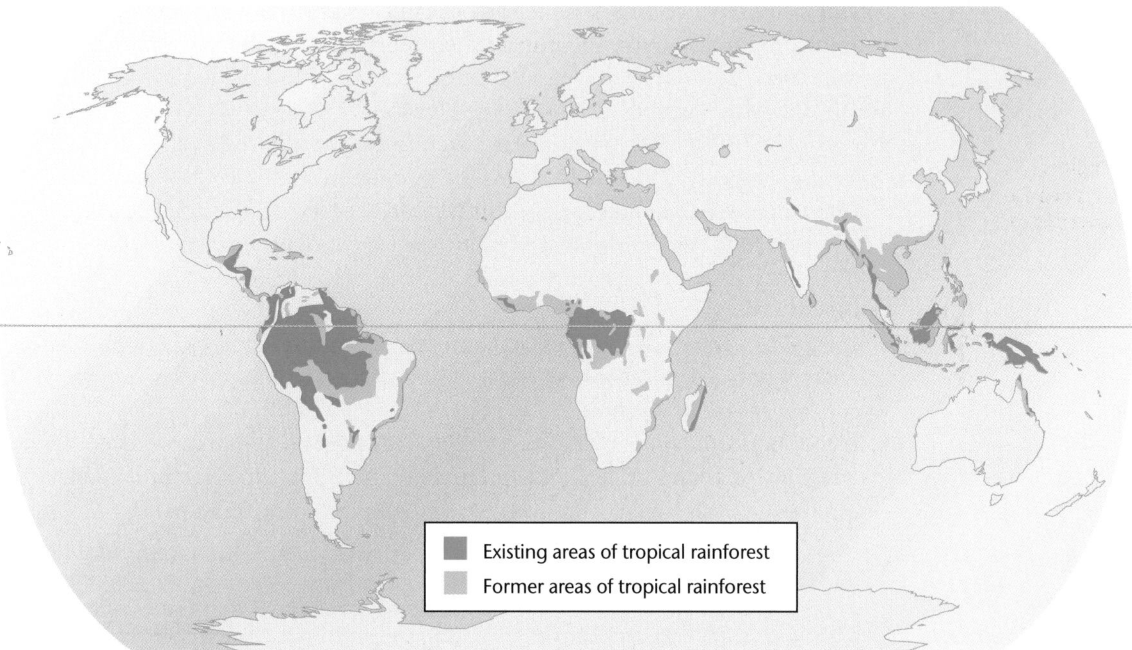

The economic, social and political causes of deforestation

Economic causes

- The demand for hardwood, such as teak, is increasing rapidly, particularly in MEDCs. Wood is in constant demand for building and furniture, both in the country of origin and for export. In Malaysia, timber and logs are the third largest export.

- Many LEDCs rely on export earnings from timber to help pay their debts and finance major development projects.
- In parts of Malaysia large rubber plantations have replaced the original forest. The latex produced provides important export earnings.
- In the Brazilian rainforest, rivers have been dammed and large areas flooded to provide water for hydroelectric power stations. An example of such a reservoir lies behind the Tucurui dam on the Tocantins River in Amazonia.
- Forest is also being cleared in Brazil so that minerals in the soil and underlying rock can be extracted. There are vast resources of bauxite and iron ore in the ground beneath the Brazilian rainforest and the Carajas project in Amazonia has resulted in the destruction of large areas of climax vegetation.
- Large cattle ranches have been developed, for example in Rondonia in the Amazon basin. Multinational companies herd beef cattle on the cleared land to provide meat for beefburgers.
- Forest has been cleared to build new roads and railways. The Transamazon Highway runs through the Amazon forest from east to west and is 5,300 km long. A 900 km railway has also been constructed to link the Carajas project with the port of São Luis, so that iron ore can be exported easily. As accessibility to the interior has improved it has allowed further economic activity.

Social causes

- Most countries with extensive areas of rainforest are still undergoing development. During the 1960s and 1970s, the population of the far east and South America increased rapidly because birth rates exceeded death rates. Population pressure led to increasing areas of rainforest undergoing clearance.

Political causes

- In most countries with a significant amount of rainforest government policies have encouraged the economic exploitation of forests, because they provide a valuable source of revenue.
- In Indonesia, the transmigration policy encouraged people to move from the overcrowded island of Java to less populated islands such as Sumatra, where rainforest was cleared to make way for settlements and agriculture.

The impacts of deforestation

The loss of rainforest has extensive impacts. These can be either positive or negative and can be divided into physical, economic, social and cultural impacts. Although they mainly occur on a local scale, some can have much wider-ranging consequences, right up to the global scale.

Physical impacts

Physical impacts affect the natural environment, so any effect on the land, soil, air, water and wildlife falls into this category.

As habitats shrink, **plant species** become endangered. When trees are cleared the food chain within the forest is disrupted. The reduction of producers affects

Mark Edwards/Still Pictures

Photograph 3.2 Erosion in Amazonia, Brazil, following loss of the rainforest

the higher trophic levels. Some **animal species**, for example tigers and orang-utans, are threatened by extinction. It has been estimated that between 1990 and 2000 there was a 30–50% decrease in the orang-utan population in the rainforests of southeast Asia.

The vegetation protects the latosol **soils** from the regular heavy tropical downpours. The dense forest canopy means that rates of interception are high, so not all the rainfall reaches the ground. Once the trees are removed, interception is halted. The topsoil is now open to erosion from the heavy rain and sediment is transported by runoff into the rivers. Infiltration rates also increase, so more nutrients and minerals are leached from the upper layers or A horizon, down into the subsoil. It is difficult for the soils to recover because their fertility is dependent on the input of litter from decaying vegetation. Deforestation removes this supply of nutrients.

Once the forest cover has been removed, soils can occasionally be further impoverished by the development of a **duricrust**. This is a hard impermeable layer in the soil or on the surface, created by the cementation of soil particles and mineral salts. It occurs when rainfall levels decrease after deforestation and minerals are drawn upwards through the soil by capillary action.

Flooding occurs more frequently following deforestation because increased soil erosion leads to more sediment being carried by the water entering the rivers. This sediment blocks the river channels and reduces their capacity.

The **microclimate** of the forest is disturbed by deforestation. There is a daily water cycle in the rainforest. Evapotranspiration is rapid in the early part of the

day, because the sun is always strong close to the equator and the lush vegetation stores contain huge amounts of moisture. Water vapour from these stores rises by convection. As it rises through the atmosphere the air temperature falls with altitude. The vapour condenses and is stored in clouds until storms during the afternoon return moisture to the land as precipitation. Once the trees are removed there is less transpiration and daily precipitation levels therefore decrease. The diurnal range of temperature increases because there is less cloud cover — the temperature rises more quickly during the day when there are few clouds in the sky and, without their protection, falls rapidly at night.

In Indonesia and Malaysia, the **air quality** has been greatly affected by large-scale slash-and-burn forest clearance. Smoke particulates released into the air have resulted in serious and dangerous smog episodes. These have been so bad that sometimes airports have had to be closed due to poor visibility and schools temporarily shut down because of the risk to children's health.

Burning wood produces carbon dioxide, so slash-and-burn clearance has contributed to the rise in carbon dioxide levels in the air in recent years and therefore to **global warming**. In addition, trees take in carbon dioxide and give out oxygen during photosynthesis. It has been estimated that tropical rainforests used to supply around one-third of atmospheric oxygen but this is falling because of deforestation.

Economic impacts

Indonesia and Malaysia have industrialised rapidly and economic development is occurring very fast in these countries. Clearance of rainforest has made space for new industrial developments. Income from the export of hardwood logged from the forest has resulted in greater levels of prosperity for many.

In Brazil, raw materials mined in the rainforest have provided valuable export earnings to help pay off debt.

Social and cultural impacts

Indigenous people have seen their traditional way of life changed as deforestation has destroyed their culture and in many cases forced them to move from their land:

- In the Amazon basin, many Amerindians, such as the Kayapo, have been forced into reservations. Some have left the rainforest for good to try their luck in the big cities of the southeast.
- As they have come into contact with the outside world disease has ravaged some indigenous populations. Lack of immunity to Western diseases, such as measles, has meant the loss of entire villages.
- In some areas migrants have been moved into the forest on government resettlement schemes. Such people are often unprepared for the harsh reality of the rainforest and find it difficult to make a living from the land. In Indonesia, the transmigration scheme has not proved successful for many of those who migrated from the island of Java to less populated outlying islands (see pages 354–355).

Soils

The origins of soil: the role of water, organic and inorganic matter

Soil has four main components:

- mineral matter, which originates from the underlying parent rock
- organic matter, which originates mainly from vegetation
- air
- water

The characteristics of soil are the result of interactions between a number of factors: climate, vegetation (organic matter), relief, drainage and the underlying parent rock, all operating through time. Human activity can have an important impact in improving or degrading soil.

Water and air

The amounts of water and air present within a particular soil depend on a number of factors. The soil water budget is strongly dependent on climate. The relationship between precipitation and potential evapotranspiration for a particular place over the period of a year can be shown by a soil-moisture graph. Figure 3.13 shows a typical soil-moisture graph for a podzol soil on the moorlands above Braemar in Scotland.

- When precipitation is greater than evapotranspiration, the dominant movement of water within the soil is downwards. This is called **leaching** or **eluviation**. It causes soluble nutrients and minerals to be washed out of the upper layers of the soil. In extreme circumstances a soil can become completely waterlogged. The water table reaches the surface and leaching ceases.
- During a warm dry season, when potential evapotranspiration is greater than precipitation, water evaporates from the ground surface and is transpired through plants. The movement of water through the soil is upward. It occurs by capillary action. Soluble minerals, such as salts, can be transported through the soil and deposited close to the surface. Capillary action can cause soils to become salinised. Such a soil has a soil-moisture deficit.

Figure 3.13 A soil-moisture graph for a podzol on moorland above Braemar, Scotland

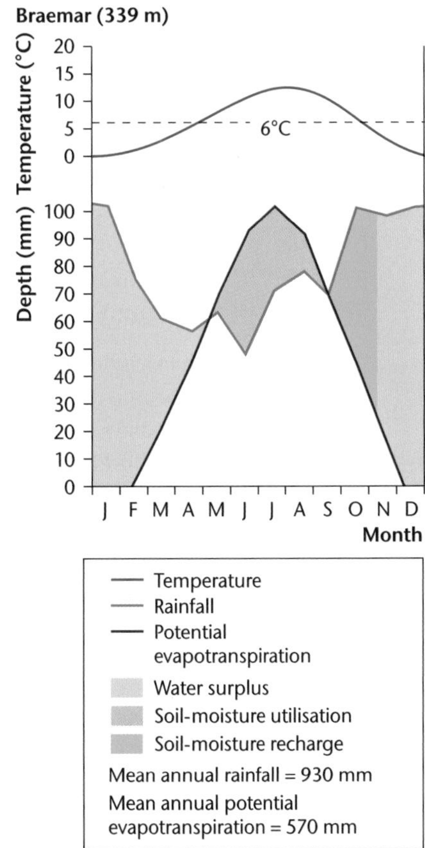

The texture and structure of a soil influence the amount of space between the soil particles for the retention of water and for aeration. Clay soils have a large number of small pores (micropores) whereas sandy soils have larger pores (macropores) which allow water to pass through more

Key terms

Azonal soil An immature soil that lacks a well-developed profile because there has been insufficient time for soil processes to create horizons.

Illuviation The washing in and deposition of material in a lower horizon of a soil which has been removed from an upper horizon by eluviation.

Intrazonal soil A type of soil whose structure reflects the dominance of single local factor, such as drainage or rock type.

Leaching/eluviation Soluble bases are removed from a soil by downward percolating water in environments where precipitation exceeds evaporation.

Soil The outermost layer of the Earth's crust, providing the foundation for all plant life. Soil is made up of organic, mineral and animal constituents differentiated into layers (horizons) of variable depth. It is created by the interaction of physical, chemical and biological processes.

Soil acidity The concentration of hydrogen ions in a soil, measured using the pH scale.

Soil structure The manner in which the particles stick together to form peds.

Soil texture The composition of the soil in terms of the varying proportions of sand, silt and clay sized particles.

quickly. If all the pores are filled with water there is no space for air in the soil and it becomes anaerobic. Under such circumstances decomposition can occur only very slowly. Anaerobic conditions in the soil occur in some upland areas in the UK, for example in the Pennines, and peat soil develops as a result of waterlogging.

Inorganic mineral matter

The inorganic component of the soil is derived from the weathering of the underlying parent rock. There are different types of weathering:

- physical weathering — freeze–thaw and onion-skin
- chemical weathering — oxidation, carbonation and hydrolysis
- biological weathering — the action of living organisms may break up the **regolith** (rock debris) in some areas

The weathered products can be divided into two groups:

- primary minerals which remain unaltered from the original parent material and are released by weathering
- secondary minerals which are produced in the soil by chemical reactions. Unlike primary minerals, these are readily soluble and are predominately carbonates, because weak carbonic acid enters soils in rain. Although it is a weak acid, carbonic acid can detach potassium, magnesium and calcium from the parent material to produce carbonates: potassium carbonate (K_2CO_3), magnesium carbonate ($MgCO_3$) and calcium hydrogen carbonate ($Ca(HCO_3)_2$)

Chemical weathering generally produces clay compounds. Even resistant rocks such as granite can be weathered to release potassium and magnesium together with sesquioxides of iron and aluminium. Quartz is released as sand grains when the parent material disintegrates. The sand and clay make up the inorganic fraction; the soluble products enter the soil.

Organic matter

Dead plants and animals, leaf litter and faecal remains are broken down by bacteria and fungi. As this organic matter decays, its previous structure becomes unrecognisable and **humus** is produced. Some of this can be recognised as a distinct layer on top of the soil. As humification continues, organic matter is incorporated into the soil to form an essential part of the clay–humus complex.

Three distinct types of humus can be recognised, each reflecting the environmental and nutrient cycle operating in the area where it is formed. Some plants take up more minerals, such as calcium and potassium, and incorporate them into structures. Such plants are rich in nutrients and, when they decay, the nutrients are returned to the soil and become incorporated into the humus. This humus is neutral or mildly acidic and is known as **mull**. It is soft, crumbly, has a blackish colour and is usually found under lowland areas covered by deciduous woodlands or grasslands. Under more acidic conditions, such as upland heath, bogs or coniferous forests, where breakdown of organic matter is slower, the plants take up, and hence return, fewer nutrients. This produces a raw, fibrous, acidic humus known as **mor**. The third type is a transitional mor-like mull, called **moder**.

An analysis of the major characteristics of soil

Soil texture

The nature of the underlying parent rock partly determines the composition and particle size of a soil. Soil texture is the composition of a soil in terms of the proportions of sand, silt and clay:

- **Sand** particles are the largest, with diameters of 0.06–2.0 mm. Soils with a high percentage of sand drain freely because the relatively large pores between the grains allow water to pass through quickly. They suffer from leaching and as a result of this have poor nutrient retention in the A horizon.
- **Silt** particles have diameters between 0.002 and 0.06 mm. Silty soils often exhibit relatively low organic retention. They are prone to waterlogging and erosion.
- **Clay** particles are the smallest, with diameters less than 0.002 mm. Soils with a high clay content have a much greater surface area available for nutrient retention. However, drainage is impeded and penetration by plant roots is difficult. Clay soils are heavy, become easily waterlogged, shrink on drying and are therefore hard to work.

Soils are made up of varying proportions of these three particle types. The most common way to illustrate this distribution is through the use of a triangular graph (Figure 3.14).

The best soils for agricultural use (loams) have relatively even proportions of all three particle types, combining the positive qualities of each. The ideal combination is 20% clay, 40% sand and 40% silt. The clay component helps to retain moisture and nutrients, the sand aids drainage and reduces the risk of waterlogging and the silt helps to bind the other particles together.

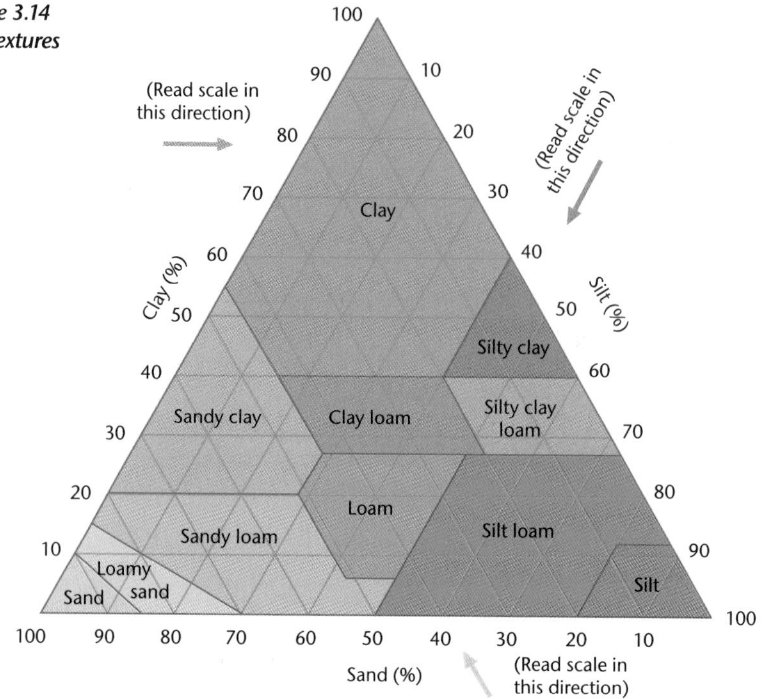

Figure 3.14
Soil textures

Soil structure

Structure is the way in which mineral particles and humus are aggregated together to form larger units called **peds**. The presence of organic matter and the gums produced during bacterial breakdown help bind the peds together. Spaces between peds allow the passage of water and soil microfauna. Five main types of ped structure are recognised:

- **Crumb (granular)** is soil made up of small breadcrumb-like particles. It contains many air spaces and drains well, which makes it good for agriculture.
- **Platy** soil has particles with horizontal axes longer than the vertical, forming small plates that overlap. It does not provide good drainage, so has poor agricultural potential.
- **Blocky** soil structure consists of larger, irregularly shaped 'blocks'. These are closely packed, but do allow some drainage and a reasonable agricultural productivity.
- **Prismatic (columnar)** structure has particles in a prism-like vertical arrangement with the vertical axis much longer than the horizontal. It is productive because it allows vertical movement of water and roots.
- In **structureless** soil, for example heavy clay soils, it is not possible to recognise any of the above four structures.

Soil acidity

Soil pH relates to the number of hydrogen ions in the soil. The pH scale runs from pH 1 to pH 14 and is logarithmic; a reading of pH 7 is neutral.

A soil with a low concentration of hydrogen ions has a high pH and is **alkaline**.

O	L	Undecomposed litter; leaf layer
	F	Partially decomposed; fermentation layer
	H	Well decomposed; humus layer
A	Ah	Dark-coloured humic horizon
	Ap	Ploughed layer in cultivated soils
	E	Eluvial horizon from which clay/sesquioxides removed
	Ea	Bleached (albic or ash-like) layer in podzolised soils
	Eb	Brown eluvial layer, depleted of clay
B	Bt	Illuvial clay redeposited (textural B horizon)
	Bh	Illuvial humus layer
	Bf/Bfe	Illuviated iron layer
	Bs	Brightly coloured layer of sesquioxide (iron/aluminium) accumulation
C		Weathered parent material

Table 3.1 Soil horizons

The higher the hydrogen-ion concentration, the lower is the pH and the more acidic the soil. Most soils fall in the range of pH 4 to 8. In the UK, most soils are slightly acidic with a pH of 5.5 to 6.5.

Soil processes and the development of horizons

A vertical section through the soil is known as a **profile** and shows the different layers, called **horizons**. The profile is the product of the balance between inputs and outputs, and the processes at work in the soil redistributing and chemically altering the various soil constituents. It is common to recognise three main horizons, which are then subdivided as shown in Table 3.1:

- **A horizon** — the upper layer of the soil where biological activity and humus content are at their maximum. This zone may lose soluble salts by drainage and downwash (eluviation)
- **B horizon** — the lower level of the soil where material removed from above is redeposited (illuviation)
- **C horizon** — the weathered parent material (regolith)

Above the A horizon are zones which consist entirely of organic matter (O). Localised conditions may produce a soil that differs from the basic A, B, C pattern. Where soils are waterlogged, for example, a **gley horizon (G)** develops.

Soil processes

A **process** can be defined as 'a series of mechanical or chemical actions on (something) in order to change or preserve it.' There are a number of processes that change soils. Many of the words used to describe these actions end in '-ation'.

Weathering breaks down the parent material and releases inorganic matter into the soil. **Humification** occurs when soil organisms break down organic matter to form humus. As organic matter decays, it releases nutrients and organic acids and these can be strong enough to break down clays and other minerals in the A horizon. The resulting chelates (organic–metal compounds) are soluble and easily transported down the profile — a process known as **cheluviation**.

The movement of soil components in any form (solution, suspension, etc.) or direction (up or down) is known as **translocation**. The removal of material from the A horizon and its movement down the soil is called **eluviation**. The deposition of this material in the lower horizon is called **illuviation**. When soluble material is removed in solution from the A horizon, the process is known as **leaching**. It is very common in UK soils. A more extreme form, operating in cool climates, is **podzolisation**, where the oxides of iron and aluminium are removed along with humus. Cheluviation also comes under this heading.

If evapotranspiration begins to exceed precipitation, leaching is limited. Calcium is no longer removed and begins to build up in the process known as **calcification**. Where evapotranspiration becomes much greater than precipitation, salts are drawn upwards in solution by capillary action. These can eventually form a hard salt deposit on the surface. This process of **salinisation** has led to serious problems in irrigated areas around the world.

When soils become waterlogged, reddish-coloured oxidised ferric iron is chemically reduced to grey-blue ferrous iron — a process known as **gleying**.

Two zonal soils: podzol and brown earth

Zonal soils are mature soils whose characteristics reflect the climate and vegetation of the area in which they are found. They have distinctive profiles, often with clearly defined horizons.

Podzol

Podzols have well-defined horizons. They are associated with the cool temperate continental climate, which occurs between 50° and 80° north of the equator, and is experienced in northwest Europe, Siberia and northern Canada. In the UK, podzols are generally found in the uplands to the north and west, where there is a moisture surplus. The predominant vegetation here is coniferous forest, moorland and heath.

The soil itself is relatively shallow, only about 1 m from the surface to the parent rock. The main reason for this is the cool climate. Although there is an abundance of moisture, there is insufficient warmth to encourage rapid chemical weathering of the parent rock. This results in slow input of inorganic material into the subsoil.

The vegetation produces acidic litter, such as pine needles. The cool climate contributes to the slow rate of humification because it is difficult for bacteria and other decomposers to survive in large numbers at low temperatures. The pH of the topsoil is generally between 3.5 and 4.2 and creates a mor humus.

Precipitation exceeds evapotranspiration, so eluviation is the main process operating within a podzol. Podzolisation and cheluviation also occur, so strong humic acids are released as the acidic mor humus is slowly broken down. Under these conditions, aluminium and iron sesquioxides are unstable and are translocated from the topsoil. This results in a sandy-textured, bleached and silica-rich A horizon. The iron and aluminium compounds are illuviated or redeposited in the B horizon, creating a red iron- and aluminium-rich layer, called an **iron pan**. Beneath this, the soil is darker (from the translocated humus) and is clay-rich.

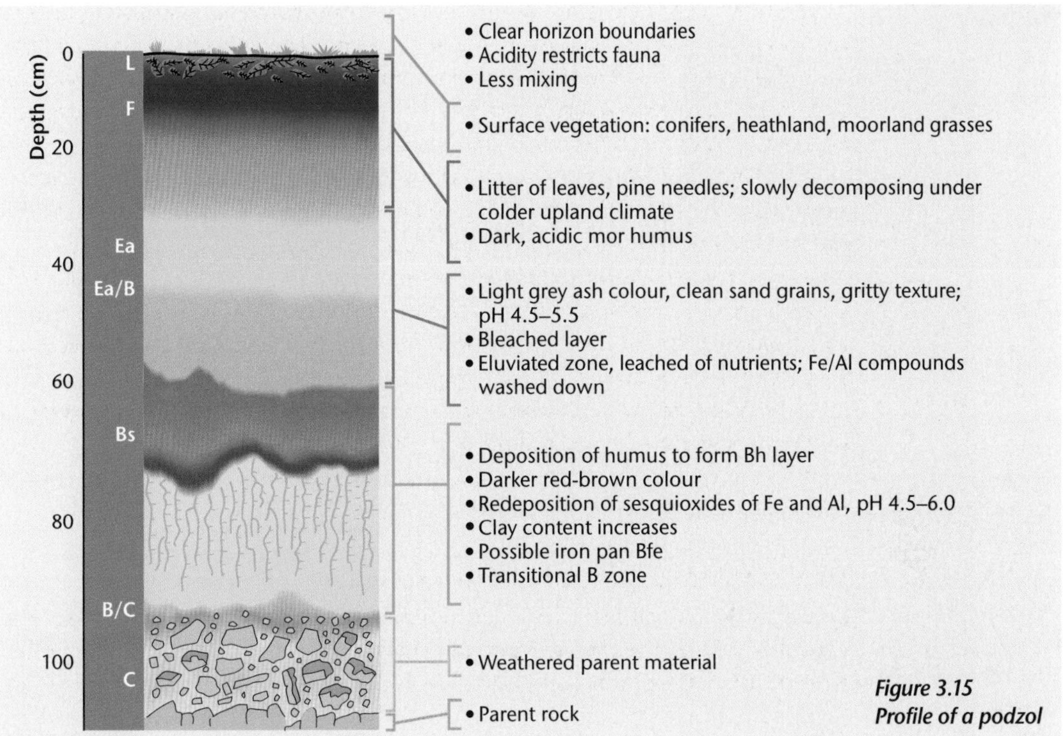

Figure 3.15
Profile of a podzol

Brown earth

Brown earths are characteristically found in the CTWM climate. This is the most common soil type of lowland western Europe, the east coast of the USA and eastern Asia. Such soils typically form under temperate deciduous woodland. However, much of this indigenous forest has been cleared for farming and the soil now lies under pasture or arable fields. This soil type is relatively fertile and can be recognised by its lack of defined horizons.

At about 2 m, brown earth is deeper than podzol. This is because it has greater inputs of both organic and inorganic matter. The main reason for this is the relatively warm and moist climate. Precipitation marginally exceeds evapotranspiration and the warm moist conditions encourage weathering of the parent rock. Warm temperatures and adequate moisture during the long growing season encourage plant growth. Leaf-fall from deciduous trees occurs in the autumn. This input of organic litter is rapidly broken down into humus during the following spring. The deciduous trees produce a relatively neutral/slightly acidic litter (pH 5–6.5). This provides a hospitable environment for detrivores, which break it down into a mull humus. Earthworms and other living organisms in the A horizon of the soil contribute towards the mull humus being incorporated into the topsoil.

Brown earth is a well-mixed soil with hazy horizons. The soil tends to be well drained and there is no impermeable hardpan layer, as in a podzol. There is some leaching, particularly during the winter when plant uptake and evapotranspiration are reduced. This is not so intense as in the podzol so cheluviation and

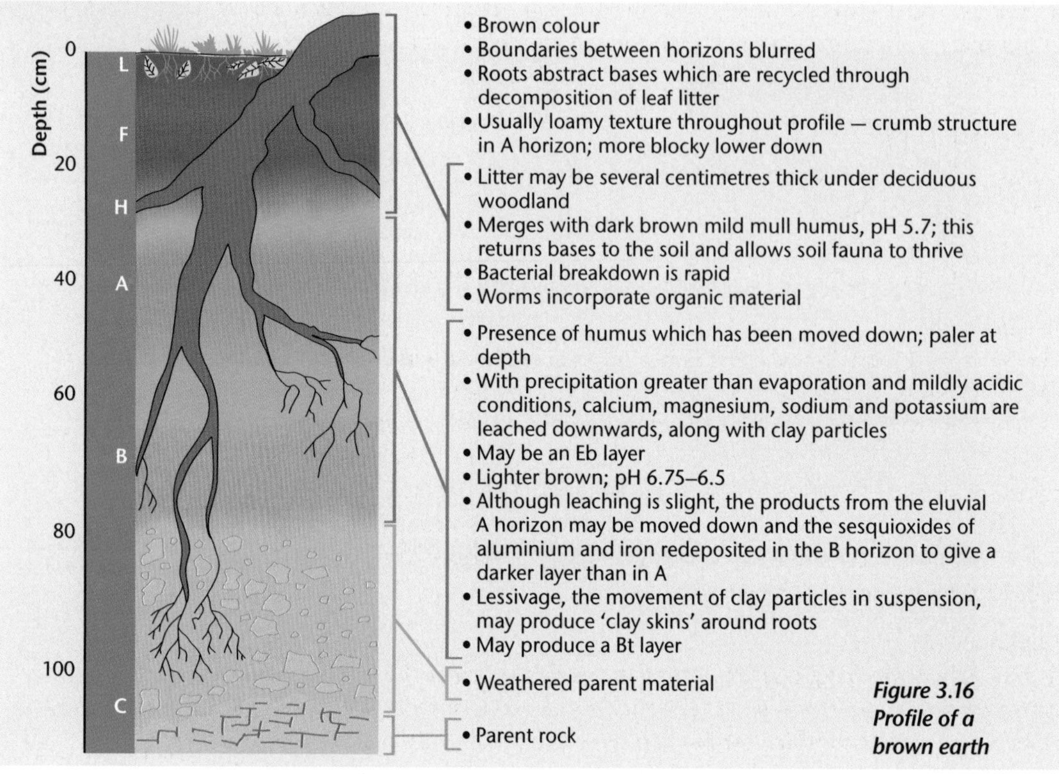

Figure 3.16 Profile of a brown earth

podzolisation do not occur. Some clay particles are eluviated by **lessivage** into the deeper layers of the soil, so the B horizon may be slightly darker in colour and enriched with clay.

Azonal and intrazonal soils

Azonal soil

An **azonal soil** is an immature soil of recent origin. It lacks a well-developed profile because it has had little time to be affected by soil-forming processes. Azonal soils are frequently disrupted by the addition of new material and are unaffected by climate and vegetation. It is impossible to recognise horizons in an azonal soil. These soils are most influenced by such factors as the origin of the parent material and the agent of deposition. They can be classified into:

- **Lithosols** — these develop at high altitude or in exposed sites where resistant parent material reduces the impact of weathering and steep slopes encourage downslope movement of loose material. This prevents the development of horizons. Scree is an example of a lithosol.
- **Regosols** — these form on unconsolidated materials, typically in a sand dune environment or on lava or ash produced by a recent volcanic eruption. Soil profile formation is disrupted by the continuing accumulation of fresh material.

- **Alluvial soils** — these consist of recent sediments deposited on floodplains or salt marsh. They are subjected to periodic flooding which leads to deposition of further sediment and this restricts soil-forming processes.

Intrazonal soil

Intrazonal soils have characteristics which reflect the dominance of a single local factor. These factors include:

- the impact of geology
- the influence of slope and its effect on the drainage properties of the soil

Geology

Limestone and chalk in particular have a high calcium carbonate content and are slightly alkaline (pH between 7.0 and 8.0). Their permeable nature ensures free drainage of water. In addition limestone is soluble and when moisture is present is attacked by a form of chemical weathering called **solution**. **Rendzina** and **terra rosa** soils develop on these parent rocks. Rendzina soils are thin, loamy and grey in colour. Terra rosa soils occur in the Mediterranean climate and are reddish in colour due to the accumulation of iron hydroxides, which remain after the soluble salts have been eluviated from the topsoil.

Drainage

In areas where the water table is close to the surface or where the underlying rock is impermeable, poor or restricted drainage may lead to the formation of **gley soils**. Gleys can develop in low-lying areas, such as valley floors, or on upland plateaus where the effect of gravity on the movement of water is restricted. Under waterlogged conditions, all the pores in the soil are filled with water, producing

Photograph 3.3 A terra rosa soil in Turkey

Amanda Barker

anaerobic conditions. (Anaerobic means the absence of free oxygen.) The decomposition of plant matter and litter on the surface is, therefore, extremely slow. Chemical weathering reduces iron compounds from an insoluble ferric form to a more soluble ferrous form. This gives the soil a grey-blue colour because the soluble iron salts are slowly removed from the system.

Relief

Soils can change along a slope, despite the fact that the climate and/or parent rock remain constant. The **soil catena** (Figure 3.17) illustrates an expected sequence of soils down a slope, in which each soil is different but is linked to adjacent types. Catenas develop over a long period of time and are, therefore, best established in areas with stable environments.

- A typical soil catena in upland Britain might have waterlogged gley soil at the top of the hill.
- A **zone of shedding** would develop on the upper parts of the slope, where the angle of the hill encouraged better drainage (and leaching) but the soil would be relatively shallow due to soil-creep and the effects of gravity. Minerals would be washed downwards through the soil giving it the characteristics of a podzol.
- A **zone of transfer** would occur further down the hill, on the middle and lower slopes. Here, there would be much throughflow of water, translocating mineral matter, so the soil would be relatively dry and still rather shallow. On the lower slopes the soil could start to get deeper and richer, resulting in a brown earth.
- A **zone of accumulation** would develop at the foot of the slope, where water, organic and inorganic matter would accumulate. Such a soil would be waterlogged and might again be a gley.

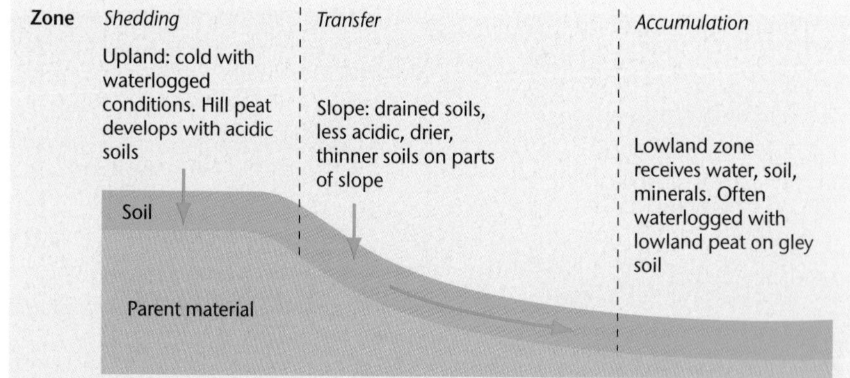

Figure 3.17 Diagram of a soil catena

Assessment exercises

Water on the land

1 Figure A is a simplified systems diagram of the drainage basin component of the hydrological cycle.

a (i) Distinguish between the inputs and outputs of the drainage basin hydrological cycle. (2 marks)

(ii) Name the transfers labelled x, y and z on the diagram. (3 marks)

(iii) How might human activity modify the drainage basin hydrological cycle? (5 marks)

b Examine the physical factors responsible for flooding. (10 marks)

(20 marks)

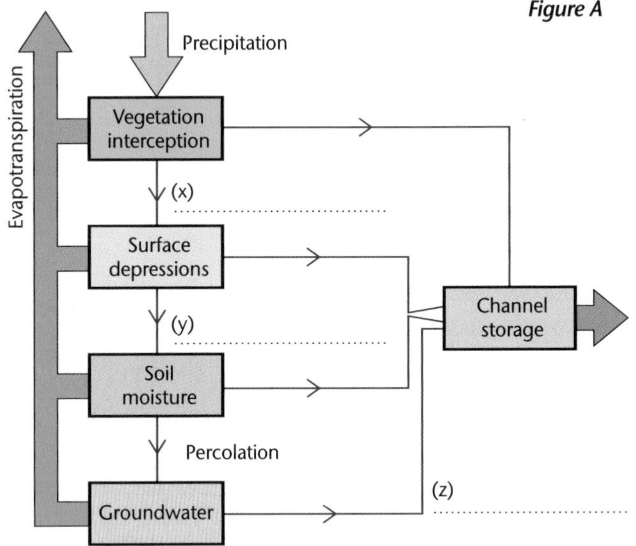

Figure A

2 Figures B and C show changes in the River Omo Delta, on the northern shore of Lake Turkana, that took place between 1975 and 1995.

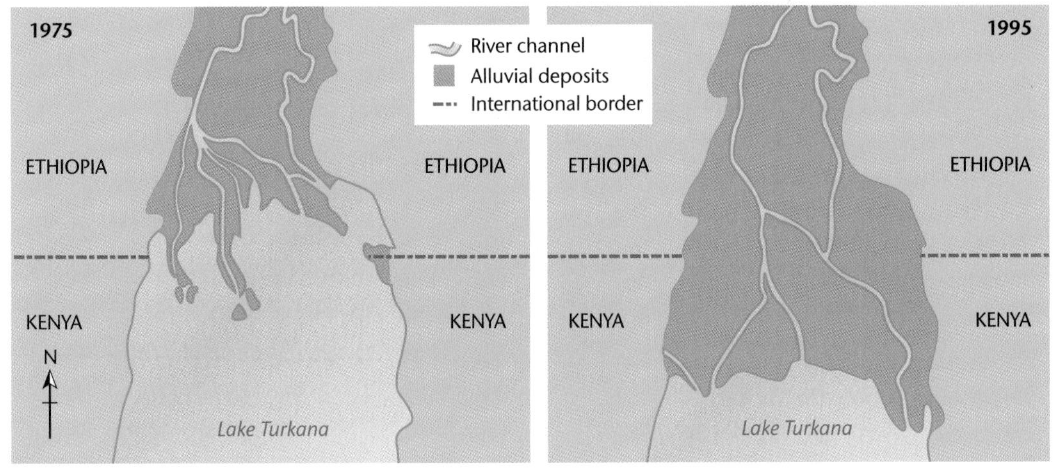

Figure B *Figure C*

a (i) Identify two changes to the delta that took place between 1975 and 1995. (2 marks)

(ii) Suggest a reason for the changes identified in (i). (2 marks)

b Why do features of deposition exist throughout the long profile of most rivers? (6 marks)

c Examine the costs and benefits of one river management scheme you have studied. (10 marks)

(20 marks)

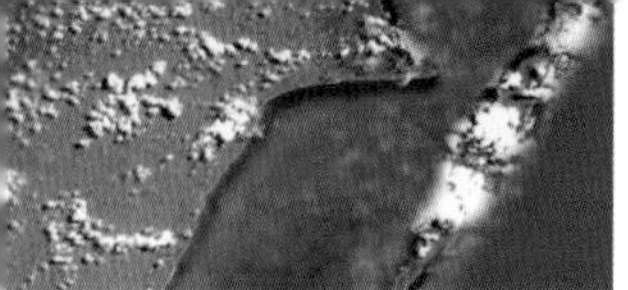

Climatic hazards and change

1 **Figure D gives information for European cities of similar latitude, within the cool temperate western maritime climate zone.**

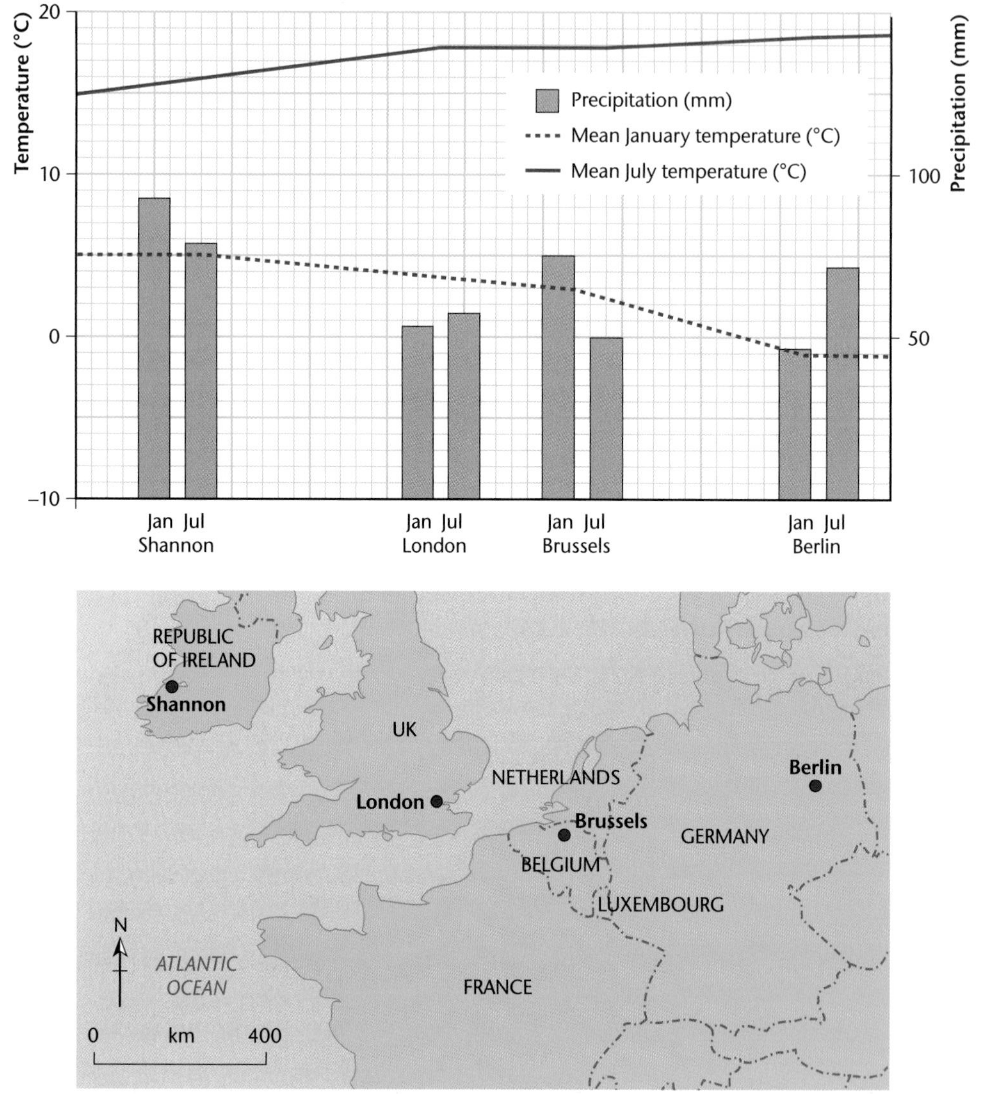

Figure D

a **(i)** **Describe the relationship between distance from the Atlantic Ocean and January precipitation.** (2 marks)

(ii) **How does the annual temperature range vary from west to east between Shannon and Berlin?** (2 marks)

(iii) **Explain the variations in temperature and precipitation shown in Figure D.** (6 marks)

b Examine the opportunities and constraints on human activity for places experiencing the cool temperate western maritime climate. (10 marks)

(20 marks)

2 Figure E demonstrates the link between severe acute respiratory syndrome (SARS) and air quality in five Chinese provinces between April and May 2003. (The air quality index takes five major pollutants into account; an index below 100 is considered healthy for the general population.)

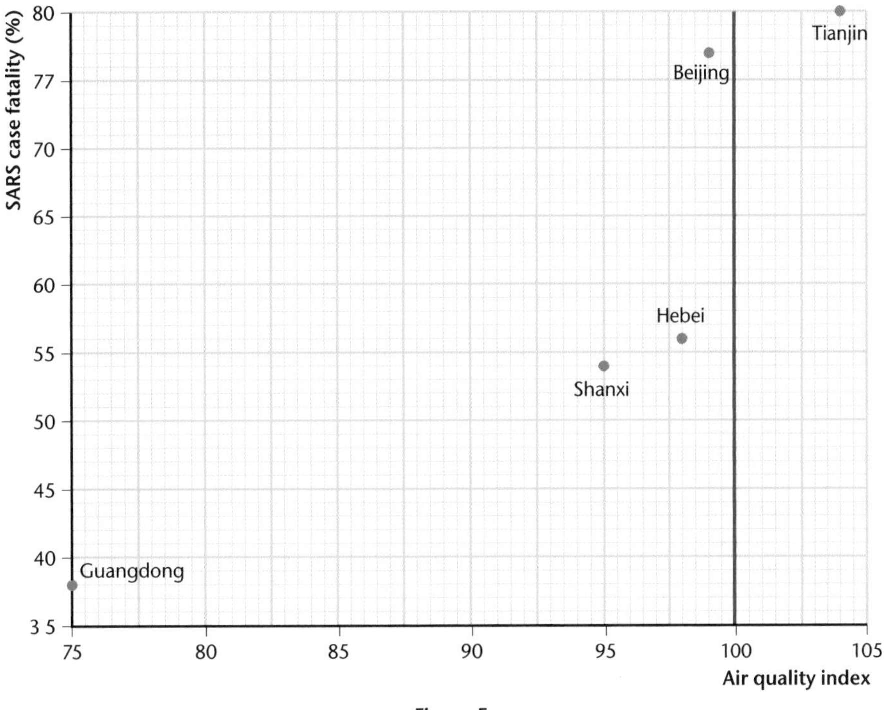

Figure E

a (i) Comment on the variations in air quality in the Chinese provinces shown in Figure E. (2 marks)

(ii) Identify and suggest a reason for the relationship between deaths and air quality suggested in Figure E. (3 marks)

b Under what circumstances do high concentrations of air pollution result in the formation of photochemical smog? (5 marks)

c Examine the success of policies designed to improve the air quality in one or more cities you have studied. (10 marks)

(20 marks)

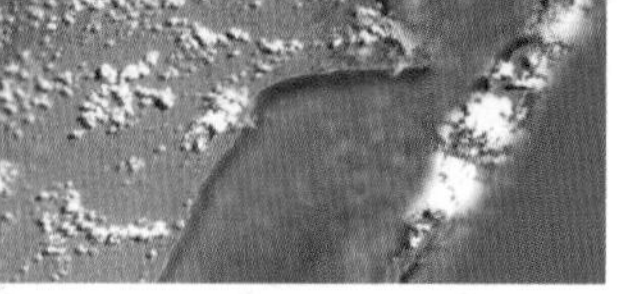

Energy and life

1 Figure F shows wildlife supported by a typical British hedge.

Figure F

At least 65 species of birds nest in hedges

Around 1,500 species of beetles, bugs, butterflies, moths and other insects

30+ species of bush make up a mature hedge

600+ species of wild flowers

200 species of invertebrates, e.g. snails and slugs

20+ species of mammals, amphibians and reptiles, e.g. badgers, toads and snakes

a (i) Identify the trophic levels within the hedge. (2 marks)

(ii) Suggest reasons for the differences between the trophic levels you have identified in (a)(i). (3 marks)

b Outline the biotic and abiotic components of a small-scale ecosystem you have studied. (5 marks)

c A global ecosystem is called a biome. Explain why deforestation in the tropical rainforest biome is of continuing concern. (10 marks)

(20 marks)

2 Figure G shows the hydrological processes operating in a podzol soil. A podzol is an example of a zonal soil.

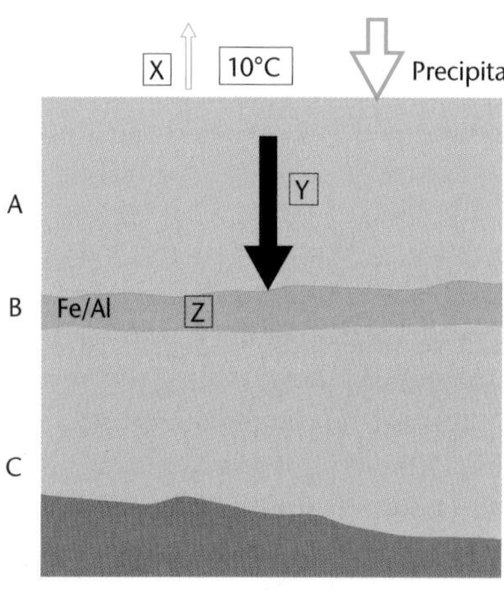

Figure G

a (i) What is a zonal soil? (2 marks)

(ii) Name the processes labelled X and Y, and the feature labelled Z on Figure G. (3 marks)

(iii) Identify the factors that most influence the characteristics of a podzol soil. (5 marks)

b A podzol soil may be found in a heathland environment in the UK. Identify and explain the sequence of events that leads to the plant succession and climatic climax in one environment you have studied. (10 marks)

(20 marks)

AS

Module 2

Core concepts in human geography

Chapter 4

Population dynamics

Population change

The population of an area alters as a consequence of both natural change and migration. The annual population change of an area is the cumulative change in the size of a population after both natural change and migration have been taken into account.

Table 4.1 Global population data

Region	Birth rate	Fertility	Death rate	Infant mortality rate	Life expectancy at birth
World	21	2.8	9	56	67
MEDCs	11	1.6	10	7	76
LEDCs	24	3.1	8	62	65
Africa	38	5.1	14	90	52
North America	14	2.0	8	7	78
Latin America	22	2.6	6	29	72
Asia	20	2.6	7	54	67
Europe	10	1.4	12	7	74
Oceania	17	2.1	7	26	75

Source: World Population Data Sheet (2004)

Natural population change

The measurement of population characteristics

Most of the countries in the world collect data about their populations, usually in the form of a census. This is a detailed collection of information on a regular basis — for example, every 10 years. The data collected include employment characteristics, ethnicity, educational attainment, patterns of social activity, and housing type and ownership.

In the UK, the data are collated by areas of local government and by postcode. The smallest area is that covered by one census collector — an area known as an **enumeration district**.

The information collected is of use to:

- governments — to provide a basis for the allocation of resources to services such as health, education and employment
- non-governmental bodies — retailers, advertisers, financial services, property developers and utilities

Censuses are not without problems. Some people object to them on the grounds that they infringe privacy. Some people do not return their census forms. Political conditions in some countries make censuses difficult to organise.

At a national government level, a census:

- records trends over the previous 10 years which can be projected forward to enable planning in a range of social services
- helps with prediction of natural population change and migration patterns
- enables the estimation of national housing demands
- enables the planning of national transport demands
- is a snapshot of the diversity of the country

For businesses and commerce, a census:

- can be linked to other data sources, such as credit card data, to provide information on regional lifestyles
- enables targeted marketing, based on postcode areas
- enables the insurance industry to assess risk more effectively
- enables retailers to invest in optimum locations where spending power is highest
- allows firms to target goods to stores according to the profile of the population. For example, supermarkets stock more prepared foods in areas where there are greater numbers of young single adults

It is easy to see, therefore, that censuses are a useful source of information for geographers and demographers.

Key terms

Birth rate A measure of an area's fertility. It is expressed as the number of live births per 1,000 people in 1 year.

Death rate The number of deaths per 1,000 people in 1 year.

Fertility The number of live births per 1,000 women aged 15–49 in 1 year. It is also defined as the average number of children each woman in a population will bear. If this number is 2.1 or higher, a population will replace itself.

Infant mortality The number of deaths of children under the age of 1 year expressed per 1,000 live births per year.

Life expectancy The average number of years from birth that a person can expect to live.

Longevity The increase in life expectancy over a period of time. It is a direct result of improved medical provision and increased levels of economic development. People live longer and this creates an older population.

Natural change The change in size of a population caused by the interrelationship between birth and death rates. If birth rate exceeds death rate, a population will increase. If death rate exceeds birth rate, a population will decline.

Changes over time and factors influencing change

Factors affecting fertility

In most parts of the world, fertility exceeds both mortality and migration. It is, therefore, the main determinant of population growth. Its importance has increased over time with the worldwide fall in mortality. Several African countries (e.g. Niger, Angola, Uganda and Somalia) have very high birth rates of over 50 per 1,000 per year. At the other end of the scale, Belarus, Bulgaria, Estonia, Italy, Russia and Spain have birth rates of only 9 per 1,000 per year. Why does fertility vary?

- The relationship with **death rate** can be important. Countries in sub-Saharan Africa have high birth rates that counter the high rates of infant mortality (often over 100 per 1,000 live births). One study of sub-Saharan Africa concluded that a woman must have, on average, ten children to be 95% certain of a surviving adult son.

Photograph 4.1 A large rural family in the Philippines watching television. Fertility rates depend on a number of factors, including economic issues, education and religion

Mark Edwards/Still Pictures

- In many parts of the world, **tradition** demands high rates of reproduction. Intense cultural expectations may override the wishes of women.
- **Education** for women, particularly female literacy, is a key to lower fertility. With education comes knowledge of birth control, more opportunities for employment and wider choices.
- **Social class** is important. Fertility decreases from lower to higher classes or castes.
- **Religion** is of major significance because both Islam and the Roman Catholic church oppose the use of artificial birth control. However, adherence to religious doctrine tends to lessen with economic development. This is particularly well illustrated in Italy. Although it is the location of the Vatican — the home of the pope — the fertility rate in Italy is very low (1.2). This suggests that some form of artificial birth control is taking place.
- **Economic factors** are important, particularly in LEDCs, where children are an economic asset. They are viewed as producers rather than consumers. In MEDCs, this is reversed. The length of time children spend in education makes them expensive, as does the cost of childcare if both parents work. In eastern Europe, economic uncertainty is a major factor causing low fertility rates.
- There have been several cases in recent years of countries seeking to influence the rate of population growth. Such **political influences** have been either to increase the population (as in 1930s Germany and Japan, and more recently in Russia and Romania) or to decrease it (as in China, with its one-child policy).

Factors affecting mortality

Some of the highest death rates are found in the LEDCs, particularly in sub-Saharan Africa. The Gambia, Mali, Sierra Leone, Malawi, Uganda and Zambia all have death rates of 20 per 1,000 or more. However, some of the lowest mortality rates are also found in countries at the lower end of the development range, for example Kuwait (2 per 1,000), Bahrain (3 per 1,000) and Mexico (5 per 1,000). Why does mortality vary?

- **Infant mortality** is a prime indicator of socioeconomic development. It is the most sensitive of the age-specific rates. Sierra Leone has an infant mortality rate of 195 per 1,000 live births. Infant mortality is falling across the world, but there are still wide variations between nations. Areas with high rates of infant mortality have high rates of mortality overall.
- **Age structure:** countries with high percentages of people below the age of 15 have low death rates. Both Kuwait and Bahrain (see above) have populations in which more than 25% are under 15.
- Areas with high levels of **medical infrastructure** have low levels of mortality.
- Life expectancy is higher in countries with higher levels of **economic development**. Poverty, poor nutrition, a lack of clean water and sanitation (all associated with low levels of economic development) increase mortality rates.

Table 4.2 Major causes of death in MEDCs and LEDCs

MEDCs	LEDCs
Heart disease and strokes	Respiratory diseases: influenza, pneumonia, tuberculosis (collectively 25% of all deaths)
Cancers	Parasitic diseases: malaria, sleeping sickness (15%)
Wars: international (e.g. two World Wars)	Wars: civil wars (e.g. Ethiopia, Sudan)
Transport-related accidents	Natural disasters (e.g. earthquakes)
	AIDS (greater impact than in MEDCs)

Around the world, mortality has fallen steadily because of medical advances. It seems people are more willing to control mortality than they are to control fertility.

The demographic transition model

The **demographic transition model (DTM)** describes how the population of a country changes over time (Figure 4.1). It gives changes in birth and death rates, and shows that countries pass through five stages of population change.

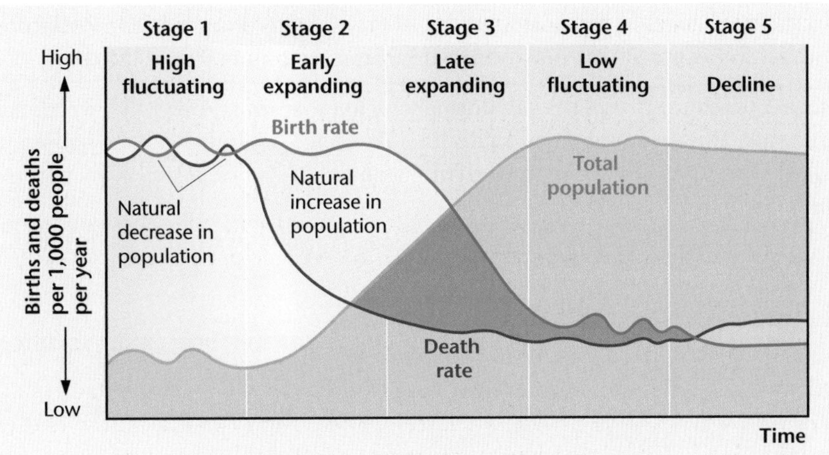

Figure 4.1 The demographic transition model

Stage 1 (high fluctuating) A period of high birth rate and high death rate, both of which fluctuate. Population growth is small. Reasons for the high birth rate include:

- limited birth control/family planning
- high infant mortality rate, which encourages the birth of more children
- children are a future source of income
- in many cultures, children are a sign of fertility
- some religions encourage large families

Reasons for the high death rate include:

- high incidence of disease
- poor nutrition and famine
- poor levels of hygiene
- underdeveloped and inadequate health facilities

Stage 2 (early expanding) A period of high birth rate but falling death rate. The population begins to expand rapidly. Reasons for the falling death rate include:

- improved public health
- better nutrition
- lower child mortality
- improved medical provision

Stage 3 (late expanding) A period of falling birth rate and continuing falling death rate. Population growth slows down. Reasons for the falling birth rate include:

- changing socioeconomic conditions, greater access to education for women
- preferences for smaller families
- changing social trends and fashions, and a rise in materialism
- increased personal wealth
- compulsory schooling, making the rearing of children more expensive
- lower infant mortality rate
- the availability of family planning systems, which are often supported by governments.

Stage 4 (low fluctuating) A period of low birth rate and low death rate, both of which fluctuate. Population growth is small and fertility continues to fall. There are significant changes in personal lifestyles. There are more women in the workforce, with many people having high personal incomes and more leisure interests.

Stage 5 (decline) A later period, during which the death rate slightly exceeds the birth rate. This causes population decline. This stage has only been recognised in recent years and only in some western European countries. Reasons for the low birth rate in this stage include:

- a rise in individualism, linked to the emancipation of women in the labour market
- greater financial independence of women
- concern about the impact of increased population numbers on the resources for future generations
- an increase in non-traditional lifestyles, such as same-sex relationships
- a rise in the concept of childlessness

Case study Demographic change in the UK

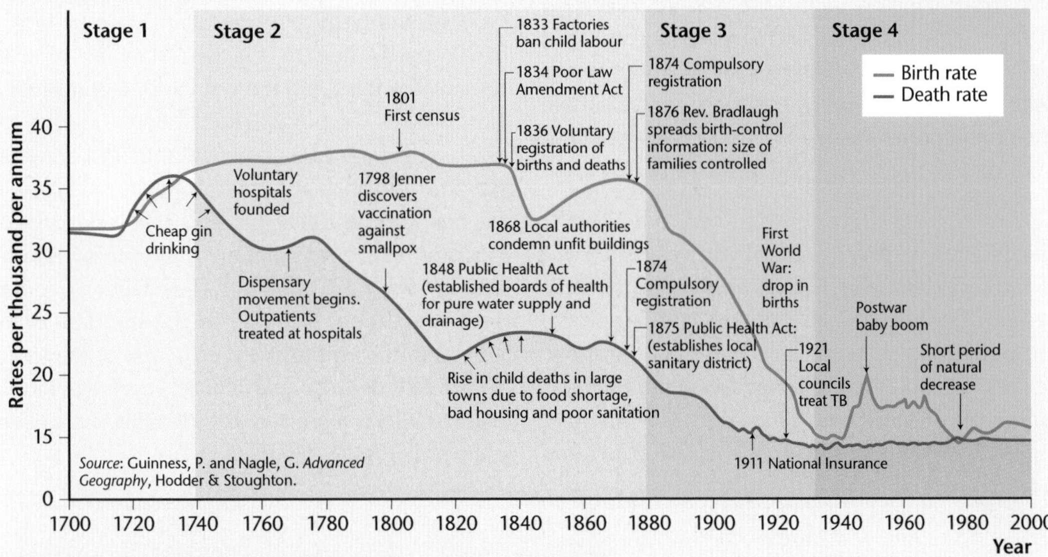

Figure 4.2 Demographic transition model in the UK, 1700–2000

During medieval times, both birth and death rates in the UK were high, at around 35 per 1,000. Generally, the birth rate was a little higher than the death rate, resulting in a slow rate of natural increase.

The birth rate tended to remain at a relatively stable level, but the death rate varied considerably. In 1348–49, the epidemic of bubonic plague, called the Black Death, killed one-third of the population. Other plagues followed in the seventeenth century, including the Great Plague of 1665. There was an increase in mortality between 1720 and 1740, which is attributed to the availability of cheap gin. This was ended by the introduction of a 'gin tax' in 1751.

Falling death rate

The period from the mid-eighteenth century to about 1875 was a time of rapid urbanisation, which alerted public officials and enlightened industrialists to the urgent need for improvements in public health. Factory owners soon recognised that an unhealthy workforce had a huge impact on productivity. The provision of clean, piped water and the installation of sewage systems, together with improved personal and domestic cleanliness, saw the incidence of diarrhoeal diseases and typhoid fall rapidly. Greater disposable income from factory wages led to more food being consumed by the working class and to a wider range of food products being demanded. At the same time improvements in farming practices and transport systems allowed this demand to be met. Better nutrition played a significant role in the decline in infant mortality.

The combination of better nutrition and the general improvements in health brought about by legislation such as the Public Health Acts of 1848 and 1869, caused the incidence of common infectious diseases such as scarlet fever and tuberculosis to diminish markedly. Public perception of cleanliness was also a major factor. Soap was a well-advertised product and the availability of cheaper cotton clothing (which is easier to wash than woollen clothing) was important.

Falling birth rate

After 1875, the continued decrease in the death rate was accompanied by a reduction in the birth rate. Medical science began to play an important role in the control of mortality, with doctors being able to administer more effective drug treatments. Surgery grew more advanced and anaesthesia became available. From the early part of the twentieth century, increasing attention was paid to maternity and child welfare, and to the health of schoolchildren. There were further advances in nutrition – for example cheap American wheat, and refrigerated meat and fruit from Australia and New Zealand began to be imported.

The decline in fertility began with the celebrated trial of two social reformers, Charles Bradlaugh and Annie Besant. They were prosecuted, and later acquitted, for publishing a book that gave contraceptive advice. The desire for smaller families at this time was due to the financial costs of looking after children, especially when education to the age of 13 became compulsory. Between 1890 and 1930, the birth rate fell from 32 per 1,000 to 17 per 1,000.

By 1940, the birth rate had fallen again to 14 per 1,000, partly due to the uncertainties of war. Immediately following the war, birth rates rose for a short while — the postwar baby boom. However by 1980, birth rates had again fallen to 14 per 1,000 and have remained at this level. The introduction of the oral contraceptive pill and the wider use of condoms have meant that the relationship between desired family size and achieved family size has remained strong. The rise in the importance of females in the employment structure of the UK in the last few decades, particularly in service industries, has further impacted on birth rates, particularly in the professional classes.

The usefulness and application of the DTM

The DTM is useful because:

- it is universal in concept — it can be applied to all countries in the world
- it provides a starting point for the study of demographic change over time
- the timescales are flexible
- it is easy to understand
- it enables comparisons to be made demographically between countries

Limitations of the DTM are that:

- the original model did not include the fifth stage
- it is eurocentric and assumes that all countries in the world will follow the European sequence of socioeconomic changes
- it does not include the role of governments
- it does not include the impact of migration

In the 1960s, people noted that many countries of the more economically developed world (MEDW) had gone through the first four stages of the model. They also noted that countries of the less economically developed world (LEDW) seemed to be in a situation similar to stage 2 — their death rates had fallen but their birth rates were still very high, leading to rapid population growth.

In the UK, as noted in the case study (page 113), stage 2 took over 100 years to complete. This was because social, economic and technological changes were introduced gradually and the death rate fell slowly. In many parts of the LEDW, the death rate has fallen much more rapidly because these changes, particularly the introduction of Western medical practices, have taken place more quickly. The birth rate, however, has stayed high and so the population has increased rapidly.

It was hoped that such countries would move into stage 3, as failure to do so could result in population exceeding available resources. This was one of the reasons that China introduced the one-child policy, forcing its population into stage 3. Malaysia also reduced its birth rate by introducing a government-sponsored nationwide family-planning programme. The outcomes of that programme, begun in the 1960s, are shown in Table 4.3.

Date	Birth rate	Death rate	Total population (millions)	Average population change (% per year)
1960	47	20	8	
1970	44	16	10	2.8 (1960–70)
1980	44	13	14	3.1 (1970–80)
1990	37	11	18	2.6 (1980–90)
2000	27	5	23	2.3 (1990–2000)

Table 4.3 Population change in Malaysia, 1960–2000

In summary, there are a number of important differences in the way that countries of the LEDW and MEDW have undergone population change. In comparison with countries now in the MEDW, those in the LEDW:

- had generally higher birth rates in stages 1 and 2
- had a much steeper fall in death rate (and for different reasons)
- had in some cases much larger base populations, so the impact of high population growth in stage 2 and the early part of stage 3 has been far greater
- in those countries in stage 3, the fall in fertility has been steeper
- had a weaker relationship between population change and economic development — governments have played a more decisive role in population management

Case study Population change in Thailand

The birth rate in Thailand has fallen rapidly, partly as a result of the National Family Planning Programme, which has been run by the Ministry of Health since 1970. This has included:

- public information programmes, to ensure that everyone knows about contraceptive methods
- advertising the benefits of the two-child family
- establishing health centres throughout the country, to provide mainly free contraception
- training paramedics and midwives, who are mainly from the local villages and are, therefore, known and trusted. They provide healthcare for mothers and babies, so more babies are surviving

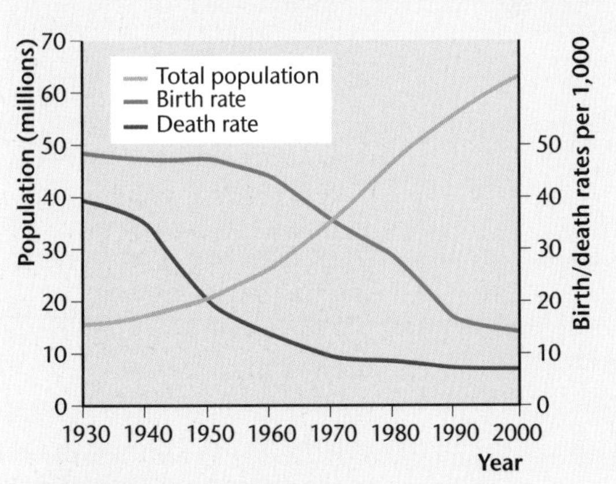

Figure 4.3 Population change in Thailand, 1930–2000

Migration

The relationship between the numbers of births and deaths (natural change) is not the only factor in population change. The balance between immigration and emigration (**net migration**) must also be taken into account. The relative contributions of natural change and net migration can vary both within a particular country and between countries.

Migration can be categorised using a number of criteria (Table 4.4).

Table 4.4 Types of migration

Criterion	Type of migration
Scale	International, regional, local
Direction	Rural–urban, urban–rural, urban–urban, MEDW to LEDW, LEDW to MEDW
Distance	Long distance, short distance, regional
Decision making	Forced (e.g. from hazards or for political safety — refugees) Voluntary (e.g. for work, retirement or family reasons)
Cause of movement	Economic, social, environmental

Migration tends to be subject to **distance-decay** — the number of migrants declines as the distance between origin and destination increases. Refugees tend to move only short distances; economic migrants travel greater distances.

Theories of migration

The push–pull model

Many factors influence the decision to migrate. They can be categorised into push factors and pull factors:

- **Push factors** are the negative aspects of the current place of residence. They include lack of employment, low wages, poor housing, poor educational opportunities, political persecution, natural hazards, starvation and war.
- **Pull factors** are the attractions of the destination. They are often the inverse of the push factors: better employment and educational opportunities, better housing and social services (health services), higher wages, family integration and political stability.

If the perceived push or pull factors are strong enough to overcome the forces of **inertia** (cost of moving, disruption of social networks), then migration will occur.

One of the most important factors in any migration is the **perception** of the individual concerned. Perception is the subjective view that a person has of the environment, which is derived from personal experience, the experience of others and the media. Through perception, a potential migrant builds up a mental image of the destination. This mental image may be partial and distorted but will be the basis of the decision by the migrant.

The mental images that migrants have, therefore, often fail to accord with reality. This is one reason why for each migration there is often a movement in the opposite direction — disillusioned migrants returning to their place of origin.

Lee's model

Lee suggested that people:

- assess and perceive the destination
- assess conditions where they are
- look at obstacles between the two, such as distance and cost
- consider personal circumstances

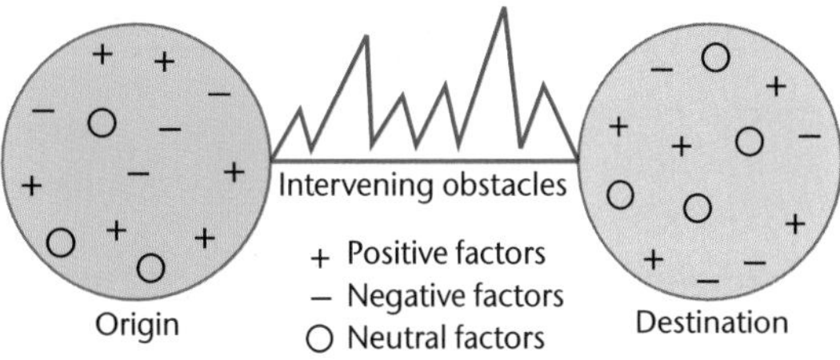

***Figure 4.4* Lee's model of migration**

The decision to migrate depends upon the number of intervening obstacles (negative factors) between origin and destination, such as mountains or international boundaries and on the balance between positive and negative factors in the origin and the destination.

Causes of migration

Migration is more volatile than fertility and mortality. It is affected by changing physical, economic, social, cultural and political circumstances. However, the wish to migrate may not be fulfilled if the constraints are too great. The desire to move within a country is generally inhibited only by economic and social factors. The desire to move to another country is usually constrained by political factors, such as immigration laws.

Table 4.5 gives examples of some major causes of migration. It classifies such movements in terms of their origin and destination; and whether the movement is voluntary or forced.

***Table 4.5* Examples of migration**

Movement	Voluntary	Forced
Between MEDCs	The 'brain drain' of doctors and scientists from the UK and Germany to the USA	
	The movement of East European workers into the UK following the expansion of the EU in 2004	Repatriation of East Germans into the new unified Germany after 1989
From LEDCs to MEDCs	Movement of Mexicans into the USA to work as casual employees in the farming communities of California	Movement of large numbers of refugees and asylum seekers in many parts of the world Movement of evacuees from Montserrat following the volcanic explosions in 1996
From MEDCs to LEDCs	Movement of aid workers from EU countries to the Sudan and Ethiopia	
Between LEDCs	The movement of migrant labour from Pakistan and Bangladesh to the oil-rich states of the Persian Gulf	Movement of Tutsi and Hutu peoples from Rwanda to the Democratic Republic of Congo, because of the fear of genocide

The changing nature of international migration

Patterns of international migration have been changing since the late 1980s. There have been increases in:

- attempts at illegal, economically motivated migration as a response to legal restrictions

Key terms

Forced migration The migrant has to migrate, because of the circumstances.

International migration The UN defines international migration as the movement of people across national frontiers, for a minimum of 1 year.

Migration A permanent or semi-permanent change of residence of an individual or group of people.

Net migration The difference between the numbers of in-migrants and out-migrants in an area. When in-migrants exceed out-migrants, there is net migrational gain. When out-migrants exceed in-migrants there is net migrational loss.

Rural–urban and urban–rural migration In LEDCs, the net migrational gain of urban areas at the expense of rural areas results in urbanisation. In MEDCs, movements from urban areas to rural areas have led to counter-urbanisation.

Voluntary migration The migrant makes the decision to migrate.

- those seeking asylum (see below)
- migration between MEDCs, particularly between countries within the EU where restrictions have been removed to allow the free movement of labour
- short-term migration, as countries increasingly place limits on work permits. It is now common for MEDCs (e.g. the UK and USA) to limit the length of work permits, even for qualified migrants coming from other MEDCs
- movement of migrants between LEDCs, particularly to those where rapid economic development is taking place, for example the countries of the Persian Gulf and the Asian economic growth areas of Singapore and Indonesia

There has been a decline in:

- legal, life-long migration, particularly from LEDCs to MEDCs. Host countries provide fewer opportunities for migrants because the number of available low-skilled jobs has dropped. Many host countries have also tightened entry requirements, and introduced more rigorous monitoring at the point of entry
- the number of people who migrate for life. Many newer migrants want to return home at some point. For example, a common feature of villages in Italy, Portugal and Greece is new housing built by returnees
- the number of people migrating with the purpose of reuniting family members, as the amount of long-term family separation reduces and many migrants eventually return home

Refugees

Refugees are defined by the UN as persons unable or unwilling to return to their homeland for fear of persecution, based on reasons of race, religion, ethnicity or political opinion, or those who have been displaced forcibly by other factors.

By 2002, the UN estimated that there were over 20 million refugees in the world. Many refugee movements are large-volume, non-selective and over short distances. They are often caused by war. Such migrations are often temporary — when the cause of the migration ends, the refugees return to their former homes. At the end of the twentieth century and the beginning of the twenty-first, major movements have included:

- 2 million from Ethiopia, Sudan and Somalia, as a result of famine and civil war
- 6 million from Mozambique, as a result of famine, civil war and flooding
- 1 million Kurds from northern Iraq fleeing oppression
- 1 million Afghans into neighbouring Pakistan, fleeing civil strife and war
- 100,000 Tamils fleeing oppression and civil war in Sri Lanka
- 7,000 residents of Montserrat fleeing a volcanic eruption in the Soufrière Hills

Asylum seekers

One definition of asylum is 'the formal application by a refugee to reside in a country when they arrive in that country'. The numbers seeking asylum have increased steadily in recent years as countries seek to curtail immigration.

The prominence of asylum seeking has increased for the following reasons:

- pressure to migrate from the poorest states is increasing because of economic decline and political instability
- improved communications enable people to learn more about potential destinations
- in real terms, the cost of transport has declined
- more gangs of traffickers are preying on would-be migrants and offering a passage to a new life

It can be difficult to distinguish between those fleeing from threats to their life and liberty and those seeking to escape poverty and improve their quality of life.

Effects of migration

Impact on population structure

Migration affects the population structure (page 125) of both the area of origin and the area of destination. Impacts on the area of origin include:

- the younger adult age groups (20–34) migrate, leaving behind an older population
- males are more likely to migrate, causing an indentation on that side of the population pyramid
- birth rates will fall and death rates will rise

Barra, an island in the Outer Hebrides (Scotland), has long experienced depopulation as a result of the poor economic prospects in this remote and isolated location (Figure 4.5).

Impacts on the area of destination:

- the proportion of the younger adult age groups (20–34) increase
- males are more likely to migrate, causing an expansion on that side of the pyramid
- birth rates rise and death rates fall

Dar-es-Salaam, the capital city of Tanzania, is a thriving international port and has long been a magnet for those seeking employment in that area of east Africa (Figure 4.6).

Social, economic, environmental and cultural effects

Migration affects both the area of origin and the area of destination. The effects of migration are social, economic, environmental and cultural (Tables 4.6 and 4.7).

Figure 4.5 Population pyramid for Barra, Scotland

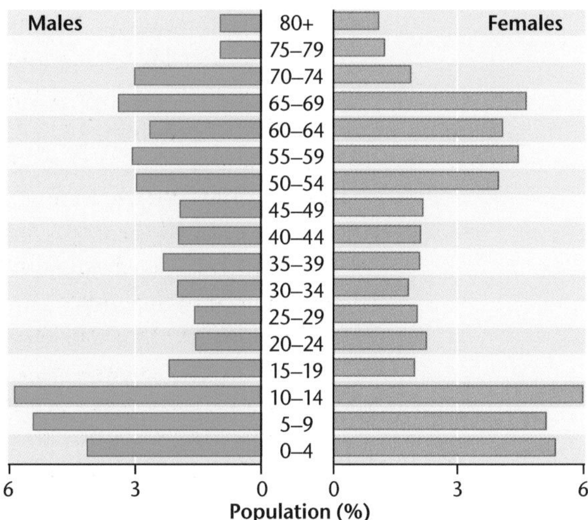

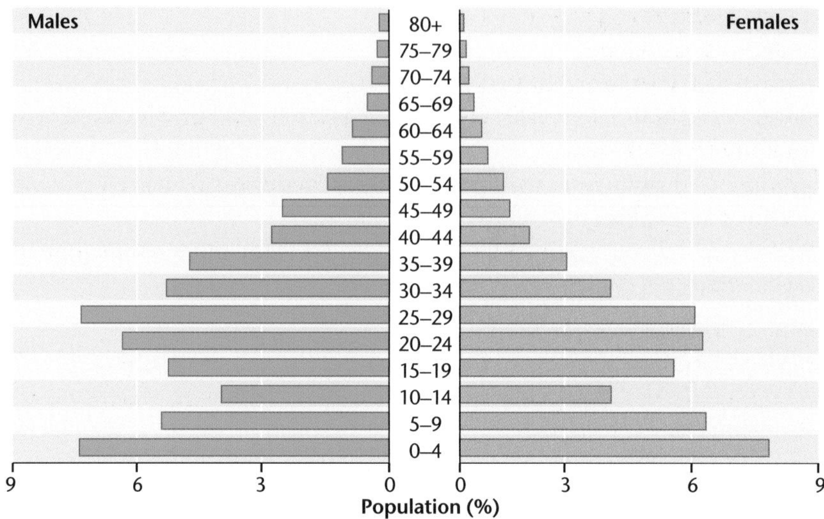

Figure 4.6 Population pyramid for Dar-es-Salaam, Tanzania

Table 4.6 The effects of migration on the area of origin

Impact	In the area of origin
Social	Marriage rates fall
	Family structures can break down
Economic	Those with skills and education leave, causing labour shortages or reduced pressure on resources such as farmland
	The area benefits from remittances sent back — an economic gain
	On their return migrants bring back new skills
Environmental	Farming declines and land is abandoned
Cultural	Departure of males and young families causes a loss of cultural leadership and tradition

Table 4.7 The effects of migration on the area of destination

Impact	In the area of destination
Social	Marriage rates rise
Economic	There is a labour surplus; those with skills and education fuel a new drive to the economy; there is greater take-up of menial jobs
	Remittances are sent back to the area of origin — an economic loss
	On returning to the area of origin, migrants export the skills they have learned — a kind of reverse 'brain drain'
Environmental	Pressure on resources
	Temporary housing and shanty towns in LEDCs; pollution; poor public health
Cultural	Arrival of a new group of people can cause friction, especially if their cultural identity is retained
	Attitudes of local people to new migrants may be both negative and positive
	Social tension may increase
	New food, clothes, music etc. are introduced into the area

Issues of economic migration: source country

Economic costs include:

- the loss of the young adult labour force
- the loss of those with skills and entrepreneurial talents, which may slow economic development
- regions where out-migration takes place may suffer from a spiral of decline that is difficult to halt
- the loss of labour may deter inward investment by private organisations, increasing dependence on governmental initiatives

Economic benefits include:

- the prospect of reduced under-employment in the source country
- returning migrants bring new skills to the country, which may help revitalise the home economy
- many migrants send remittances home, much of which is reinvested in the home economy, in projects such as new buildings and services
- there is less pressure on resources in the area, including basic supplies such as food and essential services such as healthcare

Social costs include:

- the perceived benefits of migration encourage more of the same generation to migrate, which has a detrimental effect on social structure
- there is a disproportionate number of females left behind
- the non-return of migrants causes an imbalance in the population pyramid, with long-term consequences
- returning retired migrants may impose a social cost on the community if support mechanisms are not in place to cater for them

Social benefits include:

- the population density is reduced and the birth rate decreases, as it is the younger adults who migrate
- remittances sent home by economic migrants can finance improved education and health facilities
- returning retired migrants increase social expectations in the community, for example, the demand for better leisure facilities

Issues of economic migration: destination country

Economic costs include:

- the costs of educating the migrants' children have to be borne
- there is an over-dependence of some industries on migrant labour, e.g. the construction industry in the UK
- much of the money earned, including pension payments, is repatriated to the country of origin
- increased numbers of people add to the pressure on resources, such as health services and education

Economic benefits include:

- economic migrants tend to take up the less desirable jobs

- the host country gains skilled labour at reduced cost
- the 'skills gap' that exists in many host countries is filled by qualified migrants
- costs of retirement, especially later in life, are transferred back to the source country

Social costs include:

- discrimination against ethnic groups and minorities leads to civil unrest and political extremism
- the dominance of males is reinforced, especially in countries where the status of women is low — for example, in the Persian Gulf states
- aspects of cultural identity are lost, particularly among second-generation migrants
- segregated areas of similar ethnic groups are created, and schools are dominated by migrant children

Social benefits include:

- the creation of a multiethnic and multicultural society increases the understanding of other cultures
- there is an influx of new and/or revitalised providers of local services — for example, Turkish baths and local corner shops
- there is a growth of ethnic retailing and areas associated with ethnic food outlets — for example, the 'curry mile' in Rusholme, Manchester

Case study Recent economic migration to the USA

Immigration has been a dominant trend in the demography of the USA for nearly 200 years. During this time migrants have entered the country from many parts of Europe (Britain, Ireland, Italy, Germany and other countries), and from China, west Africa and Latin America.

TopFoto

Photograph 4.2 Mexican migrant workers on a farm in San Diego, California

In 1965, an act was passed that set an annual limit of 120,000 immigrants from the western hemisphere (the Americas) and 170,000 immigrants from the eastern hemisphere (Europe and Asia). In 1990, these quotas were raised by 40%.

In the 1990s, a considerable influx took place, which reopened the immigration debate. More than 5 million immigrants arrived between 1991 and 1996. Some Americans argued that recent immigrants were taking jobs that should be theirs; others voiced concern about racial tension and the impact on the welfare system.

This immigration has been spatially selective. In 1995, 55% of all immigration was to just four states — California, New York, Florida and Texas. The main reasons for such concentrations are:

- the location of existing immigrant communities
- the availability of employment in these, the four most populous states

- the land border with Mexico for California and Texas, and Florida's proximity to Caribbean countries

In 1997, over 25% of the population of California were born outside the USA. For the city of Los Angeles the proportion is almost 40%, compared with 16% for New York.

For obvious reasons, it is difficult for the authorities to be precise about numbers of illegal immigrants. Estimates vary from 2.5 to 4 million in the 1990s. In the early 1990s, more than 1 million undocumented migrants were apprehended coming from Mexico each year. In 1996, Congress increased the number of guards on the border with Mexico, tightened asylum rules and made it harder for illegal immigrants to become legal.

There is debate as to whether these migrants are beneficial to the American economy in the long term. Some facts are:

- foreign-born residents are 35% more likely to receive public assistance than native Americans
- immigrants on average pay 32% less tax during their lifetimes than native Americans
- over a period of 40 years, the children of immigrants will pay far more to the state in taxes than they will take from it (assuming they stay in the country)
- for the public purse, the most lucrative immigrant is a 21-year-old with a higher-level education

Case study Economic migration: Germany

Following the end of the Second World War, Germany became two separate countries:

- West Germany — a capitalist country supported by the USA and western European countries, which became a powerful economic force. It had large resources of coal and developed prosperous industries of steel, chemicals, engineering, electronics, motor vehicles and consumer goods. The standard of living of the people became high.
- East Germany — a communist country supported by the former Soviet Union, which became reliant on out-dated heavy industries. Living standards were low, although there was full employment and everyone received state housing. Individual enterprise and initiative were not encouraged.

During the 1960s and 1970s, rapid economic growth led to labour shortages in West Germany. The government encouraged migration from East Germany. However, in 1963, East Germany built a fortified fence between the two countries and constructed the Berlin Wall to separate East and West Berlin (the city was inside East Germany but West Berlin was part of West Germany).

The pull of West Germany's economy attracted workers from many other countries. Unemployed building workers in the UK went to work there and large numbers (over 2 million) emigrated from Turkey.

As West Germany continued to grow economically and East Germany did not, the difference in their standards of living became greater. By the late 1980s, large numbers of East Germans (Ossies) were travelling to other east European countries such as Czechoslovakia (now the Czech Republic and Slovakia) and then crossing the border into West Germany. Their movement became symbolised by the movement past border controls of old-fashioned Trabant cars loaded with possessions.

Following brief but mass protests in East Germany, the communist government collapsed and the Berlin Wall came down in 1989. East and West Germany were reunited soon after this. At first the East Germans were delighted by their new freedom and many moved west. The old East German factories could not compete with their modern western counterparts. Many were deemed too polluting and were closed.

Germany is still a 'country divided'. Although there has been massive development in some parts of the east, especially around Berlin, other parts still suffer from high unemployment and poor housing. Despite these problems, Germany is still seen as an attractive destination by people in other countries of southern and eastern Europe – the countries of the former Yugoslavia, Albania and Greece. Germany has over four times as many migrants as the UK each year and the numbers show no sign of falling.

The German economy is relatively strong and it has extensive land borders with its neighbouring countries, which make it easy for migrants to enter.

Case study Refugee migration: Sudan

The Darfur region of Sudan has been suffering civil war since 2003. This is how the BBC website described the crisis in May 2005:

> The world's worst humanitarian crisis has been unfolding in Sudan's western region of Darfur. More than 2 million people are estimated to have fled their homes and at least 180,000 are thought to have died during the crisis. Sudan's government and the pro-government Arab militias (the Janjaweed) are accused of war crimes against the region's black African population, although the United Nations has stopped short of terming it a genocide.

How did the conflict start?

The conflict began in the arid and impoverished Darfur region early in 2003. Rebel groups began attacking government targets, claiming that the region was being neglected by central government in Khartoum. These groups, the Sudan Liberation Army (SLA) and the Justice and Equality Movement (Jem), say that the government is oppressing black Africans in favour of Arabs. For many years, there has been tension over land and grazing rights between the mostly nomadic Arabs and local farmers.

What is the Sudanese government doing?

The government admits to mobilising 'self-defence militias' following the attacks by the black rebel groups. However, it denies any links to the Janjaweed Arab militia groups, which are accused of trying to 'cleanse' large swathes of territory of black Africans. Refugees from Darfur say that, following air raids by government aircraft, the Janjaweed ride into villages on horses and camels, slaughtering men, raping women and stealing whatever they can find. Many women report being abducted by the Janjaweed and held as sex slaves for more than a week before being released. After strong international pressure and the threat of sanctions against the country, the government promised to disarm the militias, but there is little evidence of this so far. Thousands of extra police have been deployed to the area, but the local people, most of whom are now refugees, have little faith in the Sudanese security forces.

What has happened to the civilians?

More than 2 million people have left their homes and many thousands have been killed. Most have fled their destroyed villages and taken refuge in camps in the main towns of Darfur. However, there is not enough food, water or medicine in the camps. The Janjaweed patrol outside the camps, and Darfurians say that men are killed and women raped if they venture too far in search of firewood or water. Aid workers report that many thousands in the camps are at risk of starvation and disease, and 1 million children are threatened by malnutrition. Attempts by

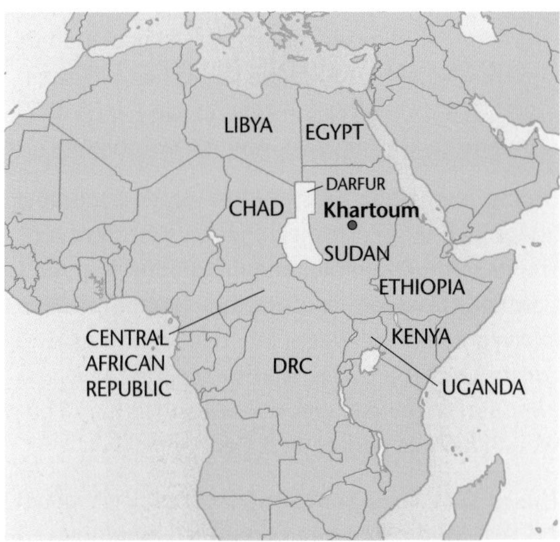

Figure 4.7 Map showing the location of Darfur

the Sudanese security forces to persuade the refugees to leave the camps and return home have led to violence and brought condemnation from the international community. Meanwhile, a drought and a big reduction in the number of active farmers means a poor harvest and heavy dependence on food aid.

As many as 200,000 people have sought refuge in neighbouring Chad. Many are also camped along a 600 km stretch of the border and remain vulnerable to attacks from Sudanese militia groups. The government of Chad is worried that the conflict could spill over the border, as its eastern areas have a similar ethnic mix to that in Darfur.

What is being done to help?

There are many aid agencies working in Darfur. However, they are unable to gain access to large parts of the region. They accuse the government of blocking their access to some areas by demanding visas and using other bureaucratic obstacles.

The government and the two rebel groups signed a ceasefire in April 2004, but this has not held. The African Union, a group of African countries, has organised peace talks and has made progress on some agreements, such as banning military flights and allowing in humanitarian aid. Some 3,000 African Union troops have been deployed in Darfur, but the Sudanese government is resisting any further increase in numbers. The United Nations has been criticised for doing too little, too late. Its Security Council agreed to impose travel bans and an asset-freeze on those who commit atrocities in the area. The Sudanese government has also hinted at a degree of autonomy for the Darfur region.

Population structure

The composition of a population according to age groups and gender is known as the age–sex structure. It can be represented by means of a **population pyramid**. Figure 4.8 shows the age–sex structure for the UK in 2001.

The vertical axis of a population pyramid has the population in age bands of 5 years and the horizontal axis shows the number or percentage of males and females. The pyramid shows longevity by its height.

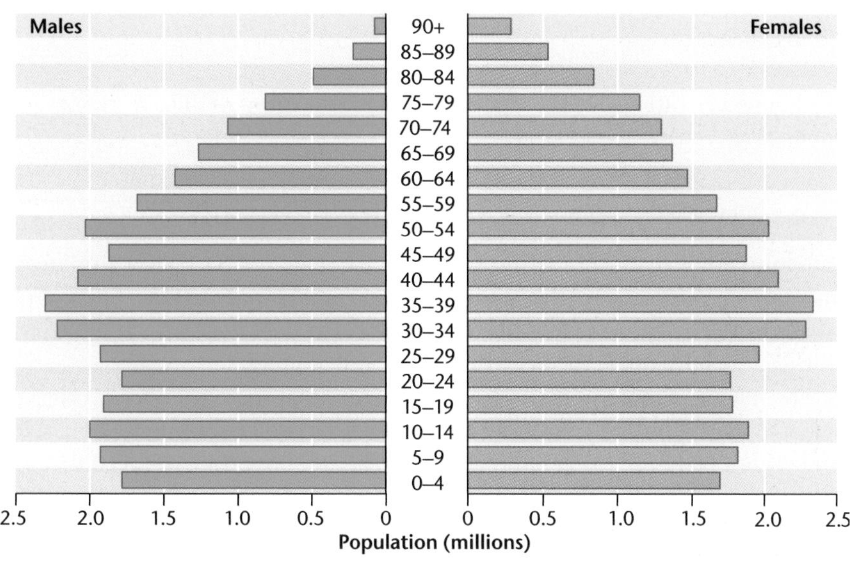

Figure 4.8 Population pyramid for the UK, 2001

Population pyramids can show:

- the results of births minus deaths in specific age groups
- the effects of migration
- the effects of events such as war, famine and disease
- an indication of the overall life expectancy of a country

Age structure can also be measured by a number of indices:

- the dependency ratio
- the support ratio
- the juvenility index
- the old-age index

The **dependency ratio** shows the relationship between the economically active (working) population and the non-economically active (dependent) population. In the EU, the dependent population is those people aged under 19 and over 60. The dependency ratio can therefore be calculated by:

$$\text{dependency ratio} = \frac{(\text{population } 0\text{–}19) + (\text{population over } 60)}{\text{population } 20\text{–}59}$$

The higher the dependency ratio, the more the non-economically active proportion is dependent on the working population.

The **support ratio** is the inverse of the dependency ratio.

The **juvenility index** is calculated by:

$$\text{juvenility index} = \frac{\text{population } 0\text{–}19}{\text{population } 20 \text{ and over}}$$

The higher the juvenility index, the greater the proportion of younger people in a population.

The **old-age index** is calculated by:

$$\text{old-age index} = \frac{\text{population } 60 \text{ and over}}{\text{population } 20\text{–}59}$$

The higher the old-age index, the greater the proportion of elderly people in a population.

The changing age–sex structure of the UK

The population pyramid for the UK for 2001 (Figure 4.8) shows a relatively smooth pyramidal shape, with some slight bulges and indentations. These slight variations can be explained by the circumstances at the time each age group was born and by subsequent factors which affected that group.`

The bulge of people in their 30s demonstrates that the birth rate was slightly higher in the 1960s than in the 1970s. There may be two reasons for this. First, the 1960s was a period of rising national prosperity and increasing personal income. In the 'swinging sixties', there was a lessening of sexual taboos and an increase in freedom for women. Second, this was the time at which people who themselves had been born in a 'baby-boom', following the Second World War, were entering their fertile years. As there were more fertile individuals, more babies were born. Most people who were parents in the 1960s were in their 50s in 2001, and feature as a slight bulge on the pyramid. These examples demonstrate that population growth is cyclical and that to some extent changes can be predicted, so long as social norms are retained.

Two further points illustrate the changing nature of a population structure. In the 2001 pyramid, there is a relatively large number of people over the age of 80. The reasons for this are complicated. People born in the period 1910–20 were often part of large families. This was both traditional and functional. Many young children died in infancy from infectious diseases and a large family acted both as a source of income and as a form of security in old age. As the century progressed, however, death rates fell (despite the devastating impact of the First World War). Improvements in medical care and the development of new drugs and treatments have meant that some of these people, particularly women, are living into their 80s and 90s.

The second point concerns the younger part of the pyramid. As mentioned above, there was an increase in birth rates in the 1960s. The people born then became fertile in the 1980s and 1990s, so a cyclical increase in birth rates would be expected at that time. This has not happened to the extent predicted because social norms have changed. In recent decades, young adults have been less willing to have children. There are various reasons for this: the increased availability of contraception, abortion and sterilisation, the growing importance of material possessions (houses, cars, holidays), and the desire of women to have careers. With hindsight, it is possible to add another factor. The economic recession of the late 1980s and early 1990s left many young adults financially insecure. Many women were forced to become the main bread winners, as male employment in mining and the manufacturing industries fell.

The net result is that in the early part of the twenty-first century, the UK has an ageing population. The proportion of the population aged 50 and over has increased significantly since the start of the twentieth century. There has also been a rise in the 'very elderly' — people aged 80 and over. Population projections suggest that by 2021 there will be more than 3 million people over 80 — 5% of the population. At the same time the number of people aged under 16 has been progressively falling. It is anticipated that in 2007, the number of people aged 65 and over will exceed those under 16 for the first time.

Links between the DTM and age–sex structure

The demographic transition model can be used to demonstrate changes in age–sex structure both spatially and over time. This can be seen in the characteristic shapes and names of the pyramids at each stage of the DTM (Figure 4.9).

- **Stage 1 (high fluctuating)** High birth rate; rapid fall in each upward age group due to high death rate; short life expectancy
- **Stage 2 (early expanding)** High birth rate; fall in death rate so more middle-aged people alive; slightly longer life expectancy

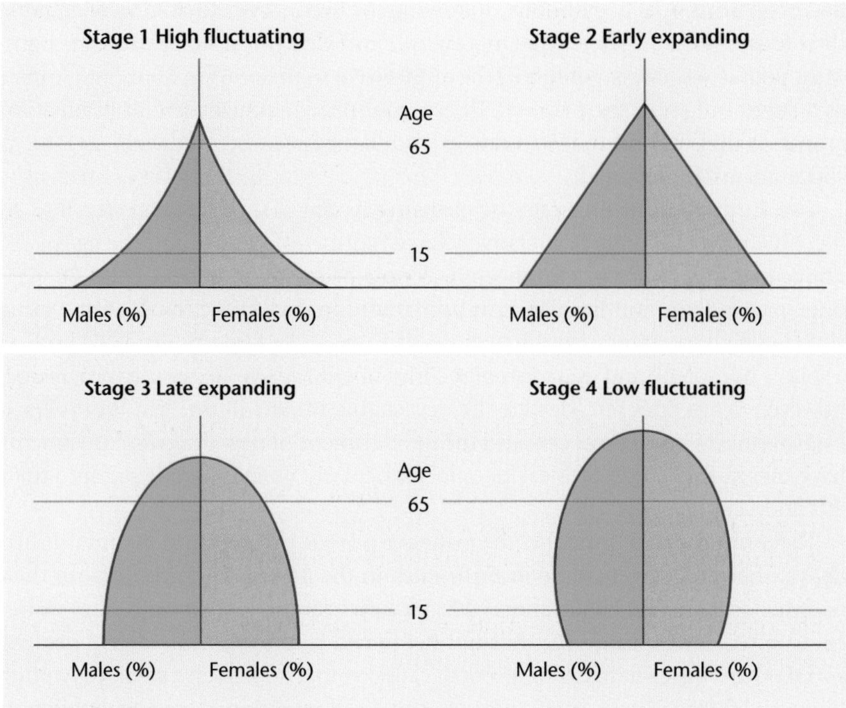

Figure 4.9 Age–sex structure and the DTM

- **Stage 3 (late expanding)** Declining birth rate; low death rate; more people living to an older age
- **Stage 4 (low fluctuating)** Low birth rate; low death rate; higher dependency ratio; longer life expectancy

An ageing population

The population of the world is ageing significantly. In 2004, 10% of the population was over the age of 60. This proportion is expected to increase to 20% by 2050. At present, 600 million people are aged 60 years and over. This is projected to increase to 1 billion by 2020 and to 2 billion by 2050. The rise in the median age of the population is caused by increased life expectancy (greater longevity) and the decline in fertility. It is called **demographic ageing**. Demographic ageing has been a concern for the MEDW for some time and it is now also beginning to alarm some countries of the LEDW. Although ageing of the population has begun later in the LEDW, it is progressing at a faster rate than in the MEDW. This is because the relative rates of decline in both fertility and mortality are much greater in the LEDW than in the MEDW.

The following demographic ageing features have been highlighted by the United Nations:

- The global average for life expectancy increased from 46 years in 1950 to 64 in 2000. It is projected to reach 74 years by 2050.
- The global median age for males was 26 in 2000 and is projected to rise to 35 years by 2050.

- In the LEDW, the population aged 60 and over is expected to quadruple between 2000 and 2050. The proportion of this population is projected to increase from 8% in 2000 to 21% by 2050.
- During the same time period, the proportion of children (16 and under) is projected to fall from 33% to 20%.
- The population aged 80 and over numbered 69 million in 2000. This is the fastest growing section of global population and is projected to increase to 394 million by 2050.
- Europe is the 'oldest' region in the world. Those aged 60 and over in 2000 formed 20% of the population and this is projected to rise to 35% by 2050.
- Africa is the 'youngest' region in the world. Those aged 15 and under accounted for 42% of the population in 2000. This is expected to decline to 24% by 2050.

Demographic ageing poses considerable problems for the world as a whole. However, it is the LEDW that faces the greatest challenge because:
- financial, health and housing resources are woefully inadequate to meet the increasing demands of the elderly
- traditional support mechanisms for old people are deteriorating in an era of rapid social change
- the significant decline in fertility is leaving fewer children to care for elderly parents

However, this is not to underestimate the considerable adjustments required in the MEDW to cope with demographic ageing. In the EU, it has been predicted that by 2025:
- there will be an increase in the number of people aged 60 and over — a further 37 million
- one-third of its population will be pensioners — 111 million people
- the working population (aged 20–59) will shrink by 13 million
- the numbers of over-60s will outnumber the under-20s, for the first time in recorded history
- there will be three times as many over-80s as there were in 2003
- there will be 9 million fewer children and teenagers — a 10% decline

These figures are summarised in Table 4.8.

Age (years)	Status	1995	2025
60+	Dependent	74 million	111 million
20–59	Economically active	203 million	190 million
0–19	Dependent	86 million	77 million

***Table 4.8* Dependent and economically active populations in the EU, 1995 and 2025**

Country	0–19 years	20–59 years	60+ years
France	–6.1	0.2	57.7
Germany	–12.1	–13.5	51.2
Ireland	–25.2	2.7	67.7
Sweden	1.2	3.7	38.1
UK	–8.2	–2.8	43.6

***Table 4.9* Predicted change in population (%) in selected EU countries by age cohort, 1995–2025**

Demographic ageing in the UK

Demographic ageing is one of the greatest challenges facing the UK today as the contrasting population pyramids for 2001 and 2050 show (Figures 4.10 and 4.11).

Figure 4.10 Distribution of the UK population by age, 2001

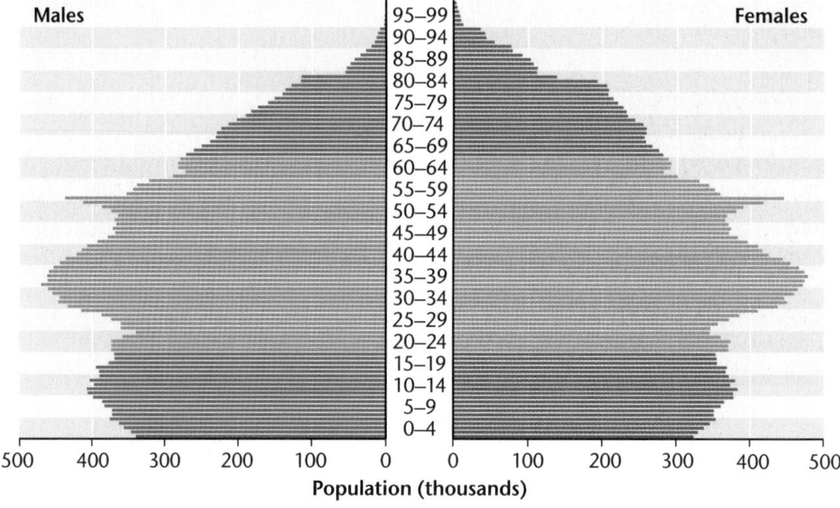

Note: The paler area highlights those aged 20–64.
Source: GAD 2002-based Pensions Commission analysis

Figure 4.11 Projected distribution of the UK population by age, 2050

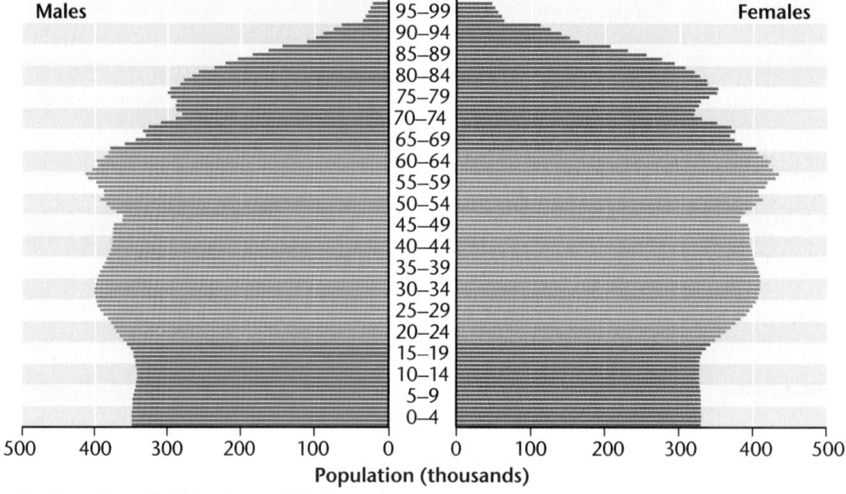

Note: The paler area highlights those aged 20–64.
Source: GAD 2002 projection, Pensions Commission

The demographic trends predict that by 2050 the proportion of the population aged 65 years and over will have almost doubled. The main impacts will be on healthcare, pensions and housing. The UK government has predicted in its most recent review that:

- the ratio of people 65 years and over to those aged 20–64 will rise from 27% in 2001 to 48% in 2050. This marks a considerable change from the very slow increase in the previous 20 years

Photograph 4.3 Elderly people in Eastbourne, UK

- average male life expectancy at 65, which rose from 12.0 years in 1950 to 19.0 in 2001, will increase further to 21.0 by 2030 and to 21.7 by 2050. Female life expectancy is higher, but will increase at a slightly slower rate
- the current low fertility rate of 1.7 children per woman will increase only slightly to 1.75 by 2025, levelling off thereafter

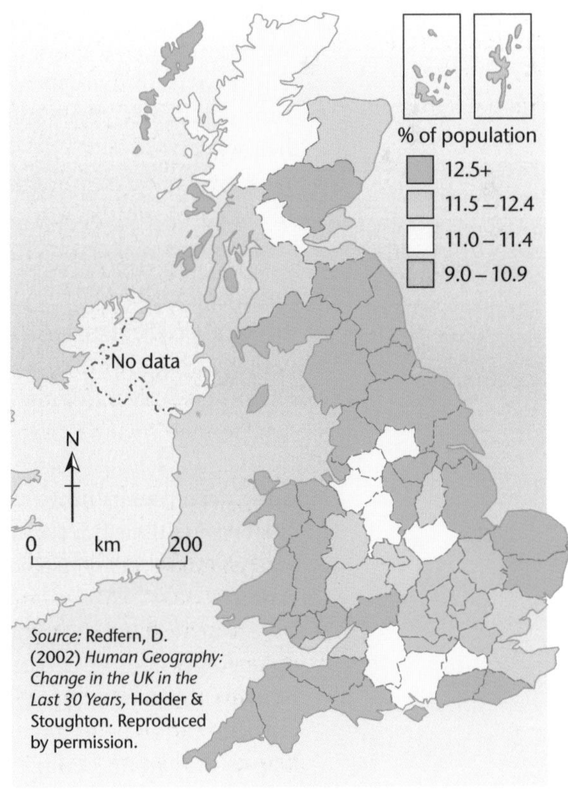

Figure 4.12 Distribution of retired people in the UK, 1996

Source: Redfern, D. (2002) *Human Geography: Change in the UK in the Last 30 Years*, Hodder & Stoughton. Reproduced by permission.

Life expectancy is influenced by socioeconomic class and by ethnic group. Men in social class 1 have about 4 years longer life expectancy at 65 than men in social class 5. Thus, longevity is greater in more affluent parts of the country. The white Irish and white British populations have the highest proportions of people aged 65 and over; the black African population has the lowest proportion of older people.

Christchurch in Dorset is the pensioners' 'capital' of the UK with one in three residents of retirement age. Eastbourne, another popular retirement centre, has the highest ratio of elderly women to elderly men. However, it is not just coastal areas with a perceived high quality of life that attract retirees. There is also evidence that the growing elderly population is migrating to the countryside.

Ageing and health

An ageing population places increasing pressure on health resources but it is important not to overstate this impact. Average healthcare costs do rise with age, but the cost of this trend could be significantly offset by people becoming healthier. Retired people continue to pay income tax and many of the other taxes that the working population pay, such as VAT and council tax. Health costs tend to be compressed into the last years or even months of life — a process termed the **compression of morbidity**.

Ageing and pensions

The state pension system transfers resources from the current generation of workers to the current generation of pensioners. As the population has aged the level of resource transfer required has increased. The system cannot be sustained in the future without significant change. Four options have been suggested:

- pensioners become poorer relative to the rest of society
- taxes and National Insurance contributions devoted to pensions increase
- the rate at which individuals save for retirement increases
- the average retirement age increases

Public responses to these options will feature in political debate in the coming years.

Another feature of demographic ageing is that the voting power of the older age group increases. The 'grey vote' is of major significance to the political parties and the needs of the elderly cannot therefore be ignored by those in power.

The economic and purchasing power of the 'grey pound' is also increasing. This is beneficial to companies that specialise in providing goods and services to older people. For example:

- in the tourist industry, cruising is a popular type of holiday with this age group
- some companies, for example Saga, provide a wide range of leisure services for older people, in this case for the over 50s
- some companies, for example B&Q and Homebase, target this age group for their workforce
- the growing number of elderly people who live alone has led to the provision of a range of support services, such as health visitors, meals on wheels, home-help cleaners and drivers for hospital visits

Ageing and housing

As the number of elderly people and the age to which they live increases, so some degree of segregation has taken place, particularly in terms of housing. Many elderly people have to decide whether or not to leave the family home when they are left on their own or have difficulty caring for themselves. Old people living alone in council houses have found that very often they do not have a choice. Housing departments move them out into sheltered accommodation or nursing homes because their houses are required for families.

Segregation based on age has manifested itself in a number of ways in towns in this country.

- On council estates, it is common to see clusters of purpose-built bungalows occupying one small part or parts of the estate. In some areas maisonettes with security access have been built. This type of housing for elderly people is provided in the belief that it is best for them to live in the community for as long as they are fit enough. They are often people who have lived in the area for many years. They have friends and relatives living locally and they are integrated into social functions such as the church or social clubs.

- A more recent provision has been sheltered accommodation — a complex of flats or units with some shared facilities, overseen by a warden or manager. In some cases purpose-built blocks of flats, some for single people and some for married couples, have been constructed. A mobile warden may oversee a number of complexes. The location of these facilities is only just beginning to establish a pattern in some urban areas.
- Nursing homes have been increasing in number to cater for the growing number of elderly people who have difficulty looking after themselves. Initially, both local authorities and private developers provided such housing, but local authorities have been cutting back their provision. In many urban areas, concentrations of nursing homes are becoming clear. They are often in both inner and outer suburbs, in areas where large Georgian and Victorian houses can either be converted or extended for this purpose. Close links with medical provision are also a factor, and some of the most financially successful nursing homes are located on a main road within a town so as to facilitate the arrival of ambulances.

LEDCs with youthful populations

In many LEDCs:

- the population pyramid has a broad base, indicating a youthful population with a large proportion of children and high fertility
- the pyramid tapers rapidly, indicating high mortality with a significant reduction in numbers in each 5-year group
- the pyramid has a narrow apex, suggesting a small proportion of elderly people
- as mortality falls in large LEDCs (e.g. India), the huge numbers of over-60s will cause major problems
- the working population is reduced by migration to MEDCs, particularly by those with skills
- there may be few relatives to act as carers (due to migration and deaths from AIDS), so the costs of care for the elderly will rise

Case study Iran

The main characteristics of the age–sex structure of Iran are shown in Figure 4.13.

There is evidence that the population growth rate in Iran is slowing down, even though it currently has a youthful population.

Writers who have studied the country state that there have been

Table 4.10 ***Population statistics for Iran, 2004***

Population	67 million
Age structure:	
0–14 years	32.6% (male, 11 million; female, 10 million). Estimated to fall to 27% by 2015.
15–64 years	62.7% (male, 21 million; female, 21 million)
65 years and over	4.7% (male, 1.6 million; female, 1.4 million)
Population growth rate	1.2%
Birth rate	17.5 births per 1,000 population
Death rate	6 deaths per 1,000 population

four revolutions for women, each of which has influenced the birth rate:

- **The urban revolution** — women who have moved to the cities (e.g. Tehran) usually have fewer children than those who stay in the rural areas. Sixty-seven per cent of Iran's population is now classed as urban.
- **The education revolution** — there has been a slow but steady increase in education for girls and women. Women who are educated are likely to marry later, become more aware of family planning (74% of Iranian women between the ages of 15 and 49 used contraception in 2004) and gain paid employment.
- **The working revolution** — women who work in the cities find it more difficult to arrange childcare, and hence have fewer children.
- **The migration revolution** — women who migrate from Iran to other Persian Gulf states and to Europe have adopted a more Westernised lifestyle with smaller families and more consumer goods. By remaining in contact with friends and relatives, they have had a big effect on social attitudes in the country.

The fertility rate in Iran has fallen to 2.5 per woman — one of the lowest in the Arab world. As fertility decreases, there will be a greater proportion of people in the economically active age range. Economists have matched the declining dependency ratio to rising rates of investment and savings. This in turn is likely to encourage foreign investment into the country. Both factors will be favourable for economic growth over the next 30 years.

Figure 4.13 Age–sex structure of Iran, 1999

Chapter 5

Settlement processes and patterns

Urbanisation and suburbanisation

The global pattern of urbanisation

At a global scale, rapid urbanisation has occurred over the last 50 years. Around 50% of the world's population lives in towns and cities. The most urbanised continents are Europe, North America, South America and Oceania; the least urbanised are Asia and Africa. However, in terms of urban growth, the number of urban dwellers is by far the largest in Asia, with 1.4 billion people living in towns and cities, which is 40% of the population.

Urbanisation is increasing most rapidly in Africa and Asia. This trend is expected to continue, so that by 2025 almost half the population of these continents will live in urban areas and 80% of urban dwellers will be in LEDCs.

In Europe, Oceania and North America, urbanisation levels peaked in the 1970s and have fallen steadily since then.

The graphs in Figure 5.2 illustrate the complexity of this topic. The predicted pattern of urbanisation based on percentages appears to vary little between 2000 and 2025. However, the pattern based on actual numbers of people is very different.

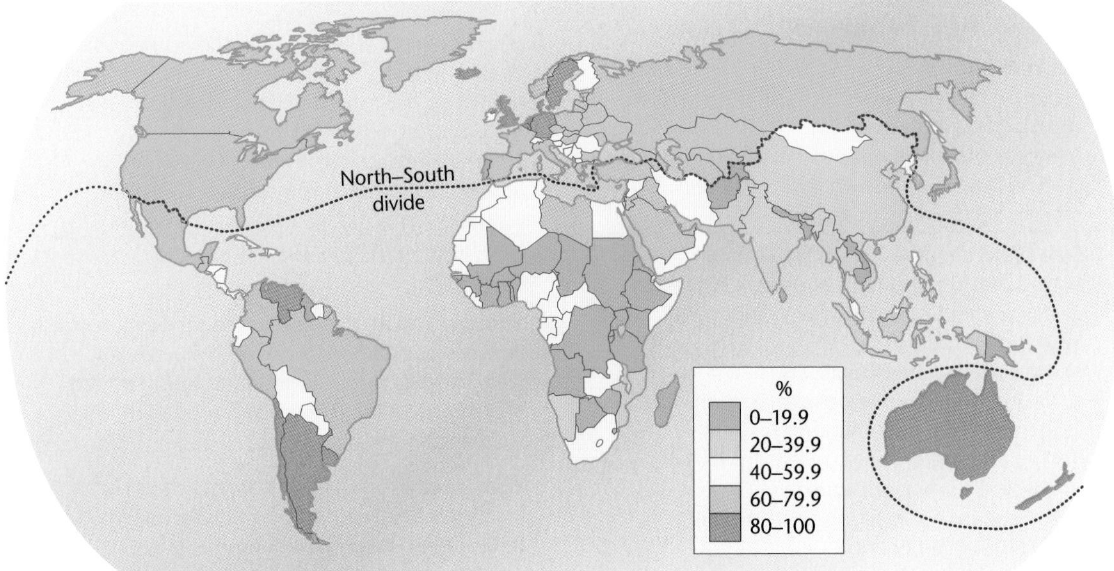

Figure 5.1 Percentage of the world's population living in urban settlements, 2000

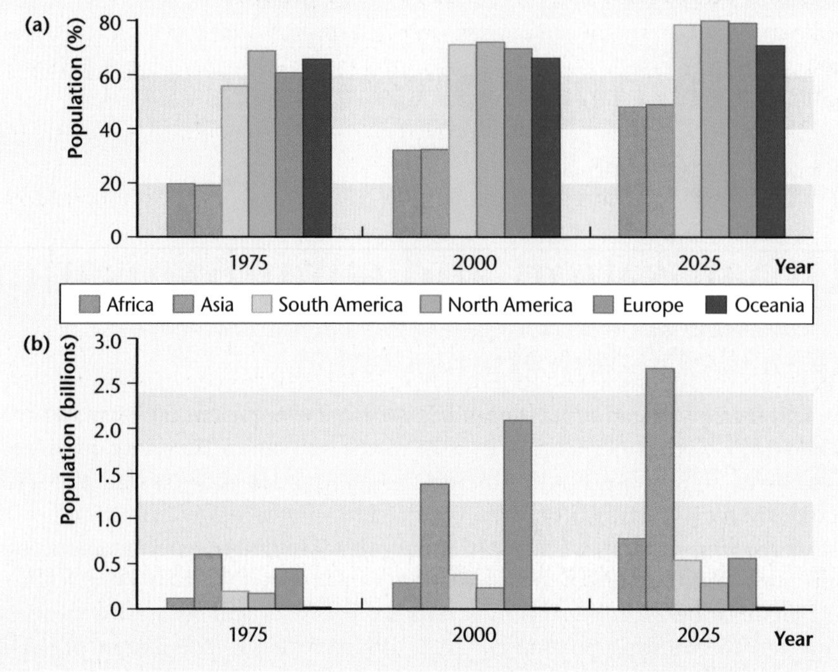

Figure 5.2 Predicted pattern of urbanisation, 1975–2025, by (a) per cent and (b) number of people

Key terms

Counter-urbanisation The movement of people from large urban areas into smaller urban areas or into rural areas, thereby leapfrogging the rural–urban fringe. It might mean daily commuting, but could also require lifestyle changes and the increased use of ICT (homeworking or teleworking).

Reurbanisation The movement of people and economic activities back into city centres. One characteristic of reurbanisation is the refurbishment, by more affluent people, of old housing stock in former run-down inner-city areas. This process is known as **gentrification.**

Size of urban area This varies according to the boundaries chosen. Each boundary is likely to give a different estimate of population. An urban area might comprise:

- the administrative boundary
- the contiguous built-up area (including both the inner and outer suburbs)
- the contiguous built-up area and the physically separate suburbs
- the contiguous built-up area and the commuter hinterland

Suburbanisation The movement of people from the inner parts of a city to the outer parts. It has been facilitated by the development of transport networks and the increase in ownership of private cars. These have allowed people to commute to work.

Urban growth An increase in the number of urban dwellers. Classifications of urban dwellers depend on the census definition of urban areas, which vary from country to country. They usually include one or more of the following criteria: population size; population density; average distance between buildings within a settlement; legal and/or administrative boundaries.

Urbanisation An increase in the proportion of a country's population that lives in towns and cities. The two main causes of urbanisation are natural population growth and migration into urban areas from rural areas.

Urban sprawl The physical spread of the urban area. It has been caused by suburbanisation and the desire for lower density housing.

The growth of millionaire cities and megacities

Increased global urbanisation has resulted in the development of many millionaire cities. There is also a significant number of enormous megacities, some of which are classed as world cities.

- **Millionaire cities** are those with more than 1 million people. India and China have the most millionaire cities in the world.
- **Megacities** are those with more than 5 million people. Some commentators suggest that 10 million is a better indicator (in this case London does not qualify).
- **World cities** are those which have great influence on a global scale, because of their financial status and worldwide commercial power.

Three cities sit at the top of the global hierarchy: New York, London and Tokyo. These cities house the headquarters of many transnational corporations (TNCs), are centres of world finance and provide international consumer services. Other major world cities include Los Angeles, Paris, Singapore and São Paulo.

Table 5.1 illustrates the changing geographical pattern of the world's ten largest cities.

Rank	1960	Population (millions)	2000	Population (millions)
1	New York	14.2	Tokyo	27.2
2	London	10.7	Mexico City	16.9
3	Tokyo	10.7	São Paulo	16.8
4	Shanghai	10.7	New York	16.4
5	Beijing	7.3	Mumbai	15.7
6	Paris	7.2	Shanghai	13.7
7	Buenos Aires	6.9	Los Angeles	12.6
8	Los Angeles	6.6	Beijing	12.4
9	Moscow	6.3	Calcutta	12.1
10	Chicago	6.0	Buenos Aires	11.9

Table 5.1 The world's ten largest cities, 1960 and 2000

The causes of urban growth

Natural population growth

Urban areas tend to have relatively low age profiles. Young adults (15–40 years), have traditionally migrated from rural areas. They are in their fertile years — the years during which people have children — and so the rates of natural increase are higher in cities than in the surrounding rural areas.

Rural–urban migration

The reasons for rural–urban migration are often divided into 'push' and 'pull' factors. **Push factors** cause people to move away from rural areas, whereas **pull factors** attract them to urban areas. In LEDCs push factors tend to be more important than pull factors.

Push factors are largely due to poverty caused by:

- population growth which means the same area of land has to support increasing numbers of people, causing over-farming, soil erosion and low yields
- fragmentation of land due to a system of inheritance that causes land to be subdivided into smaller and smaller plots

- systems of tenure that do not allow tenants to have a long-term perspective for their land, so they do not invest in it
- debt on high-interest loans taken out to support agricultural change
- desertification due to low and unreliable rainfall amounts which results in low agricultural yields
- high levels of local diseases and inadequate medical provision
- the conversion of land from subsistence agriculture to the production of cash crops. This has been done to try to pay off the interest on national debts. Land previously used to grow food for local people is now used to produce cash crops for sale to MEDCs
- natural disasters such as floods (Mozambique), tropical storms (Bangladesh) and earthquakes (Gujarat, India) have all caused people to flee previously fertile rural areas and not to return
- wars and civil strife in countries including Afghanistan, Sudan, Kashmir and Rwanda have caused people to flee their land. Fear and unexploded landmines may prevent them returning

Pull factors include the prospect of:

- employment in factories and service industries (e.g. hotels), earning better wages than those in rural areas
- earning money from the informal sector, e.g. selling goods on the street, providing transport (taxi/rickshaw driver), prostitution
- better-quality social provisions, from basic needs such as education and health-care to entertainment and tourism
- a perceived better quality of life in the city, fed by images in the media

Urbanisation in an LEDC: São Paulo, Brazil

São Paulo is the largest city in the southern hemisphere. It is also referred to as 'the richest city in the LEDW'. In 2000, the population of the metropolitan area was 17 million. It is a compact city. Its population density is 21,000 persons km^{-2}, which is twice that of Paris and three times that of Los Angeles. The city continues to grow in size — between 1991 and 2000 the population increased by 16% — but the rate of increase is slowing down. There is reduced rural–urban migration and the rate of natural increase has slowed. In addition the population of the central areas is decreasing and that of the peripheral areas is increasing. Such decentralisation mirrors that of cities in the MEDW.

São Paulo's initial site was inland, in a shallow basin on a river terrace above the River Tiete. The area developed into a centre of agriculture, based on coffee and cotton. A rail link connected it to the port at Santos on the Atlantic coast, allowing the export of these crops.

It is now a major industrial centre with:

- manufacturing industries — food processing, cars, cotton mills, steelworks, consumer goods
- service industries — commercial and financial centre, administrative centre for the state of São Paulo

Ron Giling/Still Pictures

Photograph 5.1 Housing in São Paulo

The industrial development of São Paulo owes much to foreign investment, particularly from the USA. The wealth generated by export earnings from coffee and cotton has led to continued economic development, attracting yet more migrants. The city also possesses a range of energy sources. There is a local hydroelectric power (HEP) scheme at Cubatao, while gas and oil are imported via Santos.

Another attractive feature of the city is its temperate climate due to its elevated position compared with the tropical coastal lowlands.

The environment

It has been estimated that 25% of all vehicles in Brazil circulate in São Paulo. Over 35% of households in the city own a car. The noise of traffic on the main roads into and out of the city is incessant, 24 hours a day.

In recent years, much has been done to improve air quality and reduce the levels of sulphur dioxide and lead. However, levels of other pollutants such as ozone, carbon monoxide and suspended particulates are still of concern.

The city authorities spend $1 million a day on rubbish collection. The cost has risen sharply over the last decade because of:

- a lack of strategic planning
- a growing population
- the rising amount of rubbish per person because of increased consumption

Disposing of this waste is a problem. In 2000, the city had only two landfill sites. Two huge waste incinerators, each burning 7,500 tonnes a day, came into operation during that year.

Figure 5.3 Map showing the location of São Paulo

Variations in the quality of life

Although São Paulo is relatively prosperous compared to the country as a whole, poverty and unemployment are huge problems. The city has the highest unemployment rate in the country. Like cities in the MEDW, São Paulo is moving away from dependence on manufacturing industry and is becoming more service-orientated. It is facing deindustrialisation.

In 2002, the city authorities conducted a survey of living standards. The richest district, Moema, had a Human Development Index (HDI) equivalent to the Portuguese national average; the poorest district, Marsilac, had an HDI lower than that of Sierra Leone (the world's poorest country according to the UN).

Low standards of living and social difficulties have had a significant impact on the city. In 1999, São Paulo recorded 11,500 homicides, compared with 670 in New York. The affluent elite has assembled the world's third largest fleet of urban helicopters (after New York and Tokyo), allowing them to hop from rooftop to rooftop to escape the squalor of the streets. São Paulo has 240 helipads compared with ten in New York.

Three different housing types dominate:

- **condominiums** — luxury housing blocks for affluent people constructed both within the city and on the periphery, often separated from the nearby favelas by high walls and security gates
- **corticos** — inner-city dilapidated rental accommodation in sub-divided nineteenth-century tenement buildings. Many consist of blocks of one-room dwellings in which up to four people live
- **favelas** — or informal settlements made up of small, poorly built dwellings with limited infrastructure such as water and power supplies

It is estimated that substandard housing occupies 70% of the area of São Paulo and that up to 60% of the population growth of recent years has been absorbed by the favelas. During the 1980s, the public authorities removed favelas from areas valued by the property market. The action of private property owners regaining possession of their land has driven the favelas to the poorest, most peripheral and hazardous areas — floodplains and steep hill slopes. Heliopolis is São Paulo's largest area of favelas. One hundred thousand people live here in a mix of absolute and semi-poverty.

Basic favelas are densely packed informal settlements made of wood, corrugated iron and other makeshift materials. More established favelas are made from concrete blocks, with tiles replacing the corrugated roofing material. Services are poor, with little running water, mains drainage or rubbish collection. The streets are frequently open sewers which flood when it rains. Electrical power is limited, and there is a lack of schools, teachers, hospitals and healthcare professionals. Drinking water is often polluted, leading to disease (typhoid, cholera and dysentery). Many people who live in the favelas are unemployed or under-employed, finding work in the informal sector of the economy.

Housing improvement schemes

Some large-scale improvement in favelas has occurred due to:

- residents expecting to remain where they are

- changes in public policies during the past 20 years, from slum removal to slum upgrading

A number of attempts have been made to tackle the housing problem:

- a Federal Bank was established to fund urban housing projects and to provide low-interest loans to lower- and middle-income groups
- a state cooperative helped to build housing for state workers, such as teachers
- a state development company provided housing for low-income families and financed slum-upgrading projects
- a municipally managed company was set up to build public housing, fund self-help projects and upgrade substandard housing

During the early 1990s, the authorities tried to support self-help housing schemes. The city supplied funding directly to community groups, which allowed families to either build their own or to renovate existing housing. The authorities also provided serviced plots for building with mains water, electricity, sewerage and roads — such site and service schemes were a low-cost solution to the housing problem. However, despite a great deal of publicity, the annual house building total only increased to 8,000 during this period. From 2000, this idea was re-adopted with an investment of $3 billion over the following 4 years. Individual houses attracted up to $14,000 of investment.

Santo André (population 650,000) is an area within São Paulo that has been undergoing transformation. An Integrated Programme of Social Inclusion was established here to alleviate poverty. It included the following:

- micro-credit facilities for small-scale entrepreneurs
- community healthcare agents made widely accessible
- literacy campaigns for both adults and street children
- effective local communications through the use of street theatre
- targeted government interventions aimed at fostering citizenship and local participation in decision making

Cooperation between the authorities and the local community is essential to provide the best infrastructure for health, education and other basic services.

Suburbanisation in MEDCs

Causes

Suburbanisation has resulted in the outward growth of urban development that has engulfed surrounding villages and rural areas. During the mid- to late-twentieth century, this was facilitated by the growth of public transport systems and the increased use of the private car. The presence of railway lines and arterial roads has enabled relatively wealthy commuters to live some distance away from their places of work.

To a large extent the towns and cities of the UK demonstrate the effects of past suburbanisation. In the 1930s there were few planning controls and urban growth took place alongside main roads — this was known as ribbon development. By the 1940s this growth, and the subsequent growth between the 'ribbons', became a cause for concern. This led to the creation of **green belts** — areas of open space and low-density land use around existing urban areas where further development was strictly controlled.

Since 1950, suburban expansion has increased and has been better planned. During the 1950s and 1960s large-scale construction of council housing took place on the only land available which was the suburban fringe. In the 1970s, there was a move towards home ownership, which led to private housing estates being built, also on the urban fringe. Building in these areas allowed people to have more land for gardens and more public open space, compared with housing areas nearer the town centre.

The growth of car ownership and of other forms of road transport also encouraged suburbanisation. The edge of town, where there is more land available for car parking and expansion, became the favoured location for new offices, factories and shopping outlets. In a number of cases, the 'strict control' of the green belts was ignored (or at best modified) in the light of changing circumstances.

In the green belt of the southeast England, where there is the most pressure for more housing developments, the controls have been effective. However, the future growth of the southeast is a major issue. A recent report suggested that by 2016 over 1 million new homes will be needed in the region. One consequence of this might be a re-emergence of suburbanisation.

Consequences

Suburbanised areas have experienced much change in recent years. The influx of new population has been reflected in changes to the land-use of the area. New detached and semi-detached houses and bungalows have been built, both on individual plots and on estates of varying sizes. Local shopping centres have been constructed, along with a large number of primary schools and a smaller number of secondary schools. Suburbanised areas also demonstrate other key elements of the rural–urban fringe, such as residual woodlands and parks, cemeteries, golf courses and playing fields. Many are now well-established housing areas, highly sought after in the property market.

Counter-urbanisation and reurbanisation

Counter-urbanisation

Counter-urbanisation is the process of migration of people from major urban areas to smaller urban settlements and rural areas. There is a clear break between the areas of new growth and the urban area from which the people have moved. As a result, counter-urbanisation does not lead to suburban growth, but to growth in rural areas beyond the main city. The difference between rural and urban areas is diminished as a consequence of this movement.

A number of factors has caused the growth of counter-urbanisation. One is the negative reaction to city life. Many people want to escape from the air pollution, dirt and crime of the urban environment. They aspire to what they see as the pleasant, quiet and clean environment of the countryside, where land and house prices are cheaper. Car ownership and greater affluence allow people to commute to work from such areas. Indeed, many sources of employment have also moved out of cities. Between 1981 and 1996, rural areas gained more than 1 million jobs. Improvements in technology such as the internet have allowed more freedom of location. Someone working from a home computer can access the same global system as a person in an office block in the centre of a city.

At the same time there has been a rising demand for second homes and earlier retirement. The former is a direct consequence of rising levels of affluence. Alongside this is the need for rural areas to attract income. Agriculture is currently facing economic difficulties and one straightforward way for farmers to raise money is to sell unwanted land and buildings.

Counter-urbanisation affects the layout of rural settlements. Modern housing estates are built on the edges of small settlements, while small industrial units are sited on the main roads leading into the settlement. Former open areas are built on, old properties are converted and modernised and some agricultural buildings are redeveloped as homes. As with gentrified areas in the inner cities, there is tension between the newcomers and the locals.

One of the main areas of conflict is that, despite the influx of new people, local services often close down. Bus services to many rural communities have disappeared, schools and post offices have closed, and churches have closed as parishes are amalgamated into larger units. The main reason for these changes is that the newcomers have the wealth and the mobility to continue to use the urban services some distance away.

The evidence for counter-urbanisation in an area includes:

- an increase in the use of a commuter railway station in the area, including car parking for commuters
- increased value of houses in the area
- the construction of more executive housing in the area, often on newly designated building land, following the demolition of old properties
- more conversions of former farm buildings to exclusive residences

Counter-urbanisation is one of a number of processes contributing to social and demographic change in rural settlements, sometimes referred to as the **rural turnaround**. The main changes include:

- the out-migration of young village-born adults seeking education and employment opportunities elsewhere
- the decline of the elderly village-born population, due to death
- the in-migration of young to middle-aged married couples or families with young children
- the in-migration of younger, more affluent people, which results in increased house prices

These changes do not take place uniformly within all rural settlements. There are considerable variations between and within parishes. The ones with the most change are **key settlements** that have a range of basic services and good access to commuter routes. Such settlements are called **suburbanised villages**.

Land-use patterns of suburbanised villages

Like suburban areas in towns and cities, suburbanised villages have experienced much change in recent years. The influx of new population has been reflected in changes to the land-use structure of the area. These changes include new detached and semi-detached houses and bungalows, both on individual plots and on estates of varying sizes, and the conversion of old farm buildings. The model in Figure 5.4 summarises the types of change that have occurred in suburbanised villages. Compare it with the main features of a similar village you have studied.

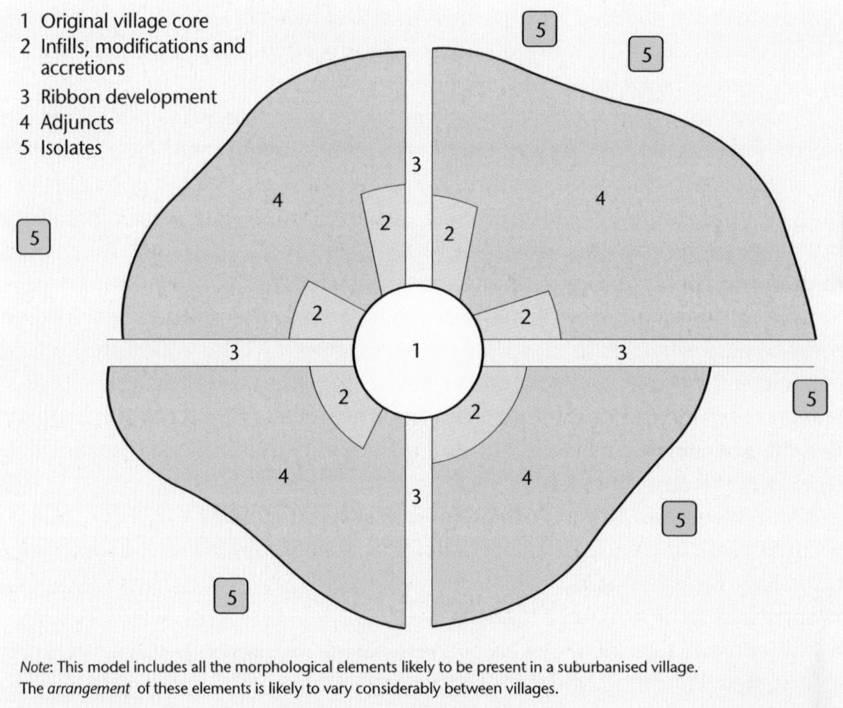

Figure 5.4 A model of a suburbanised village

Photograph 5.2 New housing in Cordrona village, near Peebles, UK

Case study The effects of counter-urbanisation: St Ives, Cambridgeshire

The small town of St Ives, in Cambridgeshire, is about 100 km north of London. It lies on the A1123, 8 km east of Huntingdon and 25 km northwest of Cambridge, just off the A14 trunk road. The town is close to both the A1 trunk road and the main east coast railway line. Regular trains to London make the area very accessible.

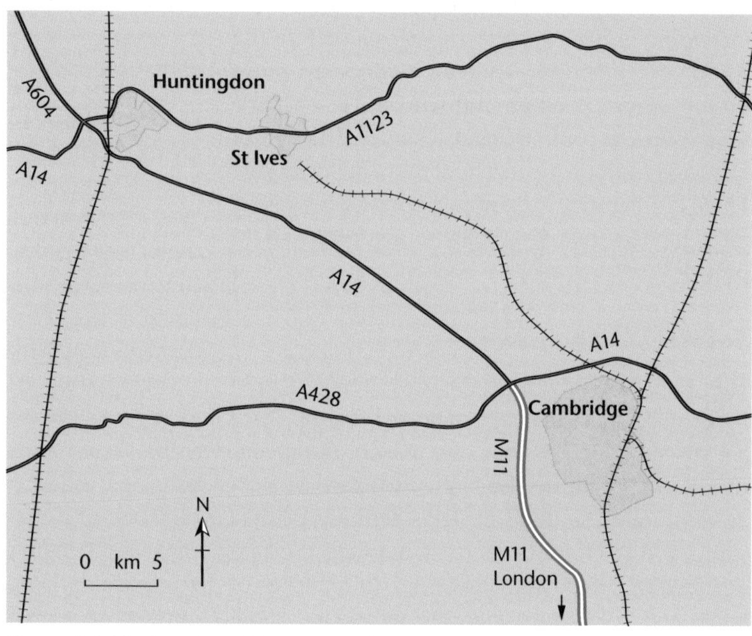

Figure 5.5 The location of St Ives, Cambridgeshire

St Ives is a picturesque riverside town, on the Great Ouse. It has a narrow six-arched bridge with a central chapel that was built in the fifteenth century. The town has connections with Oliver Cromwell and a statue in his memory stands in the market place. There are many fine Georgian and Victorian houses in the Broadway and in Bridge Street. There are also many other splendid buildings, including the Corn Exchange and All Saints Church. The building styles contribute a great deal to the character of the place and add to the attraction of living there.

The surrounding rural area is mainly farmland. However, in recent years there have been many new housing developments on the periphery of the town. A substantial number of new exclusive apartments have also been built within the heart of the town, particularly on the south bank of the Great Ouse.

Changing population and prosperity

The population structure of the town is changing. One section of the community is ageing, but another is becoming more youthful. A large proportion of the working population is now employed outside the town. There has been an influx of people from in and around London, who prefer daily commuting to living in the city. Housing in the area is affordable and a sustained boom in demand for property has been the result. People in St Ives have higher incomes and higher standards of living than those in many other parts of the UK. Recently retired people are also moving into the area. Their impact is noticeable in the increased demand for bungalows and small riverside apartment blocks.

Commuting to London increased during the 1990s. The main line was electrified and journey times were much reduced. The station at Huntingdon is about 50 minutes from Kings Cross in central London. It is estimated that 25% of St Ives' working population now commutes to London each day. These people prefer living in a rural/small town environment and travelling to London each day. An annual standard-class season ticket cost over £3,300 in 2004, but housing in London is significantly more expensive than in St Ives.

Prosperity in the town has been increasing for some elderly people who own their own properties and for families who have moved out of London, but for others there is a different picture. There is an increasing gap between those who can afford the rising cost of housing and commuting and those on low wages, such as farm workers, or on part-time wages or youth training schemes. The cost of housing is beyond the means of those on lower pay. There is a demand for low-cost housing for young local families but few builders are prepared to provide it.

Services in the town

The shops and services in the town have changed as the make-up of the population has altered. There are still supermarkets, butchers, bakers and green-grocers, but there are also high-status services such as restaurants, antique dealers, designer clothes shops and knick-knack shops. A number of estate agents have offices in the town, as do branches of banks and building societies. The secondary school roll is increasing.

As in other rural areas, the bus service to St Ives is infrequent, although it is better than many others because the town lies on a more-or-less direct route between Cambridge and Huntingdon. Bus transport is available during priority times — the start and end of the school day and on market days.

Pressure to increase the housing stock is becoming greater, fuelled by demand from commuters. There is some resistance to building more homes from the local residents, but many of these are relatively new to the area themselves and do not want their newly chosen environment changed. It is likely that additional house construction will take place because demand is so great. However, developers will be encouraged to ensure that new developments blend in as far as possible with the current urban landscape. There will need to be an acceptable density of buildings, use of appropriate construction materials, provision of sufficient open space, preservation of vistas and tasteful provision of street furniture (road signs, seating, lamp posts). Any further development must make a positive contribution to the overall character of the area.

Changes in rural settlements in the UK

Services

The main changes to services in rural settlements in the UK are summarised in Table 5.2.

Population characteristics

Remote rural populations in the UK are declining whereas accessible rural–urban fringe areas are expanding.

The consequences of decline include:

- many of the people left behind are elderly and of limited means
- houses are bought as second homes, creating a ghost-town effect for much of the year
- deprivation sets in — many of the people left cannot move away and so lead restricted lives
- a sense of isolation becomes pervasive
- breaking the spiral of decline and deprivation is the key issue

The consequences of expansion include:

- creation of several small, new housing estates, often with houses that local people cannot afford

Service	Changes for the worse	Changes for the better
Food shops	Many village stores have closed — supermarkets in small rural towns have lower prices, extended hours and some offer free bus services from local villages	The development of new types of village shop, such as farm shops and garage shops
Post offices	Many village post offices have been downgraded to part-time or 'hole-in-the-wall' facilities. Much pension business has been diverted to banks	Cooperation between some rural post offices and banks to offer combined services
Public transport	Bus deregulation led to the closure of uneconomic routes New unitary authorities subsidise their own bus services, but have withdrawn support for cross-council links Passenger numbers are falling as car ownership increases	Grants are available for community buses and taxis, such as the postal bus service that combines transport with letter delivery
Village schools	An ageing population leads to falling school rolls, and the prospect of closure As schools compete for numbers, many wealthy parents opt to educate their children privately	The opening of nurseries increases the total number of children in school Grants exist to support small schools. Shared headships also allow smaller schools to remain open
Libraries	Cuts in local services	Increased numbers of mobile libraries
Primary healthcare	Closure of some GP surgeries A decline in dental facilities	The creation of mini-health centres in larger villages Grants are available for rural GP practices and pharmacies
Village halls	A general decline in village-centred activities A withdrawal of funds for youth clubs and social facilities for the elderly	Grants for the refurbishment of many village halls

Table 5.2 Changes in rural settlements in the UK

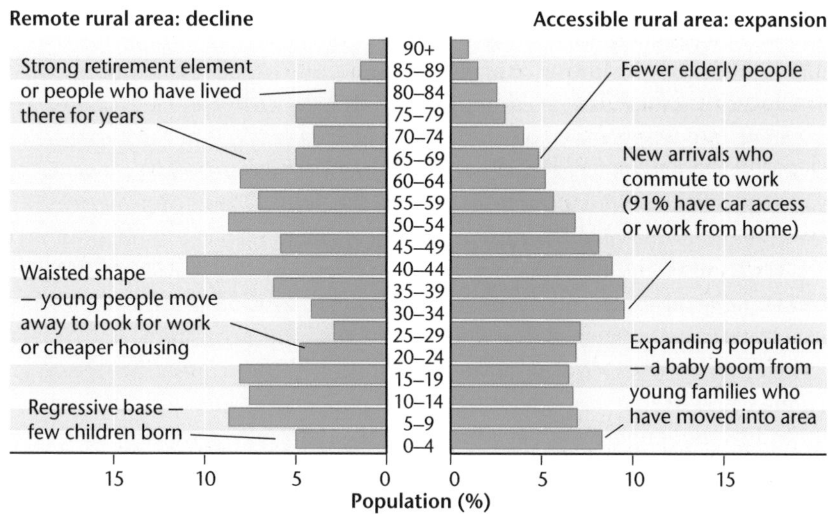

Figure 5.6 Population pyramid for two types of rural areas

- many families have two or more cars, so there is increased traffic congestion, particularly at peak times
- villages are often dormitory villages, with little life during the day
- conflicts can occur between established villagers and newcomers — local people may not feel that their values are respected
- maintaining the rural identity in an increasingly urban environment is a key issue

Reurbanisation

Reurbanisation is the movement of people into the city centre or inner city as part of the process of urban regeneration.

There are three main processes at work here:

- in-movement by individuals or groups of individuals into older housing that was previously in a state of disrepair and the subsequent improvement of that housing — **gentrification**
- in-movement by people as part of large-scale investment programmes aimed at urban regeneration in a wider social, economic and physical sense — **property-led regeneration** (through Urban Development Corporations, see Chapter 12)
- the move towards **sustainable communities** (see Chapter 12), allowing individuals and communities who live in city centres to have access to a home, a job and a reliable income, with a reasonable quality of life and opportunities to maximise personal potential through education and health provision, and through participation in local democracies

Gentrification

Gentrification is a process of housing improvement. It is associated with a change in neighbourhood composition in which low-income groups are displaced by more affluent people, usually in professional or managerial occupations. Regeneration of inner cities can take place by gentrification, but it is different from the schemes described in Chapter 12 in that it is carried out by individuals or groups of individuals, and not by supported bodies. Gentrification involves the rehabilitation of old houses and streets on an individual basis, but is openly encouraged by groups such as estate agents, building societies and local authorities.

One of the clear positive outcomes of gentrification is that the social mix of the area is changed and becomes more affluent. The purchasing power of the residents is greater, which leads to a rise in the general level of prosperity. The area becomes dominated by 'yuppies', and there is an increase in the number of bars, restaurants and other higher-status services. The very nature of the refurbishment that takes place in each house leads to the creation of local employment in areas such as design, building work, furnishings and decoration.

There are, however, clear disadvantages of gentrification. Local people on low incomes find it increasingly difficult to purchase houses, as the price of refurbished property rises markedly. Indeed, the size of the privately rented sector diminishes as more properties are sold off. Friction and conflict arise between the 'newcomers' and the original residents.

Photograph 5.3 A gentrified street in Notting Dale, North Kensington, London. One house is still swathed in scaffolding

Gentrification is taking place in the central parts of many towns and cities in the UK (Photograph 5.3). Well-documented examples include Notting Hill and Islington in London.

The use of greenfield and brownfield sites for new housing

The government's population projections in 1997 suggested that, by 2021, the population of England would rise by 3.4 million to 52.5 million, an increase of 7%. At the same time, the number of households would rise by 3.8 million, an increase of 18%, giving a total of 24 million households. Most new households want their own housing unit, which creates pressure on land.

There are two main reasons why there is likely to be a faster growth in households than in population:

- the increase in the adult population, which accounts for 77% of the growth in demand for households. This is due to the change in the age structure of the population with a fall in the proportion of younger age groups and a rise in the proportion of those in older age groups
- changes in the way in which people choose to live, in particular, more divorces and later marriages. Of the 3.8 million new households 71% will be single-person households

Some people argue that population predictions have been wrong before and that new houses should not be built until it is certain that the demand is there. However, if building is delayed, there is a danger that there will be a shortfall of suitable housing. This could result in more crowded households and inflated house prices — a real problem for young people and those on low incomes who want to buy their own homes.

The following solutions to this issue have been suggested:

- **Increasing the number of people living in homes that already exist** — there are 800,000 empty homes in England, over 80% of which are in the private sector. In the north of England many of these are abandoned houses that the owners cannot sell. Another tactic would be to provide tax incentives to encourage people to take in lodgers or to share their homes. In some areas, empty council housing is being improved. The advantages of these potential solutions are that they are cheap and do not use up new land.
- **Building new houses on brownfield sites (in towns and cities)** — the government is now talking in terms of building houses on 'previously developed land', most of which is in urban areas. Farmland, parks, allotments and playing fields are excluded. The government has set a target that, by 2008, 60% of new houses built each year will be on such land. Some say this is too low. However, there is still a mismatch between where land is available (the industrial areas of northern England) and where the pressure for housing is greatest (southeast England).
- **Building new homes near to work and leisure activities** — within the 'pedshed' — 10 minutes walk from railway stations and bus stops. To achieve this, innovative developments will be required to create high-density housing that is socially and environmentally appealing, and affordable.
- **Allowing building in rural areas and small towns on land that has not been 'previously developed'** — greenfield sites are cheaper to develop than brownfield sites and there is still plenty of rural land available. In 1991, 11% of the land in England was in urban use. It is predicted that by 2016, this will only have risen to 11.9%. Much agricultural land is not being used productively — for example, over half a million hectares were set aside in the 1990s under EU subsidy.

Table 5.3 Brownfield and greenfield sites compared

Brownfield sites	Greenfield sites
Derelict sites in urban areas	New sites, usually on agricultural land in green belts around urban areas
The land is available, but can be costly to reclaim if it has been polluted by industrial use; this information may not be readily available	Land is not available unless planning permission has been obtained; there is usually a public enquiry and a delay of several years, adding to the costs
Housing is likely to be built at a high density to reflect the cost of the land; there is less demand for such housing as it is in less fashionable areas	Housing will be relatively low density; there is great demand for such housing as it is in fashionable areas
Infrastructure is normally present, though existing facilities can become overloaded	Infrastructure costs are high as new sewerage, water, gas and electricity supplies have to be considered; new schools and health facilities may be needed too
Sites tend to be small patches of land	Sites tend to be larger
The environment is generally improved	The environment is changed from rural to urban use

Prescott plans 140,000 homes on south coast

OVER THE NEXT 20 years, the government plans to build about 140,000 homes in the Solent Gateway between Southampton and Portsmouth, with more likely to follow. There is intense opposition from local people and environmental groups.

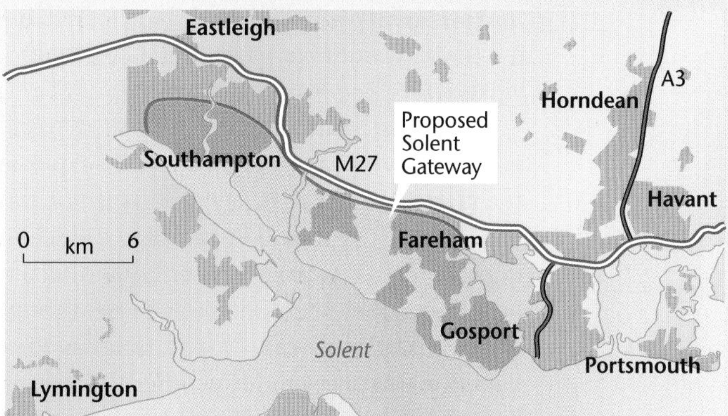

However, talks have begun with local authorities and both Portsmouth and Southampton councils have expressed interest. A spokesperson said: 'We accept the need for new housing in the region. It's just a question of where.'

The head of housing strategy in Southampton confirmed that the council has just completed a joint public consultation with other local authorities on proposals to build 80,000 new homes by 2026. A further 50,000 homes would be built under the Solent Gateway plan, much of the development taking place around the towns of Gosport and Fareham and on the fringes of Southampton and Portsmouth. This plan is driven by the need for economic growth which is below average in this area.

If the plan goes ahead much of the development will be on greenfield sites. Environmentalists are critical of this approach.

Adapted from the *Sunday Times*, May 2005

***Figure 5.7* Proposed new housing in the Solent Gateway**

It is estimated that 3.8 million new households will be required by 2021. Of these, a considerable proportion will be built in rural areas and small towns in the south and southeast of England, where demand is greatest. The main proposed areas of development are the Thames Gateway, Ashford in Kent, Milton Keynes, the Solent Gateway (Figure 5.7) and the Cambridge to Stansted M11 corridor.

The main features of brownfield and greenfield sites are summarised in Table 5.3.

Settlement hierarchy

The concept of settlement hierarchy is related to central place theory. **Central places** are settlements that provide services (or **functions**) for their own population and for people who live in the surrounding area. The area within which a central place has functional ties is known as its **sphere of influence** or **catchment**.

Each function in a central place requires a minimum population to support it — the **threshold**. Some functions, for example a public house or a post office, have low thresholds, say 500–1,000 people. These are **low-order** functions and can be found in small settlements. Larger settlements have many such establishments. **High-order** functions, for example clothes shops, car showrooms and secondary schools, have larger thresholds of several thousand people and are fewer in number. In rural areas, they are confined to market towns or larger villages.

The **range** is the maximum distance people are prepared to travel to obtain a good or service. In general, the more expensive the service or good, the greater is the range. For example, people will not travel long distances for a newspaper (bought daily) but will for an item of furniture (bought infrequently). However, improvements in personal mobility and the development of new retail outlets have meant that people are now more willing to travel further for low-order goods.

The effect of threshold and range is to create a **hierarchy** of central places. Functions with a low threshold and a low range (such as essential food and household items) are available locally in many small centres in villages and within towns. Higher-order functions that have larger thresholds and higher ranges are available only in a few larger centres. Together these create a hierarchy of central places in an area, for example:

- one regional centre (city)
- two or three sub-regional centres (large towns)
- several small towns
- many villages

The identification of a hierarchy of central places can be attempted in any area. This can be done subjectively by simply noting the types and variety of services found in a settlement.

Spheres of influence

The sphere of influence of a settlement is the area served by the functions provided. In simple terms it is a summary of all of the ranges of the goods and services provided by that settlement. The sphere of influence tends to diminish with distance away from the settlement as fewer services are provided. The sphere of influence varies according to:

- the order of the service provided — greater for higher-order services
- the proximity of a competing centre — smaller in the direction of that centre
- the density of the population — greater in areas of low population density
- the physical nature of the terrain — may be curtailed by a physical barrier, such as a river or upland area
- administrative boundaries, particularly political boundaries

Reilly's law of retail gravitation

This model is used to predict the theoretical margin (breakpoint) of the sphere of influence of competing centres. The calculations are performed using the formula:

$$D_{bk} = \frac{D_{ab}}{1 + \sqrt{(P_a/P_b)}}$$

where D_{bk} is the breakpoint distance from the smaller town, B; D_{ab} is the distance between towns A and B; P_a is the population of the larger town; P_b is the population of the smaller town.

In its simplest form, the model assumes that the larger the town, the stronger the attraction. For example:

town A; population, P_a = 625,000
town B; population, P_b = 25,000
distance from A to B, D_{ab} = 60 km
breakpoint from the smaller town is given by:

$$D_{bk} = \frac{D_{ab}}{1 + \sqrt{(P_a/P_b)}}$$

$$= \frac{60}{1 + \sqrt{625{,}000/25{,}000}}$$

$$= \frac{60}{1 + \sqrt{25}} = \frac{60}{1 + 5} = 10 \text{ km}$$

By calculating and plotting the breakpoints for a number of centres of the same order around a settlement, the theoretical sphere of influence can be identified, assuming people travel to the nearest centre. This might not be the case, but the model, like that of central places, does provide a useful vehicle for testing the reality.

Measuring the actual sphere of influence through fieldwork

To discover the sphere of influence of a settlement, you can try the following fieldwork ideas:

- Stand in the main shopping street of a settlement, outside a store in an out-of-town retail park, or outside another major service provider and ask the customers where they live. The data can then be plotted on a map (Figure 5.8).
- In shops that deliver goods, ask where they deliver to. The areas they cover can be plotted on a map.
- For larger towns, map the routes of bus services that start or terminate in the town.
- If a town publishes a local newspaper, plot the sources of the local news and advertisements.
- Ask larger local employers if they will give outline details of the catchment area of their workforce.

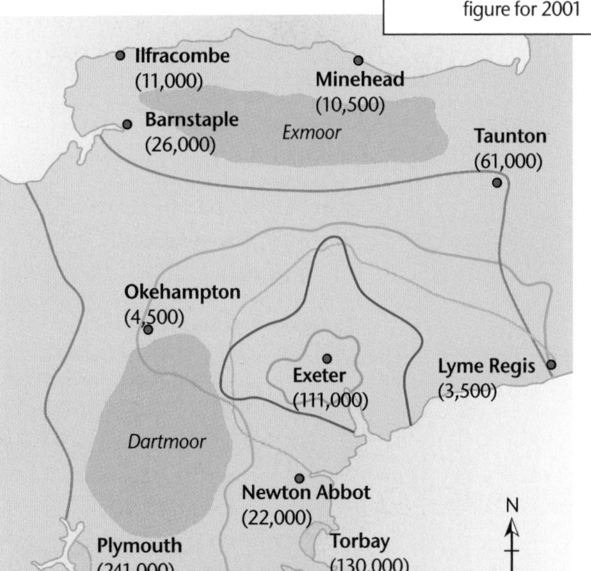

Figure 5.8 Spheres of influence of some services provided by Exeter, 2001

- Visit a large rural area and conduct a survey of which urban settlements people go to in order to obtain a variety of services and commodities (Figure 5.9).

Although some of these methods may give you a clear line, others, for example interviewing customers, will result in dots on a map. You will need to draw a line around the outer limits of these points. The result will be a series of lines around the settlement. High-order services will have wider spheres of influence than low order. The catchment areas of adjacent settlements will often overlap.

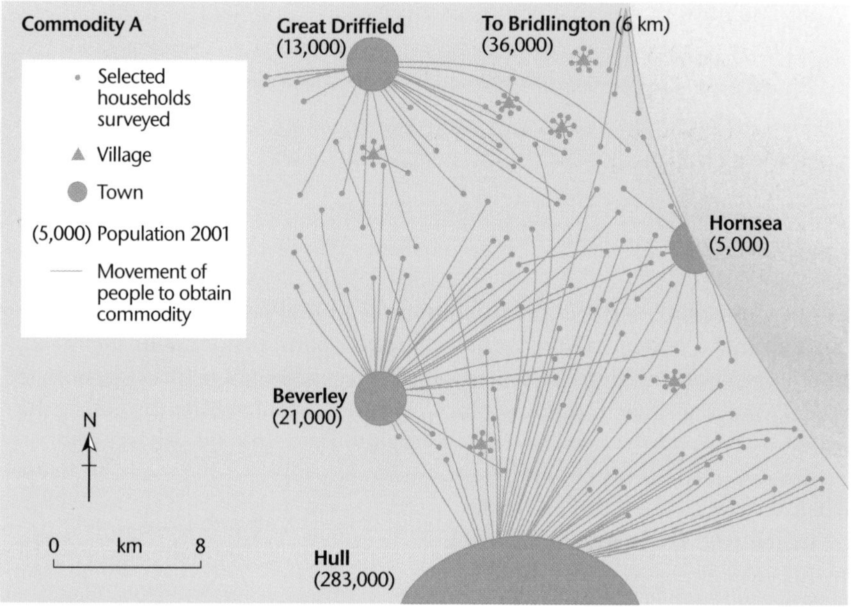

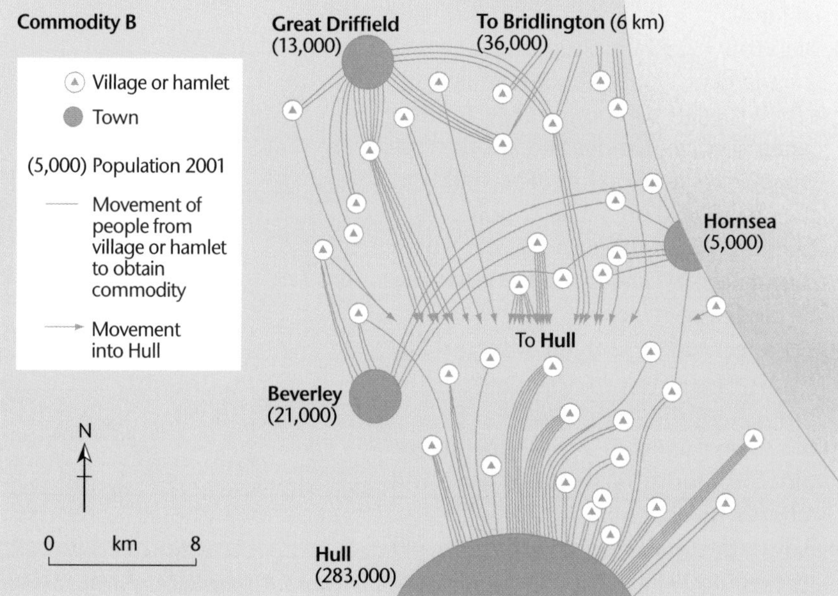

Figure 5.9 Shopping movements in north Humberside

This exercise will also enable you to study changes that are occurring:

- In retailing, the growth of out-of-town superstores and retail parks, often well outside towns, or even near small settlements (at a major road junction perhaps) is destroying the former relationship between settlement size and catchment area.
- In the recent past, local authority schools were obliged to take students from within a set catchment area — a line drawn on a map. In recent years, government policy has been to encourage schools to compete with each other for students. As a result, their catchment areas increasingly overlap.
- In the health service, GPs are encouraged to 'shop around' for hospital services rather than just sending patients to the nearest hospital.

All of this means that the strength of the idea of a sphere of influence of a settlement is beginning to weaken.

Chapter 6

Economic activity

Secondary activities

Industrial change in the UK

Since the mid-1970s the UK, in common with other industrialised countries, has seen massive changes in its manufacturing industry. Some industries have undergone major decline, whereas others have grown markedly. Many of the areas of growth have been stimulated by investment from overseas.

Manufacturing industry has declined in its relative importance both in terms of employment and in its contribution to the national economy. Over 7 million people were employed in manufacturing in the mid-1970s, but by 2002 the number had fallen to less than 4 million. This progressive decline has been called **deindustrialisation**.

The main aspects of manufacturing change can be summarised as follows:

- manufacturing in the UK has declined and this has caused job losses and severe economic problems for communities once based on traditional manufacturing industries
- industrial revival, from both private and public investment, has had an uneven impact, with some areas still suffering the social and economic effects of industrial closures
- massive investment from overseas, and technological developments from research and development institutions, have contributed to industrial revival
- manufacturing industry now employs fewer workers than the growing service-based industries
- areas of the UK not traditionally linked with manufacturing have gained jobs more rapidly than urban areas
- the use of high technology in manufacturing processes has created its own requirements for industrial location, and has had a significant effect on working practices within industry
- sensitivity towards the environment, both locally and nationally, is a major influence on decision making

Key terms

Globalisation The close economic interdependence between the leading nations of the world in trade, investment and cooperative commercial relationships.

Manufacturing industry Companies that convert raw materials into finished goods or which assemble components made by other manufacturing companies.

Multinational corporations (MNCs, transnationals) Capitalist enterprises that organise the production of goods and services in more than one country.

Newly industrialised countries (NICs) Countries that have undergone rapid, generally successful, industrialisation since the 1960s. Many people see the rise of NICs as a key element in the process of globalisation.

Decline in traditional manufacturing

The main manufacturing industries that have declined in the last 30 years are those which were established in the nineteenth century. Their growth was based on the use of coal and imported raw materials, such as iron ore and cotton. A key aspect of their development was the ability to export the finished products to other countries, particularly Britain's former colonies. For these reasons the main industrial areas were either on the major British coalfields or at coastal ports on deep-water estuaries (Figure 6.1). These industries have been given a variety of collective names, including 'smokestack' because of their link to coal, and 'sunset' because of their decline in importance.

Examples of such industries include:

- textiles — woollen cloth in West Yorkshire (Leeds, Bradford, Huddersfield) and cotton cloth in Lancashire (Bolton, Bury, Burnley)
- steel in Sheffield, Middlesbrough and south Wales
- shipbuilding in Newcastle, Sunderland, Belfast and Glasgow
- chemicals in the northeast (Middlesbrough) and the northwest (Widnes and Runcorn)

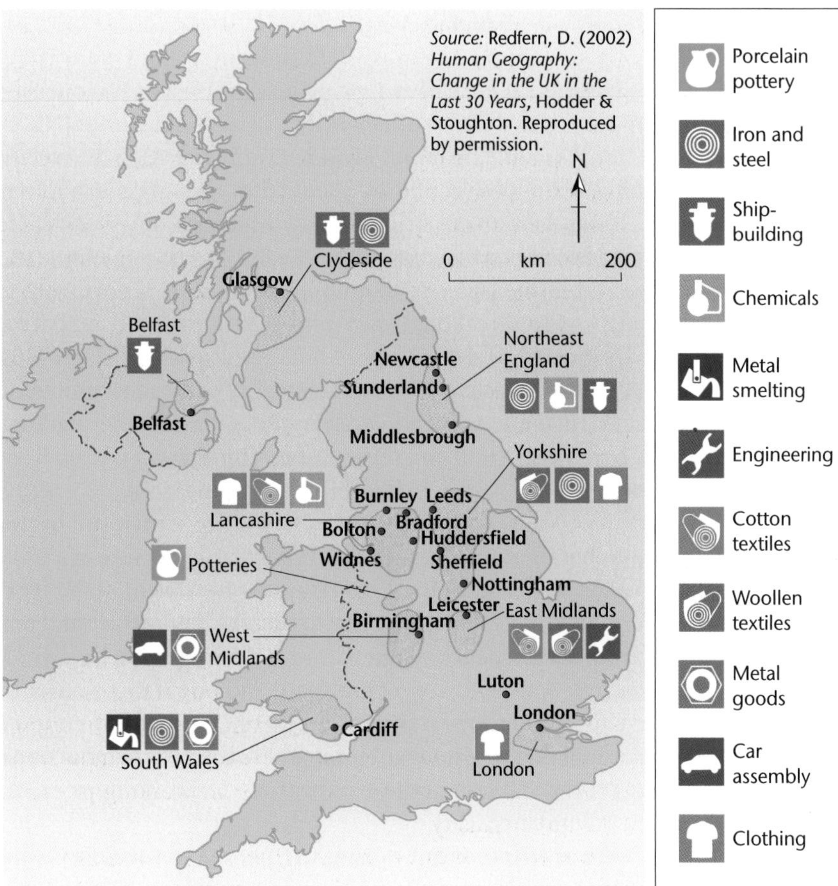

Figure 6.1 Traditional industrial areas in the UK

Getty Images

Photograph 6.1 A Cunard liner, the Queen Mary, *under construction in Glasgow, 1934*

- the car industry and component suppliers in older locations, for example Birmingham and other parts of the West Midlands, and Luton
- clothing, food processing, and other port industries in the East End of London
- pottery and other household goods in the area around Stoke

Reasons for the decline

There are many reasons for the decline in manufacturing. Some relate to changes within the UK, some to factors elsewhere in the world.

An increased use of **mechanisation**, such as automation, robotics and computerised production lines, has reduced the number of workers needed for the manufacturing process. In particular the tasks undertaken by unskilled and semi-skilled workers have been mechanised, reducing the number of people employed in manufacturing.

An inability to compete on price has caused UK industry to lose many of its overseas markets, as well as its home market. Competition from overseas countries producing similar products, particularly the newly industrialised countries (NICs) of the Pacific Rim (Hong Kong, Singapore, Taiwan, South Korea), has severely disadvantaged UK industry. In these countries, production costs are much lower, mainly because of lower labour costs. Outdated buildings and inefficient equipment have also added to production costs in the UK.

Working practices within the UK were traditional, or 'Fordist'. They involved the division of labour — the breaking down of a task into small repetitive fragments, each of which could be done at speed by workers with little specialist training. Such practices were characteristic of mass assembly lines which produced standardised products. In the newer industrial areas more flexible working practices, in terms of both production and the use of machinery and labour, have resulted in multi-tasking — one worker being able to do several jobs.

A world economic **recession** in the early 1980s combined with a rise in the value of sterling meant that the cost of British manufactured goods rose at a time when worldwide demand was falling. The Conservative government at the time believed that manufacturing industry should strive to become competitive and not be protected by government assistance. A number of industries formerly owned by the government, such as British Steel, were privatised and forced to 'go it alone'. Subsidies and other support mechanisms were dropped. Rationalisation took place, concentrating production in a smaller number of highly-mechanised units so as to remain competitive. Uncompetitive industries closed. In most cases, rationalisation meant redundancy.

Political factors were also important during the period of manufacturing decline under the Conservative government which was in power from 1979 to 1997.

This government wanted a less unionised labour force, particularly in the mining and manufacturing industries, and set out to 'defeat' many of the trade unions, and reduce their power. A previous Conservative government had suffered at the hands of trade unions in the coal mining and motor vehicle industries, and this one came to power soon after the 'winter of discontent' in 1979 during which the unions were thought by many to have overstepped their powers.

During the late 1990s and the early 2000s, the problems of **global overcapacity** previously suffered by the iron and steel and shipbuilding industries began to appear in the motor vehicle industry. The two 'giants' of the industry, Ford and General Motors, decided to cease car assembly at Dagenham and Luton respectively due to the falling demand for cars in Europe. The global strategies of these two firms do not allow for spare capacity, and there are worries that this will affect other manufacturers in the years to come, particularly as the major players in the industry continue to merge to share design and production costs.

Finally, although traditional manufacturing in the UK has declined (Figure 6.2 and Table 6.1), the overall output of manufacturing industry in the country has increased. This has been due to the expansion of new factories making motor vehicles, computers and related equipment, and other electrical goods. Clearly, de-industrialisation has been selective in both the industries and the areas it has affected.

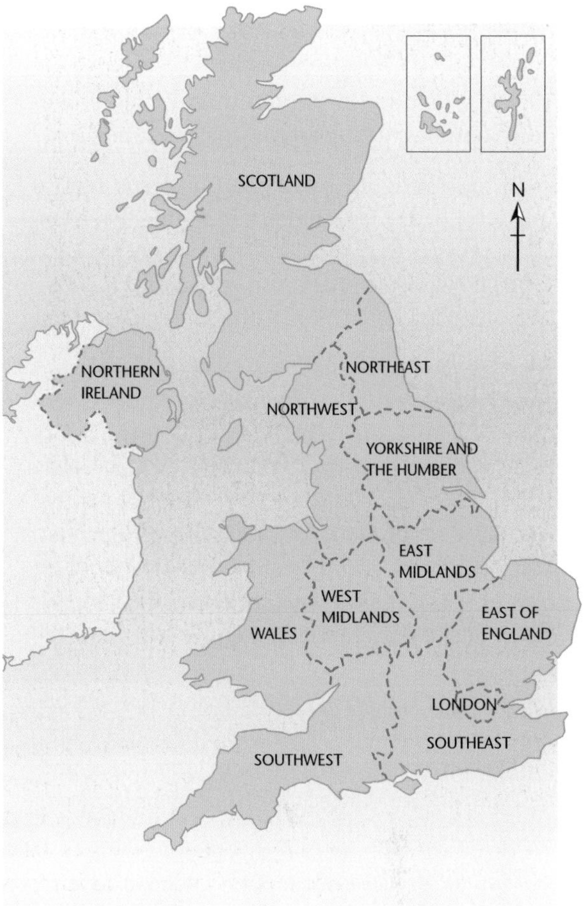

Figure 6.2 Standard regions in the UK

Table 6.1 Changes in manufacturing employment by standard region in Great Britain, 1981–2003

Standard region	1981 (thousands)	1995 (thousands)	2003 (thousands)	Percentage change 1981–2003 (%)
London and southeast	1,683	883	825	–51.0
East of England	186	139	130	–30.0
Southwest	396	281	259	–34.6
West Midlands	801	511	481	–40.0
East Midlands	533	398	380	–29.3
Yorkshire and the Humber	579	398	350	–39.6
Northwest	800	469	430	–46.2
North	339	222	205	–39.5
Wales	238	227	215	–9.7
Scotland	502	319	291	–42.1
Great Britain	6,057	3,847	3,566	–41.1

Case study The steel industry in Consett, County Durham

The steel industry in Consett is an example of a declining industry in a declining manufacturing area.

In the mid-1960s the British Steel Corporation had a workforce of 250,000, producing nearly 25 million tonnes of steel at 23 locations in Britain. By the mid-1990s its workforce had been reduced to 55,000, with a production of 14 million tonnes at just four locations.

This reduction was a consequence of huge over-capacity around the world, with new steel-making facilities being developed in places such as India, South Korea and Taiwan. The response of the European nations was to rationalise production. Many high-cost inland locations such as those at Consett in northeast England (Figure 6.3) and at Bilston in the West Midlands were closed. Only the biggest and most efficient integrated works (Redcar-Lackenby, Scunthorpe, Llanwern and Port Talbot) survived in Britain. In 1999 British Steel merged with the Dutch company Hoogovens to form Corus, and this company announced the closure of the Llanwern steel-making plant in February 2001.

Steelworks are very much dependent on ease of transport of raw materials. They need access to wide, deep, sheltered estuaries through which coal and iron ore are imported from countries such as Australia, Brazil and Liberia. These same ports can be used for exporting the finished steel, and railway transport can be used for home markets.

Consett

Steel-making in Consett began in 1840, based around local deposits of coking coal and blackband iron ore. By the late 1880s the furnaces at Consett were producing 10% of the nation's steel. A company town grew up around the steelworks, which meant that most of the houses and shops were owned by the steel company.

The closure of Consett steelworks was announced in 1980, on economic grounds. Production was to be transferred to the more cost-efficient works on the coast at Redcar-Lackenby. The local raw materials had long since been exhausted, and losses were high due to the small capacity of the works. The main market for the Consett plant, ship-building on the Rivers Tyne and Wear and at Barrow-in-Furness, had also largely closed down.

Closure of the works resulted in the immediate loss of 4,000 jobs, and the town faced economic disaster. Male unemployment in the town was set to rise to 30%, adding to the unemployment caused by the decline of the surrounding coal industry. This was exacerbated by the subsequent closure of another large industry — a ball-bearing manufacturer.

Regeneration

Shortly after the closure of the steelworks a number of organisations (private businesses, local government agencies and the local authority) set up the Derwentside Industrial Development Agency. This encouraged various companies to move into the area, the most famous of which were Derwent Valley Foods (makers of Phileas Fogg snacks), which employs 80 people, and Blue Ridge Care, a manufacturer of disposable nappies. Over 200 companies,

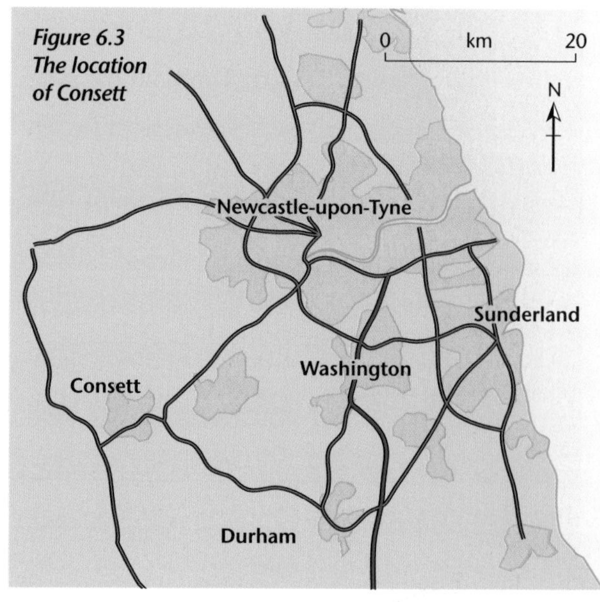

Figure 6.3 The location of Consett

some computer-based, have been established in new purpose-built units, creating over 3,500 jobs in total. These companies were encouraged by grants and loans, but also by the substantial improvements made to the local environment, such as the greening over and landscaping of the spoil tips.

The area's economy changed considerably over the 20 years from 1980 to 2000. The early 1980s saw the area in a position of economic weakness. Between 1980 and 2000 Derwentside lost over 16,000 coal-mining jobs, 6,000 steel-related jobs and over 4,000 other jobs. Between 1977 and 1981 manufacturing employment declined by 66%, and in 1982 unemployment approached 30%, with a total of 8,900 people registered as unemployed.

During the same 20-year period (from 1980 to 2000), the industrial development programme successfully assisted 180 businesses to start up or grow in the Derwentside area, creating over 6,000 new jobs. Over 90% of these jobs were in manufacturing. The area's economy diversified and strengthened, but it still remains weak in comparison to that of the UK generally.

One of the main remaining problems is educational attainment. This is below both regional and national levels, with 18% and 40% of adults having low levels of literacy and numeracy respectively. Similarly, there are low attainment levels in both GCSE and A-level qualifications, at 25% and 31% below national levels respectively.

Areas of new and expanding manufacturing industry

The majority of new manufacturing industries in the last 10–20 years in the UK have been high-technology industries, such as computers and computer-related equipment, telecommunications and microelectronics. In addition, many traditional industries, for example the car assembly industry, have advanced by adopting new technologies and working practices. A key feature of this type of industry is research and development (R&D). This is needed to develop new products and update existing lines, as well as keeping 'ahead of the game' in product design.

For these 'new' industries, a highly skilled and qualified workforce is essential, while access to raw materials is less important. They have therefore become concentrated in areas where the workforce can be attracted or is available, or in places where the government encourages them to locate. They are often described as 'footloose' because they are not tied to certain locations, like traditional manufacturing, and as 'sunrise' because of their growth. At a local scale they tend to be located on new industrial estates on the edges of towns, or alongside motorways for efficient transport (Figure 6.4).

The following are the main areas of new industrial growth:

- 'silicon glen' in central Scotland
- the Cambridge area and along the M11
- the 'sunrise strip' of the M4 corridor
- the 'Honda valley' in south Wales, and the Honda assembly plant at Swindon
- the new car assembly plants in the northeast (Washington) and East Midlands (Burnaston)
- many small light industrial estates in 'rural' areas, e.g. East Anglia and Sussex

Reasons for growth and location of new industry

The reasons for these changes in industrial growth and location reflect changes within the UK, and global economic factors.

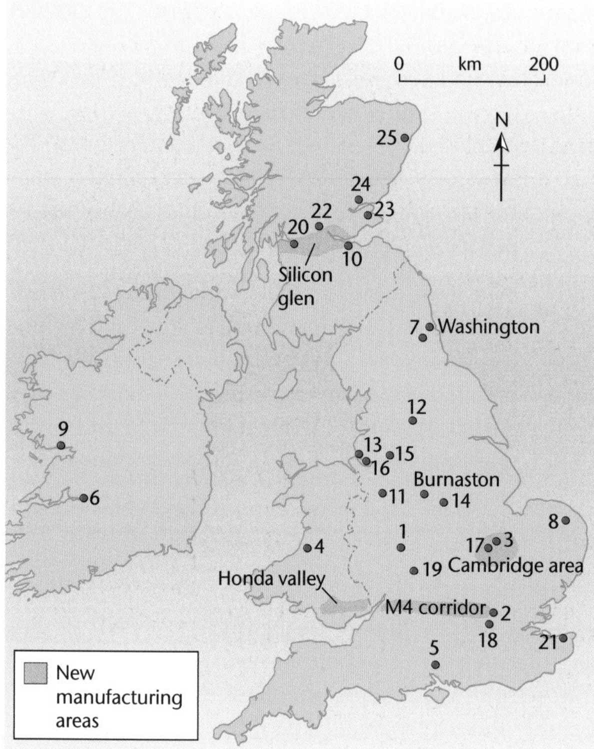

Science/research parks

1 Aston Science Park
2 Brunel Science Park
3 Cambridge Science Park
4 Cefn Llan Science and Technology Park
5 Chilworth Research Centre
6 Cooperative Education Centre
7 University of Durham Industrial Research Laboratories
8 University of East Anglia Industrial Liaison Unit
9 University College Galway Industrial Liaison Office
10 Heriot Watt Research Park, Edinburgh
11 Keele University Science Park
12 Listerhills High Technology Development
13 Liverpool University R&D Advisory Unit
14 Loughborough Technology Centre
15 Manchester University/Manchester Science Park
16 Merseyside Innovation Centre
17 St Johns Innovation Park, Cambridge
18 Surrey University/Surrey Research Park
19 University of Warwick Science Park
20 Scottish Development Agency and Universities of Glasgow, Strathclyde, and West of Scotland Science Park
21 Applied Statistics Research Unit, University of Kent, Canterbury
22 Stirling University Innovation Park
23 St Andrews Technology Centre
24 Dundee Technology Park
25 Aberdeen Science and Research Park

***Figure 6.4* New manufacturing areas and science/research parks in the UK**

Growth

There has been massive **inward investment by overseas transnational companies**, for example by Japanese, South Korean and German firms (Figures 6.5 and 6.6). In the case of the motor vehicle industry a number of Japanese car manufacturers have come to Britain and built huge new plants, the three largest being Nissan, Toyota and Honda. Nissan was the first. It began production in 1986 with an initial output of 100,000 cars per year, rising to over 270,000 in 1993. Its factory at Washington in the northeast of England was the largest single investment by a

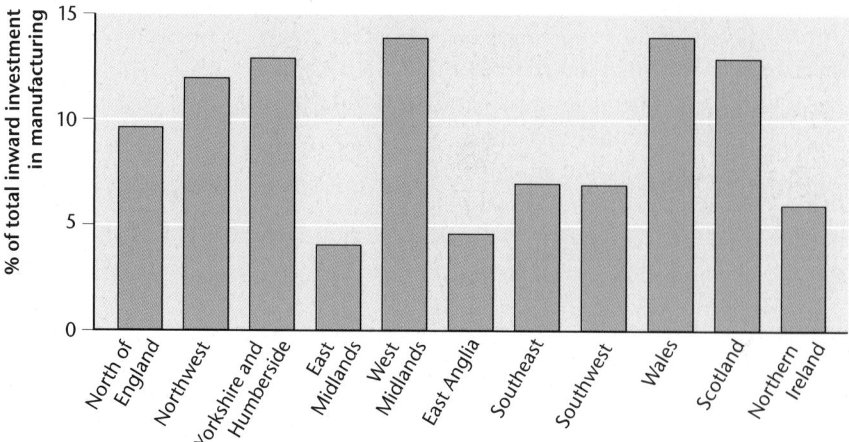

***Figure 6.5* Location of inward investment in manufacturing in the UK by standard region, 1999**

Japanese company in Europe. Other similar investments followed. A large Toyota plant was built next to the A38 trunk road at Burnaston in north Derbyshire, and a Honda assembly plant at Swindon on the M4. Inward investment in other parts of Britain has not always been as successful — examples are the Fujitsu (Japan) and Siemens (Germany) factories in the northeast of England which were both subsequently closed down.

Aid packages from various levels of government (local and national), or from government-sponsored bodies, have encouraged overseas and home investment in certain areas of the UK. It is clear that the major investments by Nissan and Toyota described above were partly attracted by the financial packages they were offered.

Others
Taiwan
Australia
Other European
France
Germany
Japan
North America
Source: AQA
Total number of jobs: 118,753

***Figure 6.6* Origin of jobs created in manufacturing in the UK by inward investment, 1998–2000**

The revival of old industrial areas and the reindustrialisation of new areas has been a policy of most governments over the last 30 years, with varying degrees of commitment. A wide variety of regional policies has been set up to try to redress imbalances of economic and social development. These have included:

- Assisted Areas — carefully defined parts of the UK in which government grants may be given to persuade firms to locate. At various times in the last 30 years these have been called Special Development Areas, Development Areas and Intermediate Areas, and varying levels of incentives have been offered.
- Enterprise Zones — areas at a more local scale to which industry was attracted by the removal of certain taxes (local and national) and local authority planning controls. Typical Enterprise Zones were small, 100–200 hectares in size, sometimes

Nissan

***Photograph 6.2* Robot assembly in the body shop at Nissan's Washington factory**

built on greenfield sites and sometimes on areas within inner cities with 'development potential' (often a euphemism for empty and derelict).
- Urban Development Corporations and other urban regeneration schemes (for more details see pages 395–396).

The growth of new industries has allowed the **transfer of technology** to the UK. This is the movement of new working practices and other innovations into the country, including:
- The just-in-time (JIT) system of production. This is designed to minimise the costs of holding stocks of raw materials and components by carefully planned scheduling and flow of resources. It requires a very efficient ordering system and reliability of delivery. JIT was introduced to Britain by car manufacturers such as Nissan. In car plants there is hourly delivery of some parts, and many component manufacturers have been forced to relocate close to the assembly plants. Another requirement of JIT is zero defects and total quality control. Car manufacturers have close and strong links with their suppliers, which are monitored rigorously.
- The concept of teams of flexible multi-tasking workers who rotate jobs between them. This helps to increase skill levels. In car assembly, it means that production can be designed to fulfil the needs of the individual customer. Standardised products are fewer, and a greater range of specialised products is made. It also allows more flexible production which can meet even the smallest alteration in market demand at short notice. This links into the following two points.
- The use of 'envoys' — representatives from a 'buying' industry who are permanently based in the factories of component suppliers. They can pass on directly any required changes to design and specification at short notice.
- The use of 'milkmen' — representatives from a 'buying' industry who regularly visit the factories of component suppliers to inform them of required changes to design and specification.

Location

The development of numerous motorways, airports and high-speed rail links for ease of **communication** has been a major factor in the location of new manufacturing. For industries such as these, speed of access is important both for people and for raw materials and products.

Some industries have located close to universities which provide both **research expertise** and a pool of highly skilled/intelligent labour. An example of this is the Cambridge Science Park (see case study).

An **attractive environment**, such as a rural or landscaped out-of-town location, may also be an important locational factor. Many business and science parks have been built on greenfield sites where the relatively low cost of land has been an advantage. The high quality of the environment is thought to assist in the creative development required by such industries.

Such developments are also favoured by many local authorities because there is little direct environmental impact on the surrounding area, other than the use of greenfield sites. However, it is increasingly difficult to gain permission for development on such areas (for more details see 'Planning issues' on page 179).

Case study The Cambridge Science Park

The first and biggest science park in the UK was the Cambridge Science Park (Table 6.2), on the northern edge of this famous university city (Figure 6.7). There are well over 700 hi-tech companies within the Cambridge region (known as 'silicon fen') which employ over 20,000 people. The growth of the science park is clearly linked to the nearby university and its pool of highly educated and technologically qualified workers and scientists. These individuals have generated high personal incomes which have enabled entrepreneurship to develop even further. Research and development are encouraged by the university, which provides some of the facilities.

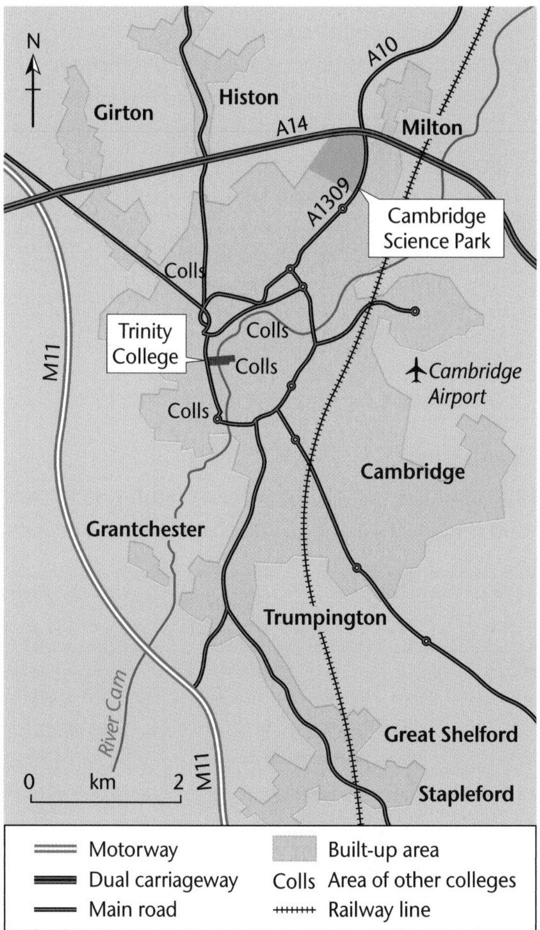

Figure 6.7 The location of the Cambridge Science Park

Economic activity	Number of companies
Computer systems and software	17
Research and development	10
Biotechnology	10
Pharmaceutical	6
Medical equipment	4
Associated services (e.g. licensing, patenting, travel)	4
Communications	3
Animal medicine	2
Health preparations	2
Investment/venture capital	2
Management/scientific consultancy	2
Others (e.g. lasers, structural engineers)	9

Years in science park	Number of companies
0–5	20
6–10	25
11–15	12
16–20	10
21–25	3
26+	1

Size of unit (square feet)	Number of companies
0–1,999	15
2,000–9,999	25
10,000–19,999	16
20,000–29,999	5
30,000–39,999	4
50,000–59,999	2
60,000–69,999	1
90,000–99,999	1
220,000–229,999	1

Number of employees	Number of companies
0–10	15
11–30	20
31–50	11
51–75	9
76–100	3
101–125	3
126–150	2
151–175	1
201–250	3
350	2
450	1
560	1

Table 6.2 The Cambridge Science Park — summary data, 2005

The building of the M11 and electrification of the railway have improved access to Cambridge and acted as growth factors. Since 2002 the creation of new clusters has occurred in the park, specifically in the areas of photonics and nanotechnology. A new Centre of Molecular Materials for Photonics and Electronics (CMMPE) has been opened. This is bound to encourage more companies to move into the area, keen to take advantage of the **synergy** that will develop. Synergy is the intense localised interaction between different companies (research organisations, banks, entrepreneurs, service organisations) on the same site which creates benefits for all participants. It is sometimes summarised as '2 + 2 = 5'.

Case study The M4 corridor

The M4 corridor to the west of London follows the route of the M4 motorway through Reading, Newbury, Swindon and Bristol and into south Wales (Figure 6.8).

Many high-technology industries have located here, including information technology industries, computer-based industries, telecommunications and microelectronics. Research and development sites are also widespread, some connected to private industries and others to government institutions.

Advantages of the area

The location has a number of advantages:

- both the M4 (running west to east) and the A34 (running north to south) provide good road communication
- the electrified railway line west from Paddington provides a quick route into central London for business meetings
- Heathrow airport on the M4 provides easy overseas access
- the government research centres (Aldermaston and Harwell) already in the area have encouraged related industries to locate here
- inward migration of people from elsewhere in the UK seeking highly paid employment has created a skilled and motivated workforce
- nearby universities, such as Oxford, Brunel and Reading, have stimulated research projects and encouraged further development of expertise. Business parks and science parks similar to the one at Cambridge have become established across the area, encouraging the exchange of ideas and information
- the attractive environment of the Thames Valley and other nearby areas such as the Cotswolds, Mendips, Chilterns and Marlborough Downs provide homes for the highly paid workers

Swindon

Swindon lies halfway between London and Bristol, and owes its origin to the railway line between

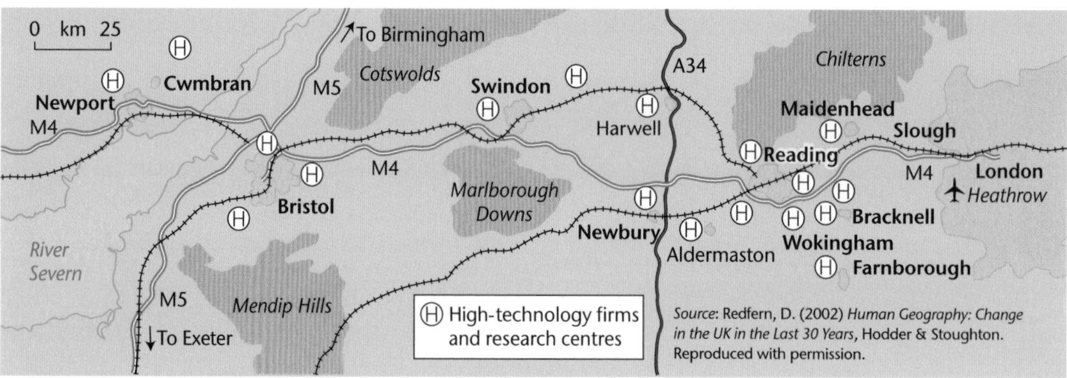

Figure 6.8 The M4 corridor

London and south Wales. It was the engineering centre of the Great Western Railway. Today it has attracted, like the rest of the corridor, a wide range of high-technology industries such as Intel, a leading microprocessing company. The percentage of people employed in manufacturing has gone down in Swindon (as it has in every other UK town), but the nature of that manufacturing industry has significantly changed.

An indication of the increasing wealth of Swindon is the fact that major service industries — the insurers Allied Dunbar and Commercial Union, and the Nationwide Building Society — have moved their administrative headquarters to the town.

Industrial growth in newly industrialised countries

Newly industrialised countries (NICs) are those that have undergone rapid, generally successful, industrialisation since the 1960s — the manufacturing sectors of their economies have expanded rapidly. The rise of NICs can be seen as a key element in the process of globalisation.

The first wave of NICs was in Asia: Taiwan, South Korea, Hong Kong and Singapore. These became known as the Asian Tigers. Economic growth in such countries was the result of:

- import substitution — industries were increasingly geared to replacing imports in the home market
- the creation of free-trade zones and export-processing areas
- the active support of national governments, particularly in encouraging export industries, state planning and setting up free trade and economic priority zones

Japanese companies stimulated growth in the Asian Tigers. When they first decided to locate abroad, they looked to the most developed of their neighbours. Further investment came from multinational corporations (MNCs) in the West, particularly the USA.

The favourable factors that encouraged MNCs to locate in the Asian Tigers included:

- a reasonably well-developed infrastructure
- good skill levels — people in such NICs were regarded as their greatest resource because they were relatively well educated
- low wage levels compared with the home countries of the MNCs
- financial incentives from host governments encouraging MNC investment
- general political stability
- labour and other laws favouring overseas investors
- good geographical location — for example, the situation of Singapore allows it to funnel the flow of trade between the Indian and Pacific Oceans

As the economies of the first wave of NICs developed, wage levels began to rise, which resulted in MNCs looking elsewhere to set up operations. This led to the growth of a second wave of NICs that included such countries as Malaysia and Thailand. In recent years, a third wave of NICs has grown up that includes China and India.

Case study South Korea: a first-wave NIC

The Korean War (1950–53) devastated the country and led to it being split into North and South Korea.

South Korea was a poor country with a low GDP and seemingly no prospects. However, in the early 1960s the economy took off and substantial rates of growth were achieved over the following 30 years. By 1996, it was able to join the Organization for Economic Cooperation and Development (OECD) — the grouping of the world's richest nations.

Throughout this period the economy prospered, wage levels increased, the quality of life for South Korea's population improved and life expectancy rose from 47 (1955) to 75 (2002). In 1988, South Korea was able to afford to stage the Olympic Games in Seoul.

Reasons for growth in South Korea include:

- the state was involved in many companies and owned some of them
- the prime objective for the country was to be keenly competitive in global markets and to achieve and sustain high volumes of exports
- state-directed bank loans, at very low or negative real rates of interest, allowed some industries to invest and expand at a fast rate
- large business conglomerates, known as *chaebol*, came to dominate the economy. The largest four, Daewoo, Samsung, Hyundai and Lucky Goldstar (LG), accounted for over half of South Korea's exports
- export success encouraged the largest *chaebol* to diversify, which was seen as a sign of strength when growth rates were high
- the military-run governments of the 1960s and 1970s held wages below productivity levels
- the government controlled trade union activity, banning much of it

The economic crises of the late 1990s affected all the NICs of the Pacific Rim. South Korea was hit badly because of a downturn in many industries in which the country specialised. Other factors included increased wages (which by that time were higher than those in many European countries) and the emergence of lower-cost competitors, such as China. The *chaebols* also had massive debts that they found difficult to service at a time of falling revenues.

Under pressure, the country increasingly opened its economy to foreign competition, which further eroded profits. Daewoo was in such a poor economic state that it was taken over by the US company, General Motors.

Case study China: a third-wave NIC

Since 1995, economic expansion has been so great that China has been referred to as 'the new workshop of the world'. A number of economic reforms have been put in place that have stimulated massive foreign direct investment (FDI).

In 2002, China:

- overtook the USA to become the world's largest recipient of FDI — over $52 billion
- became the fifth largest global trader. China now exports more to the USA than Japan does, and has taken over from the USA as the largest exporter to Japan
- manufactured approximately 50% of the world's computers, 60% of its bicycles, and over half of its shoes
- became the world's second largest importer of oil after the USA
- consumed 55% of the world's cement
- became a member of the World Trade Organization

The huge concentration of investment in China has pulled finance away from industrial centres in the rest of Asia. Over 23,000 Japanese companies operate in the country. A number of important high-technology nuclei have been developed to concentrate the investment of foreign and indigenous companies in this important and expanding business sector.

One example is Zhongguancun, close to the capital Beijing. This high-tech nucleus based near China's most prestigious universities has over 4,000 companies, including the multinational giants Motorola, Nokia, IBM and Founder. New firms are constantly arriving to take advantage of the low-cost but well-educated workforce. The area is a Special Economic Zone, attracting companies with tax incentives, reduced rents and rapid processing of operating permits. Infrastructure has been considerably upgraded and entire neighbourhoods of housing have been cleared to make way for new buildings.

Some Chinese companies are now buying up distressed businesses in Japan, where the long economic slump has caused major problems. In many cases, the Chinese company has relocated manufacturing to China where wages are as little as one-tenth of their Japanese equivalents.

Motor-vehicle production is a key industry in China's economic development. The country is now the fastest growing vehicle market in the world and has attracted investment from the major global manufacturers — Ford, General Motors, Volkswagen, Honda, Toyota and Nissan. The largest indigenous company, SAIC, has also considered joint ventures with European manufacturers.

Multinational corporations

Multinational corporations (MNCs) are capitalist enterprises that organise the production of goods and services in more than one country. Another definition of an MNC is a firm that has the power to coordinate and control operations in more than one country, even if it does not own them. For example, Nike is an MNC but does not make any clothes or shoes itself. It contracts out production to companies in South Korea and Taiwan. These companies themselves also operate factories in lower-wage countries such as the Philippines and Vietnam.

Multinational corporations are the driving force behind **economic globalisation**. As the rules regulating the movement of goods and investment have been relaxed and the sources and destinations of investment have become more diverse, such companies have extended their reach. There are now few parts of the world where the influence of MNCs is not felt and in some areas they are a powerful influence on the local economy. Many MNCs are also involved in a web of collaborative relationships with other companies across the globe.

According to the United Nations Conference on Trade and Development (UNCTAD), there are now over 40,000 companies in the world that have activities in more than one country. The USA still dominates — nearly half of the world's top 500 companies have their headquarters there.

Many MNCs are involved in intense global competition, which has led to several sectors being dominated by only a few companies. In the following sectors, the ten largest corporations in the world control the following market percentages:

- 35% of the pharmaceuticals industry
- 70% of the computer industry
- 85% of the pesticides industry
- 86% of telecommunications

Many MNCs are organised in a **hierarchical** manner, with the headquarters and research and development departments in the home country (country of origin) and branch manufacturing plants overseas. As an organisation becomes more global, regional headquarters and, in some cases, regional research and development departments, are introduced in the manufacturing areas.

Case study Toyota: an MNC

Toyota was founded in 1930 in Japan and remained a Japanese-based company until the late 1950s. After 1945, it grew as an export-based company, producing vehicles from eight plants and developing a 'just-in-time' system in 1959.

In 1959, Toyota began the move to manufacturing overseas, at first using Japanese-manufactured parts but later looking for local suppliers. The first overseas plant was set up in Brazil.

In the late 1980s, Toyota began to manufacture in the USA, first in California and then in Kentucky and Indiana. The company also began to make moves into the European market, with a technical centre in Belgium (1987), a link with Volkswagen in Hannover, Germany (1987) and a large plant at Burnaston (Derby, UK, 1992) in order to gain a foothold in the EU (80% of Burnaston's production is destined for Europe).

This early development was followed by a second European plant at Valenciennes (France), and a link with Peugeot Citroen for production of small cars. With Citroen, Toyota is also considering moving eastwards into countries that have just joined the EU (e.g. Poland). In 2002, Toyota established a German-based Formula I racing team to put itself on a par with other manufacturers.

Toyota's present headquarters are in Tokyo. The company employs over 200,000 people in 24 countries. Once entirely Japanese owned, it now has foreign shareholders (over 10%). It has a 24% share in its component manufacturers, including Denso (Japan), which is the fourth largest parts maker in the world, employing 85,000 people.

Explaining Toyota's success

Toyota has become a successful global automobile manufacturer because:

- **research** and **development** was carefully targeted to market needs
- the business ties its suppliers closely to the company through a **vertical integration** system
- **'just-in-time'** production systems were adopted early
- the company operates large and fully **automated** assembly plants
- it has a number of **joint ventures** in technology, particularly with Japanese computer companies
- it applies **labour management** policies
- it has sought **alliances** with other manufacturers with regard to specific targets, such as small cars in eastern Europe
- it has been given Japanese **government support** and host government support (both direct and indirect) when establishing plants overseas

The impact of MNCs on developing countries

When MNCs open operations in developing countries they have a great impact on the economic, social, cultural and political life of that country. They may also impact on the environment.

Positive impacts include:

- an inflow of capital to help stimulate economic development
- creation of employment opportunities
- transfer of technological and entrepreneurial skills to the host country's population

- an increase (through taxes) in government income to be spent on infrastructure, health and education
- a growth in local companies supplying raw materials and components to MNC factories and undertaking construction work
- a stimulus for further economic development (the multiplier effect causes increased spending power in the host nation's population)
- development of trade links and a source of foreign revenue

Negative impacts include:

- the country becomes economically dependent upon MNCs
- MNCs are run from overseas and the parent company may take the decision to move to another, cheaper location
- incentives to attract an MNC may divert funds from other sectors of the economy
- MNCs often exploit the local labour force and do not always transfer all skills — for example managers may be brought in from the parent country
- the arrival of MNCs can have a disastrous effect on local industry
- the political influence of MNCs can affect the political sovereignty and the policies of the country
- MNCs can encourage increased rural–urban migration as they often locate in the capital (core) region
- environmental laws less rigorous than those in the parent country may be exploited (see Bhopal case study below)
- the national culture may be undermined with a Westernisation of attitudes and consumption patterns
- capital in the form of profits often goes to the parent country

Case study The impact of an MNC: Bhopal

On 3 December 1984, toxic gas leaked from a Union Carbide factory in Bhopal, Madya Pradesh, India, killing thousands of people. Union Carbide estimates that 3,800 were killed. Municipal workers, who loaded bodies onto trucks for burial in mass graves or incineration on mass pyres, believe they shifted at least 15,000 bodies. People are still dying from the after-effects.

How the disaster happened

The Bhopal factory was built in the 1970s. Union Carbide believed that India represented a huge untapped market for its pest control products. However, sales never met the company's expectations. Indian farmers, struggling to cope with droughts and floods, could not afford Union Carbide's pesticides. The plant, which never reached its full capacity, proved to be a loss-making venture and ceased active production in the early 1980s. However, vast quantities of dangerous chemicals remained; three tanks continued to hold over 60 tonnes of methyl isocyanate (MIC). Although MIC is a particularly reactive and deadly gas, the Union Carbide plant's elaborate safety system was allowed to fall into disrepair.

Regular maintenance had also lapsed and, on the night of 2 December, when an employee was flushing a corroded pipe, multiple stopcocks failed and allowed water to flow freely into the largest tank of MIC. An uncontrolled reaction occurred, the tank was blown out of its concrete bunker and a deadly cloud of MIC, hydrogen cyanide and other chemicals was released. It was blown by the prevailing winds and settled over much of Bhopal. Soon after, people began to die.

The effects of the gas cloud

Aziza Sultan, a survivor, remembers:

> At about 12.30 a.m. I woke to the sound of my baby coughing badly. In the half-light I saw that the room was filled with a white cloud. I heard a lot of people shouting. They were shouting 'run, run'. Then I started coughing with each breath seeming as if I was breathing in fire. My eyes were burning.

Another survivor, Champa Devi Shukla, remembers that,

> It felt like somebody had filled our bodies up with red chillies, our eyes tears coming out, noses were watering; we had froth in our mouths. The coughing was so bad that people were writhing in pain. Some people just got up and ran in whatever they were wearing or even if they were wearing nothing at all....Those who fell were not picked up by anybody, they just kept falling, and were trampled on by other people. People climbed and scrambled over each other to save their lives – even cows were running and trying to save their lives and crushing people as they ran.

People started dying in hideous ways. Some vomited uncontrollably, went into convulsions and fell dead. Others choked to death, drowning in their own body fluids. Many died in the stampedes through narrow gullies. The gases burned the tissues of the eyes and lungs and attacked people's nervous systems. They lost control of their bodies. Urine and faeces ran down their legs and women suffered spontaneous miscarriages.

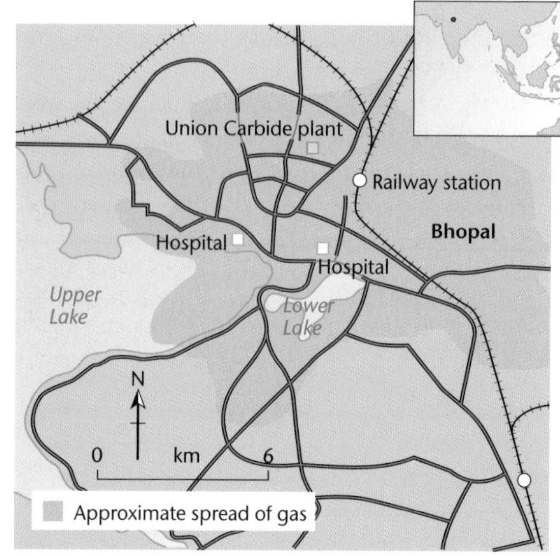

Figure 6.9 Map showing the location of the Bhopal disaster

Since the disaster, survivors have been plagued with an epidemic of cancers, menstrual disorders and children born with severe disabilities. People are

Photograph 6.3 A victim of Bhopal shows his burns during a protest march in Delhi, 1990

TopFoto

still dying from the effects of the contamination. According to Rashida Bi, a survivor who lost five gas-exposed family members to cancers, those who escaped with their lives 'are the unlucky ones; the lucky ones are those who died on that night'. Both Union Carbide and its new owner Dow Chemical have refused to release information about the effects of MIC, claiming that these are a trade secret . The site has never been cleaned up, and a new generation is being poisoned by the remaining pollutants.

Union Carbide's response

It was not until 1989 that Union Carbide, in a partial settlement with the Indian government, agreed to pay out some $470 million in compensation. The victims were not consulted in the settlement discussions and many felt that their compensation was inadequate. Victims of the gas attack eke out a perilous existence; 50,000 Bhopalis are unable to work due to their injuries. The lucky survivors have relatives to look after them; many survivors have no family left.

The Union Carbide Corporation was charged with culpable homicide, a criminal charge whose penalty has no upper limit, but refused to appear before an Indian court. Union Carbide also remains liable for the environmental devastation the accident caused. Environmental damages were not addressed in the 1989 settlement, and the contamination continues to spread. These liabilities became the property of the Dow Corporation, following its 2001 purchase of Union Carbide. However Dow has consistently maintained that it is not liable for the Bhopal accident.

Adapted from **www.bhopal.org**

Tertiary and other activities

Changing patterns of retailing in the UK

The traditional pattern of retailing is based on two key factors:

- easy, local access to goods such as bread, milk and newspapers which are purchased on a regular basis, often daily and particularly so if perishable
- willingness to travel to a shopping centre for goods with a higher value which are purchased less often, such as household and electrical goods, clothes and shoes

For many years, these factors led to a two-tier structure of retailing. Local needs were met by corner shops in areas of terraced housing, and by suburban shopping parades. Higher-value goods were purchased in the town centre (the central business district or CBD) and required a trip by bus or car. In the last 30 years technology (in the form of the motor vehicle) has had a major influence on the patterns of retailing.

In the 1970s **supermarkets** and **superstores** began to be built in residential areas and town centres. These stores sold a full range of food and non-food items, including brand names and shop brands, at the same check-out. This idea expanded into larger **hypermarkets** that also sold electrical goods and clothing and often had smaller specialist retail outlets under the same roof. An important factor in the development of these establishments was the use of the private car to load up once or twice a week with the 'family shop'.

In the 1980s **non-food retail parks** expanded. These housed DIY, carpet and furniture stores such as Do-it-All, B&Q, MFI and Carpetland. Many such parks

Table 6.3 Out-of-town shopping centres

Shopping centre	Location	Approx. number of shops
Braehead	Near Glasgow	100
MetroCentre	Near Gateshead	320
Trafford Centre	Near Manchester	320
Meadowhall	Near Sheffield	270
Merry Hill	Near Birmingham	230
Cribbs Causeway	Near Bristol	150
Bluewater	Dartford (south of Thames)	330
Lakeside	Thurrock (north of Thames)	350

were constructed on the outskirts of towns or cities, with easy access to main roads, again to attract the car user. The buildings were of a warehouse type construction, often uniform in design, each distinguished by the display on the outside and by the internal design.

In the 1990s huge **out-of-town shopping centres** were built on the periphery of large urban areas and close to major motorways. They often had their own motorway junctions. Some of the best-known shopping areas in the country come into this category: MetroCentre (near Gateshead), Meadowhall (near Sheffield), the Trafford Centre (near Manchester), and Bluewater and Lakeside on either side of the Thames east of London (Table 6.3 and Figure 6.10).

Figure 6.10 Location of out-of-town shopping centres in the UK

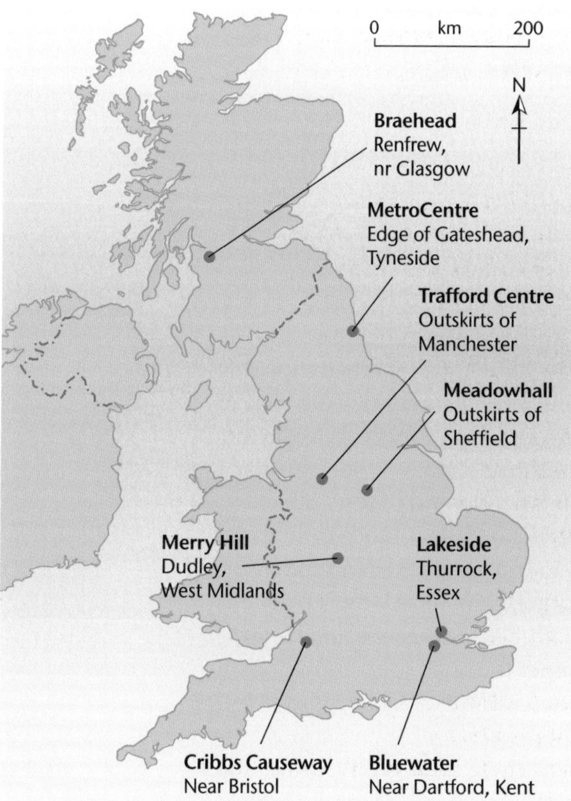

In the twenty-first century we are seeing the beginning of e-commerce and e-tailers — electronic home shopping using digital and cable television systems. The impact of this form of retailing on other types of shops has yet to be seen. However, it does seem that this type of shopping is unlikely to affect existing shopping locations seriously. People still want to examine items before purchase, and e-tailers depend upon mail delivery services, both road and rail based, none of which can guarantee next-day delivery.

Effects on the CBD

During each of these phases of retail change, the traditional town centre has continued to exist. At several times this area of retailing has been said to be dying, and in some small towns there has been a general decline. Evidence that was often quoted in the 1990s was the closure of branches of Marks and Spencer in a number of small towns. Shop closures in some cities did take place, with consequent job losses.

MetroCentre

Photograph 6.4 Inside MetroCentre, Gateshead

An increase in the numbers of charity and low-price shops and a greater emphasis on office developments in town centres are also given as evidence of decline.

However, town centres still flourish. In some cases, the CBD has moved slightly in one or more directions. In other cases, new indoor shopping areas or malls have been built. The Eldon Centre in Newcastle and the Arndale Centres in many towns are examples. Another feature has been the gentrification of shopping areas, as in the case of Brindley Place in Birmingham.

Response of the CBD

The decline of CBDs is a cause for concern. Run-down city centres can become dangerous at night. Dereliction, increased numbers of low-grade shops and lack of investment all encourage a cycle of decay. Planners see the CBD as an important social and cultural meeting point for a city. A declining CBD accelerates the success of out-of-town shopping centres.

A number of strategies are being devised to help city centres fight back, including:

- the establishment of business and marketing management teams to coordinate activities
- the provision of more attractive shopping environments with pedestrianisation, new street furniture, floral displays, paving and landscaping
- the construction of all-weather shopping malls that are air-conditioned in the summer and heated in the winter, often with integral low-cost parking
- the encouragement of specialist areas, such as open street markets, cultural quarters and arcades
- the improvement of public transport links to the heart of CBDs, with rapid transit systems, park-and-ride schemes and shopper buses
- the extensive use of CCTV and emergency alarm systems to reduce crime and calm the fears of the public, particularly women

- the organisation of special shopping events such as Christmas fairs, late-night shopping and Sunday shopping
- conservation schemes that enhance the ambience of heritage cities such as Chester, York, Bath and Cambridge

Many cities are also encouraging functions other than retailing to increase the attractions of their CBDs, including:

- developing a wider range of leisure facilities that people visit in the evening, such as café bars, restaurants, music venues (e.g. the 'Arenas' in many city centres), cinemas and theatres
- promoting street activity (e.g. Covent Garden in London)
- developing a wide range of nightlife, such as 'clubbing' in Manchester and Leeds (but there are negatives associated with this as a high level of policing is necessary)
- establishing theme areas, such as the gay area in Manchester, or the cultural quarters of Sheffield and Stoke
- developing flagship attractions (e.g. the National Museum of Photography, Film & Television in Bradford)
- encouraging residential use to return to city centres, in the form of either gentrification or new up-market apartments

Effects on the rural–urban fringe

Large areas have been devoted to major retail parks and this has involved the following:

- redevelopment and/or clearance of a large area of cheap farmland or a brown-field site
- the creation of extensive areas of car parking (the Trafford Centre has 10,000 spaces)
- the construction of a link to a motorway interchange or outer ring road
- the development of other transport interchange facilities — bus station, supertram, railway station
- the construction of linked entertainment facilities, e.g. Warner Village cinemas, fast-food outlets

Factors affecting retail change

A number of factors have combined to produce the changes in retailing described above.

Increased mobility

Nearly all the changes described arise from increased ownership and use of the private car. Car parking in city centres is expensive and relatively restricted. Access to such areas is by means of congested roads. Out-of-town retail areas have large, free areas of car parking. Locations next to motorway junctions offer speedy access, which makes reaching them less stressful. Even at a local level, it is often easier to pull into a petrol-station forecourt to make a low-level purchase than to find a parking space outside a suburban shopping parade. Petrol stations are no longer just places people go for fuel. They can also buy newspapers, bread, milk, vegetables, fast food, lottery tickets and often obtain money from a cash machine. The local petrol station has become the corner shop of the twenty-first century.

The changing nature of shopping habits

People now purchase many items as part of a weekly, fortnightly, or even monthly shop. The use of freezers in most homes means items that once had to be purchased regularly for freshness can now be bought in bulk and stored. This technology has dovetailed with the changing nature of employment. In many cases, either both income earners or the sole income earner in a family does not have time to shop daily. Retailers have responded to this by developing more 'ready-made meal' products that can be stored in a domestic freezer.

Changing expectations of shopping habits

An increasing number of people use shopping as a family social activity, involving more than just the act of shopping. Consequently, many of the larger shopping areas combine retailers with cinemas, restaurants, fast-food outlets, and crèches and entertainment areas. For example, the White Rose Centre near Leeds has an area set aside for men who accompany their partners but do not wish to 'shop until they drop'! It is claimed that at the Bluewater shopping centre near Dartford you are never more than 100 m away from a coffee bar. Such marketing ploys are used to make the customer feel much more at ease.

The changing nature of retailing

There are only a few supermarket/hypermarket companies, each of which strives to be more competitive than the others. They seek to build on cheaper out-of-town locations and to increase their economies of scale. In this way they can afford to reduce prices and provide large car-parking areas.

Changing attitudes of politicians and planners

Politicians believe that retail development in out-of-town locations has gone far enough. New life has to be injected into existing CBDs to avoid the problems of economic decline in these areas. Similarly, traffic congestion in out-of-town locations has to be reduced. A number of the major shopping areas identified above have sought permission to expand and, in most cases, this has been refused. Some supermarket chains are turning their attention back to their existing and new CBD outlets. For example, Sainsbury's has developed new Sainsbury's Local stores which do not sell the full range of goods found in its larger outlets but stock items targeted at local needs. Tesco has followed suit with its Express range of local stores.

Attitudes to the development of out-of-town retailing

Those in favour of out-of-town retailing believe it provides greater opportunities to shop without the need to travel into city centres. It also provides greater employment opportunities for local people, especially for students at weekends or young mothers who want to work part time.

Those opposed to out-of-town retailing believe it causes an increase in traffic in the area, which creates problems of safety, pollution, noise and parking in local residential streets. All-night shopping means continual movement of both cars and delivery lorries which may cause unacceptable noise levels at night.

Case study An out-of-town retail area: the Trafford Centre, Manchester

When the Trafford Centre was opened in 1998 many people were concerned about the effect it would have on Manchester's CBD. Nearly 5.4 million people (almost 10% of the UK population) live within 45 minutes' drive of the centre. It was designed to be more than just a shopping centre, with a 1,600-seat food court, an 18-lane ten-pin bowling alley and a 20-screen cinema.

Advantages

The Trafford Centre offers the following:

- 10,000 free car parking spaces
- facilities for the disabled which are regularly spaced within the complex. These include a Shop Mobility Unit offering scooters and wheelchairs
- a weatherproof, air-conditioned and safe environment
- its own security system, with a tannoy and a meeting point for lost children
- a full range of peripheral services, such as a post office, banks and travel agents

Disadvantages

It has the following disadvantages, typical of out-of-town retail areas:

- heavy build-ups of traffic on the access road network, e.g. the M60, at certain times of the year, such as Christmas and Bank Holidays
- the atmosphere within the complex is artificial, although there are themed sections which reflect the styles of Italy, Chinatown and New Orleans
- all the outlets are those of national chain stores — it is too expensive for local or independent businesses to become established in the centre
- public transport services to the centre are restricted, which makes access difficult for elderly shoppers in particular. In 2003, 91% of visitors came by car. However, there are plans to provide a Metrolink connection and a rail link to the centre
- it is difficult for poorer people to gain access to the centre — for example, the homeless are usually kept out by security staff

Summary: out-of-town vs CBD

Advantages

City-centre advantages include:

- good public transport access
- new shopping malls
- newly refurbished areas
- pedestrianised streets
- more varied outlets including independent shops

Out-of-town advantages include:

- one-stop shopping
- free parking
- cheap land
- good accessibility
- economies of scale
- planned shopping environment
- purpose-built buildings on retail parks

Disadvantages

City-centre disadvantages include:

- congestion

- cost of car parking
- decline of some services, due to competition
- land for redevelopment is more expensive
- less space for development

Out-of-town disadvantages include:
- a car usually required for access
- excludes low-income earners and non-car owners
- large amounts of land are required

Planning issues

Conflicts have arisen over the building of new retail, business and science parks, which have have been developed on greenfield sites on the edge of urban areas. Some of these, such as the building of the Trafford Centre (see case study) have been well publicised, but there are many smaller local issues. Such conflicts are resolved by market processes, planning processes or, in some cases, a combination of the two.

Market processes operate in an environment in which the ability to pay the going rate takes precedence over any local or national concerns. Often, objectors cannot afford to outbid the developer and the development goes ahead with the minimum of consultation. When it does occur, consultation often takes the form of an opportunity to voice objections or propose counter-arguments, with no right to independent arbitration or appeal.

Planning processes attempt to provide a means by which local authority planners:
- listen to the local community
- listen to the organisation responsible for a proposal
- have overall development control

A refusal by a local authority planning committee to grant planning permission may lead to an appeal or may result in the developer going to a higher body, for example the Department for Environment Food and Rural Affairs. Planning processes are costly, in terms of both time and money. Planning committees may:
- require, or negotiate, modifications in order to appease those opposing the plans
- require the developer to provide additional facilities (such as better road access), which the authority would otherwise have to fund. Such benefits may help to reduce local opposition

Planning committees have to weigh up:
- the gains from the proposal against its negative aspects
- the conflicts between differing groups within a local community
- the wider benefits of a local scheme vs the local opposition

Exploring personal attitudes and values

Conflicts about, for example, out-of-town shopping developments provide an opportunity for you to explore your own attitudes and values, as well as considering those of others.

- **Attitudes** are sets of beliefs that predispose a person, group or organisation to perceive and act towards people, environments and situations in a particular way.
- **Values** are the extent to which people attribute worth, or weight, to those attitudes.

People with differing attitudes will hold a range of views about any proposed development. In the most basic terms, they will either be in favour, against, or have no view.

Some people will be in favour of a proposal because they are responsible for the decision in the first place. They are the decision makers, the planners, the developers — those who are most likely to gain from the development. Other people in favour of a scheme will have calculated that the advantages to them will outweigh the disadvantages. All such people therefore have attitudes based on values.

Other people will oppose the scheme, and will have recognised that the disadvantages of the proposal, for them, outweigh the advantages. They may be affected directly or indirectly; some in the short term, others in the longer term.

When answering examination questions about attitudes and values, it is essential to ensure that each of the participants in the conflict you are writing about is clearly identified. Companies, pressure groups, affected sub-groups (e.g. elderly people and young mothers) must be named and their attitudes clearly outlined. In some cases, you may be asked for *your* attitude. When this happens, state your views clearly, and then give the *reasons* why you believe them to be correct. Marks will not be awarded for your views, they will be given for the quality of the argument that supports them; in other words, your attitudes and values.

Assessment exercises

Population dynamics

1 Figure A shows how birth rates, death rates and natural increase changed in Mexico between 1950 and 2000.

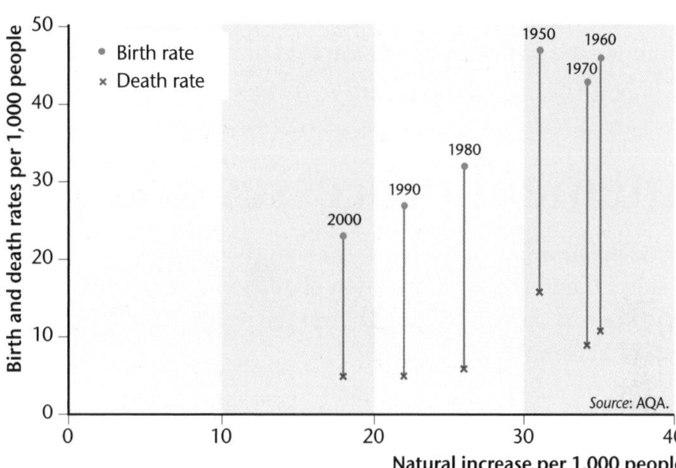

Figure A
Change in birth rates, death rates and natural increase in Mexico, 1950–2000

a (i) State the natural increase in Mexico's population in 1970 and 1990. (2 marks)

(ii) With reference to Figure A, state the stages of the demographic transition model into which Mexico fitted in 1950 and 2000. (3 marks)

(iii) Outline reasons for the variations in natural increase shown in Figure A between 1950 and 2000. (5 marks)

b Explain why the pattern of population change in some countries does not follow that predicted by the demographic transition model. (10 marks)

(20 marks)

2 Figure B illustrates the population structure of Afghanistan in 2000 and the projected structure for 2050.

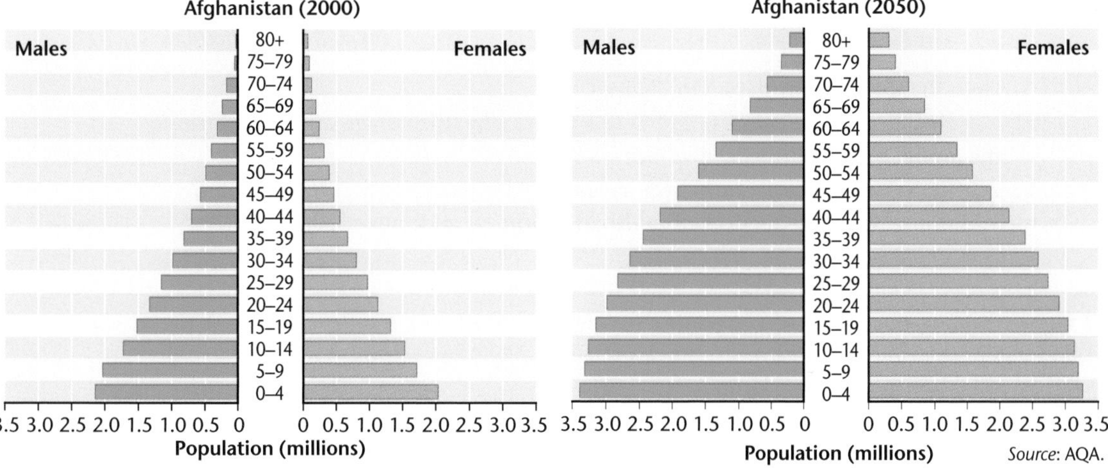

Figure B Population structure of Afghanistan in 2000 and projected structure for 2050

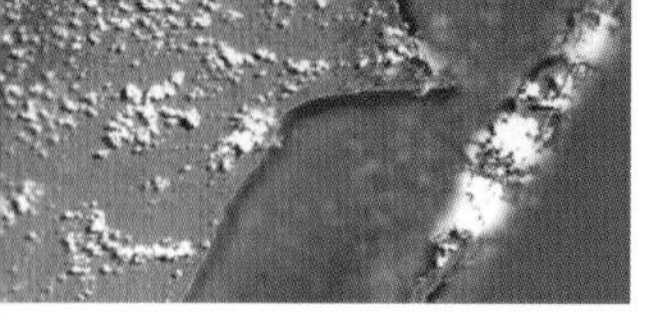

a (i) These pyramids show absolute numbers on the horizontal axes but percentages are more commonly used. Give advantages of using a percentage scale. (2 marks)

(ii) Identify the ways in which the population structure is expected to change between 2000 and 2050. (3 marks)

(iii) Explain why the changes identified in (ii) will occur. (5 marks)

b In recent years, many refugees have fled from Afghanistan to seek safety in the UK. Examine the push factors that can lead to refugee migrations. (10 marks)

(20 marks)

Settlement processes and patterns

1 a State the meaning of the term counter-urbanisation. (2 marks)

b Figures C and D give information about a village in southeast England. Figure C gives census data and Figure D gives the result of a 25% sample survey to show the age of housing in the village.

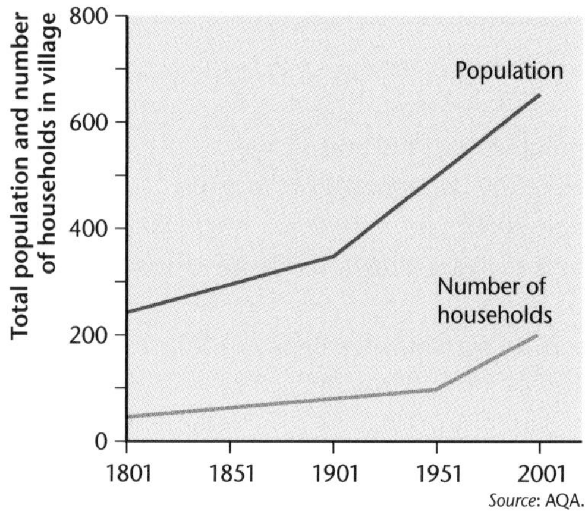

Figure C Census data

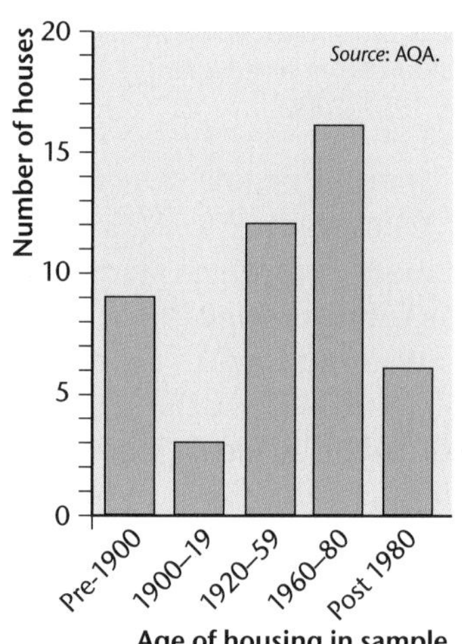

Figure D Age of housing

(i) Describe the changes shown in Figure C. (3 marks)

(ii) Use evidence from Figures C and D to suggest why this village might conform to the model of a suburbanised village. (5 marks)

c In recent years, many people have been encouraged to move back into our inner cities. Examine the consequences of re-urbanisation on an inner city in the UK. (10 marks)

(20 marks)

2 Figure E shows the results of a shopping survey conducted on a market day by a sixth-form student in the market town of Buckingham. Reilly's law was used to calculate the break point between neighbouring settlements.

a (i) What information is needed to calculate the break point between two towns. (2 marks)

(ii) Referring to Figure E, suggest reasons why the theoretical sphere of influence around Buckingham is not perfectly round. (3 marks)

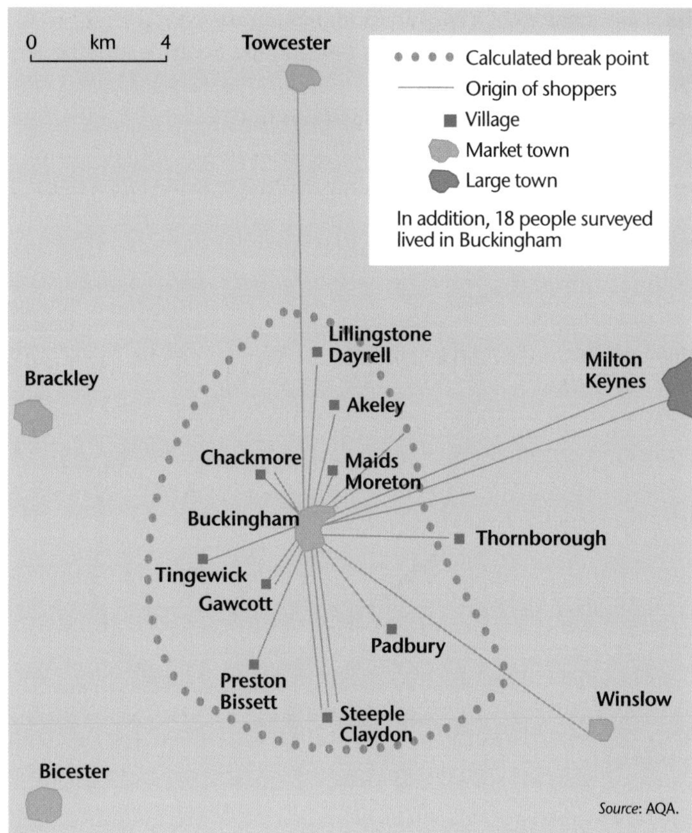

Figure E
Results of a shopping survey in Buckingham

b How can the range and threshold of a central place be determined? (5 marks)

c Using an example, outline the problems caused by rapid urbanisation in one less economically developed country you have studied. (10 marks)

(20 marks)

Economic activity

1 Table A shows the employment structure of two selected cities. Seoul is located in an NIC (newly industrialised country), where many multinational companies operate.

	Berlin (Germany)	Seoul (South Korea)
Manufacturing	12.2	23.8
Construction	9.3	10.0
Electricity production	1.0	0.5
Wholesale	12.4	22.0
Hotels	4.1	7.1
Transport	6.5	6.0
Financial	3.1	5.2
Public administration	11.2	3.6
Education	7.5	5.8
Health	11.3	7.4
Other services	21.4	8.6

Note: Employment stated as % of total employed.
Source: UN Human Settlements Questionnaire, 1999.

Table A
Employment structure of Berlin and Seoul

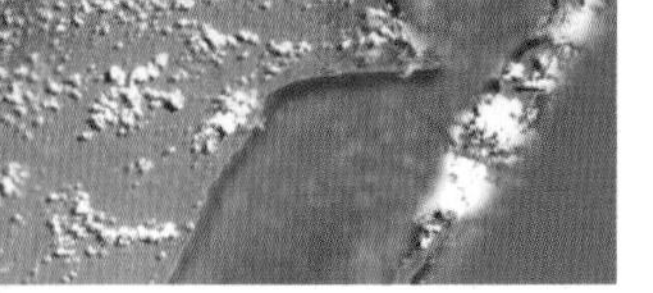

a (i) State the main features of a multinational company. (2 marks)
(ii) Contrast the employment structures of Berlin and Seoul, using the terms secondary and tertiary industry. (3 marks)
(iii) Suggest reasons for the differences identified in (ii). (5 marks)
b Identify and comment on the environmental and economic impacts of multinationals on an NIC you have studied. (10 marks)
(20 marks)

2 Figure F shows the location of DIY stores in and around the city of Oxford, some of which are in retail parks.

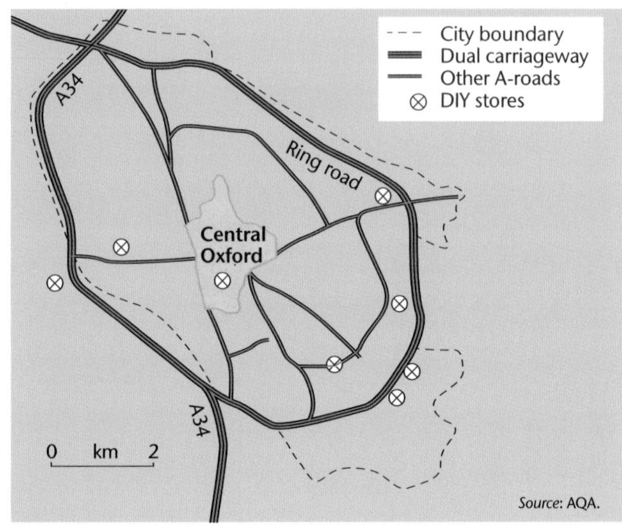

Figure F DIY stores in and around Oxford

a (i) Identify the main features of a retail park. (2 marks)
(ii) Describe the pattern of location of DIY stores shown in Figure F. (3 marks)
(iii) Suggest reasons for the pattern identified in (ii). (5 marks)
b Explain why recent industrial growth (other than retailing) has occurred within certain areas of the UK. (10 marks)
(20 marks)

AS Module 3

Geographical skills

Chapter 7

Geographical skills

AQA specification A requires you to develop a number of geographical skills. You must be able to:

- identify geographical questions and issues, select appropriate sources and effective methods and establish effective approaches to enquiry
- identify, select and collect quantitative and qualitative evidence from primary sources, including fieldwork, by using a range of techniques
- identify, select and collect quantitative and qualitative evidence from secondary sources, including maps at a range of scales, photographs, statistical data, geographical literature, information and communication technology, remotely sensed imagery and geographical information systems (GIS)
- organise, record and present such evidence in cartographic and diagrammatic form and make use of information and communication technology where appropriate
- describe, analyse, evaluate and interpret evidence and develop the ability to draw conclusions
- evaluate enquiry methods and develop an understanding of the limitations of evidence obtained and conclusions drawn

The geographical skills that are dealt with in this chapter will be tested in Unit 3 papers at each examination session. The material to be tested will be taken from the categories of basic, cartographic, graphic, statistical, ICT and investigative skills. Investigative skills are very important and you must participate in personal investigative work in the field to ensure you are familiar with these.

Basic skills

There are a number of basic skills with which you should be familiar. These include:

- **drawing sketches** — these are important as a descriptive and analytical tool. You should be able to draw sketches in the field to record information and to sketch photographs
- **analysing photographs** — you should be able to interpret photographs of different areas. When carrying out investigative work, you should be able to use photographs as descriptive and analytical tools
- **labelling** — you should be able to annotate base maps, sketch maps, Ordnance Survey (OS) maps, diagrams, graphs, sketches and photographs
- **literacy skills** — these are particularly important because much information is communicated in writing

Using field sketches and photographs

In your personal investigation, field sketches and photographs are excellent ways to record exactly what you have seen. Field sketches enable you to pick out from the landscape the features that you wish to identify and perhaps comment upon. They are particularly useful in physical geography investigations. Coastal geomorphology lends itself to this method — for example, Figure 7.1 shows a field sketch of beach nourishment. However, there is no reason why the technique cannot be used in an urban study. Sketching does not require artistic talent. It is far more important in geographical investigations to produce a clear drawing with good and useful labels.

If you lack the confidence to produce sketches but need to show detail from the area under investigation, then taking photographs is just as valid. However, you must not use them as an attractive 'space-filler' in your report. Any photographs you include must be annotated or labelled. A photograph is only useful when the reader is directed to the information it shows.

***Figure 7.1* A field sketch made on a coastal survey**

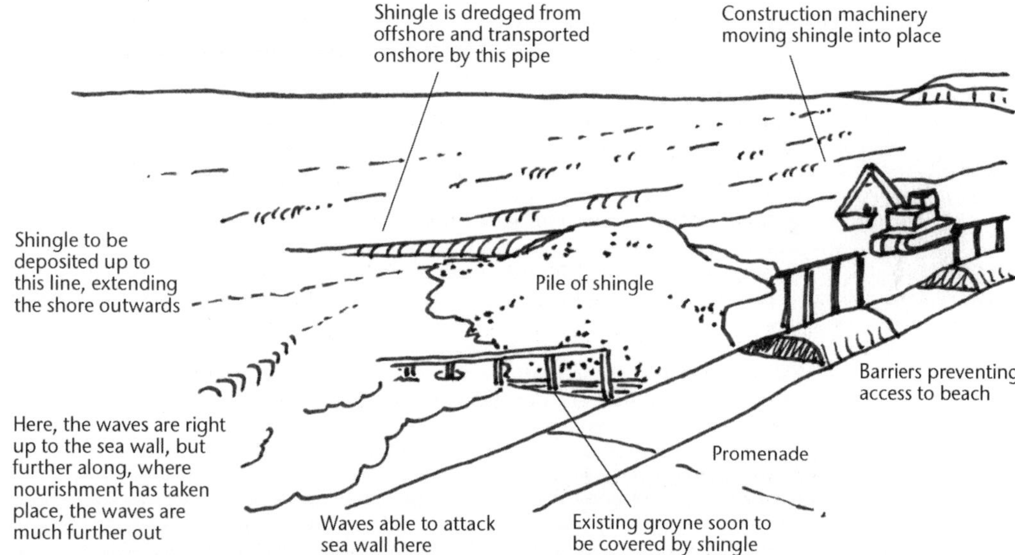

Cartographic skills

Cartographic skills fall into two main categories:

- the reading and interpretation of maps
- the production of maps in order to present information

You should be able to read and interpret:

- maps in atlases
- OS maps at a range of scales, particularly 1:50,000 and 1:25,000

- Goad maps for CBD studies (these indicate the use of buildings and open space)
- weather maps (synoptic charts)

Isoline (isopleth) maps

If you have collected data from different places, they can be represented by points on a map. It is possible to draw a map on which all points of the same value are joined by a line. This allows patterns in a distribution to be seen.

The best known example of such isolines (also called isopleths) is on Ordnance Survey maps where contour lines join places of the same height. This technique can be applied to a number of other physical factors, such as rainfall (**isohyets**), temperature (**isotherms**) and pressure (**isobars**), as well as human factors, such as travel times (**isochrones**) for commuters and shoppers.

Choropleth maps

A choropleth is a map on which data values are represented by the density of shading within areas. The data are usually in a form that can be expressed in terms of area, such as population density per square kilometre. To produce such a map certain stages have to be followed:

- The material has to be grouped into classes. Before you can do this you have to decide on the number and range of classes required to display your data clearly.
- A range of shadings has to be devised to cover the range of the data. Darkest shades should represent the highest figures and vice-versa. It is good practice not to use the two extremes of black and white because black suggests a maximum value, while white implies that there is nothing within the area. A suitable method of shading is shown in Figure 7.2.

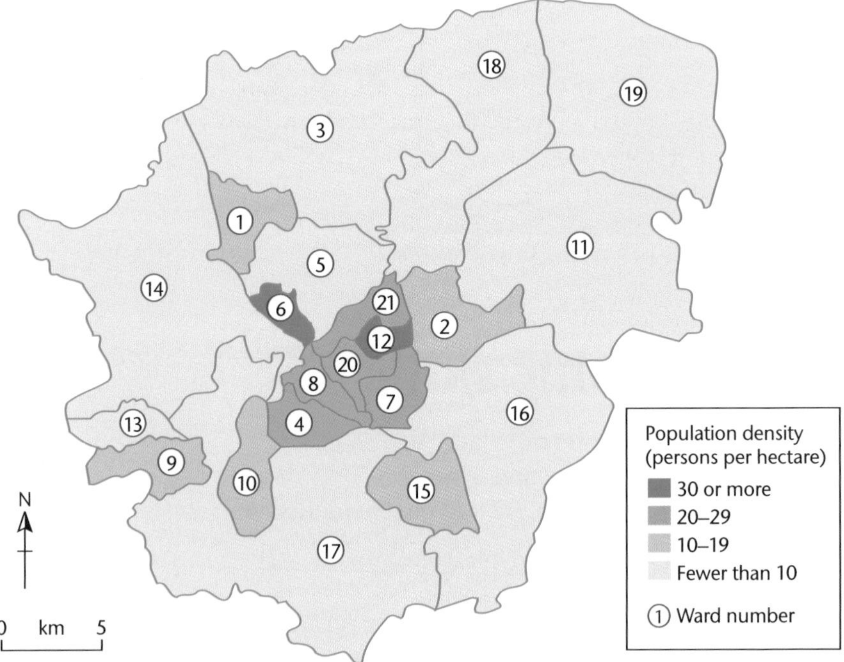

***Figure 7.2** Choropleth map showing population density in a metropolitan borough in northern England, 1991*

Choropleth maps are fairly easy to construct and are visually effective as they give the reader a chance to see general patterns in an areal distribution. There are, however, a few limitations to the method:

- It assumes that the whole area under one form of shading has the same density, with no variations. For example, on maps of the UK the whole of Scotland may be covered by one category, when it is obvious that there could be large variations between the central populated areas and the Highlands.
- The method implies abrupt changes at the drawn boundaries which will not be present in reality.

Sketch maps

Sketch maps can be produced to illustrate the location of a case study or an area of personal investigation, and the site or situation of settlements. They should be presented with good and useful labels.

Graphical skills

Arithmetic (line) graphs

Arithmetic graphs are appropriate when you want to show absolute changes in data. For example, they are suitable for showing changes in production through time, population change or stream discharge. When several lines are plotted on the same graph, it is important to recognise whether it is a simple or a compound line graph:

- On a simple line graph, the line represents the actual values of whatever is being measured on the vertical axis.
- On a compound line graph, the differences between the points on adjacent lines give the actual values. To show this, the areas between the lines are usually shaded or coloured and there is an accompanying key (Figure 7.3).

It is possible to show two sets of data on the same graph. The left hand vertical axis can be used for one scale and the right hand vertical axis for a different scale, as on Figure 7.3. This can often give a useful visual impression of the connection between two sets of data.

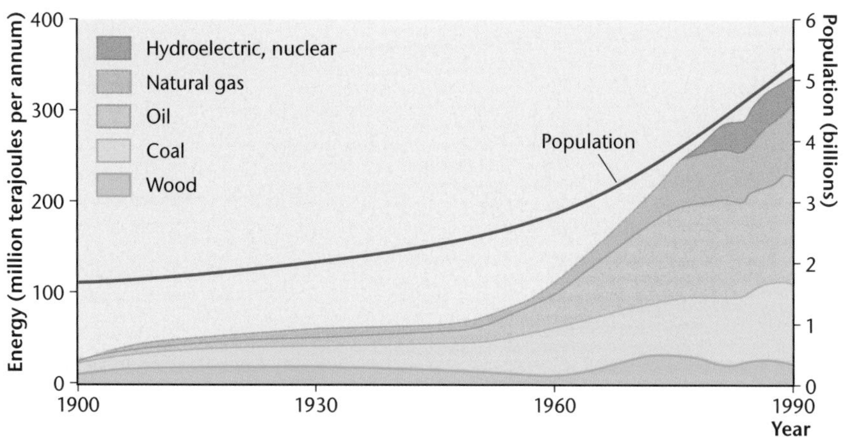

Figure 7.3 A compound line graph showing twentieth-century trends in world use of selected energy sources. Total world population is shown as a simple line

When using arithmetic graphs you should:

- plot the independent variable on the horizontal axis and the dependent variable on the vertical axis. If you are plotting data over time, time should always be plotted on the horizontal axis
- try to avoid awkward scales and remember that the scale you choose should enable you to plot the full range of data for each variable
- clearly label the axes
- use different symbols if you are plotting more than one line

Logarithmic graphs

A logarithmic graph is drawn in the same way as an arithmetic line graph except that the scales are divided into a number of cycles, each representing a tenfold increase in the range of values. If the first cycle ranges from 1 to 10, the second will extend from 10 to 100, the third from 100 to 1,000 and so on.

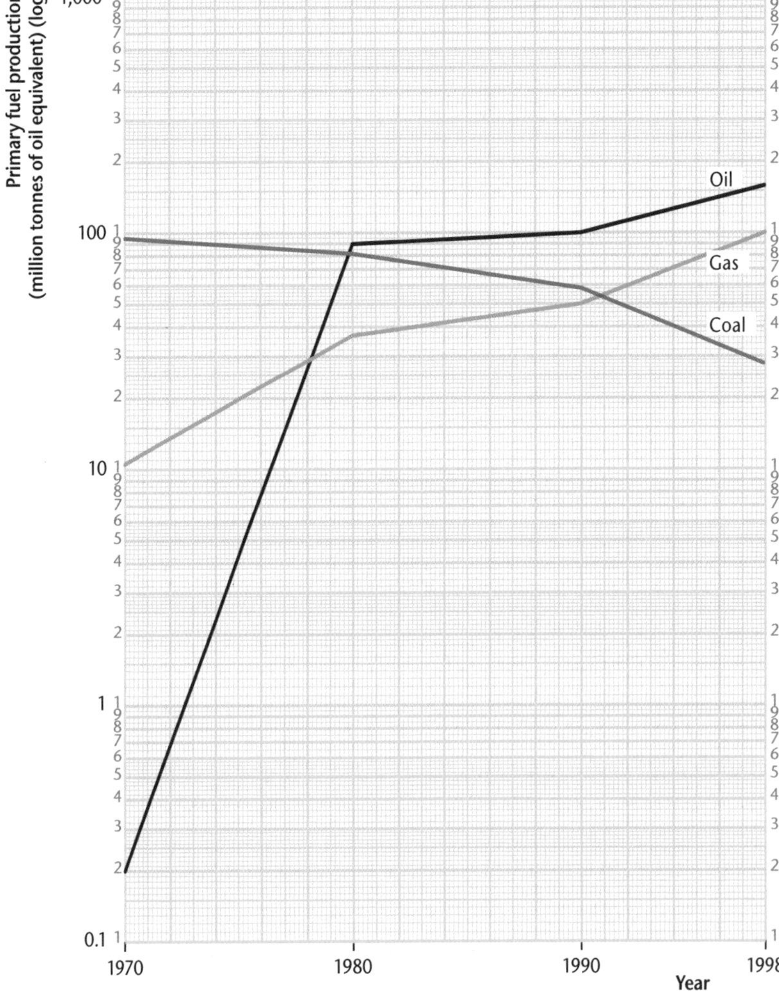

Figure 7.4 Semi-logarithmic graph showing UK production of primary fuels over time

You may start the scale at any exponent of 10, from as low as 0.0001 to as high as 1 million. The starting point depends on the range of data to be plotted.

Graph paper can be either fully logarithmic or semi-logarithmic (where one axis is on a log scale and the other is linear or arithmetic). Semi-logarithmic graphs are useful for plotting rates of change through time, where time appears on the linear axis (Figure 7.4). If the rate of change is increasing at a constant proportional rate (e.g. doubling each time period), it will appear as a straight line.

Logarithmic graphs are good for showing rates of change — the steeper the line, the faster the rate. They also allow a wider range of data to be displayed.

Remember that you cannot plot positive and negative values on the same graph and that the base line of the graph is never zero, as this is impossible to plot on such a scale.

Bar graphs

A bar graph (or chart) has vertical columns rising from a horizontal base. The height of each column is proportional to the value that it represents. The vertical scale can represent absolute data or figures as percentages of the whole.

Bar graphs are easy to understand. Values are obtained by reading off the height of the bar on the vertical axis. Bar graphs show relative magnitudes very effectively (Figure 7.5). Using an appropriate scale, it is also possible to show positive and negative values on the same graph — for example, profit and loss (Figure 7.6).

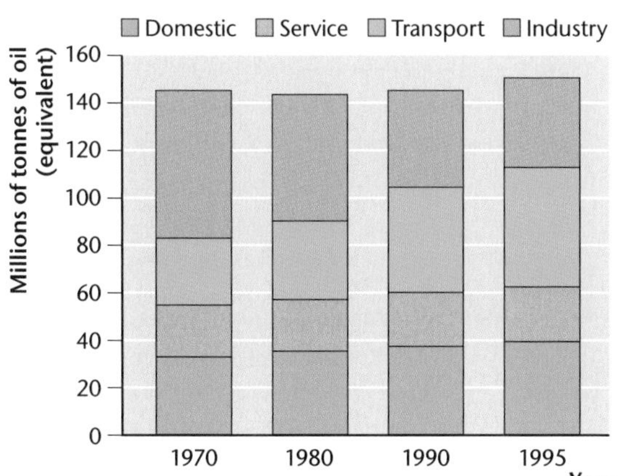

Figure 7.5 A compound bar graph showing UK final energy consumption by sector, 1970–95

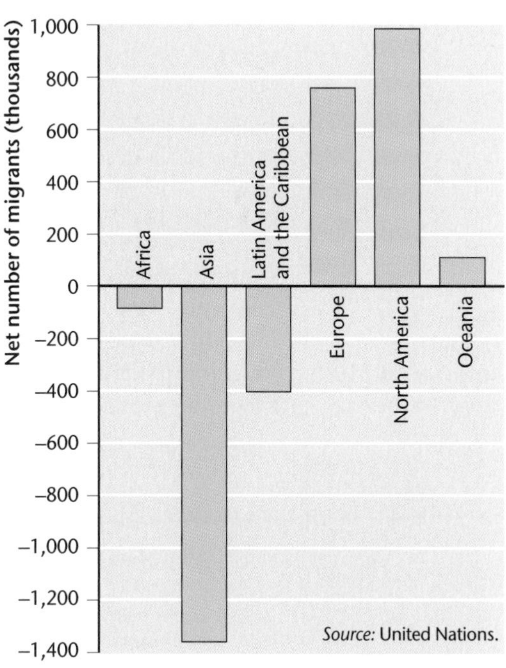

Figure 7.6 A gain–loss bar chart showing annual net migration totals in the world's major areas, 1990–95

Scattergraphs

Scattergraphs are used to investigate the relationship between two sets of data. They can be used simply to present data, but they are particularly useful in identifying patterns and trends in the relationship that might lead to further inquiry.

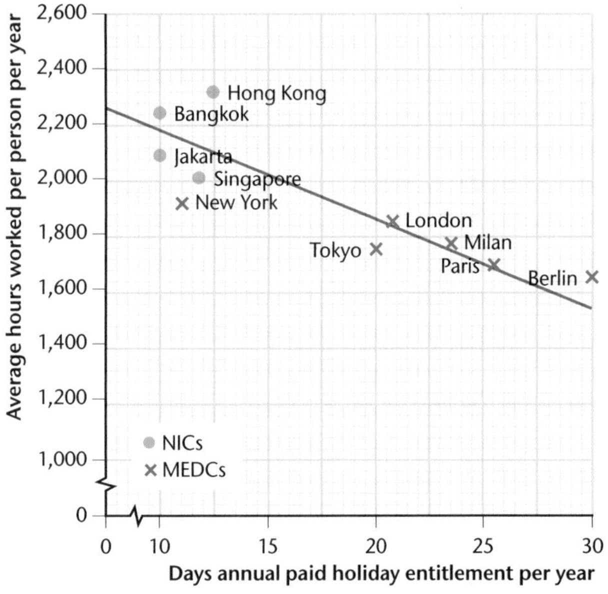

Figure 7.7 A scattergraph showing working patterns in selected cities in MEDCs and NICs, 2000

A general trend line (**best-fit**) can be added to the graph so that the relationship can be easily observed. This is the red line in Figure 7.7. If it runs from bottom left to top right, it indicates a positive relationship; if it runs from top left to bottom right, the relationship is negative.

Other features of scattergraphs include:

- they can be plotted on arithmetic, logarithmic or semi-logarithmic graph paper
- the independent variable goes on the horizontal axis and the dependent variable on the vertical axis
- it is possible for a correlation to emerge even when a relationship is only coincidental
- points lying some distance from the best-fit line are known as **residuals** (anomalies). These can be either positive or negative. Identification of residuals may enable you to make further investigations into other factors that could have influenced the two variables

Pie charts (divided circles)

The pie chart is divided into segments according to the share of the total value represented by each segment. This is visually effective — the reader is able to see the relative contribution of each segment to the whole. On the other hand, it is difficult to assess percentages or make comparisons between different pie charts if there are a lot of small segments.

Figure 7.8 Pie charts showing Malaysia's changing pattern of exports

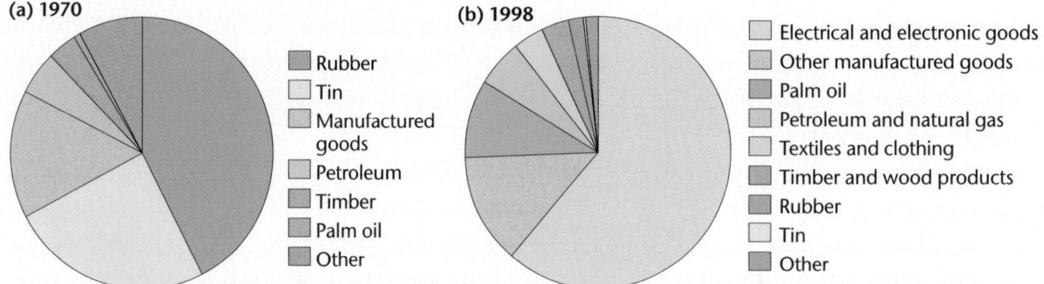

Triangular graphs

Triangular graphs are plotted on special paper in the form of an equilateral triangle (Figure 7.9). Although this looks, on the surface, to be a method that has widespread application, it is only possible to use it for a whole figure that can be broken down into three components expressed as percentages. The triangular graph cannot therefore be used for absolute data or for any figures that cannot be broken down into three components.

The advantage of using this type of graph is that the varying proportions and their relative importance can be seen. It is also possible to see the dominant variable of the three. After plotting, clusters will sometimes emerge, enabling a classification of the items involved (Figure 7.10). The items plotted could be, for example, MEDCs/LEDCs or types of soil.

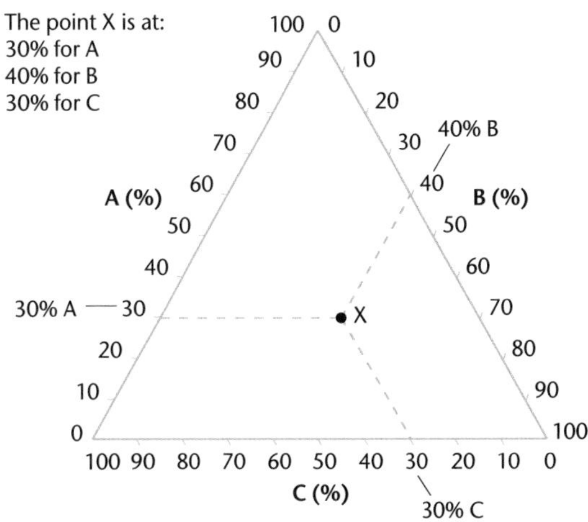

Figure 7.9
A triangular graph

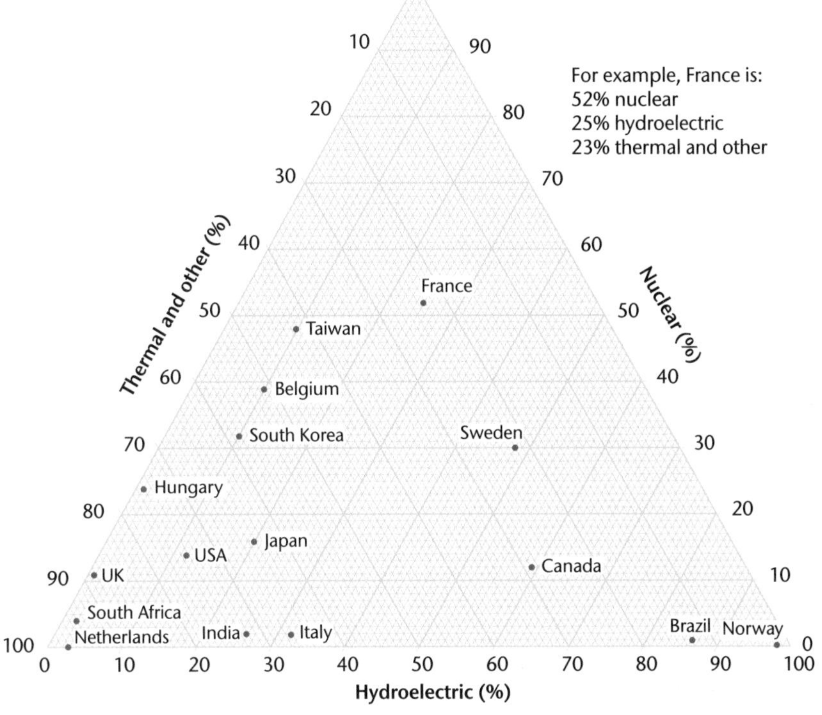

Figure 7.10
Triangular graph showing percentage of electricity produced by generating source for selected countries

Long sections and cross sections

These methods are useful for describing and comparing the shape of the land. Long sections are mostly used in river studies; cross sections can be drawn for a number of landscape features. This method essentially consists of constructing a graph showing height on the vertical scale against distance on the horizontal scale.

It is usual to take the horizontal scale from the map that you are using, but to use a different vertical scale. If you are working with a standard OS map, the scale would reduce your section, in most cases, to a line showing very little variation.

It is therefore necessary to adopt a larger scale on the vertical axis, but care must be taken that it is not massively exaggerated, changing the gentlest of slopes into the north face of the Eiger! The degree of exaggeration can be calculated and presented with your finished work. For example, if you are taking the horizontal scale from a 1:50,000 OS map 1 cm represents 500 m. If you select a vertical scale of 1 cm to represent 100 m, the vertical exaggeration is 5.

Kite diagrams

Kite diagrams are a useful way of showing changes over distance, particularly in vegetation (Figure 7.11). One axis is used for distance and the other for individual plant species. The width of the kite, representing a single species, enables a visual comparison to be made of the distribution of vegetation at any point in the section.

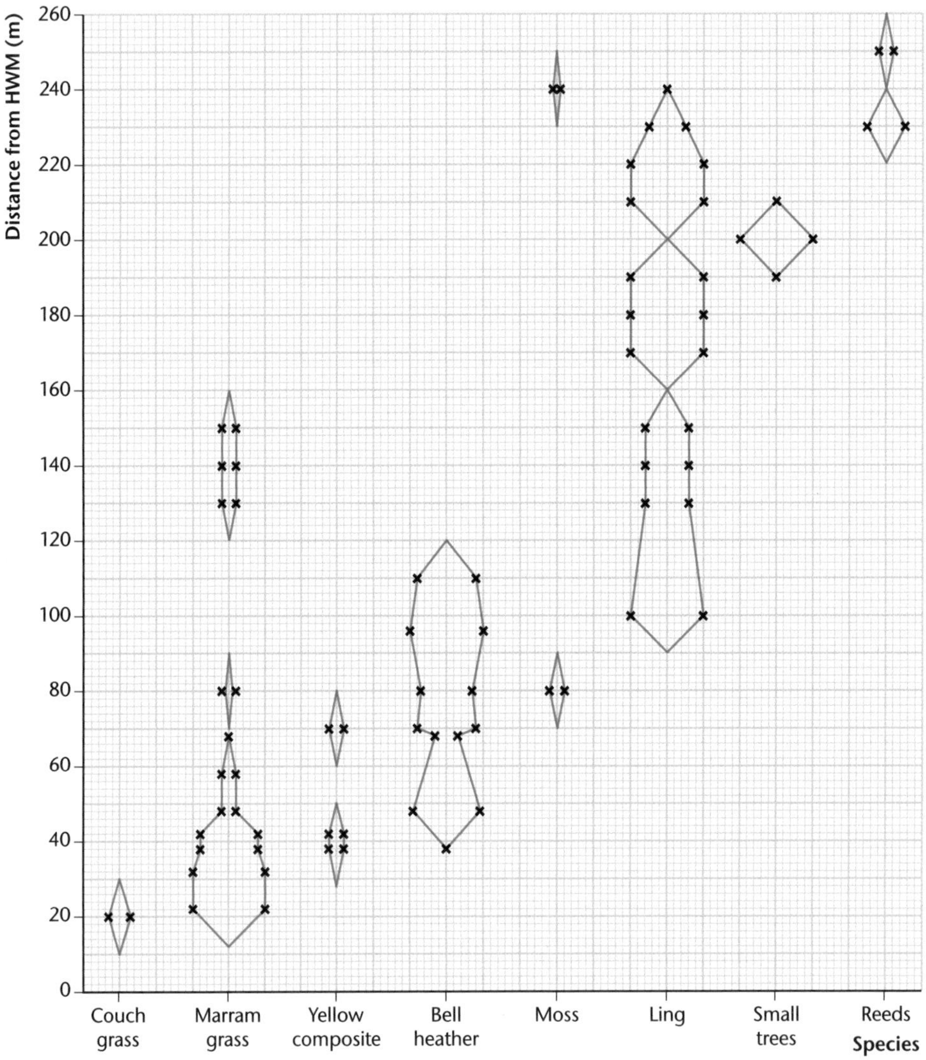

***Figure 7.11* Kite diagram showing a transect across a dune area in Dorset**

Storm hydrographs and population pyramids

Storm hydrographs are covered in Chapter 1 of this book and population pyramids in Chapter 4. You are expected to be familiar with the construction and use of both these types of graph.

Statistical skills

Measures of central tendency

There are three such measures.

Arithmetic mean

The mean is calculated by adding up all the values in a data set and dividing the total sum by the number of values in the data set. So,

$$\bar{x} = \frac{\sum x}{n}$$

The arithmetic mean is of little value on its own and should be supported by reference to the standard deviation of the data set.

Mode

This is the value which occurs most frequently in a data set. It can only be identified if all the individual values are known.

Median

This is the middle value in a data set when the figures are arranged in rank order. There should be an equal number of values both above and below the median value. If the number of values in a data set is odd, then the median will be the

$\frac{(n+1)}{2}$ item in the data set.

So, for example, if the total number of items in a data set is 27, the median will be the fourteenth value in the rank order of the data.

If the number of values in the data set is even, the median value is the mean of the middle two values. Any calculation of the median is best supported by a statement of the inter-quartile range of the data (see page 196).

Distribution of the data set

It is possible that each of these measures of central tendency could give the same result, but they are more likely to give different results. For them each to give the same result the distribution of a data set would have to be perfectly 'normal', and this is extremely unlikely when using real data. It is more likely that the distribution of the data set will be skewed (see Figure 7.14, page 198). The more it is skewed, the greater the variation in the three measures of central tendency.

None of these measures gives a reliable picture of the distribution of the data set. It is possible for two different sets of data to have the same values for mean, mode and median. Measures of the dispersion or variability of the data should therefore also be provided.

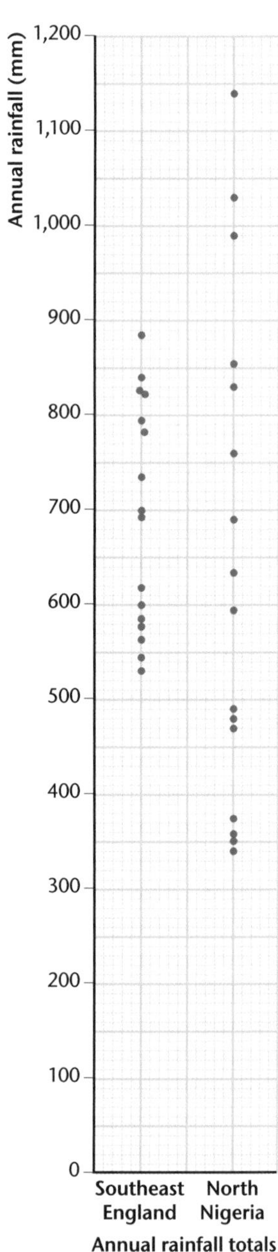

Figure 7.12 Dispersion graph showing rainfall in two selected locations over a 16-year period

Measures of dispersion or variability

There are three measures of dispersion or variability: range, inter-quartile range and standard deviation.

Range

This is the difference between the highest value and the lowest value in a data set. It gives a simple indication of the spread of the data.

Inter-quartile range

The inter-quartile range is calculated by ranking the data in order of size and dividing them into four equal groups or quartiles. The boundary between the first and second quartiles is known as the upper quartile and the boundary between the third and fourth quartiles is the lower quartile. They can be calculated as follows:

- the upper quartile (UQ) is the value that occurs at $\frac{(n+1)}{4}$ in the data set when arranged in rank order (from highest to lowest)
- the lower quartile (LQ) is the value that occurs at $\frac{3(n+1)}{4}$ in the data set

The difference between the upper and lower values is the inter-quartile range:

IQR = UQ – LQ

The IQR indicates the spread of the middle 50% of the data set about the *median* value, and thus gives a better indication of the degree to which the data are spread, or dispersed, on either side of the middle value.

Dispersion graphs

Dispersion graphs (Figure 7.12) are used to display the main patterns in the distribution of data. The graph shows each value plotted as an individual point against a vertical scale. It shows the range of the data and the distribution of each piece of data within that range. It therefore enables comparison of the degree of bunching of two sets of data.

Box-and-whisker plots

Box-and-whisker plots (Figure 7.13) provide more detail on the range and spread of data. To produce these:

- calculate the median and the upper and lower quartiles. Plot these as short bars running parallel to the horizontal axis

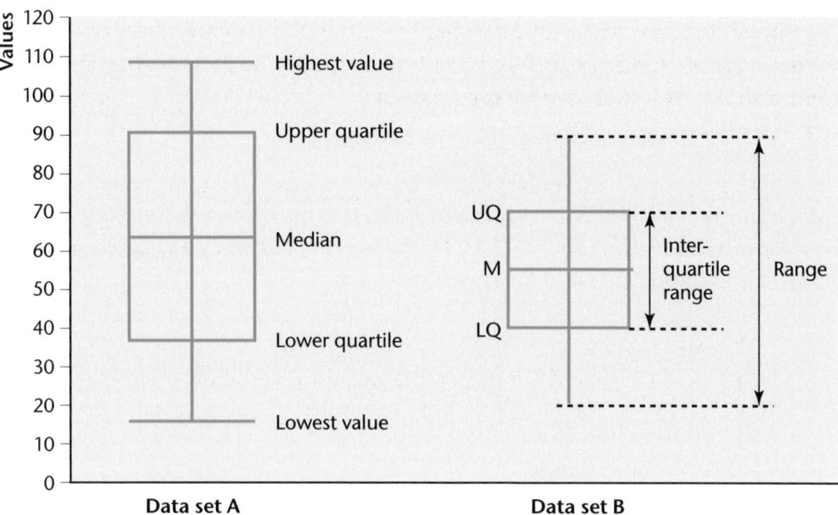

Figure 7.13 A box-and-whisker plot showing two sets of data

- draw vertical lines from the upper quartile value to the lower quartile value to **box** this spread of data. This box represents the inter-quartile range and contains 50% of the data
- mark the highest and lowest values by drawing lines parallel to the horizontal axis. Join these to the box

These '**whiskers**' show the range of the data.

Histograms

Histograms are used to show the frequency distribution of data. They use bars to indicate the frequency of each class of data, but do not confuse them with bar graphs. Histograms are used to simplify and clarify data that are easier to analyse when placed into groups, or classes, than when presented as individual data. In this way large amounts of data can be reduced to more manageable proportions which make it possible to see some of the trends present.

Before drawing a histogram you need to group the data, and this can be difficult. You need to illustrate differences between classes while keeping the variation within each class to an absolute minimum. You will need to establish:

- the number of classes to be used
- the range of values in each class — the class interval

The number of classes you use must depend upon the amount of data you have collected. Choose too many classes and you will have insufficient variation between them and may finish up with too many 'empty' classes; choose too few and you will have difficulty in recognising trends within the data.

One way of deciding on the number of classes is to use the formula:

number of classes = 5 × log of the total number of items in the set

If, for example, you had data about the size of 120 pebbles on a beach, the maximum number of classes would be:

5 × log 120 = 5 × 2.08 = 10.4

You would therefore select 10 classes.

The range of values is influenced by the number of classes that you have decided to use. This is shown by the formula:

$$\text{class interval} = \frac{\text{range of values (highest to lowest)}}{\text{number of classes}}$$

If, for example, you had data ranging from 96 to 5 and you required four classes, the class interval would be:

$$\frac{96-5}{4} = 22.75$$

It is important that class boundaries are clearly defined so that all individual pieces of data can be assigned without difficulty. Class intervals of 0–25, 25–50, 50–75, 75–100 should therefore be replaced with 0–24.9, 25–49.9, 50–74.9, 75–100, which do not overlap.

The number of classes and the interval will be influenced by the type of data with which you are dealing and the purpose to which they are being put. You will need to decide exactly what you are trying to illustrate or analyse. The distribution that you finish up with will fit into one of three categories:

- If your distribution has a modal class in the middle with progressively smaller bars to each side, then it is similar to the **normal** distribution (Figure 7.14a).
- If the modal class lies in the lower classes, then the distribution is said to show **positive skew** (Figure 7.14b).
- If the modal class lies to the upper end, the distribution is said to show **negative skew** (Figure 7.14c).

Figure 7.14 Histograms showing different distributions

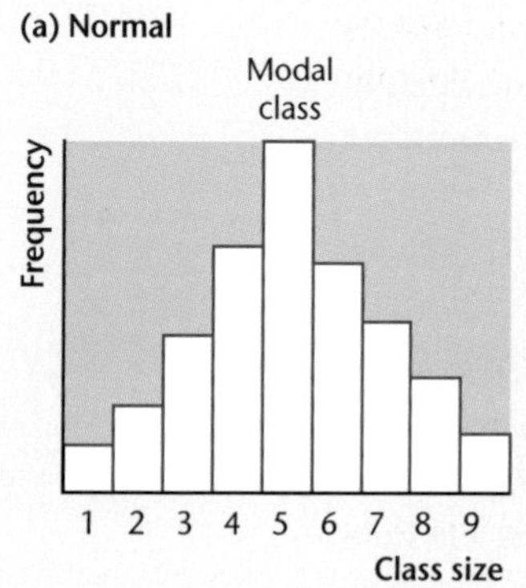

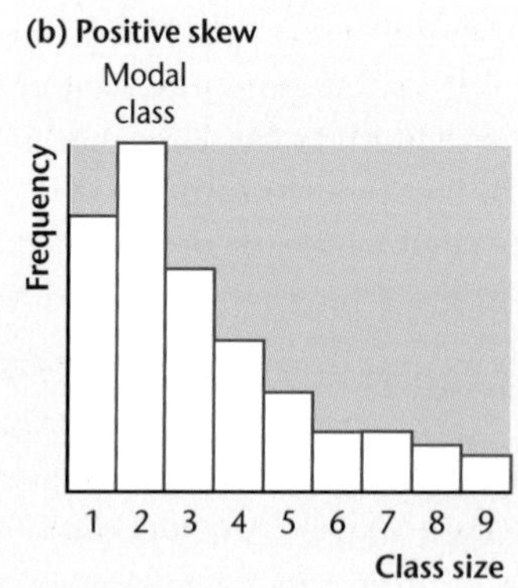

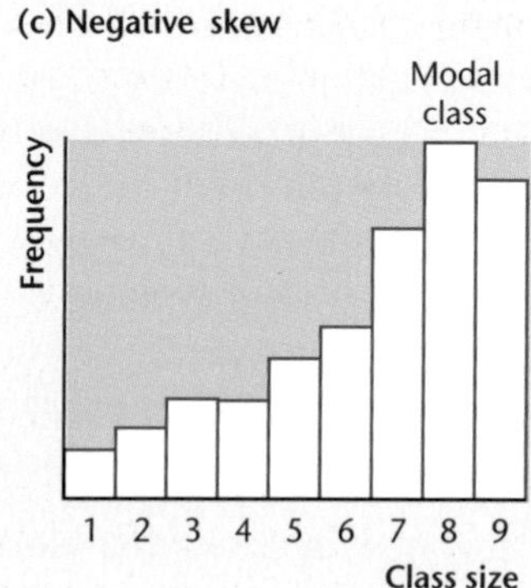

Standard deviation

Standard deviation measures the degree of dispersion about the *mean* value of a data set. It is calculated as follows:

- the difference between each value in the data set and the mean value is worked out
- each difference is squared, to eliminate negative values
- these squared differences are totalled

- the total is divided by the number of values in the data set, to provide the variance of the data
- the square root of the variance is calculated

$$\text{standard deviation} = \sqrt{\frac{\Sigma(\bar{x} - x)^2}{n}}$$

The standard deviation is statistically important as it links the data set to the normal distribution. In a normal distribution:

- 68% of the values in a data set lie within ±1 standard deviation of the mean
- 95% of the values in a data set lie within ±2 standard deviations of the mean
- 99% of the values in a data set lie within ±3 standard deviations of the mean

A low standard deviation indicates that the data are clustered around the mean value and that dispersion is narrow. A high standard deviation indicates that the data are more widely spread and that dispersion is large. The standard deviation also allows comparison of the distribution of the values in a data set with a theoretical norm and is therefore of greater use than just the measures of central tendency.

Measuring correlation: the Spearman rank correlation coefficient

Comparisons are made between two sets of data to see whether there is a relationship between them. Note that even if there is a relationship between two variables, this does not prove a causal link. In other words, the relationship does not prove that a change in one variable is responsible for a change in the other. For example, there may be a direct relationship between altitude and the amount of precipitation in a country such as the UK. These two variables (altitude and precipitation) are clearly linked, but a decrease in one does not automatically cause a decrease in the other — they are simply related to each other.

There are two main ways in which relationships can be shown:

- using scattergraphs (see page 191)
- measuring correlation using the Spearman rank correlation coefficient

The Spearman rank correlation coefficient is used to measure the degree to which there is correlation between two sets of data (or variables). It provides a numerical value which summarises the degree of correlation, so it is an example of an objective indicator. Once it has been calculated, the numerical value has to be tested statistically to see how significant the result is.

The test can be used with any data set consisting of raw figures, percentages or indices which can be ranked. The formula for the calculation of the correlation coefficient is:

$$R_s = 1 - \frac{6\,\Sigma d^2}{n^3 - n}$$

where d is the difference in ranking between the two sets of paired data and n is the number of sets of paired data.

The method of calculation is as follows:

- rank one set of data from highest to lowest (highest value ranked 1, second highest 2 and so on)
- rank the other set of data in the same way
- beware of tied ranks. In order to allocate a rank order for such values, calculate the 'average' rank they occupy. For example, if there are three values which should all be placed at rank 5, add together the ranks 5, 6 and 7 and divide by three, giving an 'average' rank of 6 for each one. The next value in the sequence will be allocated rank 8
- calculate the difference in rank (d) for each set of paired data
- square each difference
- add the squared differences together and multiply by 6 (A)
- calculate the value of $n^3 - n$ (B)
- divide A by B, and take the result away from 1

The answer should be a value between +1.0 (perfect positive correlation) and –1.0 (perfect negative correlation).

Some words of warning

- You should have at least 10 sets of paired data, as the test is unreliable if n is less than 10.
- You should have no more than 30 sets of paired data or the calculations become complex and prone to error.
- Too many tied ranks can interfere with the statistical validity of the exercise, although it is appreciated that there is little you can do about the 'real' data collected.
- Be careful about choosing the variables to compare — do not choose dubious or spurious sets of data.

Interpreting the results

When interpreting the results of the Spearman rank test consider the following:

What is the direction of the relationship?

If the calculation produces a positive value, the relationship is positive, or direct. In other words, as one variable increases, so does the other. If the calculation produces a negative value, the relationship is negative, or inverse.

How statistically significant is the result?

When comparing two sets of data, there is always a possibility that the relationship shown between them has occurred by chance. The figures in the data sets may just happen to have been the right ones to bring about a correlation. It is therefore necessary to assess the statistical significance of the result. In the case of the Spearman rank test the critical values for R_s must be consulted. These can be obtained from statistical tables, but Table 7.1 shows some examples.

According to statisticians, if there is a >5% possibility of the relationship occurring by chance, the relationship is not significant. This is called the rejection level.

The relationship could have occurred by chance more than five times in 100, and this is an unacceptable level of chance. If there is a <5% possibility, the relationship is significant and therefore meaningful.

If there is a <1% possibility of the relationship occurring by chance, the relationship is very significant. In this case, the result could only have occurred by chance one in 100 times, and this is very unlikely.

How does this work? Having calculated a correlation coefficient, examine the critical values given in Table 7.1 (ignore the positive or negative sign). If your coefficient is greater than these values, the correlation is significant at that level. If your coefficient is smaller, then the relationship is not significant at that level.

n	0.05 (5%) significance level	0.01 (1%) significance level
10	± 0.564	± 0.746
12	0.506	0.712
14	0.456	0.645
16	0.425	0.601
18	0.399	0.564
20	0.377	0.534
22	0.359	0.508
24	0.343	0.485
26	0.329	0.465
28	0.317	0.448
30	0.306	0.432

Table 7.1
Critical values for R_s

For example, suppose you had calculated an R_s value of 0.50 from 18 sets of paired data. 0.50 is greater than the critical value at the 0.05 (5%) level, but not that at the 0.01 (1%) level. In this case, therefore, the relationship is significant at the 0.05 (5%) level, but not at the 0.01 (1%) level.

Worked example: Spearman rank test

Survey: size of shingle along a storm beach

The beach in question is aligned from southwest to northeast and the dominant approach of the waves is from the southwest. The main ridge appears to increase in height with distance from the southwest. The shingle appears to decrease in size and become more rounded towards the northeast. This may indicate that the direction of longshore drift is from the southwest to the northeast, meaning that the further the shingle is moved, the more it is affected by attrition and, therefore, reduced in size. A scattergraph would show the general trend of the relationship between distance and size. However, there are anomalies, so a correlation test would be useful to decide the strength of that relationship.

The raw data are shown in Table 7.2.

The data required for the calculation of R_s between distance and the mean shingle size are shown in Table 7.3.

$$R_s = 1 - \frac{6\Sigma d^2}{n^3 - n}$$

$$\Sigma d^2 = 996.5$$

$$R_s = 1 - \frac{6 \times 996.5}{15^3 - 15}$$

$$= 1 - \frac{5{,}979}{3{,}360}$$

$$= 1 - 1.78$$

$$= -0.78$$

Table 7.2 The characteristics of shingle along a storm beach

Distance from SW end of beach (m)	Height (m)	Mean shingle diameter (cm)	Roundness index
60	5.5	8.4	1.72
180	7.5	8.5	1.77
300	8.0	7.7	1.63
420	11.5	8.1	1.48
540	11.0	6.1	1.58
660	7.5	5.8	1.63
780	10.0	6.2	1.60
900	10.5	7.2	1.41
1,020	10.0	7.5	1.36
1,120	11.0	6.2	1.33
1,220	14.0	6.5	1.35
1,340	12.5	5.8	1.23
1,460	18.0	4.8	1.18
1,580	13.5	5.0	1.17
1,700	15.0	5.8	1.25

Table 7.3 Data for the calculation of R_s

Distance (m)	Rank	Mean shingle size (cm)	Rank	Difference in rank (d)	d^2
60	15	8.4	2	13	169
180	14	8.5	1	13	169
300	13	7.7	4	9	81
420	12	8.1	3	9	81
540	11	6.1	10	1	1
660	10	5.8	12	2	4
780	9	6.2	8.5	0.5	0.25
900	8	7.2	6	2	4
1,020	7	7.5	5	2	4
1,120	6	6.2	8.5	2.5	6.25
1,220	5	6.5	7	2	4
1,340	4	5.8	12	8	64
1,460	3	4.8	15	12	144
1,580	2	5.0	14	12	144
1,700	1	5.8	12	11	121
					996.5

The coefficient indicates that there is a negative relationship between the two sets of data — as the distance increases, the mean shingle diameter decreases.

The result is significant at the 0.01 significance level. The R_s value is greater than the critical value when $n = 15$ (0.63). The possibility that such a result occurred by chance is very low — less than 1 in 100.

This statistically reliable result supports the subjective perception of the longitudinal changes with distance from the southwest end of the beach.

ICT skills

You are required to be able to:

- use photographs, both aerial and ground
- use satellite images
- use databases, e.g. population/development data and census material
- use the internet for research and to keep case studies up to date
- extract information from videos, television programmes and CD-ROMs

Investigative skills

At AS, you are required to develop the following skills:

- identification of geographical questions and issues
- establishment of effective approaches to enquiry
- identification, selection, collection and evaluation of quantitative and qualitative evidence from primary (including fieldwork) and secondary sources
- processing, presentation, analysis and interpretation of evidence
- drawing conclusions and showing an awareness of the validity of such conclusions
- an awareness of health and safety considerations in fieldwork, through risk assessment

Investigative skills always form part of the Unit 3 paper. You must therefore participate in personal investigative work in the field to ensure you are familiar with such skills. The final section of the exam paper requires you to display evidence of fieldwork with regard to the identification of geographical questions and issues and the identification, selection and collection of evidence from primary and secondary sources.

Your fieldwork investigation

Once you have established the aims and hypotheses of your investigation, you should work out what data you need to collect and what methods you will use. Investigations at AS are based on your own observations. This means using such techniques as questionnaires, interviews, river measurements, pedestrian surveys and urban transects. Secondary data from published sources can be added. Two very different ways of collecting primary data are described in detail below: sampling and river surveys.

Sampling

Sampling is used when it is impossible, or simply not necessary, to collect large amounts of data. Collecting small amounts of carefully selected data will enable you to obtain a representative view of the feature as a whole. You cannot, for example, interview all the shoppers in a market town or all the inhabitants of a village, but you can look at a fraction of those populations and from that evidence indicate how the whole is likely to behave.

When you have established the need for a sample survey, you will have to decide on a method that will collect a large enough representative body of evidence. If, for example, you are interviewing the inhabitants of a village, you must ensure that your interviews cover all age ranges in the population.

Types of sampling

The main types of sampling technique you need to consider are random, systematic and stratified (quota).

A **random** sampling is one that shows no bias and in which every member of the population has an equal chance of being selected. The method usually involves the use of random number tables.

In **systematic** sampling, samples are taken at regular fixed intervals, for example every tenth person or house. On a beach you could decide to sample sites at 100 m intervals, and select pebbles at each location using the intersection points on the grid in a quadrat.

Stratified sampling is based on knowing something in advance about the population or area in question. For example, if you are surveying a population and you know its age distribution, your sample must reflect that distribution. If you are surveying an area in which you know the distribution of soil types, samples should be taken in proportion to the area covered by each type of soil. For instance, if a particular soil covers 40% of the area, 40% of the total sample points should be within the area covered by that soil.

Bias in sampling

It is possible, through poor choice of sampling method or insufficient evidence, to achieve a result that is unrepresentative of the population in question. Taking all samples on the same day of the week or outside the same shop could lead to a distortion in a shopping survey, for example.

Sample size

The size of sample usually depends upon the complexity of the survey being used. When using a questionnaire it is necessary to sample sufficient people to take into account the considerable variety introduced by the range of questions. Sample size can be restricted by practical difficulties and this may affect the reliability of results. Your aim should be to keep the sampling error as small as possible. You are not a professional sampler and cannot be expected to conduct hundreds of interviews, but on the other hand, sampling only 20–30 people in a market survey is not representative of the population as a whole.

Point sampling

Point sampling is carried out in surveys which involve, for example, studies of land use, vegetation coverage, soil sites and selection of such items as pebbles in longshore-drift studies. Point sampling involves the use of a grid. That produced by Ordnance Survey is ideal, but for field surveys a quadrat can be used. A **quadrat** is a frame enclosing an area of known size (often 1 m^2), and may be subdivided by a grid made of wire or string. Both random and systematic sampling can be carried out within this framework.

Collecting data for river surveys

A number of measurements can be made within the channel of a river.

Speed of the river

The best and easiest way to measure the speed of flow in a river is to use a flow meter that either gives a direct reading or allows you to calculate the speed using a conversion chart. Without a flow meter, it is possible to calculate the speed by using a piece of wood or cork as a float (some people swear by dog biscuits). The procedure is as follows:

- Measure out a 10 m length of the river.
- Measure the time it takes the float to cover the distance.
- Repeat several times and at various points across the flow.
- Find the average time — this gives the surface speed.
- Multiply by 0.8 to find the true speed of the river across the whole channel.

Cross-section area and wetted perimeter

Cross-sectional area can be calculated using the following procedure:

- Run a tape across the river along the waterline from bank to bank.
- Along this tape, calculate the depth of water at 50 cm intervals (this distance can vary according to the width of the river).
- Transfer this information to graph paper, making sure that you use the same scale for the vertical and horizontal axes.
- Having produced a cross-section diagram, count the squares (the size of which you already know) inside the line and by a simple multiplication you will have the cross-section area of the channel at that point.

You can also measure the wetted perimeter from such a diagram.

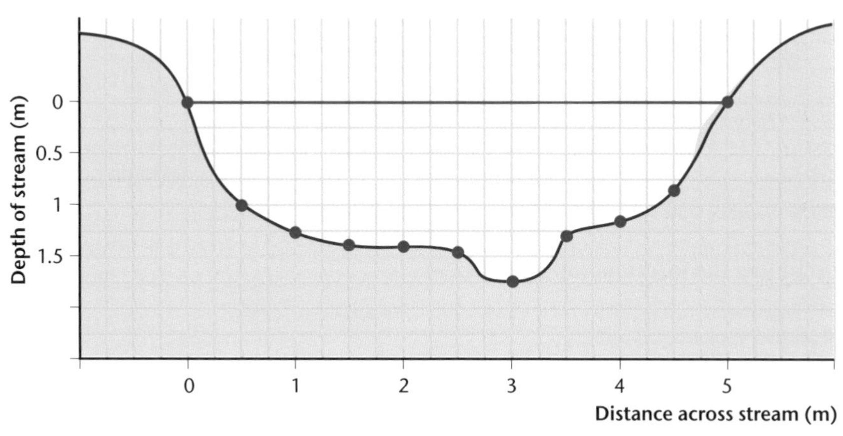

Figure 7.15 River cross-section and wetted perimeter

River discharge

To calculate river discharge:

- Calculate the speed of flow ($m\ s^{-1}$) as described above.
- Calculate the cross-sectional area (m^2) as described above.
- Multiply the two values to give the discharge in cumecs ($m^3\ s^{-1}$).

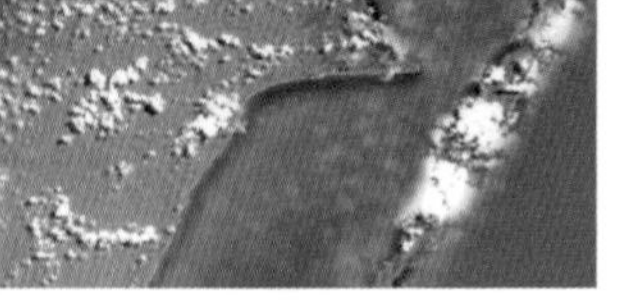

Assessment exercises

Module 3 is assessed by a geographical skills paper based on a resource booklet, which is pre-released to candidates before the examination. In the assessment exercises below resource material is included in the questions. The material that would have been placed in the booklet, rather than the examination paper, is listed at the end of each topic.

In the examination, you have a choice of answering a physical geography question or one based on a human geography topic. Both types are given here. One topic is drawn from Module 1: Core concepts in physical geography and the other from Module 2: Core concepts in human geography.

The physical environment

Global warming

1 **Figure A shows the areas of the world where carbon dioxide emissions have originated since 1800.**

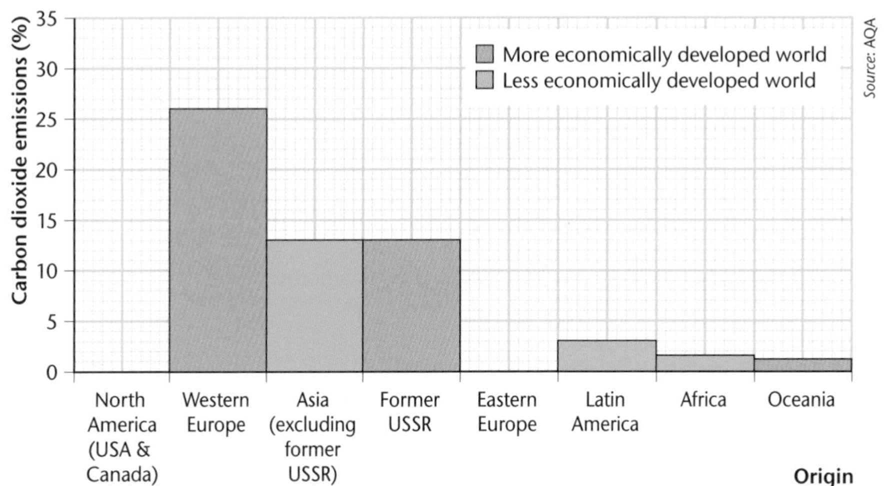

Figure A Carbon dioxide emissions since 1800

Complete Figure A by adding the information given below:

- **Eastern Europe: 6.6%**
- **North America (USA and Canada): 35.0%** (3 marks)

2 **Describe and suggest reasons for the variations in the origins of carbon dioxide, as shown in Figure A.** (6 marks)

3 **Figure B shows the long-term change in the amounts of carbon dioxide in the atmosphere and temperature levels over the same period. Figures C and D show the same information, but over the short term, i.e. since 1860.**

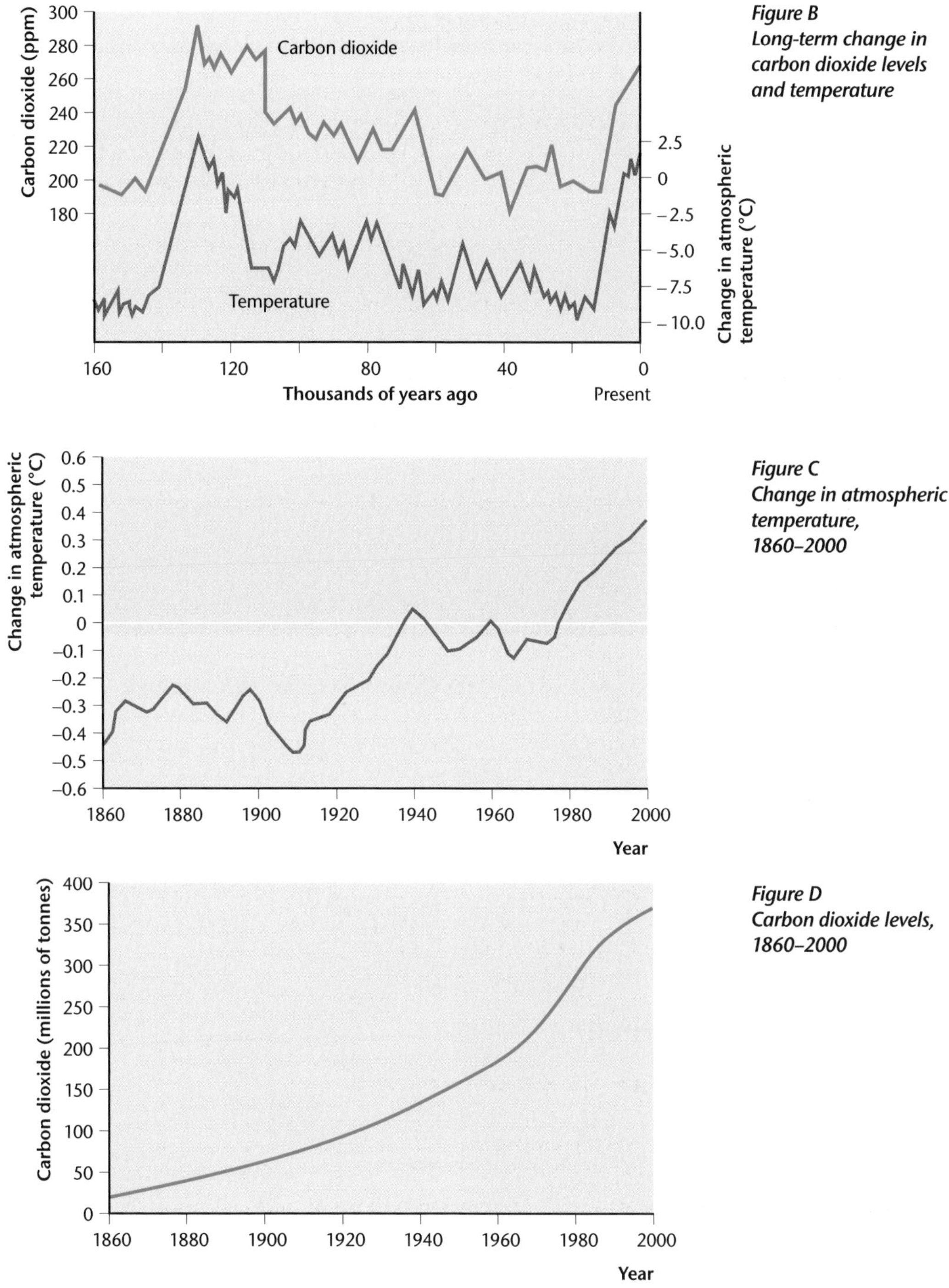

Figure B
Long-term change in carbon dioxide levels and temperature

Figure C
Change in atmospheric temperature, 1860–2000

Figure D
Carbon dioxide levels, 1860–2000

Describe the trends that are shown by Figures B, C and D. Comment on the extent to which responsibility for these trends reflects both natural and human causes. (8 marks)

4 Photograph A shows one of the Maldive Islands in the Indian Ocean. Label Photograph A to show how the island is vulnerable to the effects of global warming. (5 marks)

Photograph A
An island in the Maldives

5 Figures E and F show the proportion of the Arctic Ocean covered by ice today and the predicted amount left by 2080.

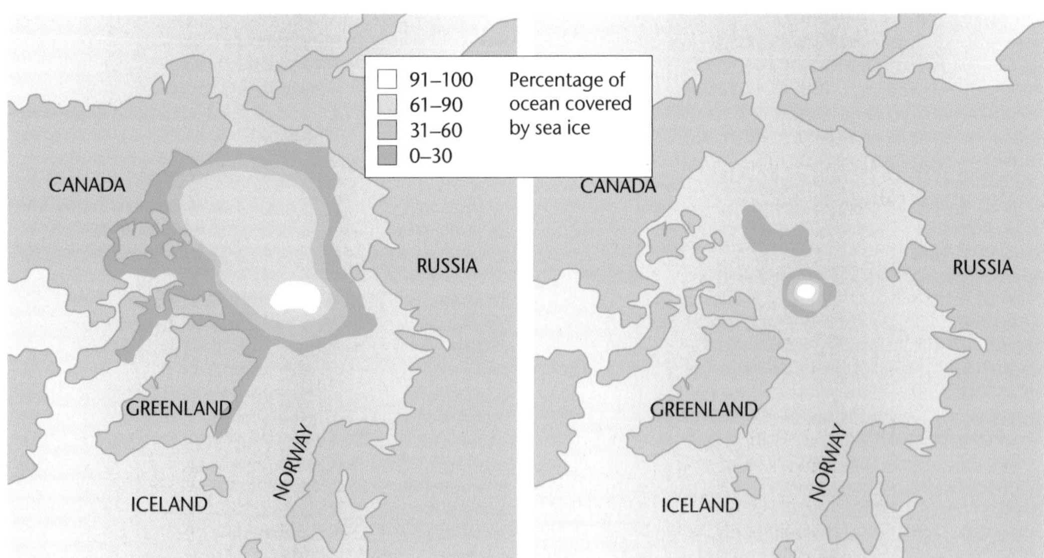

Figure E Percentage of Arctic Ocean covered by ice, 2005

Figure F Predicted percentage of Arctic Ocean covered by ice, 2080

Describe the expected changes in the amount of Arctic ice between now and 2080. (4 marks)

6 Figure G shows some of the possible consequences of global warming for Britain.

Salt water would pollute fresh water

Temperature would rise by 1.5–4.5°C

Trees: deciduous trees would replace conifers

Vines would flourish

Plants: crocuses and daffodils would only grow in the north

More forest fires

Butterflies: some species would move northwards

Sea level would rise by 20–40 cm

Birds: arctic species, such as capercaillie, ptarmigan, snow bunting and dotterel would face extinction

Skiing: loss of snow would force Aviemore to close down

Flooding: defences would need to be provided or rebuilt in low lying areas in:
East Anglia
Lincolnshire
Thames Estuary
Solway Firth
Ribble Estuary

Wetlands and inland marshes would dry up. Birds such as greenshank and dunlin would be under threat

Solway Firth
Ribble Estuary
LINCOLNSHIRE
EAST ANGLIA
Thames Estuary
KENT
N
0 km 200

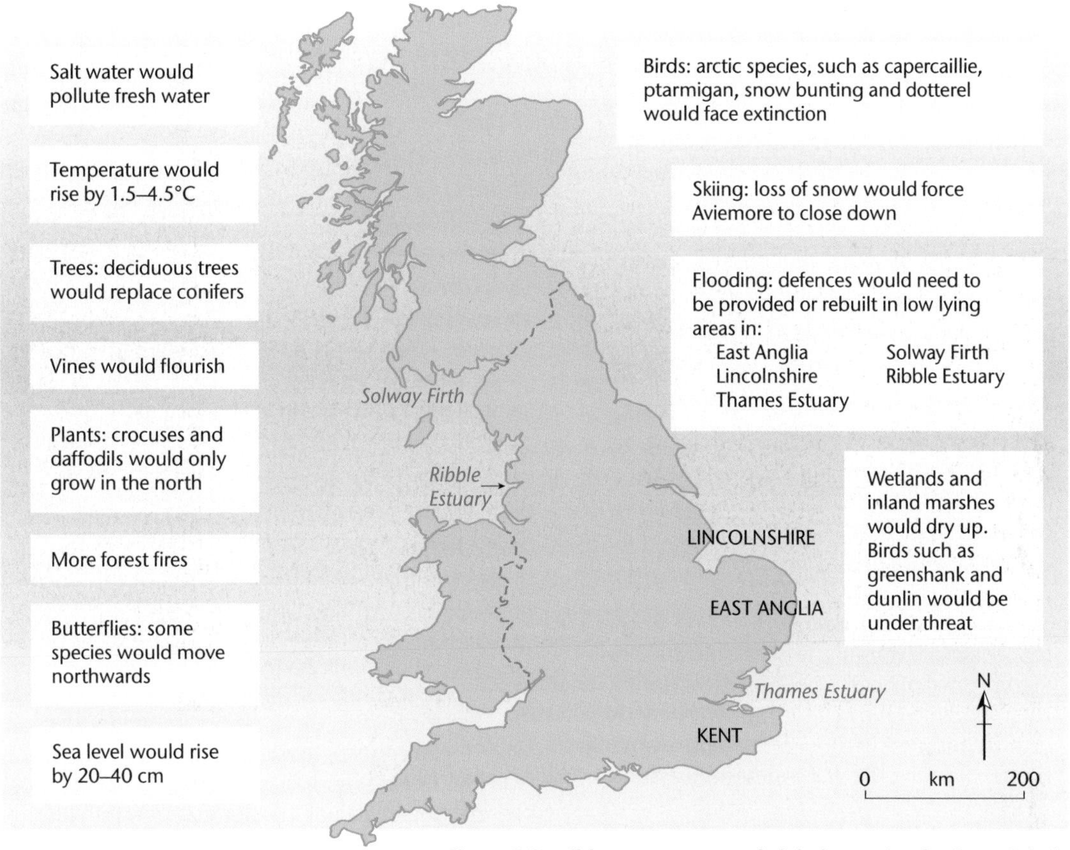

Figure G Possible consequences of global warming for Great Britain

Using Figure G, outline and explain the environmental and economic consequences of global warming for Britain. (8 marks)

7 Figure H (on page 210) contains information extracted from an article on global warming which appeared in a geographical publication.
With the help of Figure H, comment on the issues raised in seeking to reduce the problem of global warming. (8 marks)

8 You have experience of geography fieldwork as part of your course.
a For *any* geographical fieldwork study that you have undertaken, briefly outline its aim. (2 marks)
b For your chosen study, identify one item of primary data which was collected. Briefly state how it was collected, the sampling method used and reasons for adopting the sampling method described. (6 marks)

(50 marks)

The following would have been included the resource booklet:

- Figures B, C, D, E, F, G, H

Problem recognition

Some scientists believe that a cooling might result from greenhouse gas emissions. Initial global warming might later lead to more global evaporation, creating a negative feedback in which solar radiation would be prevented from reaching the Earth's surface by increased cloud cover.

Because of this scientific uncertainty, many countries are currently unwilling to spend money finding alternatives to the burning of fossil fuels — let alone cooperate in a world agreement to tackle global warming.

Unequal responsibilities

The main culprits in global warming are just a few developed countries. These countries have spewed vast quantities of greenhouse gases into the atmosphere. Yet they have been asking developing countries to find alternatives to burning fossil fuels.

Understandably, the developing countries see this as unfair. They argue — as India did very vigorously during the 1992 Earth Summit — that they should be allowed to enjoy the benefits of industrialisation without restriction, even if it means harming the global environment.

Tackling global warming: will carbon credits work?

Since 1992, governments from across the globe have been working together to tackle global warming. In 1992 over 160 of them signed a Convention on Climate Change at the first Earth Summit in Rio de Janeiro, Brazil. The convention established a set of targets for reducing the emission of carbon dioxide and other greenhouse gases into the atmosphere.

In late 1997 a follow-up meeting was held in Kyoto, Japan, where a Climate Change Protocol set more specific targets for pollution mitigation and proposed a scheme to enable governments to reach these targets. It is called a 'pollution credit system' and the first greenhouse gas to be reduced using this system is to be carbon dioxide. The scheme was due to be ratified and implemented after an intergovernmental meeting in the Hague in November 2000. However, disagreements over the details of the scheme mean that it will probably not come into force until 2002. How will the scheme work? And will it succeed in lowering carbon dioxide emissions?

The system works as follows. Each country is given an annual carbon dioxide pollution limit. Countries which exceed their limit must pay for the privilege by one or a mixture of the following:

- paying a fine
- paying for ways to reduce domestic carbon dioxide emissions (e.g. by investing in wind or solar power)
- buying a portion of the 'unused' pollution from a country which is not exceeding its annual pollution limit

For instance, let's take the perspective of a major US power company which is partly responsible for the country's carbon dioxide emissions being 15% higher today than they were in 1990. That company could either:

- pay for 'cleaner' technologies to be installed in its power plants
- pay for an old, 'dirty' power station in a less developed country like China to be fitted with cleaner technologies (like a 'carbon scrubber')
- pay for an area of Brazilian rainforest to be conserved for 20 years in order to prevent it being logged and burnt (burning wood is a major reason why atmospheric carbon dioxide levels have increased over the last 10 years)

Wealth inequalities between countries

Levels of wealth and development between countries remain as uneven as ever. While countries such as the USA and Japan are phenomenally rich and others — such as Taiwan and Mexico — are fast developing, some countries are desperately poor and will remain so for the foreseeable future (e.g. Ethiopia, Burkina Faso and Burundi). For many of these poorer countries protecting the environment is an expensive luxury. For instance, though the burning of wood releases carbon dioxide into the atmosphere, it is also an essential means of cooking food and keeping warm for many poor people in the less economically developed world.

Figure H Global warming

The human environment

Migration

1 Figure I shows the city of Cambridge divided into wards. Figure J shows the relationship between the population percentage change in each ward (1981–91) and the percentage of population who migrated into Cambridgeshire within the last year. Complete Figure J by adding the information given in Table A.

Table A Population information about Cambridgeshire

	Population change (%)	Migration into Cambridgeshire (%)
Arbury	–2.3	2.3
Castle	13.4	11.4

(4 marks)

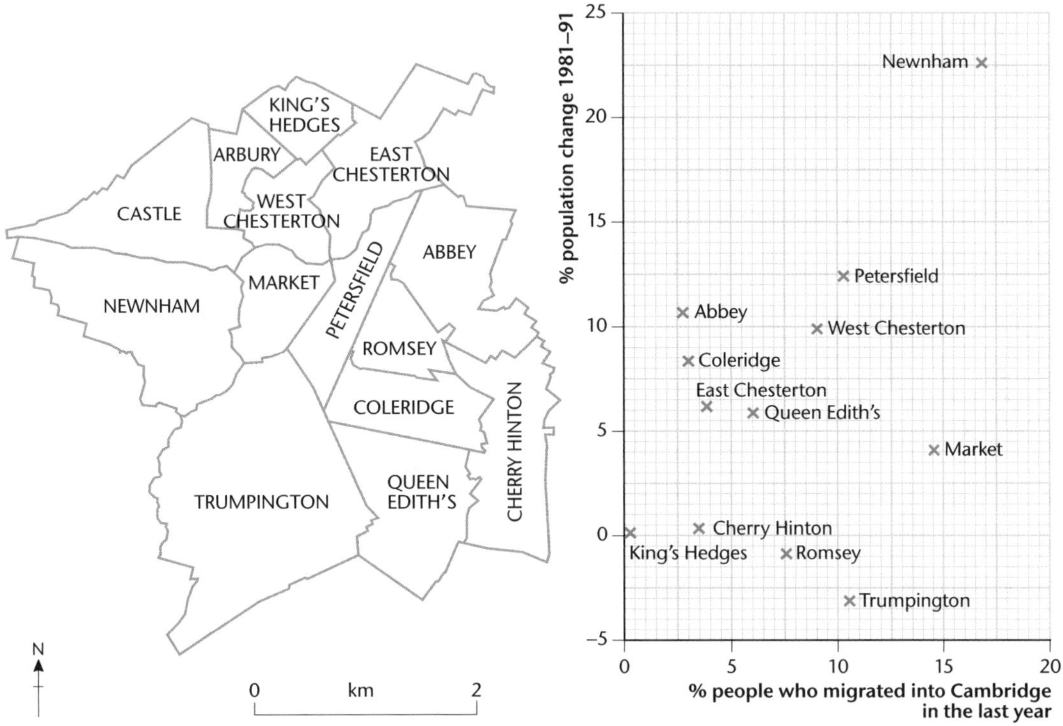

Figure I The city of Cambridge, divided into wards

Figure J Population change in Cambridgeshire, 1981–91

2 Using Figure I, describe and suggest reasons for the relationship shown in Figure J. (8 marks)

3 On the Ordnance Survey map extract (Figure K), locate the area north of the A14. Label the map to identify the evidence of

a recent growth

b the reasons such locations are attractive to in-migrants. (8 marks)

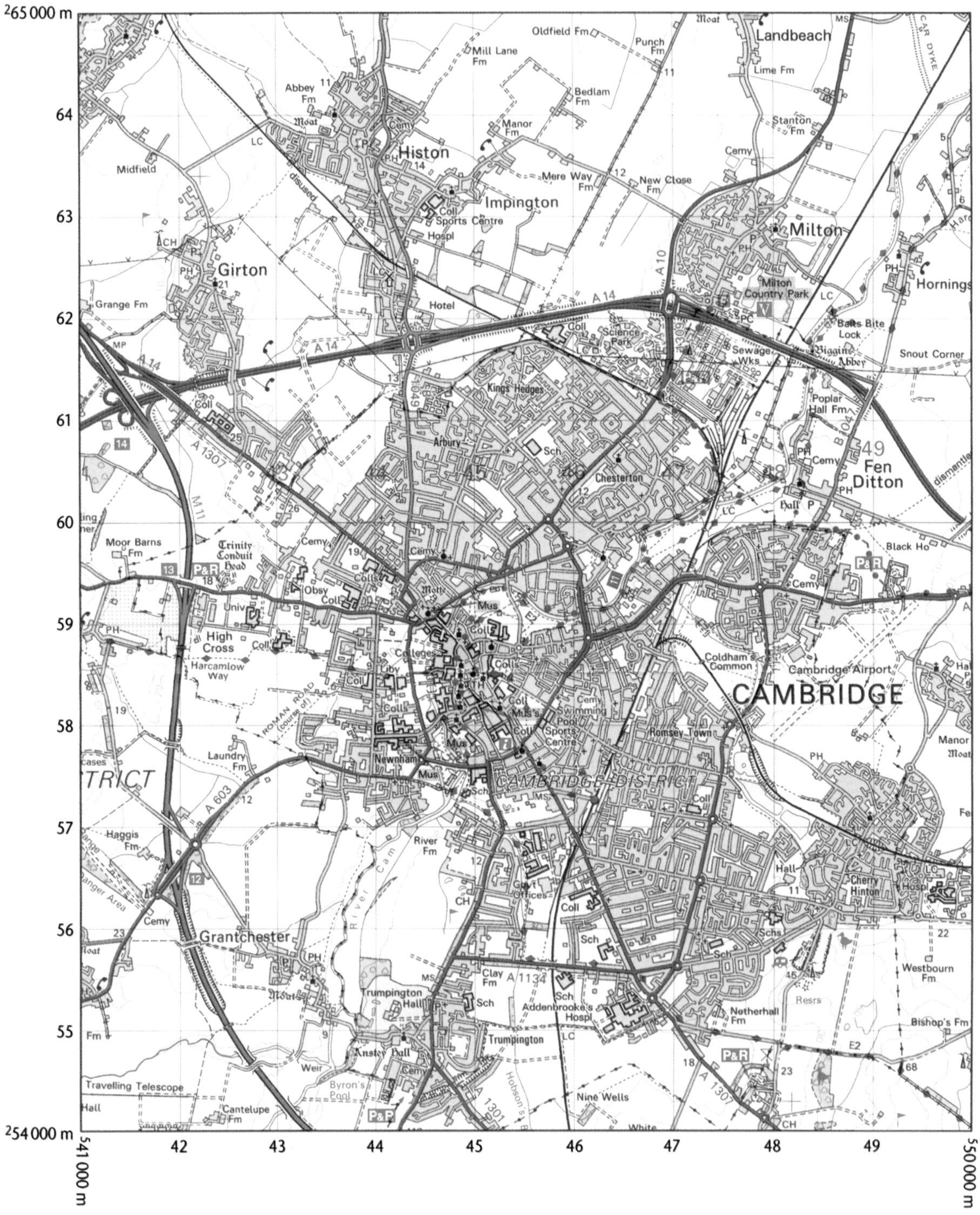

Figure K An Ordnance Survey map of Cambridgeshire

4 The distribution of refugees by host country is shown on Figure L. Describe and comment on the pattern shown by Figure L. (7 marks)

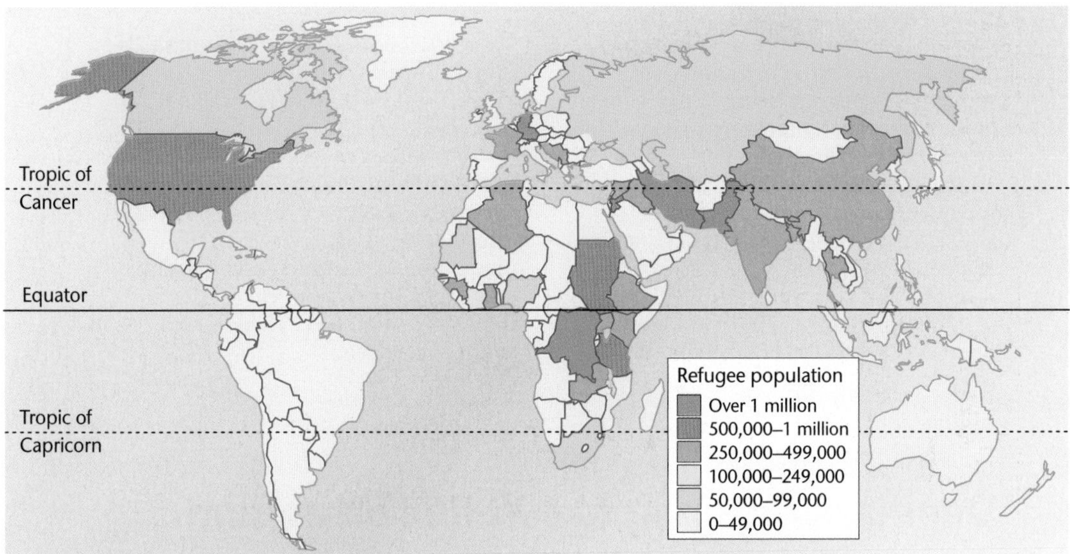

Figure L The distribution of refugees by host country, 1995

5 The two extracts from newspaper articles in Figure M (page 214) relate to different types of refugee movements. Table B lists some concepts relating to migration. Outline the meaning of the following concepts that are given on Table B:

a positive factor
b negative factor
c intervening obstacle (6 marks)

Table B Migration concepts

Concept	Illustration
Positive factor at origin	Family ties
Negative factor at origin	
Intervening obstacle	
Positive factor at destination	
Negative factor at destination	Demand that foreigners pass tests in local language

6 Complete Table B by identifying an illustration of the remaining concepts in the newspaper articles in Figure M. (3 marks)

7 Distinguish between economic and political causes of migration and suggest a link between them. (6 marks)

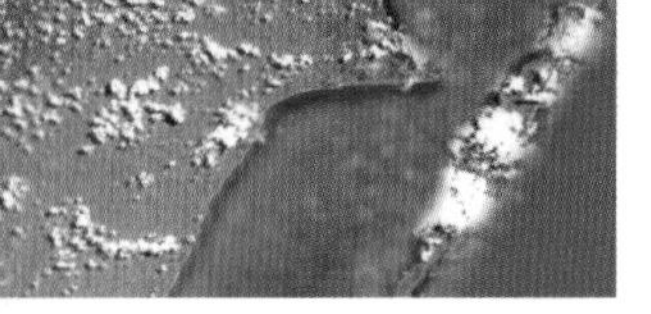

Volcano refugees spend third day without food

An international relief operation began in central Africa yesterday as hundreds of thousands of refugees fleeing Congo's erupting volcano, Nyirangongo, spent a third day without food or clean water.

Homeless after lava swallowed up much of the town of Goma, hordes of refugees huddled together on the streets of Gysenyi in neighbouring Rwanda.

The UN built two camps outside Gysenyi but by last night only 4,700 of the several hundred thousand displaced people had received food and water. The immediate threat is from the poisoned waters of Lake Kivu. With no fresh water available, refugees have no alternative but to drink from the lake.

The first medical assistance arrived yesterday. Twenty of the first 60 patients treated had dysentery. Others had respiratory diseases and eye infections caused by the lava fumes.

A spokesman said: 'There is a real risk of a cholera epidemic'

Adapted from the *Daily Telegraph*, April 2001

Denmark calls halt to soft line on asylum

Denmark, which prided itself as an immigrants' haven, yesterday dumped its liberal asylum policies in favour of a law designed to prevent all but a few foreigners from settling there.

The uncompromising 'new policy for foreigners' put forward by the centre-right government was approved by 59 votes to 48, thanks to support from the anti-immigration Danish People's Party.

Human rights' groups view the law as a 'racist' reaction to 11 September. It ends Denmark's reputation within the EU as a beacon of liberalism and multiculturalism,

The law tightens rules for asylum, cuts benefits for migrants by up to 50% and ends the automatic right to bring in a spouse.

It extends the waiting period for citizenship from 3 to 7 years. Before they can acquire nationality, foreigners have to pass tests in written and spoken Danish and in Danish culture.

About 7% of the 5.3 million population is of foreign descent.

Adapted from the *Daily Telegraph*, June 2002

Figure M Types of refugee movement

8 You have experience of geography fieldwork as part of your course.

a For *any* geography fieldwork study that you have undertaken, outline the *aim*, one *objective* and the *theory/concepts* that provided the idea for study. (3 marks)

b For your chosen study, identify one item of *primary data* which was collected. Outline the method of collection and how one risk related to this collection was minimised. (5 marks)

(50 marks)

The following would have been included in the resource booklet:

- Figures I, K, L, M

The Ordnance Survey map extract (Figure K) would have been presented in the resource booklet, together with Figure I, to give candidates a chance to make themselves familiar with the area. A black-and-white copy of the area north of the A14 would have been included in the examination paper.

A2

Module 4

Challenge and change in the natural environment

Chapter 8

Coast processes and problems

The coast and marine energy

Coastlines are important to the human race. Fifty per cent of the world's population live on coastal plains and in other locations with easy access to the sea. The coastline itself consists of a series of different zones in which specific conditions prevail that depend on factors such as tides, wave action and the depth of the sea. Figure 8.1 illustrates how these zones relate to each other:

- **Backshore** is the area between the high water mark (HWM) and the landward limit of marine activity. Changes normally take place here only during storm activity.
- **Foreshore** is the area lying between the HWM and the low water mark (LWM). It is the most important zone for marine processes in times that are not influenced by storm activity.
- **Inshore** is the area between the LWM and the point where waves cease to have any influence on the land beneath them.
- **Offshore** is the area beyond the point where waves cease to impact upon the sea bed and in which activity is limited to deposition of sediments.

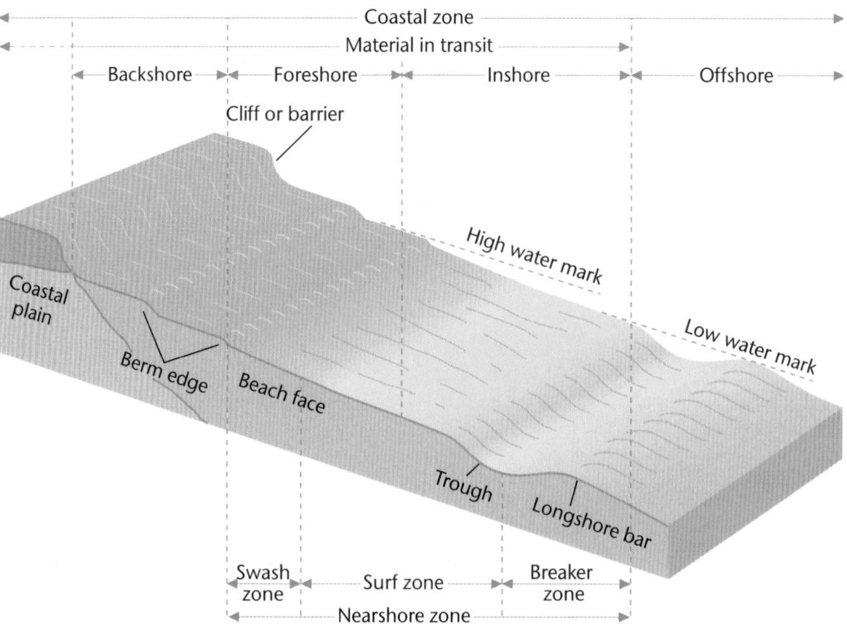

Figure 8.1 Coastal zones

There are a number of factors that determine the shape, form and appearance of a coastline:

- **wave** size, frequency, type, energy produced and direction
- **local sea currents**
- **longshore drift**
- **tides**
- **depth of water offshore**
- type and amount of **sediments offshore**
- **rock type and structure**
- **sub-aerial processes**: runoff, weathering and mass movement
- **land-based agents of erosion**: rivers and glaciers
- **climate and weather**
- **fetch** — the distance over open sea that a wind blows to generate waves; the longer the fetch, the greater the potential for large waves
- **long-term sea-level change** — eustatic (worldwide) and isostatic (local)
- **coastal ecosystems** — sand dunes, salt marshes and mangroves
- the presence of **coral**
- **human activity**

Coastlines are **dynamic** environments that are undergoing continual change. In the short term, tides, waves and longshore drift change the shape, form and appearance of elements of a coastline. Changes in sea level bring about long-term change. The shape of the British Isles has altered continually over the last few thousand years. At the end of the Pleistocene glaciation, Britain was joined to the rest of the European continent. Rising sea levels from around 9,000 years ago eventually formed the Straits of Dover, much of the English Channel and the North Sea (Figure 8.2).

The position of the coastline is continually changing. In some places, land is being lost to wave erosion and sub-aerial processes. In other parts, land is being gained by deposition. In Roman times, the Holderness coastline of Yorkshire was several kilometres further east of its present position. However, erosion of the mainly boulder-clay cliffs has resulted in the loss of 29 villages with many modern settlements only surviving because of extensive coastal protection schemes. At the present time, the small village of Mappleton is the most threatened by this action (Photograph 8.1).

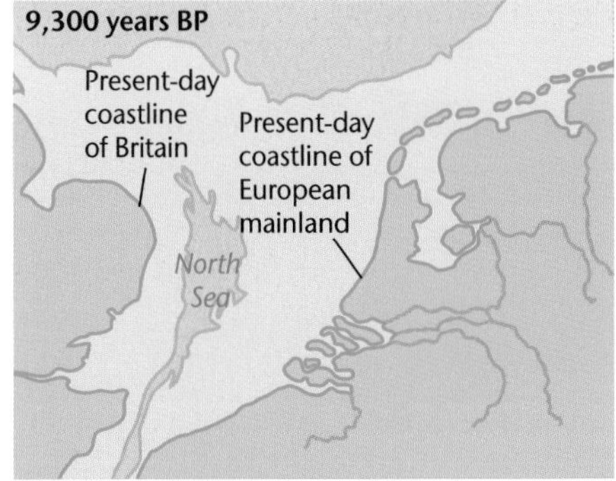

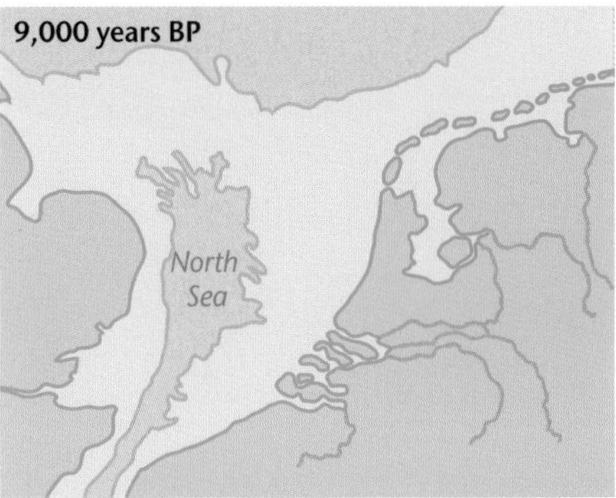

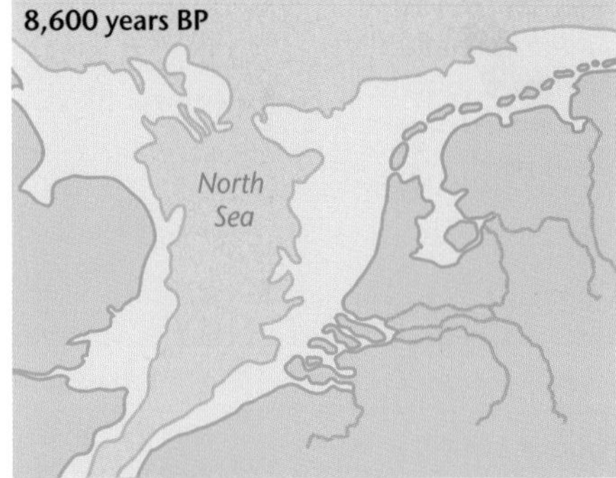

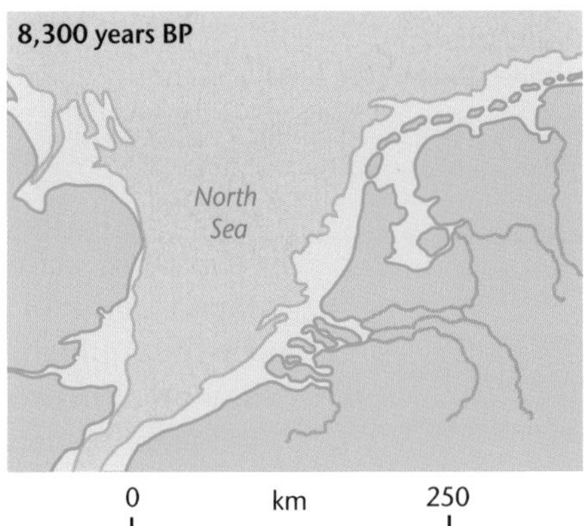

Figure 8.2 The growth of the North Sea

TopFoto

Photograph 8.1 Mappleton on the Holderness coast is threatened as cliffs have eroded over recent years

There have been repeated warnings that other parts of the east coast of England could be threatened if the sea breaks through coastal defences. In East Anglia, in the winter of 2004, there was a real threat that this would happen in the Aldeburgh area and that the line of the coast would be completely redrawn. Even though the sea did not break through, inhabitants of the area remain pessimistic about the future. The attitude of DEFRA (Department for Environment Food and Rural Affairs) is that there is not enough money to meet every flood and coastal defence need and as the Aldeburgh area is sparsely populated, the value of property defended is not high enough to justify the cost. The newspaper extract from October 2004 (Figure 8.3) shows the extent to which the coastline would be redrawn in this area if the sea were to break through the coastal defences.

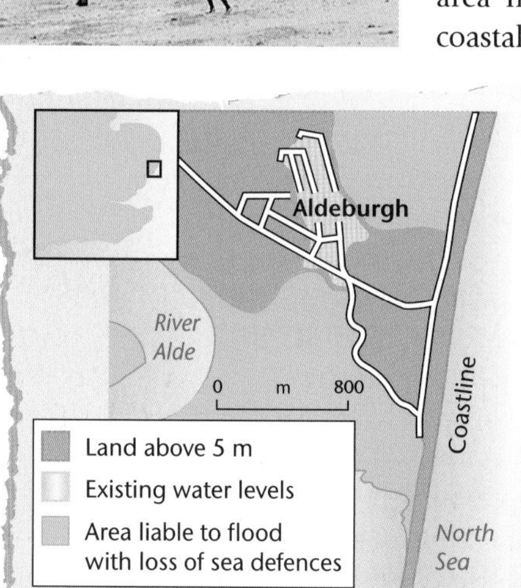

Aldeburgh could become an island and the Suffolk coastline could alter as far south as Felixstowe if the sea breaks through obsolete sea defences this winter, experts have told local residents.

Among the features under threat if the sea wall is breached at Bawdsey is a line of four Martello towers, built to fend off invasion by Napoleon, including one that is now at 'imminent risk' of sliding into the sea.

The Environment Agency accepts the need for repairs but says the area is too thinly populated for funding.

Figure 8.3 Extract from the Daily Telegraph, October 2004

The coast as a system

A coastline is regarded as an **open** system because inputs are received, and outputs are transferred, across the boundary of the system.

Inputs consist of:

- **Energy** to drive the system. This is provided by waves, winds, tides and currents. The input is irregularly boosted by storm surges and tidal waves. **Spatial** variations in energy result from variations in the strength of the wind, the fetch, and the number and intensity of storms. Storms are most frequent in mid-latitudes where low-pressure systems often dominate and in the tropics where low-pressure systems (tropical storms/hurricanes) occur. There are also

temporal variations on a seasonal and even a daily scale. For example, in the mid-latitudes depressions are more frequent in winter whereas in the part of the tropics that is in the northern hemisphere, the hurricane season is in late summer and autumn.

- **Sediment**, provided within the system from the erosion of coastlines by waves. However, most sediment comes from outside the system. It is brought mainly by rivers, which transport a whole range of different sediments from land to sea. Weathering and mass-wasting also contribute material from cliff-faces.
- **Changes in sea level.**
- **Human activities.**

Coastline **processes** are mainly those associated with erosion, constructive wave action, longshore drift and the wind. Longshore drift is the main agent that relocates materials from coastlines dominated by erosion processes to areas where depositional landforms are constructed, such as beaches, spits and bars. Wind can also carry material, in this case from the shoreline inland.

The **outputs** of the system are:

- coastal **landforms**, both erosive and depositional
- accumulations of **sediment** above the tidal limit
- loss of **wave energy**

Key terms

Coastal management Controlling development and change within the coastal zone. Good management takes into account both physical and environmental considerations as well as the views of residents and other interested groups, in order to create a balanced policy.

Marine processes Processes operating upon a coastline that are connected with the sea, such as waves, tides and longshore drift.

Sub-aerial processes Processes operating on the land but affecting the shape of the coastline, such as weathering, mass movement and runoff.

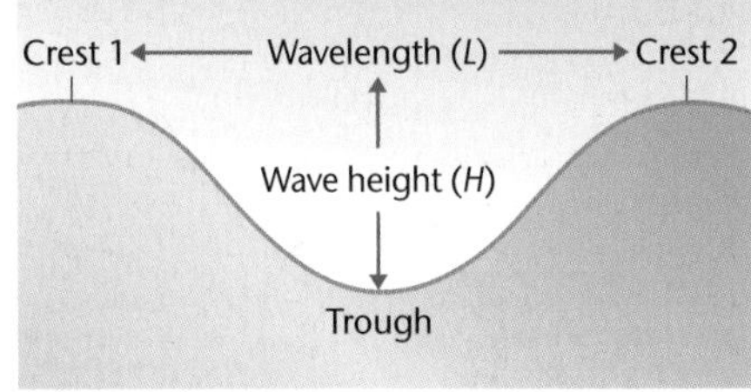

Figure 8.4 Wave terminology

Waves

Waves (Figure 8.4) are created by transfer of energy from the wind blowing over the sea surface. The energy acquired by waves depends upon the strength of the wind, the length of time it is blowing and the distance over which it blows (**fetch**). As waves approach shallow water, friction with the sea bed increases and the base of the wave begins to slow down. This has the effect of increasing the height and steepness of the wave until the upper part plunges forward and the wave 'breaks' onto the beach (Figure 8.5). The rush of water up the beach is known as **swash** and

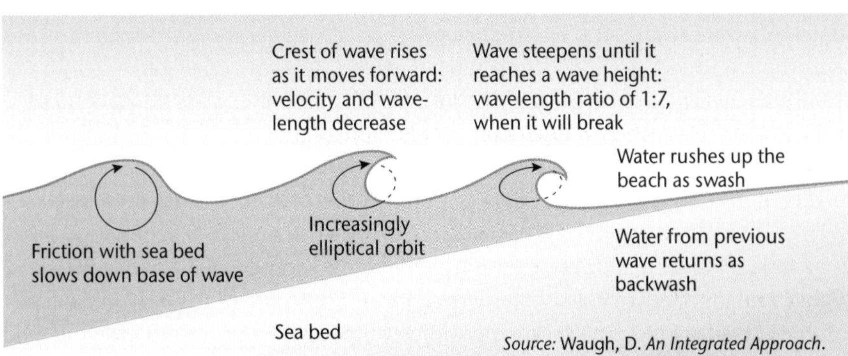

Figure 8.5 Wave movement

any water running back down the beach into the sea is the **backwash**. Waves can be described as constructive or destructive.

Constructive waves

Constructive waves (Figure 8.6) are usually associated with long fetch. They tend to be low waves, but with a long wavelength, often up to 100 m. They have a low frequency of around six to eight per minute. As they approach the beach, the wave front steepens only slowly, giving a gentle spill onto the beach surface. Swash rapidly loses volume and energy as water percolates through the beach material. This tends to give a very weak backwash which has insufficient force to pull sediment off the beach or to impede swash from the next wave. As a consequence, material is slowly, but constantly, moved up the beach, leading to the formation of ridges (or **berms**).

Figure 8.6
A constructive wave

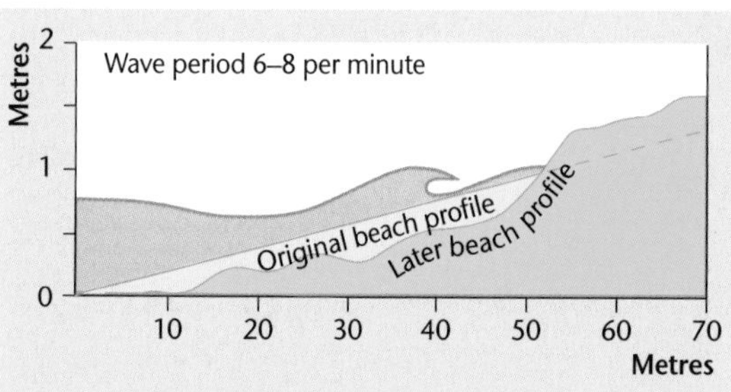

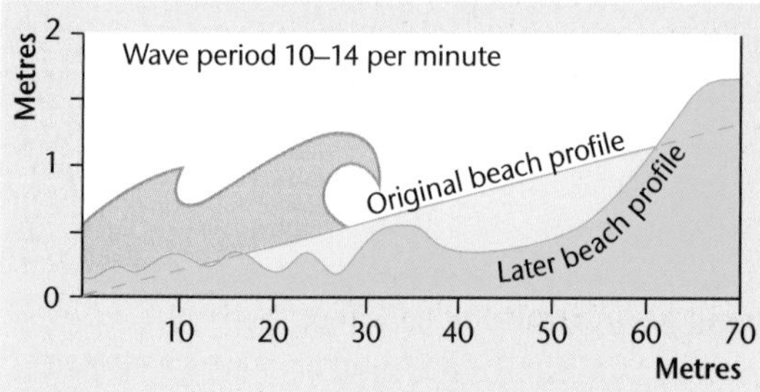

Figure 8.7
A destructive wave

Destructive waves

Destructive waves (Figure 8.7) tend to occur when the fetch is shorter. They are high waves with a steep form and a high frequency (10–14 per minute). As they approach the beach, they rapidly steepen and, when breaking, they plunge down. This creates a powerful backwash as there is little forward movement of water. It also inhibits the swash from the next wave. Very little material is moved up the beach, leaving the backwash to pull material away. Destructive waves are commonly associated with steeper beach profiles. The force of each wave may project some shingle well towards the rear of the beach where it forms a large ridge known as the **storm beach**.

Effects of waves

Most beaches are subject to the alternating action of constructive and destructive waves. Constructive waves build up the beach and result in a steeper beach profile. This encourages waves to become more destructive (as destructive waves are associated with steeper profiles). With time, though, destructive waves move material back towards the sea, reducing the beach angle and encouraging more constructive waves. So the pattern repeats itself. This type of **negative feedback** should encourage a state of **equilibrium**, but this is impossible as other factors, such as wind strength and direction, are not constant.

When waves approach a coastline that is not of a regular shape, they are **refracted** and become increasingly parallel to the coastline. Figure 8.8 shows a headland separating two bays. As each wave nears the coast, it tends to drag in the shallow water which meets the headland. This causes the wave to become higher and steeper with a shorter wavelength. That part of the wave in deeper water moves forward faster, causing the wave to bend. The overall effect is that wave energy becomes concentrated on the headland, causing greater erosion.

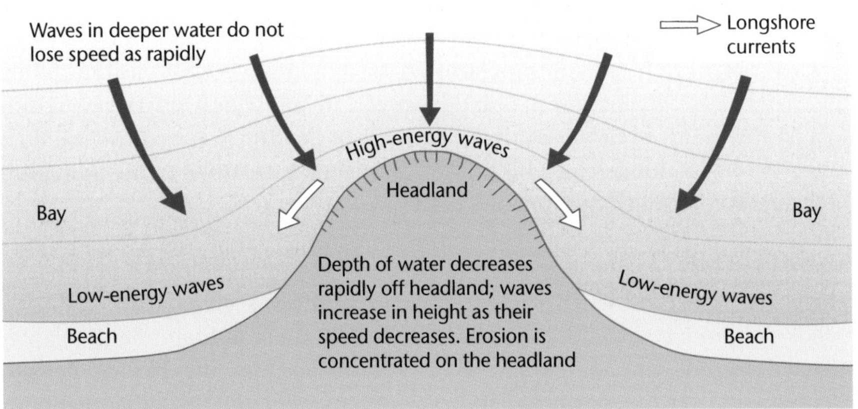

Figure 8.8
Wave refraction

The low-energy waves spill into the bay, resulting in beach deposition. As the waves pile against the headland, there may be a slight local rise in sea level that results in a longshore current from the headland, moving some of the eroded material towards the bays and contributing to the build up of the beaches.

Tides

Tides are the periodic rise and fall in the level of the sea. They are caused by the gravitational pull of the sun and moon, although the moon has much the greatest influence because it is nearer. The moon pulls water towards it, creating a high tide, and there is a compensatory bulge on the opposite side of the Earth (Figure 8.9). In the areas of the world between the two bulges, the tide is at its lowest.

As the moon orbits the Earth, the high tides follow it. Twice in a lunar month, when the moon, sun and Earth are in a straight line, the tide-raising force is strongest. This produces the highest monthly tidal range or **spring tide**. Also twice

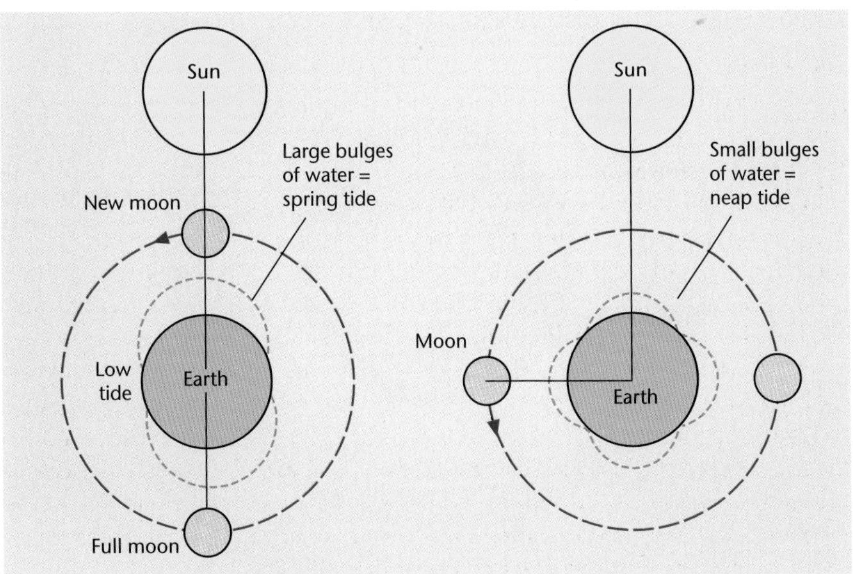

Figure 8.9
The causes of tides

a month, the moon and sun are positioned at 90° to each other in relation to the Earth. This alignment gives the lowest monthly tidal range, or **neap tide**.

Tidal range can be a significant factor in the development of a coastline. Along the coasts of the Mediterranean Sea, tidal ranges are low. This restricts wave action to a narrow width in the coastal zone. In parts of the British Isles, however, tidal ranges are high. This gives a wide zone of wave attack, resulting in the formation of wide wave-cut platforms in many places.

Storm surges

There are occasions when meteorological conditions giving rise to strong winds can produce much higher water levels than those at high tide. Two areas affected by this phenomenon are the North Sea and the Bay of Bengal. Depressions over the North Sea and cyclones affecting the Bay of Bengal both produce low-pressure conditions that have the effect of raising sea levels.

Case study The North Sea storm surge, 1953

The 1953 event was the most serious storm surge in the twentieth century to hit the coasts of countries bordering the North Sea. The reasons for the build up of water in the southern part of the sea were:

- a deep Atlantic depression moved across Scotland, deepening all the time, and by the time it had reached the coast of Denmark, the central pressure had fallen to around 970 mb
- such a rapid fall of pressure could have been responsible for a rise in the surface of the sea of about 0.5 m

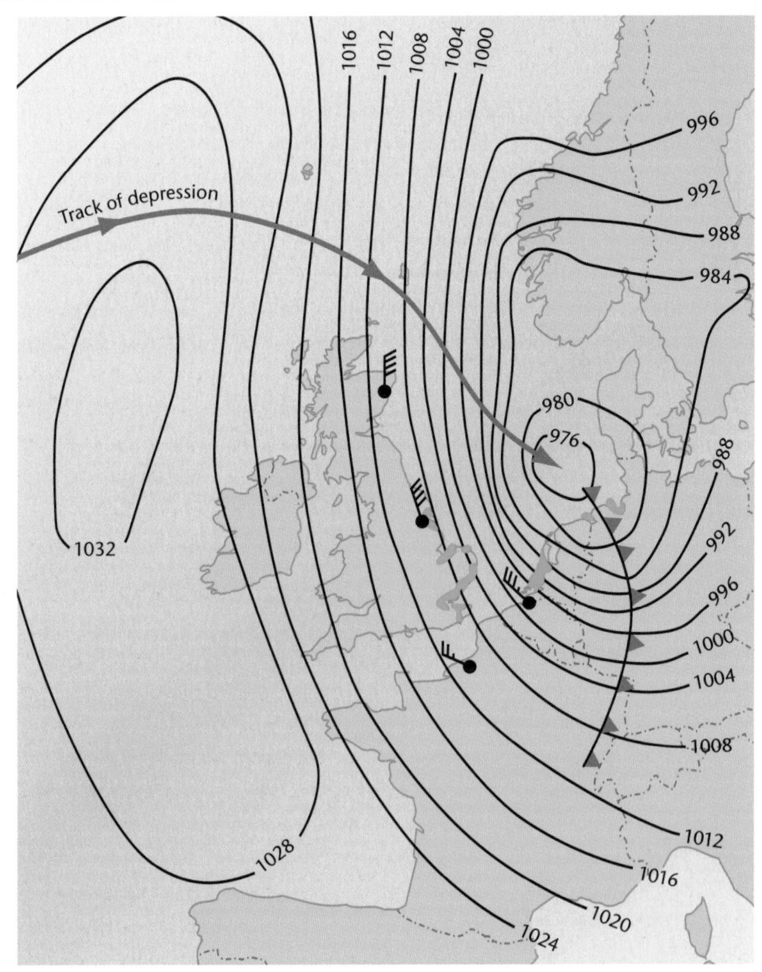

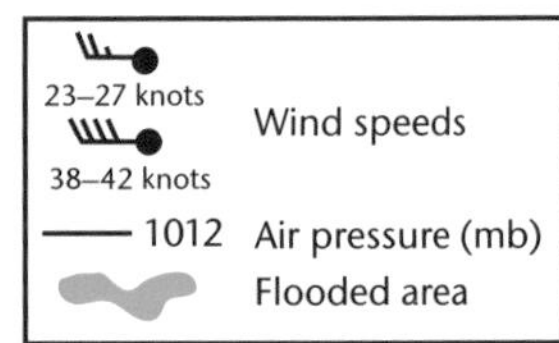

***Figure 8.10** The meteorological conditions of the North Sea storm surge, 1 February 1953*

- with an anticyclone lying to the west of the British Isles, a steep pressure gradient developed which resulted in strong winds moving south across the North Sea
- with the large fetch from the north, storm waves were produced that were over 6 m high
- all this coincided with high spring tides and rivers discharging into the sea at flood levels

With so much water pushing through the North Sea, it is not surprising that the consequences for southeast England were severe. Sea defences were breached in several places, particularly in those areas that depended upon sand dunes for protection, and thousands of hectares of low-lying land were flooded. There was a great deal of damage to property. Communication systems and agriculture were disrupted — there were huge livestock losses. Over 250 people were drowned.

In the Netherlands the damage was even greater. The dyke system, which protects huge areas of land, was breached. Over 1,800 people lost their lives and about 10% of the country's agricultural land was flooded. The Dutch government resolved that this should not happen again. Its response was to plan the Delta Scheme (page 249). The fear of a repeat in the Thames estuary led to the construction of the Thames Barrier (Photograph 8.6, page 241).

Case study Storm surges in Bangladesh

Bangladesh has the worst record in the late twentieth century for storm surges. Serious events occurred in 1970, 1985 and 1991. During a storm surge high winds, associated with cyclones forming to the south, push water northwards up the increasingly narrow Bay of Bengal. This water eventually hits the coast of densely populated Bangladesh. The country stands almost at sea level, covering most of the delta of the River Ganges. When cyclones hit, massive waves sweep water onto the land. The water level can rise by over 10 m.

Storm surges travel many kilometres inland, destroying farmland, villages and infrastructure, ruining crops and drowning livestock and people. The estimated death toll in the cyclone of 1970 was over 300,000. Most buildings in the villages are flimsy constructions made from wood and are easily swept away by the flood waters. The influx of salt water also causes long-term problems for the country. Soils are contaminated, which greatly affects the food supply, leaving many people dependent upon aid.

Bangladesh is beginning to fight back, taking steps to protect the coastal population from such surges (page 252). There is, however, increasing international concern about the possible effect of global warming on the country, as world sea levels are expected to rise during the twenty-first century.

Strong winds drive waves ahead of the storm, and this also builds up water levels. The shape of both areas means that water is increasingly concentrated into a space that is decreasing in size. High tides or, in the case of the Bay of Bengal, high river discharge, intensifies the effect. The North Sea storm surge of 1953 claimed many lives in southeast England and the Netherlands (see case study above). Bangladesh, at the head of the Bay of Bengal, has suffered from many storm surges. The most devastating storm surge of recent years occurred in 1970.

Longshore drift

When waves approach the shore at an angle, material is pushed up the beach by the swash in the same direction as the wave approach. As the water runs back down the beach, the backwash drags material down the steepest gradient, which

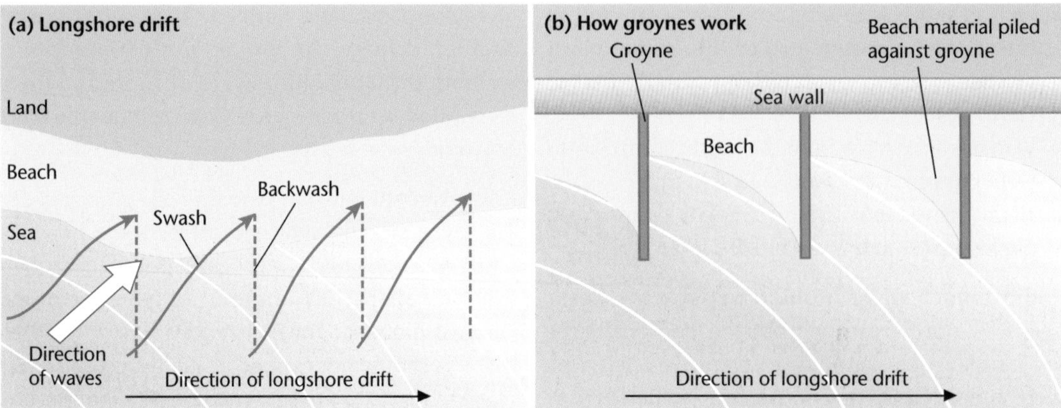

Figure 8.11 Longshore drift

is generally at right angles to the beach line. Over a period of time, sediment moves in this zig-zag fashion down the coast (Figure 8.11). If the material is carried some distance it will become smaller, more rounded and better sorted.

Obstacles such as groynes (wooden breakwaters) and piers interfere with this drift, and accumulation of sediment occurs on the windward side of the groynes, leading to entrapment of beach material. Deposition of this material also takes place in sheltered locations, such as at the head of a bay, and where the coastline changes direction abruptly — here spits tend to develop.

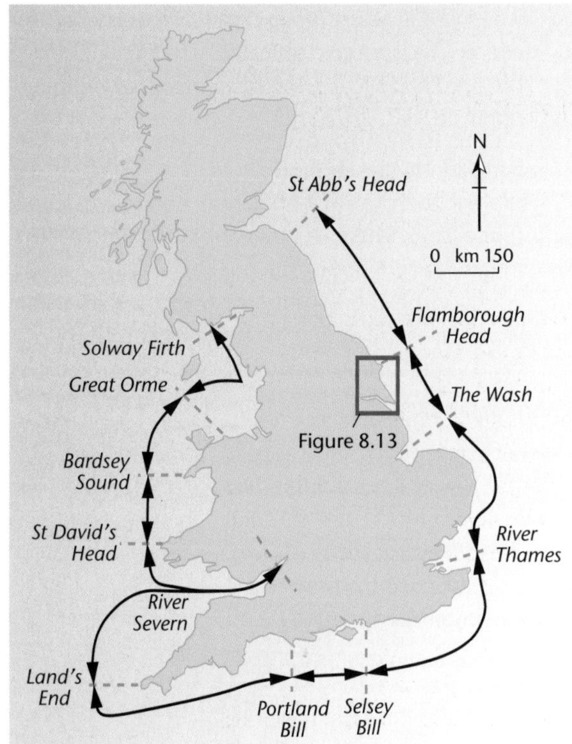

Figure 8.12 The sediment cells around England and Wales

Sediment cells

Coastal sediment comes from a variety of sources, including the sea bed, beaches, river channels and estuaries, and cliff erosion. The source of sediment which leads to the build up of certain depositional features around the British coast is in dispute. Research has suggested that sediment movements occur in distinct areas or **cells**, within which inputs and outputs are balanced. Along the coastline of England and Wales, 11 of these sediment cells have been identified (Figure 8.12). These are distinct areas of coastline separated from other areas by well-defined boundaries, such as headlands and stretches of deep water. In theory, sediment cells can be regarded as closed systems from which nothing is gained or lost. However, in reality, it is easy for fine sediments to find their way around headlands into neighbouring cells.

Sediment cells vary in size. The larger ones are divided into smaller sections (**sub-cells**), to allow closer study and management.

An example of a sub-cell is the one that operates between Flamborough Head and the Humber Estuary on the east coast of England (Figure 8.13).

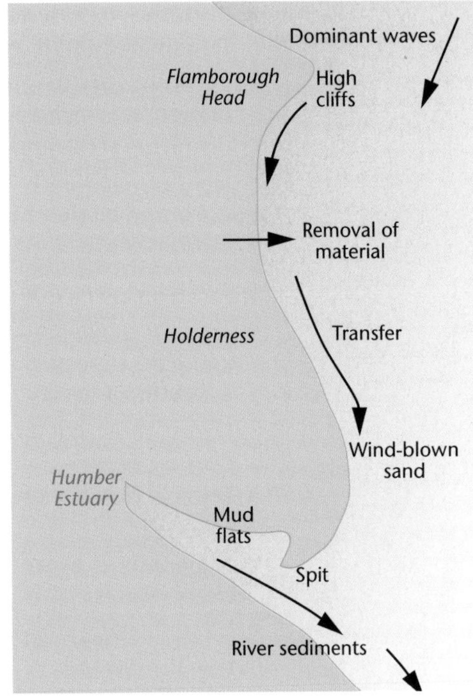

Figure 8.13 Detail of the Flamborough Head–Humber Estuary sub-cell

High-energy and low-energy coastlines

High-energy coastlines are those in which wave power is strong for a greater part of the year, for example the western coast of the British Isles. The prevailing and dominant wind direction on these coasts is westerly and they face the direction of the longest fetch. The maximum recorded wave height on western coasts is therefore greater than that on eastern coasts. For example, waves of up to 30 m have been recorded on the west coast of Ireland.

Many estuaries, inlets and sheltered bays are **low-energy** environments where wave heights are considerably lower. Here, waves spread outwards and energy is dissipated, leading to the deposition of transported material. Enclosed seas also contain low-energy environments. The Baltic Sea, for example, contains some of the longest depositional landforms in the world, mainly because of its sheltered waters and low tidal range.

Marine erosional processes and landforms

Processes of marine erosion

When waves break on a coastline they often do so with considerable energy. It has been estimated that waves breaking against the foot of a cliff can generate energy of 25–30 tonnes m^{-2}. There are several ways in which waves are able to erode coastlines:

- **Hydraulic action (wave quarrying)** — a breaking wave traps air as it hits a cliff face. The force of water compresses this air into any gap in the rock face, creating enormous pressure within the fissure or joint. As the water pulls back, there is an explosive effect of the air under pressure being released. The overall effect of this over time is to weaken the cliff face. Storms may then remove large chunks of it. This process can also lead to extensive damage to sea defences. Some coastal experts also point out that the sheer force of water itself (without debris) can exert an enormous pressure upon a rock surface, causing it to weaken. Such an activity is sometimes referred to as **pounding**.
- **Abrasion/corrasion** — the material the sea has picked up also wears away rock faces. Sand, shingle and boulders hurled against a cliff line will do enormous damage. This is also apparent on intertidal rock platforms, where sediment is drawn back and forth, grinding away at the platform.

- **Attrition** — the rocks in the sea which carry out abrasion are slowly worn down into smaller and more rounded pieces.
- **Solution (corrosion)** — although this is a form of weathering rather than erosion, it is included here as it contributes to coastal erosion. It includes the dissolving of calcium-based rocks (e.g. limestone) by the chemicals in sea water and the evaporation of salts from water in the rocks to produce crystals. These expand when they form and put stress upon rocks. Salt from sea-water spray is capable of corroding several types of rock.

There are many factors that affect the rate of erosion:

- **Wave steepness and breaking point** — steeper waves are higher-energy waves and have a greater erosive power than low-energy waves. The point at which waves break is also important — waves that break at the foot of a cliff release more energy and cause more damage than those that break some distance away.
- **Fetch** — how far a wave has travelled determines the amount of energy it has collected.
- **Sea depth** — a steeply-shelving sea bed at the coast will create higher and steeper waves.
- **Coastal configuration** — headlands attract wave energy through refraction.
- **Beach presence** — beaches absorb wave energy and can therefore provide protection against marine erosion. Steep, narrow beaches easily dissipate the energy from flatter waves, while flattish, wide beaches spread out the incoming wave energy and are best at dissipating high and rapid energy inputs. Shingle beaches also deal with steep waves as energy is rapidly dissipated through friction and percolation.
- **Human activity** — people may remove protective materials from beaches (sand), which may lead to more erosion, or they may reduce erosion by the construction of sea defences (discussed later). Sea defences in one place, however, may lead to increased rates of erosion elsewhere on the same coastline.

Geology

Several geological factors affect the rate of erosion.

Lithology refers to the characteristics of rocks, especially resistance to erosion and permeability. Very resistant rocks such as granite, and to a lesser extent chalk, tend to be eroded less than weaker materials such as clay. Some rocks are well-jointed (e.g. limestone), which means that the sea can penetrate along lines of weakness, making them more vulnerable to erosion. Variation in the rates at which rocks wear away is known as **differential erosion**.

The **structure** and variation of the rocks also affects erosion. When rocks lie parallel to the coast, they produce a very different type of coastline than when they lie at right angles. Figure 8.14 shows two contrasting types of coastline that can be found close to one another in Purbeck (southern England). The southern part of the coast has the rocks running parallel to it — known as a **concordant** coastline. Here the resistant Portland limestone forms cliffs, and these have protected the coast from erosion, only allowing the sea to break through in a few

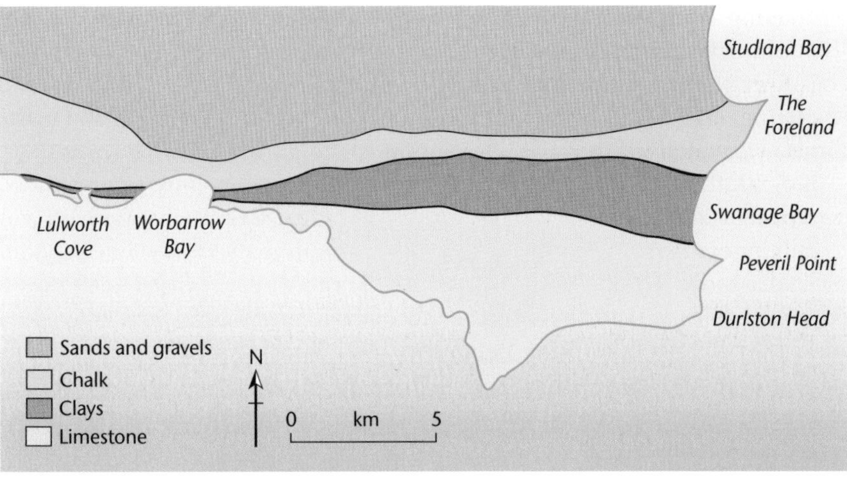

Figure 8.14
The Purbeck coast

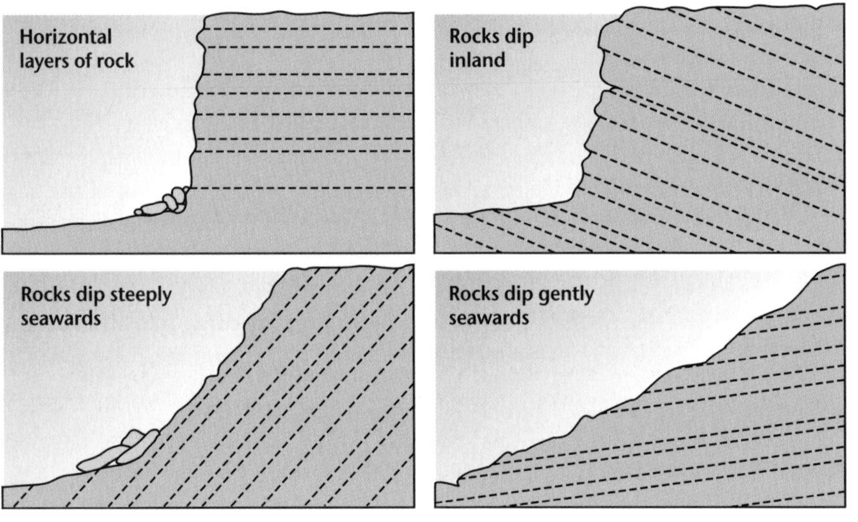

Figure 8.15
The influence of rock strata on coastlines

places (the large area of Worbarrow Bay and the small area of Lulworth Cove) to the clay behind.

To the east, the rocks run at right angles to the coast (known as **discordant**), allowing the sea to penetrate along the weaker clays and gravels and produce large bays (e.g. Swanage Bay) flanked by outstanding headlands (The Foreland and Peveril Point).

The **dip** of the rocks is also a major factor. The steepest cliffs tend to form in rocks that have horizontal strata or which dip gently inland, whereas rocks that dip towards the coast tend to produce much more gently sloping features (Figure 8.15).

Sub-aerial processes

In addition to marine processes, there are also sub-aerial (land-based) processes which shape the coastline. These processes come under the general headings of

weathering and **mass movement**. Solution was included in the marine processes listed above because it is a major process that combines with erosion to produce coastlines. Other weathering processes that can be effective include frost shattering, exfoliation (thermal expansion), biological weathering and other forms of chemical weathering than solution.

Biological weathering is quite active on coastlines. Some marine organisms, such as the piddock (a shellfish), have specially adapted shells that enable them to drill into solid rock. They are particularly active in chalk areas where they can produce a sponge-like rock pitted with holes. Seaweed attaches itself to rocks and the action of the sea can be enough to cause swaying seaweed to prise away loose rocks from the sea floor. Some organisms, algae for example, secrete chemicals capable of promoting solution.

Mass movement is common on coastlines, particularly those that are steep, and includes the following:

- **rock falls** from cliffs undercut by the sea
- **landslides** on cliffs made from softer rocks or deposited material, which slip down when lubricated
- **mudflows** — heavy rain can cause fine material to flow downhill where it sometimes takes on the appearance, and movement, of a glacier
- where softer material overlies much more resistant materials, cliffs are often subject to **slumping**. With excessive lubrication, whole sections of the cliff face may move downwards with a slide plane that is concave, producing a rotational movement. Slumps are a very common feature of the British coast, particularly where glacial deposits form the coastal areas, e.g. east Yorkshire and north Norfolk. Figure 9.28 (page 276) shows a typical rotational slump in an area where glacial deposits form cliffs on top of an impermeable clay layer.

Features produced by coastal erosion

Headlands and bays

Figure 8.14 shows the impact of geology on a coastline. There are many similar parts of the British coastline where there are areas of alternating resistant and less resistant rocks. The less resistant rocks experience most erosion and develop into bays, while the more resistant rocks become headlands. Because of refraction, the headlands receive the highest-energy waves and are more vulnerable to the forces of erosion than are the bays. The bays experience low-energy waves that allow sediment to accumulate and form beaches. These act to protect that part of the coastline.

Where the rocks run parallel with the coast, as in Purbeck (Figure 8.14), it is possible for continued erosion to break through the more resistant rocks on the coast and begin to attack the weaker strata behind. If that happens, a cove will form which will be enlarged by erosion into a bay. In Purbeck, the sea has broken through the more resistant Portland stone to form Lulworth Cove (Photograph 8.2) in the clay behind (although there is some evidence that this could have been a former river mouth). Just along from Lulworth Cove is Stair Hole. Here the sea enters through two arches and has begun to work its way along the weaker clays (Figure 8.16).

Photograph 8.2 Aerial view of Lulworth Cove, Dorset. Worbarrow Bay is visible beyond

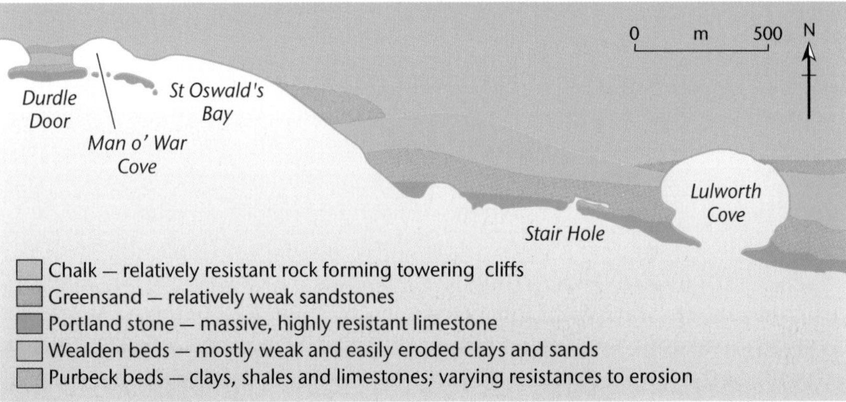

Figure 8.16 The geology of south Purbeck

Wave-cut platforms

When high and steep waves break at the foot of a cliff they concentrate their erosive capabilities into only a small area of the rock face. This concentration eventually leads to the cliff being undercut, forming a feature known as a **wave-cut notch**. Continued activity at this point increases the stress on the cliff and in time it collapses.

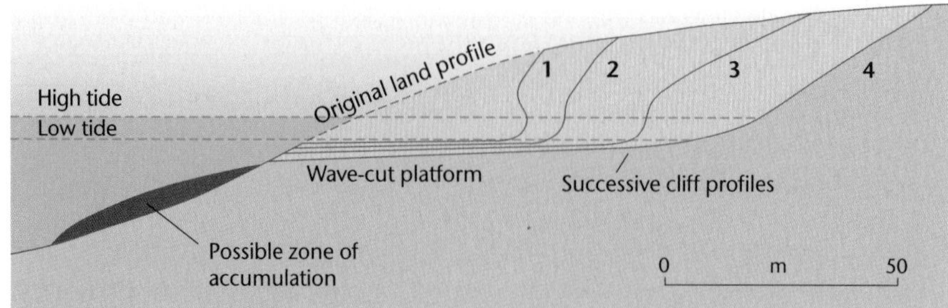

Figure 8.17 Formation of a wave-cut platform

The cliff begins to retreat, leaving at its base a gently sloping (less than 5°) wave-cut platform (Figure 8.17). When viewed from a distance, the platform looks remarkably even as it cuts across the rocks, regardless of their hardness. On closer inspection, the platform is often deeply cut into by abrasion from the huge amount of material that is daily carried across it, and by the effects of chemical action.

The platform continues to grow and, as it does, the waves break further out to sea and have to travel across more platform before reaching the cliff line. This leads to a greater dissipation of wave energy, reducing the rate of erosion on the headland and slowing down the growth rate of the platform. There tends, therefore, to be a limit to how big the feature can grow and some experts have suggested that growth beyond 0.5 km is unusual.

Geos, caves, blowholes, arches, stacks and stumps

These features are all independently observable on British coastlines, but they also represent a sequence of events in the erosion of a cliff or headland. On any cliff line the sea will attack the weakest parts such as cracks, joints or along bedding planes. Along a joint, the sea will cut inland, widening the crack to form a narrow, steep-sided inlet known as a **geo**.

In other circumstances the cliff is undercut and a **cave** is formed, usually from a combination of marine processes. If erosion continues upwards, it is possible for the cave to be extended to the top of the cliff, where a **blowhole** will form. Much more likely is that the cave will extend backwards to meet another, eventually creating a hole all the way through the headland, known as an **arch**.

As the cliff recedes and the wave-cut platform develops, the arch will eventually collapse, leaving its isolated portion as a **sea stack** standing above the platform. With time, the sea will exploit the wave-cut notch at the base of the stack, leading eventually to its collapse. A small raised portion of the wave-cut platform may be left marking the former position of the stack. This is known as a **stump**.

There are several well-known areas of Britain where these features stand out. Flamborough Head in Yorkshire has a well-developed wave-cut platform in chalk, along with sea caves, arches and a large blowhole. In the old red sandstone rocks of the Orkney Islands there is a well-known stack, the Old Man of Hoy, and the Needles on the Isle of Wight are another example of the same feature, although they look different because they are formed from chalk.

On Purbeck, in the Portland stone (a highly resistant limestone), the sea has cut the well-known arch of Durdle Door. Also on Purbeck (Figure 8.14) the chalk escarpment culminates in The Foreland and its detached pieces that are known as Old Harry Rocks. Figure 8.18 is a sketch of this area, where the sequence from headland to stack can be clearly seen. Marine erosion and sub-aerial processes will eventually reduce the upstanding parts of this area to a wave-cut platform.

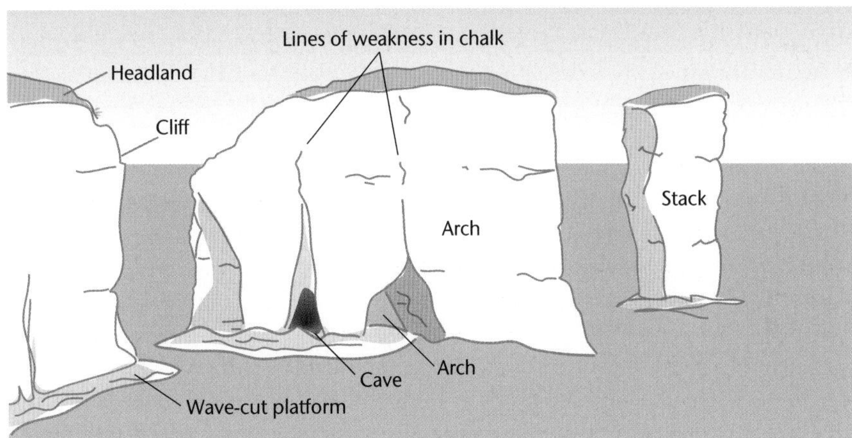

Figure 8.18 **Coastal erosion features seen at Old Harry Rocks, Purbeck**

Marine depositional processes and landforms

Features of coastal deposition

Deposition occurs on coastlines where sand and shingle accumulate faster than they are removed. It often takes place where the waves are low energy or where rapid coastal erosion provides an abundant supply of material.

Beaches

Beaches represent the accumulation of material deposited between low spring tides and the highest point reached by storm waves. They are mainly constructed from sand and shingle. Sand produces beaches with a gentle gradient (usually under 5°) because its small particle size means the sand becomes compact when wet, and allows very little percolation. Most of the swash therefore returns as backwash, little energy is lost to friction, and material is carried down the beach. This leads to the development of **ridges** and **runnels** in the sand at the low-water mark. These run parallel to the shoreline and are broken by channels that drain the water off the beach (Figure 8.19).

Shingle may make up the whole, or just the upper parts of the beach. The larger the size of the material, generally the steeper is the gradient of the beach (usually 10–20°). This is because water rapidly percolates through shingle, so the backwash is somewhat limited. This, together with the uneven surface, means that very little material is moved down the beach.

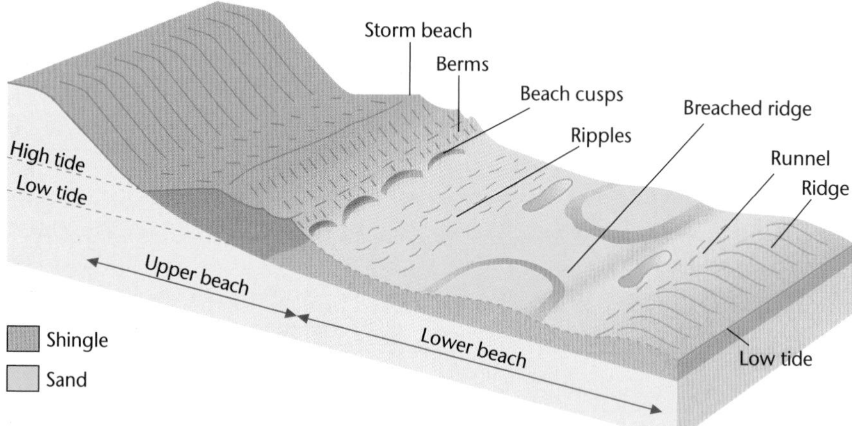

Figure 8.19 Beach features

At the back, strong swash at spring high-tide level will create a **storm beach**, a ridge composed of the biggest boulders thrown by the largest waves. Below this will be a series of ridges marking the successively lower high tides as the cycle goes from spring to neap. These beach ridges are known as **berms** and are built up by constructive waves. **Cusps** are semicircular-shaped depressions which form when waves break directly on to the beach and swash and backwash are strong. They usually occur at the junction of the shingle and sand beaches. The sides of the cusps channel incoming swash into the centre of the embayment and this produces a stronger backwash in the central area which drags material down the beach, deepening the cusp.

Below this, **ripples** are developed on the sand by wave action or tidal currents.

Spits and bars

A spit is a long, narrow piece of land that has one end joined to the mainland and projects out into the sea or across an estuary. Like other depositional features, it is composed of sand and/or shingle and the mixture very much depends upon the availability of material and the wave energy required to move it.

Figure 8.20 shows the formation of a spit. On the diagram, the prevailing winds and maximum fetch are from the southwest, so material will be carried from west to east along the coast by the process of longshore drift. Where the coastline changes to a more north–south orientation, there is a build-up of sand

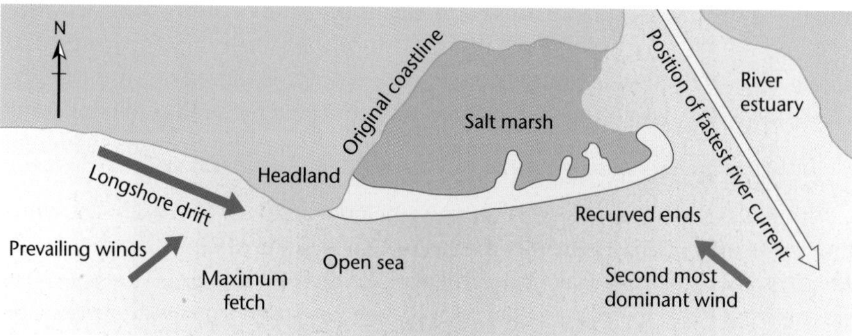

Figure 8.20 The formation of a spit

and shingle in the more sheltered water in the lee of the headland. As this material begins to project eastwards, storms build up more material above the high-water mark, giving a greater degree of permanence to the feature. Finer material is then carried further eastward, extending the feature into the deeper water of the estuary.

Increasingly, though, the end of the spit begins to curve round as wave refraction carries material round into the more sheltered water. The second most dominant wind direction and fetch may contribute to this, pushing the spit material back towards the mainland. Several curved ends may develop during a period of southeast weather until the dominant southwest movement reasserts itself. The spit cannot grow all the way across the estuary as the material will be carried seaward by the river and the deeper water at the centre inhibits growth.

Spits are often associated with two other features:

- **Sand dunes** form as dried out sand is blown to the back of the spit where it increasingly accumulates. Stability is achieved if vegetation such as marram grass begins to colonise the area and hold the dunes together.
- **Salt marshes** form as low-energy, gentle waves enter the sheltered area behind the spit and deposit the finer material such as silt and mud. This builds up to form a feature which is then colonised by vegetation.

Around the British coasts, well-known spits are found at Borth (west Wales), Dawlish Warren (Devon), Hurst Castle (Solent, Photograph 8.3), Orford Ness

Aerofilms

Photograph 8.3 *Aerial view of Hurst Castle Spit*

Figure 8.21 The spit at Orford Ness

(East Anglia, Figure 8.21) and Spurn Head (Humber estuary). A spit that joins an island to the mainland is known as a **tombolo**. The best example in Britain is Chesil Beach on the south coast of England. This links the Isle of Portland to the mainland and is about 30 km long.

If a spit develops across a bay where there is no strong flow of water from the landward side, it is possible for the sediment to reach across to the other side. In this case, the feature is known as a **bar**. Some bars, however, may simply be the result of the onshore migration of material from offshore as sea levels rose following the last ice age. Slapton Ley, a bar formed in Devon, is believed to have come about in this way. Recent work on Chesil Beach has suggested a similar cause, although the spit was probably formed by a combination of onshore migration of sea bed materials and longshore drift.

Other factors affecting coastlines

Long-term sea-level change

Tides are responsible for daily changes in the levels at which waves break on to the land, but the average position of sea level relative to the land has changed through time. Although sea levels have been fairly static since the last ice age, many changes took place during the Quaternary glaciation that reflected both the advance and retreat of the ice. A typical sequence would have run as follows:

- **Stage 1** As the climate begins to get colder, marking the onset of a new glacial period, an increasing amount of precipitation falls as snow. Eventually, this snow turns into glacier ice. Snow and ice act as a store for water, so the hydrological cycle slows down — water cycled from the sea to the land (evaporation, condensation, then precipitation) does not return to the sea. As a consequence, sea level falls and this affects the whole planet. Such a worldwide phenomenon is known as a **eustatic** fall.
- **Stage 2** The weight of ice causes the land surface to sink. This affects only some coastlines and then to a varying degree. Such a movement is said to be **isostatic** and it moderates the eustatic sea-level fall in some areas.
- **Stage 3** The climate begins to get warmer. Eventually the ice masses on the land begin to melt. This starts to replenish the main store and sea level rises worldwide (eustatic). In many areas this floods the lower parts of the land to produce **submergent** features such as flooded river valleys (**rias**) and flooded glacial valleys (**fjords**).

- **Stage 4** As the ice is removed from some land areas they begin to move back up to their previous levels (isostatic readjustment). If the isostatic movement is faster than the eustatic, then **emergent** features are produced such as **raised beaches**. Isostatic recovery is complicated as it affects different places in different ways. In some parts of the world it is still taking place as the land continues to adjust to having masses of ice removed. Today, the southeast of the British Isles is sinking while the northwest is rising. This reflects the fact that the ice sheets were thickest in northern Scotland and that this was the last area in which the ice melted.

As mean global temperatures continue to rise, there is an inevitable consequence for sea levels. As more standing ice melts, particularly in Antarctica and Greenland, fresh water will be released into the oceanic store. This could have serious implications for many islands in the Pacific Ocean and for low-lying coastal areas.

Submergent features

Rias are created by rising sea levels drowning river valleys. The floodplain of a river will vanish beneath the rising waters, but on the edges of uplands only the middle and upper course valleys will be filled with sea water, leaving the higher land dry and producing this feature. In Devon and Cornwall, for example, sea level rose and drowned the valleys of the rivers flowing off Dartmoor and the uplands of Cornwall. Good examples are the Fowey estuary in Cornwall and the Kingsbridge estuary in south Devon. Rias have a long section and cross profile typical of a river valley, and usually a dendritic system of drainage (Figure 8.22).

Fjords are drowned glacial valleys typically found on the coasts of Norway, southwestern New Zealand, British Columbia in Canada, southern Chile and Greenland. The coast of western Scotland contains fjords which are not as well developed as those in the areas above because the ice was not as thick and did not last for the same length of time.

Fjords have steep valley sides (cliff-like in places) and are fairly straight and narrow (Figure 8.23). Like glacial valleys, they have a typical U-shaped cross section with hanging valleys on either side. Unlike rias, they are not deepest at

Figure 8.22 A ria

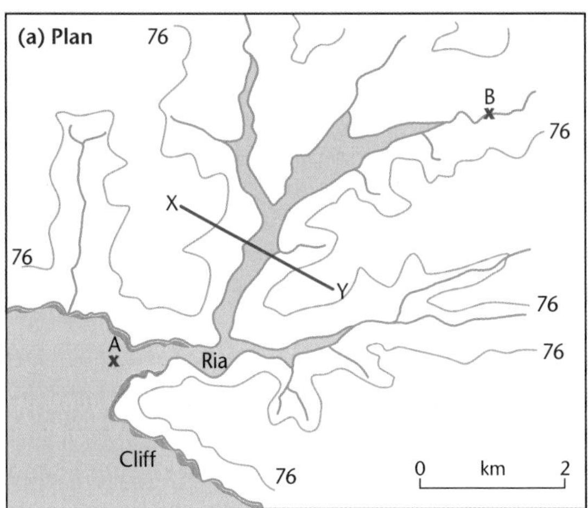

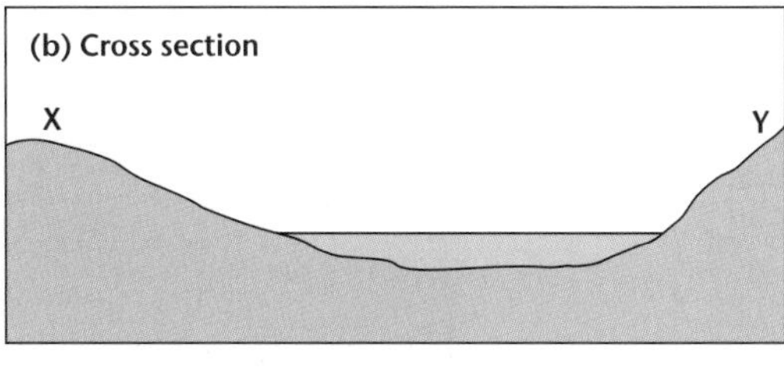

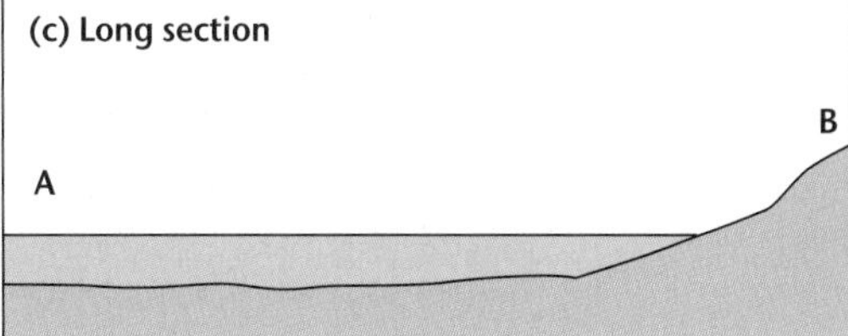

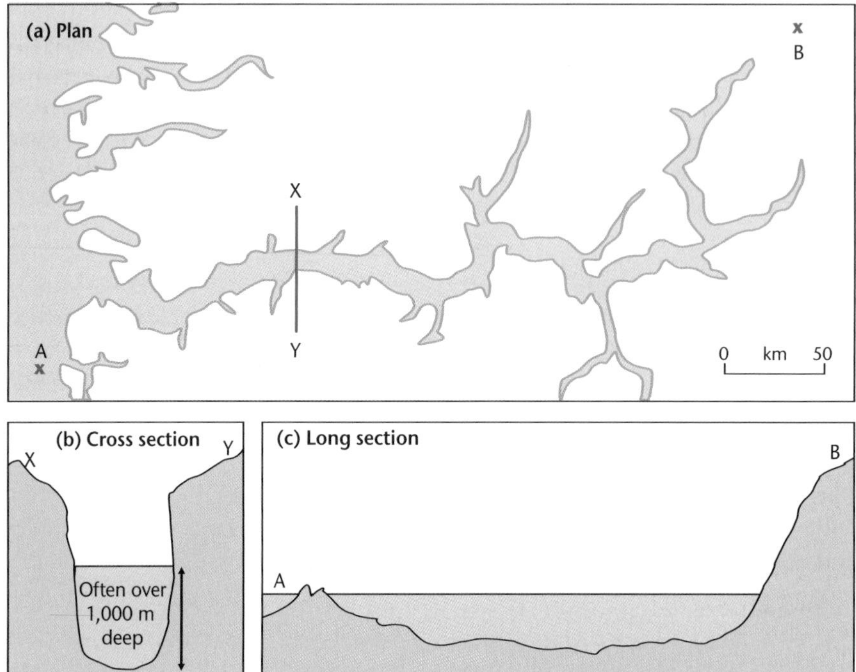

Figure 8.23 A fjord

Photograph 8.4 The entrance to Milford Sound fjord, New Zealand

the mouth, but generally consist of a glacial rock basin with a shallower section at the end, known as the **threshold**. They were formed when the sea drowned the lower part of glacial valleys that were cut to a much lower sea level. Good examples include Sogne Fjord in Norway, which is nearly 200 km long, and Milford Sound in New Zealand (Photograph 8.4).

Emergent features

Raised beaches are areas of former wave-cut platforms and their beaches which are at a level higher than the present sea level. Behind the beach it is not unusual to find old cliff lines with wave-cut notches, sea caves, arches and stacks. Raised beaches are common around the coasts of western Scotland where three levels have been recognised, at 8 m, 15 m and 30 m. Because of differential uplift these are only approximate heights.

On the west of the Isle of Arran there is a well-developed raised beach north of Drumadoon. This has a relict cliff, arches, stacks and caves, including the well-known King's Cave. This beach is around 4 or 5 m above present sea level and is probably the equivalent of the 8 m beach. It was clearly produced when the sea was at that level, which initially suggests that the sea has fallen to its present level. However, we know that sea levels have *risen* considerably (eustatic) since the end of the last ice age, so the beach must have reached its raised position by isostatic rising of the land. The land locally must have risen faster than the eustatic rise in sea level to create this emergence.

Vegetation, sedimentation and stabilisation

Coastal sand dunes

Coastal sand dunes are accumulations of sand shaped into mounds by the wind (Photograph 8.5). They represent a dynamic landform. Beaches are the source of the sand which, when dried out, is blown inland to form dunes. Sand is moved inland by a process known as **saltation** (a bouncing action which is also seen in particles moved along by running water).

During the day, the wind on the coastal fringe is generally from the sea. Air moves in response to the small pressure differentials set up by the warmer land

Malcolm Skinner

Photograph 8.5 Sand dunes at Formby, Merseyside

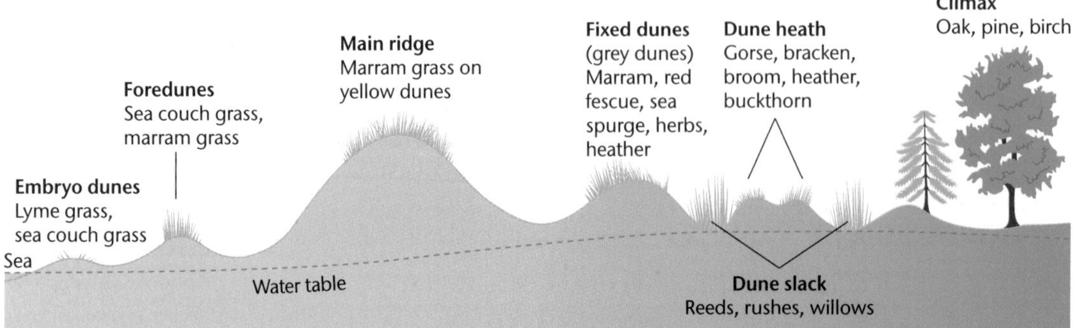

Figure 8.24 A typical sand-dune transect

and the colder sea. When there is a large tidal range, large amounts of sand may be exposed at low tide, and this further contributes to dune formation. The sequence of sand-dune development (Figure 8.24) is as follows:

- Sand may become trapped by obstacles (seaweed, rock, driftwood) at the back of the beach, possibly on the highest berm or storm beach. Sand is not a very hospitable environment for plant growth so only very hardy plants will begin to colonise here. Such plants are called **pioneers** — examples of sand-dune pioneers are sea rocket and prickly saltwort.
- The first dunes to develop are known as **embryo dunes**. They are suitable for colonisation by grasses such as sea couch, lyme and marram. These are able to grow upwards through accumulating wind-blown sand, stabilising the surface. As a result low, hummocky dunes are formed. Marram is a robust plant which spreads vigorously by underground shoots (rhizomes). This is still a difficult environment and plants need certain features to survive. Sea couch has succulent leaves to store water, prickly saltwort has thorn-like leaves which reduce transpiration and conserve water, and marram possesses long tap roots to draw moisture from the water table. Plant growth of this kind adds organic matter to the dunes which aids water retention.
- Upward growth of embryo dunes raises the height to create dunes that are beyond the reach of all but the highest storm tides. These **foredunes (mobile dunes)** are initially yellow, because they contain little organic matter, but as colonisation increases, plants like marram begin to add humus to the sand. As a result, the dunes look more grey in colour and may reach heights in excess of 20 metres.
- The dunes inland gradually become **fixed.** An organic layer develops which improves nutrient supply and water retention, allowing more plant colonisation. Lichens, mosses and flowering plants begin to appear and marram is slowly replaced by red fescue grass. Other plants include creeping willow and dewberry.
- In places **dune slacks** develop. These are depressions within the dunes where the water table is on or near the surface and conditions are often damp. Rushes, reeds, mosses and willows can be found, but the plants present will very much depend upon the amount of moisture.
- Behind the yellow and grey dunes, the supply of beach sand is gradually cut off, giving smaller dune features. This area is often referred to as **dune heath,** and

heather, gorse, broom and buckthorn are the main plants. Towards the rear of the dune system, woodland may occur with trees such as pine, birch and the occasional oak. This is beginning to lead into the climatic climax vegetation for the British Isles, but in many areas the dunes may be planted with conifers to stabilise the area. If this is the case, then the vegetation is said to be a plagio-climax (short of the climatic climax because of human interference). Within this system, it is possible to find **blowouts** where wind has been funnelled through areas and removed the sand.

Sand dunes are an example of a **succession**, a plant community where the structure develops over time. At each stage, certain species have evolved to exploit the particular conditions present. Initially only a small number of species will be capable of thriving in a harsh environment. These hardy pioneering plants gradually modify the conditions by altering such things as the mineral and moisture content of the soil and the amount of shade. As each new plant species takes hold, the process is repeated. Changes made by the plants present allow other species, better suited to this modified habitat, to succeed the old species. When the succession has reached a point where it is in balance with the climatic conditions, a climax is said to have been reached. A succession that develops on sand is called a **psammosere**.

Salt marshes

In sheltered river estuaries or behind spits, silt and mud are deposited by rivers or gentle tides to form intertidal mudflats. Upon these, vegetation will develop which, like that of the sand-dune environment, changes through time. The succession that develops (Figure 8.25) is known in this case as a **halosere** (tolerant of salty conditions) and follows these stages:

- Mudflats are formed by deposition of fine material. This may be aided by the growth of eelgrass that slows currents and leads to further, uneven, deposition.
- **Pioneers** begin to colonise the area. These are plants able to tolerate salt and periodic submergence by the sea. They are known as **halophytes** and examples include glasswort, sea blite and *Spartina*. *Spartina* has two root systems — a fine mat of surface roots to bind the mud, and long, thick, deep roots that can secure it in up to 2 metres of deposited material. This enables the plant to trap

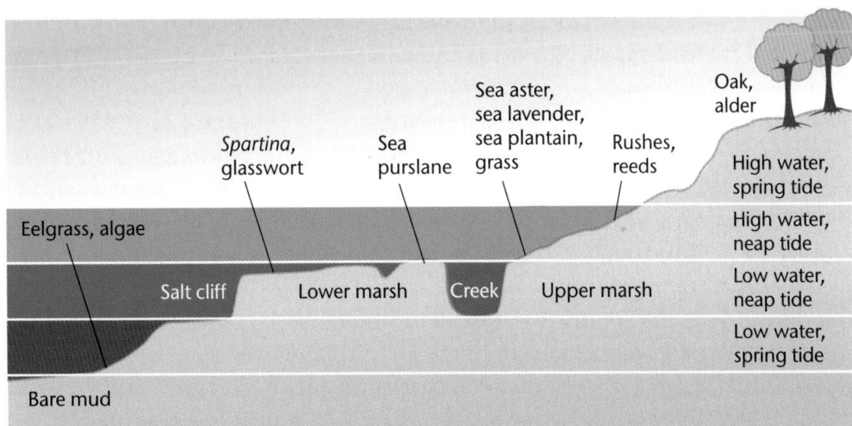

Figure 8.25 The structure of a salt marsh

more mud than other pioneers, and thus it has become the dominant vegetation on tidal flats in the British Isles.

- The pioneers gradually develop a close vegetation over the mud and this allows colonisation by other plants such as sea aster, marsh grass and sea lavender. These form a dense mat of vegetation up to 15 cm high. The growth of vegetation has the effect of slowing the tidal currents even further and this, together with the vegetation's ability to trap particles, leads to more mud and silt accumulation. Dead organic matter also helps to build up the surface, which grows in height at anywhere between 1 and 25 mm per year.
- As mud levels rise, complex creek systems develop that channel the tides and these deepen as the marsh becomes higher. Hollows may form where sea water becomes trapped and evaporates, leaving salt-pans in which the salinity is too great for plants to survive. As the land rises above sea level, rushes (such as *Juncus* species) and reeds become established, eventually leading to the growth of trees, such as alder, ash and then oak to complete the succession. This land is now rarely covered by the sea.

Coastal problems

Coastal flooding

Coastal flooding, which is confined to coastal plains, deltas and river estuaries, results from water levels being increased to substantially above normal high-tide levels. This can be brought about by:

- waves and surges generated by the passage of a tropical cyclone (hurricane)
- tsunamis
- a combination of low pressure, high tide levels and high river discharge (see the case study of the North Sea storm surge in 1953, page 222)

Although coastal flooding is a natural process, the onset of global warming means that there is an increased and growing risk of extensive coastal flooding today. Among the places most at risk are many small island states in the Indian and Pacific Oceans — for example the Maldives, Seychelles, Tonga and the Cook Islands. Certain densely populated delta regions are also at great risk, including the Nile delta in Egypt and the Ganges delta in Bangladesh (see page 223). A rise in sea level of 1 m would, for example, inundate 25% of Bangladesh. The list of river estuaries at risk includes the Thames. London has been under threat of flooding for a long time. The 1953 storm surge in the North Sea prompted a debate that led to the construction of the Thames Barrier. This was completed in 1982 (Photograph 8.6). Figure 8.26 shows coastal defences on the Thames estuary and Figure 8.27 the trend in the height of storm surge events at London Bridge.

Other areas of the UK that could be exposed to an increased danger of coastal flooding include the Severn, Dee and Mersey estuaries, Morecambe Bay, the Wash in Lincolnshire and East Anglia, the Solway Firth and the firths of Forth and Clyde in Scotland. Storm surges that were expected to occur only once in a 100-year period might now become a one in 50-year or even a one in 10-year event.

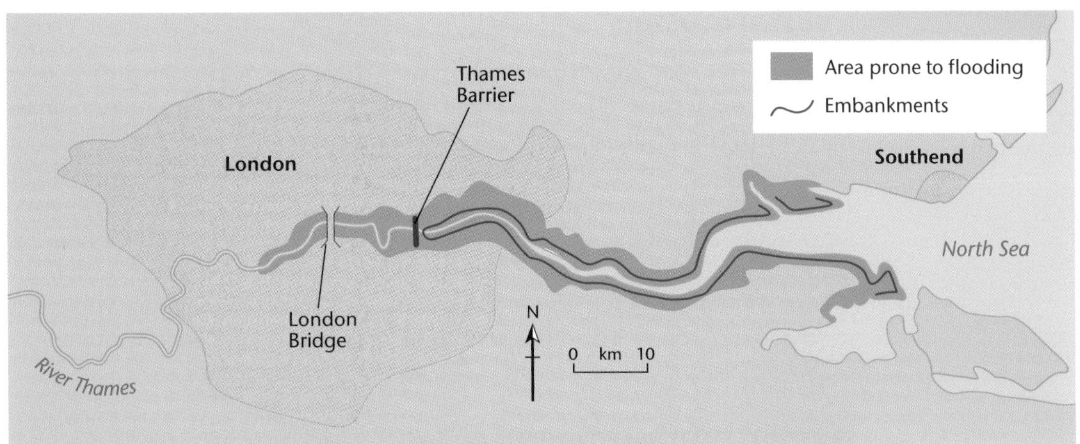

Figure 8.26
Thames estuary coastal defences

TopFoto

Photograph 8.6
The Thames Barrier

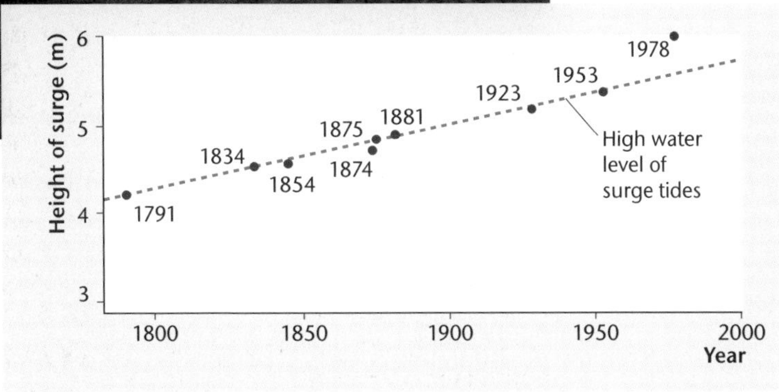

Figure 8.27
The height of storm surge events at London Bridge

Coastal erosion

The processes that are involved in coastal retreat are **marine erosion** (waves attacking vulnerable coastlines) and sub-aerial processes leading to **mass movements** (rock falls, landslides, mudflows and slumping). Like coastal flooding, coastal erosion is a natural process which is a vital part of a dynamic coast system. The coastline, however, is attractive for a wide range of human activities. In England for example, at least one-quarter of the coastline has been developed for housing, industry, agriculture and leisure activities, and many of the world's major cities are in coastal locations. This means that an increasing number of people are vulnerable to coastal hazards. It is also true that some human activities are contributing to coastal problems, because of both deliberate and accidental changes.

Human impacts on the coast

Offshore dredging

As the demand for sand and gravel for the construction industry has increased, offshore dredging has become increasingly common. It was originally thought that this would have no effect upon the coastal system. However, it was soon discovered that offshore deposits supply material to beaches. In places where beach material is moved by longshore drift removal of undersea deposits mean it is not replaced and more erosion occurs. Offshore dredging in the nineteenth century off the Devon coast resulted in the diminishing of the beach at Hallsands and, during one violent storm, the destruction of the village behind the beach. Such activity is now carefully controlled and subject to licensing.

Destabilisation of sand dunes

A sand dune is a fragile environment that is easily disrupted by human activities. Most damage is caused by the removal of vegetation either by agriculture (overgrazing) or by tourism (trampling the dunes). This can lead to **blowouts** during which large amounts of sand may be carried inland and deposited on valuable agricultural land. Management strategies include:

- replanting vulnerable areas with plants such as marram grass and stabilising the surface with sacking or wire mesh
- afforestation with conifers
- selective grazing
- restricting access by fencing off areas
- providing boardwalks for tourists
- giving tourists information about potential damage

Disturbance of estuarine environments

Estuarine environments can be disturbed by a number of human activities, including:

- reclamation for agricultural purposes
- building ports and settlements
- dredging channels for navigation
- building flood defences which prevent further salt-marsh development
- water pollution

Case study The collapse of Holbeck Hall, Scarborough, 1993

Holbeck Hall, one of Yorkshire's premier coastal hotels, was built on top of the cliffs behind South Bay in Scarborough at the end of the nineteenth century. Although the cliffs here consist largely of clay, the hotel was not considered to be in any danger, because it was at least 60–70 m away from the edge.

All this changed in the early summer of 1993 when a period of dry weather cracked much of the clay on the cliff top. This dry period was followed by heavy rainfall that penetrated the cracks and began to lubricate the clay along certain lines of slippage. The first warning came on 3 June when cracks began to appear in the hotel lawns and rose garden towards the edge of the cliff. The following morning, more cracks appeared and sections of the garden began to slide towards the beach. By late afternoon, the area of slides had reached the hotel buildings, resulting in the collapse of the terraces and the conservatory. In the early evening the collapse had affected the main part of the hotel, a large section of which fell into the slide and began to move towards the beach (Figure 8.28). As a result of this, the remainder of the hotel had to be demolished by contractors.

The owners of the hotel sued the local authority for being 'in breach of its duty of care to maintain the supporting land and the undercliff it owned between the hotel grounds and the sea'.

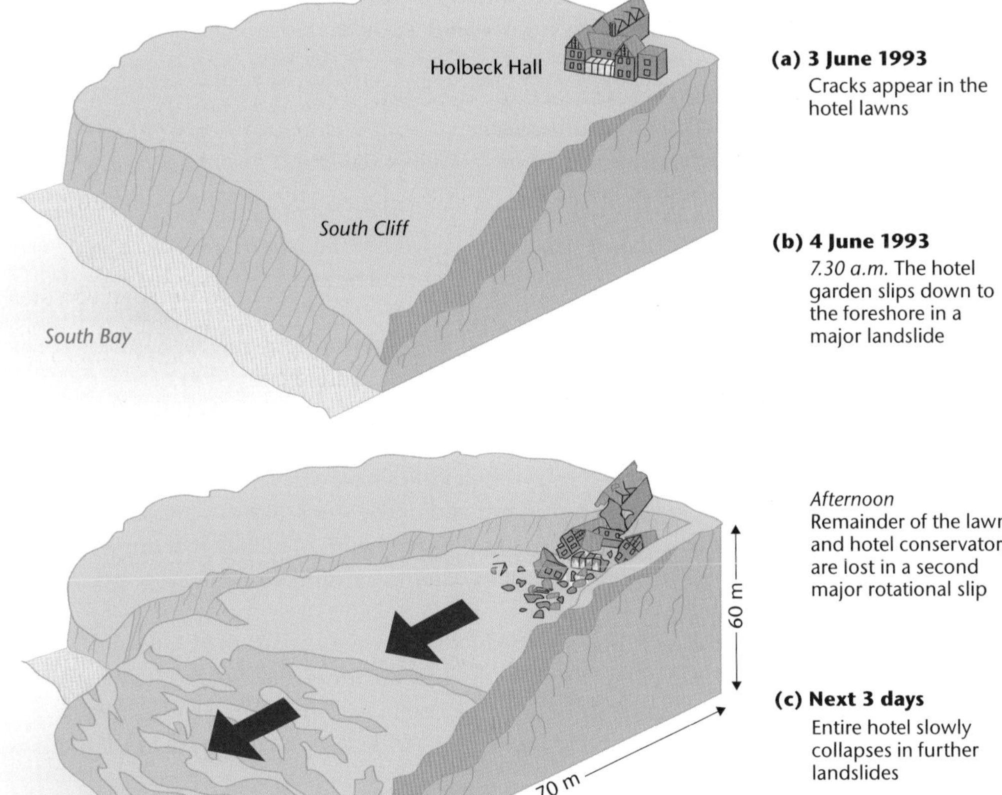

Figure 8.28 The collapse of Holbeck Hall, Scarborough

Although there have been attempts to manage and protect estuarine environments, their economic importance means that success is variable. In recent years, salt marsh has been recognised as an important feature of coastal defence. One policy that is being actively encouraged is 'managed retreat' of the coastline. If old sea defences, such as walls, are abandoned, low-lying land will be flooded. This will be reclaimed naturally by marsh plants. The new area of marsh will act as a defence against rising sea levels.

Degradation of coral reefs

Coral reefs are unique among marine ecosystems in that they are built up entirely by biological activity. Reefs are produced by coral polyps — very simple organisms with small cylindrical bodies and a ring of tentacles at one end surrounding a mouth. Many live in colonies in shallow tropical seas, where they build reefs. Coral polyps can only live within a relatively confined set of conditions:

- water temperature of at least 18°C, and preferably 23–25°C
- water depth of 25 m or less
- enough light for photosynthesis by the tiny algae (zooxanthellae) which live symbiotically with corals and provide them with 98% of their food requirement
- minimum salinity levels of 30–32 psu
- relatively sediment-free water
- wave action to ensure water is well-oxygenated

Coral reefs are under enormous environmental pressure, and it is believed that at least 10% of them are dead or degraded beyond recovery. Reefs are being damaged at a greater rate that they can self-repair. The main threats come from:

- **Global warming** — as oceans warm, corals become stressed and expel their zooxanthellae. It is the algae that provide colour and food, so the corals turn white or 'bleach' and die. Change in sea temperature can also be caused by the local effects of El Niño. In addition, global warming causes sea levels to rise and corals cannot keep pace.
- **Increased storm levels** — hurricanes have a devastating effect on reefs, particularly if the coral is diseased and under stress. Storm waves often pound reefs into rubble. They also produce vast amounts of rainfall that can wash quantities of sediment into the reef area. Global warming could increase the number and magnitude of storms.
- **The crown of thorns starfish** — this creature occurs in plagues and attacks coral reefs. A rise in numbers in several areas has resulted in excessive reef damage. Biologists believe the rise in starfish numbers is caused by nutrient enrichment from the land and overfishing which has killed off a number of their predators.
- **Rapid population growth in coastal areas** — this has a number of effects including deforestation of coastal areas, leading to greater sedimentation of reefs; construction of harbours; and pollution from agricultural chemicals, from the growth of industry and from sewage.

- **Increased tourism** — this leads to damage by boat anchors and divers; pollution from boats; and dredging for harbours and marinas.
- **Commercial exploitation** — coral mining for building materials, lime and for making jewellery.
- **Overfishing** — direct damage is caused by certain fishing activities (e.g. blast fishing), and overfishing, which upsets the balance of the food chain.
- **Acidification of the sea** — acidification is the result of the build-up of carbon dioxide in the atmosphere. Chemical processes then turn the gas into carbonic acid. This has a severe impact on organisms that have calcium in their shells.

A number of initiatives were developed in the 1990s to address the problem. These included the International Coral Reef Initiative (1993) and the International Year of the Coral Reef (1997).

Coastal management strategies

With or against nature?

Management strategies can work either with or against natural processes. Working *with* nature means allowing the natural processes of erosion to occur (**managed retreat**) and not spending money on the defence of the coastal area. This is now applied to large stretches of coastline in the UK where there are few settlements. **Soft engineering** techniques, for example beach nourishment, are also used.

Working *against* nature usually occurs where there is significant capital investment — buildings and communications — in the coastal region and these have to be protected. Protection involves the construction of sea walls, revetments, groynes and other examples of **hard engineering**. The costs of such defences are justified by the expense of replacing sea-damaged buildings and infrastructure.

Coastal protection schemes

Coastal areas contain a variety of landforms which are increasingly coming under pressure from both natural processes and human activities. In response to this, a range of protection and management strategies has been put into place in many coastal areas. These solutions are often relatively successful but, in some cases, the solutions themselves cause other problems. Coastal management has two main aims:

- to provide defence against flooding
- to provide protection against coastal erosion

Other aims of management include:

- stabilising beaches affected by longshore drift
- stabilising sand-dune areas
- protecting salt marshes

There are a number of approaches to defence of the coast.

The hard engineering approach

Hard engineering involves the building of some type of sea defence, with a specific purpose (Figure 8.29):

- **Sea walls (sometimes recurved)** aim to absorb wave energy. The recurved structure throws waves backwards. Sea walls must have a continuous facing because any slight gap will be exploited by hydraulic action. They also need drain outlets so that water does not accumulate behind them.
- **Rock armour (rip-rap)** consists of large boulders dumped in front of a cliff or sea wall to take the full force of the waves.
- **Gabions** operate on the same principle as rip-rap, but the boulders are contained within a steel wire-mesh cage.
- **Revetments** are concrete or wooden structures placed across the beach to take the full force of wave energy.
- **Groynes** are wooden or steel breakwaters built nearly at right angles to waves (usually 5–10° to the perpendicular to prevent scouring on the downdrift side of the groyne). They are built to control longshore drift but will also break up the waves as they hit the coast. Halting the bulk of longshore drift in an area may have serious effects down the coast where it will cut off the supply of beach material and could leave the coast exposed to erosion.
- **Cliff fixing** is often done by driving iron bars into the cliff face, both to stabilise it and to absorb some wave power.
- **Offshore reefs** force the waves to break offshore which reduces their impact on the base of cliffs.

Hard engineering has several disadvantages:

- structures can be expensive to build and to maintain (to repair a sea wall can cost up to £5,000 per metre)
- defence in one place can have serious consequences for another area of coast
- defence structures may not keep pace with rising sea levels
- structures are sometimes an eyesore, spoiling the landscape

Figure 8.29 Examples of hard engineering solutions

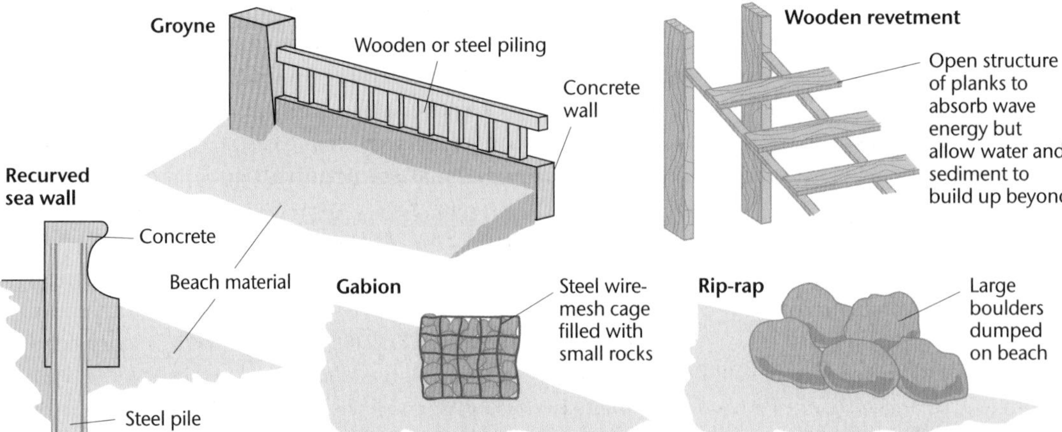

Case study Coastal management on the Isle of Wight

The Isle of Wight Council, like all others on the UK coast, has four coastal defence options:

- **Hold the line** — retain the existing coastline by maintaining current defences or building new ones where existing structures no longer provide sufficient protection.
- **Do nothing but monitor** — on some stretches of coastline it is not technically, economically or environmentally viable to undertake defence works. The value of the built environment here does not exceed the cost of installing coastal defences.
- **Retreat the line** — actively manage the rate and process by which the coast retreats.
- **Advance the line** — build new defences seaward of the existing line.

The examples of different approaches highlighted on Figure 8.30 are described below.

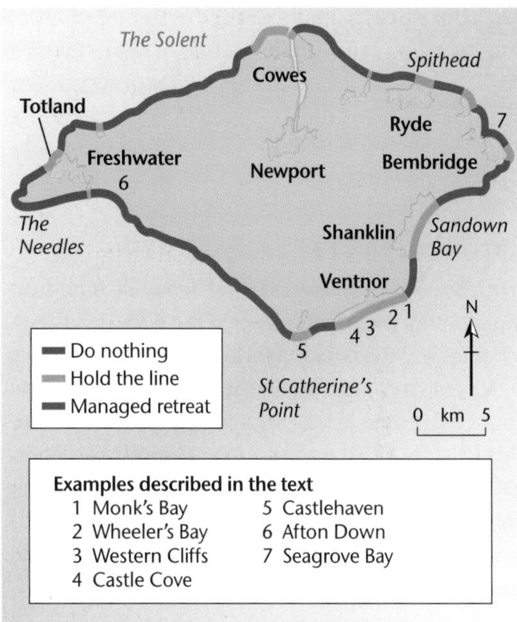

Figure 8.30 Isle of Wight coastal defences

Monk's Bay (1)

Cliff failure resulting from a combination of high-energy destructive waves and high rainfall during the severe storms of the winter of 1990/91 gave additional impetus for upgrading coastal defence here. The scheme involved constructing an **offshore breakwater**, six **rock groynes** and a **rock revetment** to reinforce the existing sea wall using 25,000 tonnes of Swedish granite. It also required **beach nourishment** using 17,000 m^3 of sand and gravel, **reprofiling** the slope and installing **land drainage** to check the active mass movement of the cliffs on the western side of the bay.

The collective value of the property far exceeded the £1.4 million cost of the scheme. It was completed in 1992 but sedimentation of the rock groynes has since been a problem.

Wheeler's Bay (2)

The ageing sea walls were in danger of collapse which would have reactivated ancient landslides. Property on the cliff behind was becoming unsaleable. Over 15,000 tonnes of Norwegian granite was placed seaward of the existing defences to form a **rock revetment** and the coastal slopes were **regraded to make a shallower profile** before installing **land drainage**. The scheme was completed in 2000 at a cost of £1.6 million and has led to a recovery in property values.

Western Cliffs (Ventnor) (3)

High-energy waves were removing chalk blocks which protected an ancient landslide complex upon which houses had been built. There was a danger that the landslides would be reactivated if sufficient chalk was removed. £1.2 million of Carboniferous limestone was brought in from the Mendip Hills in Somerset to construct a 700 m long **rock revetment** along the base of the cliffs using blocks weighing 6–8 tonnes. A series of limestone **rock groynes** was also constructed at 100 m intervals at the base of the cliffs.

Castle Cove (4)

The existing wooden revetments were being left progressively ineffective as the clay cliffs retreated. Property valued in excess of £10 million was increasingly at risk as coastal processes activated ancient landslides. The scheme stabilised the environmentally-sensitive cliffs by removing the topsoil, **stabilising the slopes** with thousands of tonnes of chalk and installing **land drainage** before replacing the top-soil. The cliff was protected by a **rock revetment** of Somerset limestone, a concrete walkway and a **gabion wall**. The defences cost £2.3 million and were completed in 1996.

Castlehaven (5)

Landslides have removed part of a road here and are threatening property worth over £20 million. A scheme to stabilise the cliffs and protect them from active coastal processes has been proposed, but the council is unable to obtain funding from the Department for Environment Food and Rural Affairs (DEFRA) because of objections from nature conservationists. They are concerned about the impact of land drainage on soft cliff habitats that support many rare insects and plants. A public enquiry will be held to see if the scheme is environmentally acceptable.

East of Freshwater (6)

Where the A3055 passes over a chalk ridge at Afton Down, it is now within 11 metres of the cliff edge. Sea defences to prevent further cliff erosion would be economically unjustifiable and environmentally unacceptable. The council has therefore devised a scheme that **stabilises the cliff top** by anchoring the top of the cliff-face chalk on the landward side of the road. The cost is £750,000.

Seagrove Bay (7)

The crumbling sea walls (maintained by residents) and unstable slopes forced the council to intervene and protect property as part of its 'hold the line' policy. A scheme costing just under £1 million, and completed in 2000, included a new concrete **sea wall** with 200 metres of **rock revetment** placed in front of the wall to dissipate the energy of the waves. **Rock groynes** were constructed as a further layer of protection. Mass movement on the soft clay cliffs has been significantly reduced by installing **land drainage**.

The soft engineering approach

Soft engineering uses natural systems for coastal defence, such as beaches, dunes and salt marshes which can absorb and adjust to wave and tide energy. It involves manipulating and maintaining these systems, without changing their fundamental structures. **Beach nourishment** is the attempt to replace material that has been lost through longshore drift. It is not unknown for local councils to move material from one end of a beach to the other before the start of the tourist season.

Managed retreat

This involves abandoning the current line of sea defences and then developing the exposed land in some way, perhaps with salt marshes, to reduce wave power. In this way the scale of hard sea defences can be reduced. There have been proposals in some areas to ban new developments on the coast. In California, for example, there are already requirements on some stretches of coastline that building must be a certain distance from the shore.

Do nothing!

In recent years a school of thought has grown up that asks whether the coast *should* be protected. Tens of millions of pounds are spent annually in the UK on coastal protection and it might be cheaper to let nature take its course and pay compensation to those affected. Figure 8.31 is a newspaper report on the findings of the House of Commons select committee on agriculture in August 1998.

We must surrender our land to the sea, say MPs

Huge tracts of Britain's coastal land, especially along the east and south coast, should be surrendered to the sea as part ofa 'peaceful accommodation' with nature, MPs said yesterday.

They set out a stark vision of a dramatically different coastal and riverside landscape complete with floodplains and regularly water-logged farmlands as mankind showed more 'humility' in the face of the sea.

Describing the millions spent on flood prevention and coastal defences as an unsustainable and 'deluded' waste of money, the agricultural select committee said it was time to give up the fight along much of the East Anglian and southeast coasts.

Daily Telegraph, 6 August 1998

Figure 8.31

The committee suggested that large tracts of land should be 'surrendered to the sea' as trying to protect them was a waste of money.

Flood protection schemes

Many of the world's coastlines are at threat of flooding. This threat can only become worse with the advent of global warming. MEDCs have the capital and technical expertise to construct dams, barriers, sea walls and dykes. A low-lying country such as the Netherlands is clearly at risk from flooding, particularly on the delta of the rivers Waal, Scheldt, Lek and Maas. Forty years ago the Delta Plan was conceived in the Netherlands to control these rives. Barriers were built to prevent the sea from inundating areas of land, as it had during the North Sea storm surge of 1953 (see case study, page 222).

Case study Coastal management schemes, the Netherlands

Management of the Dutch coastline is divided into three main areas: the delta region, the Zuider Zee and the coastal dune area.

The delta region

In its natural state, the delta region is an area consisting of islands and peninsulas running between the distributaries of the rivers Waal (Rhine), Maas, Lek and Scheldt. Flooding has been a major problem here, but the disastrous floods of 1953 forced the Dutch government to design a scheme that would control similar events in the future. The Delta Plan (Figure 8.33) consists of:

- a series of dams that seal off the channels between the large islands to keep out the sea
- two channels to allow ships to reach the ports of Rotterdam and Antwerp
- the creation of some fresh water areas
- the East Scheldt dam, which is unlike those that had already been built (fixed dams). Pressure from environmentalists has resulted in the building of a storm surge barrier with sluice gates that can be lowered in times of need. The area behind the dam has remained as salt water, preserving salt marshes and mudflats for wildlife

The Delta Plan has reduced the length of defended coastline from 800 km to 80 km.

Zuider Zee

The Zuider Zee was originally a long inlet of the sea that threatened large areas of low-lying coastlands when high spring tides were backed by northerly winds. A 30 km barrier was completed by 1932, which created a fresh water lake, the Ijsselmeer.

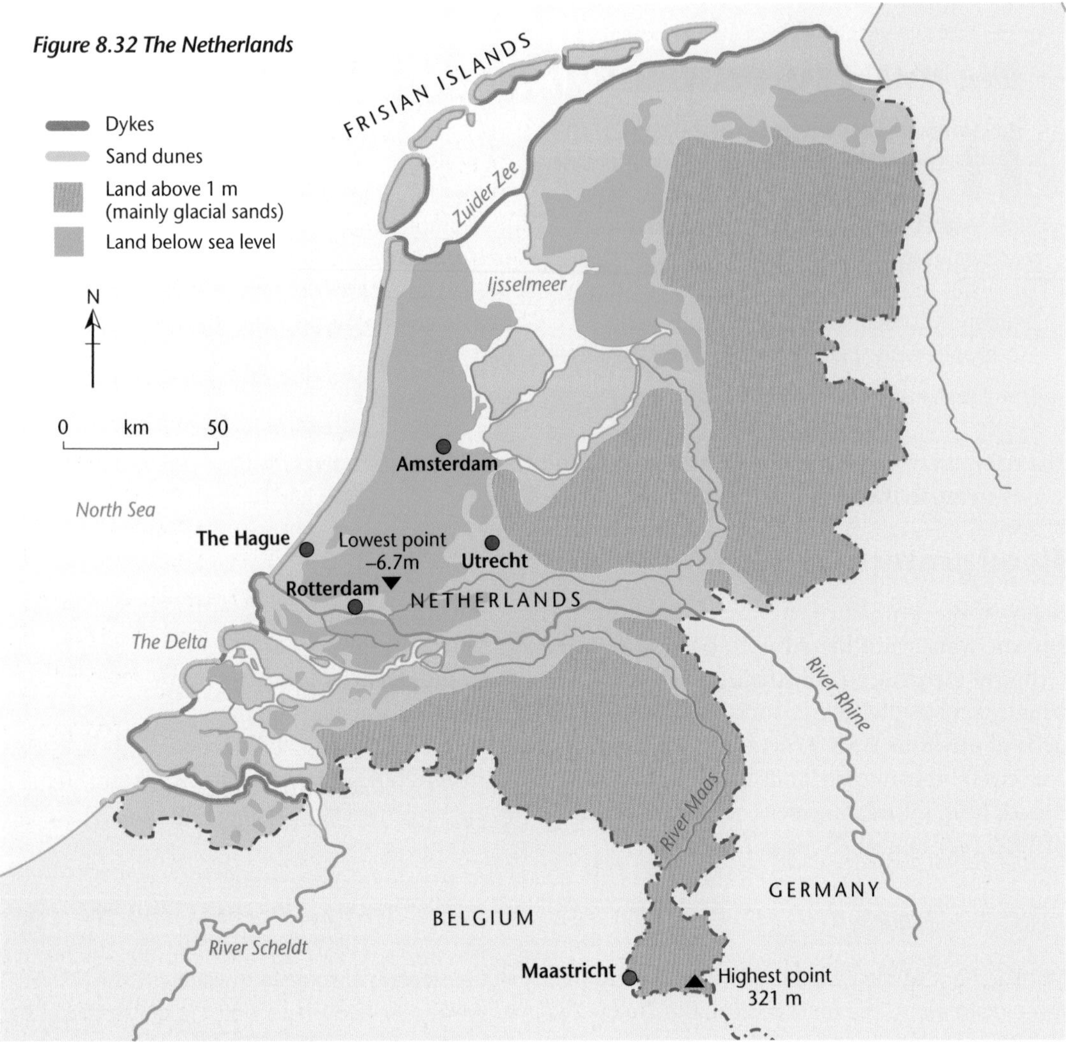

Figure 8.32 The Netherlands

This lake has been largely reclaimed as a series of polders (artificial land) providing areas for urban expansion and agriculture.

The coastal dune area

The Dutch dunes occupy an area of over 42,000 hectares, making them the largest area of continuous duneland in Europe. Currents and waves remove sand in some areas and deposit it elsewhere. Each year, some 7 million m^3 of sand are washed away. Only part of this is deposited elsewhere along the coast. The sand balance is therefore negative. As the nearshore underwater sand disappears, the beaches are gradually lowered, leading to damage to the dunes behind the beach. The main protective measures carried out include:

- sand mixed with water is pumped up from the sea bed up to 20 km out at sea. It is then transported to the Dutch coast and sprayed on to the beaches. This **sand replenishment** is accompanied by the construction of groynes to hold sand on the beaches
- grasses and trees are planted to hold the sand and reduce surface wind speeds
- sleeper dykes are placed below the dunes to keep them bedded down
- certain areas are fenced off to prevent access and trampling

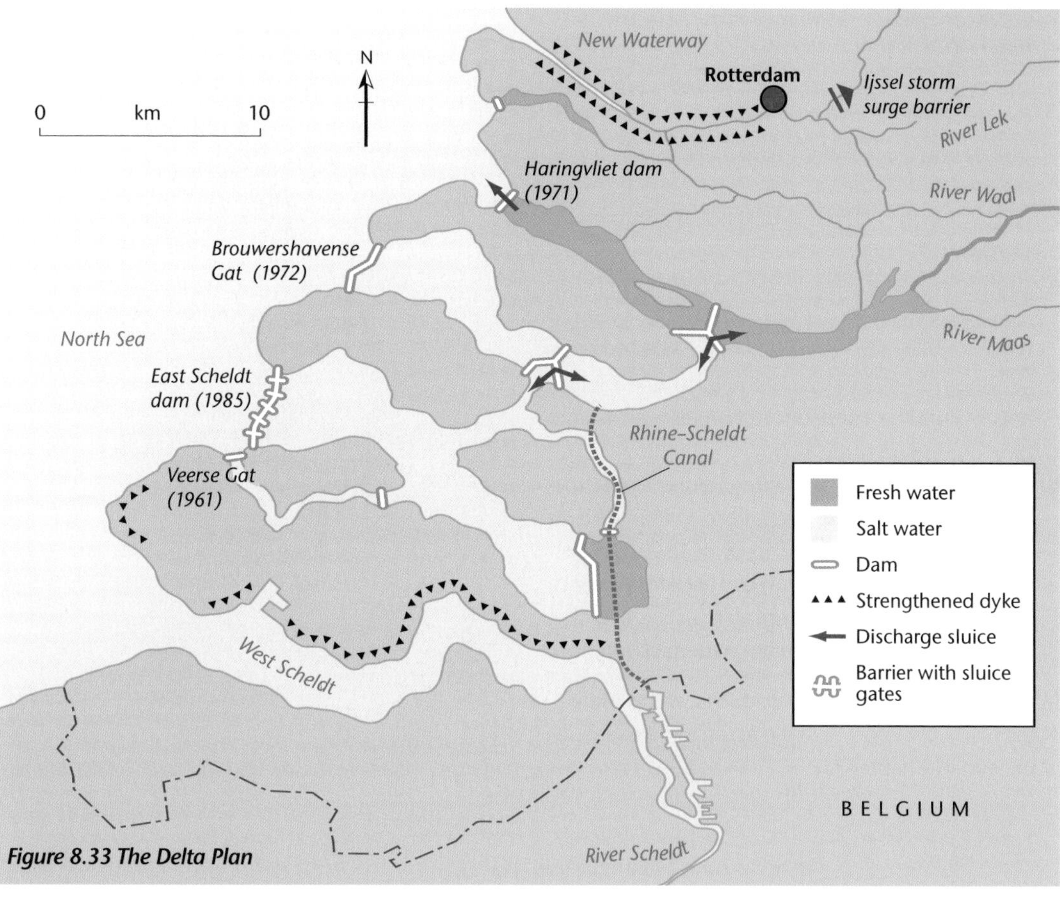

Figure 8.33 The Delta Plan

Case study Management of the Sefton coast, northwest England

The Sefton coast, north of Liverpool, is the largest dune area in England, extending for over 17 km. The sand-dune system around Formby Point experienced continual erosion throughout the twentieth century, the point itself losing about 700 m between 1920 and 1970. Natural erosion levels were compounded by the effects of dredging, spoil dumping and wall construction associated with the development of the ports of Liverpool and Preston. This significantly altered the shape of the sea bed in Liverpool Bay, leading to increased wave energy focusing on Formby Point (Figure 8.34).

At present, the rate of dune erosion at Formby Point is up to 5 m per year, with significant erosion occurring when major storms coincide with high tides.

This area attracts large numbers of people to its beaches, dunes and pine forests. The forest is the home of one of the few remaining colonies of red squirrels in the British Isles, which is a further attraction. During the 1960s and 1970s, the coast was popular with holidaymakers heading for the sea. The frontal dunes suffered greatly as a result of this access. In recent years, problems have arisen with off-road vehicles breaking up the dunes and destroying the vegetation. Sand is also removed from the area by commercial contractors for the foundry trade and glass polishing.

The **Sefton Coast Management Scheme** has included:

- close monitoring of visitor access with controls in certain areas
- prohibiting the use of off-road vehicles in most of the area
- controlling the extraction of sand for commercial purposes
- suggestions that, where the natural dune landscape has been destroyed by the pine plantations, removing the tree and scrub cover from the existing frontal areas would help to re-establish and maintain a spectrum of habitats, including bare dunes and dune slacks
- a project to recreate the natural dune landscape destroyed by the pine plantations to the north of Formby, at Ainsdale. Removal of the trees has encouraged re-colonisation by specialised plants such as yellow bartsia and animals such as the protected sand lizard and the natterjack toad

Note: The Sefton coast, and its dunes, is the subject of the fieldwork enquiry in the assessment exercises at the end of Chapter 15.

Figure 8.34 The Sefton coast

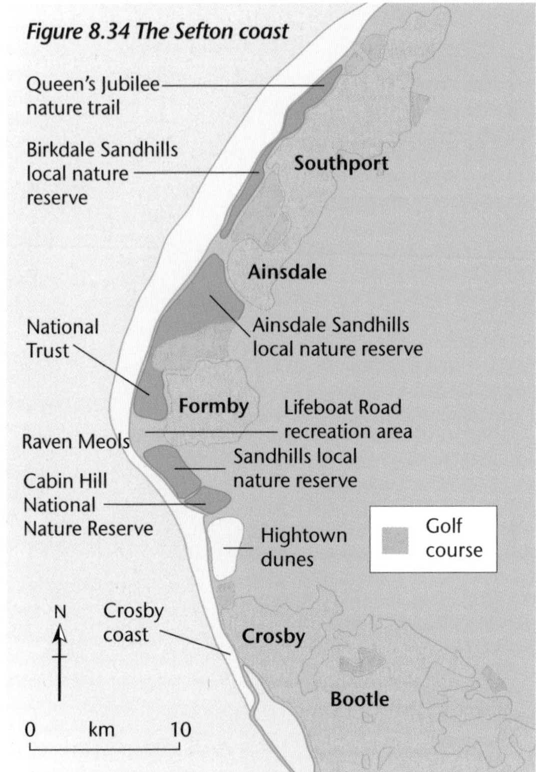

In areas such as Bangladesh, little money has been spent upon coastal defences. The policy has been to allow the delta to be inundated but to defend the capital city, Dhaka. A flood wall has been built for this purpose. However, the wall means that water is unable to flow back into the river when the flood recedes. Flood warnings are given, but it is difficult for Bangladeshis to respond to these because there is very little high ground to which they can escape. Some areas do have shelters in which people can congregate in case of storm and flood. It has been estimated that over 10,000 shelters are needed but fewer than 500 have been built. The economic disruption caused by flooding is one of the factors that contributes to Bangladesh's weak economic development. Bangladesh now has a Coastal Embankment Project — more embankments are being built, together with a series of sluices. Mangroves have also been planted on the coast because mangrove swamps act as a natural buffer against sea incursions. There are some positive signs. In 1997, a tropical cyclone warning in the Cox's Bazaar area of the country allowed the evacuation of over 300,000 people. As a result, the death toll in the disaster was below 100.

Coastal barrages

A barrage is an example of a solid, hard-engineering scheme to prevent flooding on major estuaries and other large sea inlets. A barrage acts as a dam across an estuary and prevents the incursion of seawater. Good examples of such

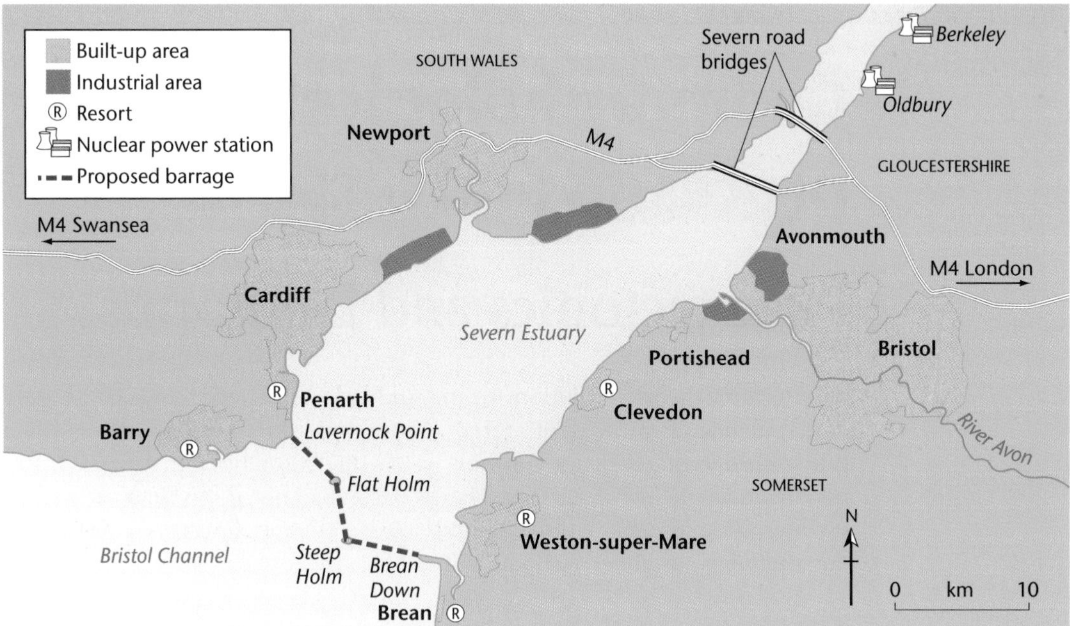

Figure 8.35 ***The proposed Severn barrage***

constructions are those that are part of the Delta Plan in the Netherlands (see case study, page 249).

Besides controlling flooding, barrages can create large freshwater lakes behind them, which may be associated with land reclamation schemes. The environmental lobby has opposed such schemes because they lead to the loss of valuable mudflat areas. These include breeding grounds for a wide variety of birds. Such schemes are also expensive, both in terms of feasibility studies and construction.

The **Cardiff Bay barrage** in Wales was completed in 1999. However, there had been strong opposition from environmental groups and local residents, who feared damage to their houses from a higher water level. The barrage (1.1 km in length) includes a fish pass to allow salmon to reach breeding grounds in the River Taff and three locks for maritime traffic. The areas around the freshwater lake created behind the barrage (200 hectares) have been regenerated, with attractions such as the Wales Millennium Centre, the National Assembly for Wales, a sports village and shopping areas on the waterfront. Over 6,000 new houses have been built.

There have been several proposals to put barrages across other major inlets in the UK, including the Wash, the Severn Estuary and Morecambe Bay. A **Severn Estuary barrage** (Figure 8.35) has been proposed in many forms. The barrage would carry major communications across its surface and generation of electricity using tidal power could be incorporated into the scheme. However, the estuary is an important breeding ground for many species of birds, particularly waders and waterfowl, and there are several wetland nature reserves including the internationally renowned Wildfowl and Wetlands Trust reserve at Slimbridge. This, along with opposition from people involved in some aspects of the tourist industry, has meant that no proposals have ever been given the green light. Another stumbling block is the several billion pounds that it would cost.

Chapter 9

Geomorphological processes and hazards

Plate tectonics and landforms

Plate tectonic theory revolutionised the study of earth science. As soon as maps of the Atlantic Ocean were produced, people noticed that the continents either side seemed to fit together remarkably well — the bulge of South America fitting into the indent below west Africa. Francis Bacon had noted this fit as early as the seventeenth century but it did not attract any serious attention as no one thought the continents could move about.

The theory of plate tectonics

In 1912 a German, Alfred Wegener, published his theory that a single continent existed about 300 million years ago. He named this super-continent Pangaea, and maintained that it had later split into the two continents of Laurasia in the north and Gondwanaland in the south. Today's continents were formed from further splitting of these two masses. Wegener published this **theory of continental drift** and claimed that it was supported by several pieces of evidence that these areas were once joined.

Geological evidence for the theory included:

- the above-mentioned fit of South America and Africa
- evidence of the glaciation of the late Carboniferous period (290 million years ago), deposits from which are found in South America, Antarctica and India. The formation of these deposits cannot be explained by their present position; they must have been formed together and then moved. There are also striations on rocks in Brazil and west Africa which point to a similar situation
- rock sequences in northern Scotland closely agree with those found in eastern Canada, indicating that they were laid down under the same conditions in one location

Biological evidence for the theory included the following:

- fossil brachiopods found in Indian limestones are comparable with similar fossils in Australia
- fossil remains of the reptile Mesosaurus are found in both South America and southern Africa. It is unlikely that the same reptile could have developed in both areas or that it could have migrated across the Atlantic
- the fossilised remains of a plant which existed when coal was being formed have only been located in India and Antarctica

Development of the theory

Wegener's theories were unable to explain how continental movement could have taken place and his ideas gained little ground. From the 1940s onwards, however, evidence began to accumulate to show that Wegener could have been correct.

The mid-Atlantic ridge was discovered and studied. A similar feature was later discovered in the Pacific Ocean.

Examination of the ocean crust either side of the mid-Atlantic ridge suggested that sea-floor spreading was occurring. The evidence for this is the alternating polarity of the rocks that form the ocean crust. Iron particles in lava erupted on the ocean floor are aligned with the Earth's magnetic field. As the lavas solidify, these particles provide a permanent record of the Earth's polarity at the time of eruption (palaeomagnetism). However, the Earth's polarity reverses at regular intervals (approximately every 400,000 years). The result is a series of magnetic 'stripes' with rocks aligned alternately towards the north and south poles (Figure 9.1). The striped pattern, which is mirrored exactly on either side of a mid-oceanic ridge, suggests that the ocean crust is slowly spreading away from this boundary. Moreover, the oceanic crust gets older with distance from the mid-oceanic ridge.

Figure 9.1 Magnetic 'stripes' on the Atlantic Ocean floor

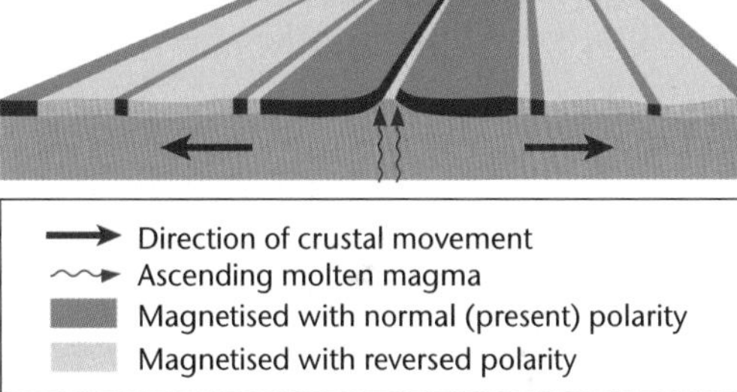

Sea-floor spreading implies that the Earth must be getting bigger. As this is not the case, then plates must be being destroyed somewhere to accommodate the increase in their size at mid-oceanic ridges. Evidence of this was found with the discovery of huge oceanic trenches where large areas of ocean floor were being pulled downwards.

Key terms

Global structures The major surface relief features of the planet that cover both oceanic and continental areas. They include fold mountains (ancient and young), rift valleys, oceanic ridges, oceanic trenches, island arcs, the abyssal plain (ocean basins) and the continental slope and shelf.

Hazard An event that threatens life and property. Remote volcanic and earthquake events that pose no threat to life or property are not hazard events. Without human involvement they are simply natural processes. One definition of a hazard is 'a perceived natural event which threatens both life and property — a disaster is the realisation of the hazard'.

Mass movement The downhill movement of weathered material under the influence of gravity.

Plates The lithosphere (the crust of the Earth and the upper part of the mantle) is divided into a number of sections called plates. These rigid slabs float on the underlying semi-molten mantle (asthenosphere) and are moved by convection currents within it.

Plate tectonics A theory that explains the formation and distribution of the Earth's major structural features in terms of a series of plates that make up its surface.

Weathering The natural breakdown of rocks in situ (i.e. in their original position). It is different from erosion, in that there is no movement of materials except where gravity is involved.

The Earth's layers

Before the development of plate tectonic theory, earth scientists divided the interior of the Earth into three layers: the crust, the mantle and the core. The **core** is made up of dense rocks containing iron and nickel alloys and is divided into a solid inner core and a molten outer one, with a temperature of over 5,000°C. The **mantle** is made up of molten and semi-molten rocks containing lighter elements, such as silicon and oxygen. The **crust** is even lighter because of the elements that are present, the most abundant being silicon, oxygen, aluminium, potassium and sodium. The crust varies in thickness — beneath the oceans it is only 6–10 km thick but below continents this rises to 30–40 km. Under the highest mountain ranges the crust can be up to 70 km thick.

The theory of plate tectonics has retained this simple threefold division, but new research has suggested that the crust and the upper mantle should be divided into the lithosphere and the asthenosphere. The **lithosphere** consists of the crust and the rigid upper section of the mantle and is approximately 80–90 km thick. It is divided into seven very large plates and a number of smaller ones (Figure 9.2). Plates are divided into two categories, oceanic and continental, depending on the type of material from which they are made (see Table 9.1). Below the lithosphere is the semi-molten **asthenosphere**, on which the plates float and move.

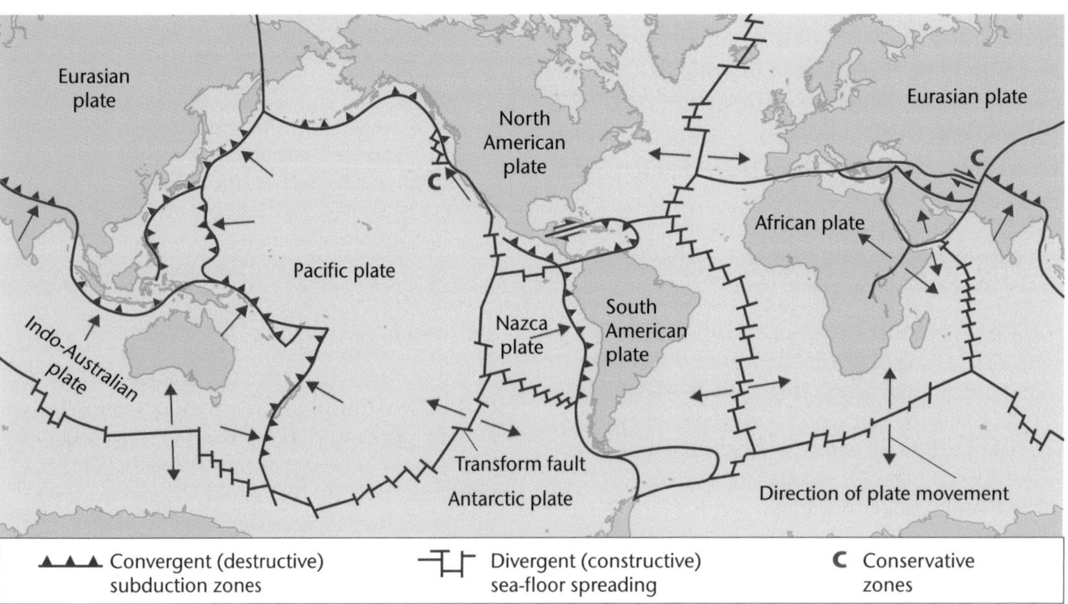

Figure 9.2 Tectonic plates and their margins

Table 9.1 Differences between continental and oceanic crust

	Continental crust	Oceanic crust
Thickness	30–70 km	6–10 km
Age	Over 1,500 million years	Less than 200 million years
Density	2.6 (lighter)	3.0 (heavier)
Composition	Mainly granite; silicon, aluminium and oxygen (SIAL)	Mainly basalt; silicon, magnesium, oxygen (SIMA)

Hot spots around the core of the Earth generate thermal convection currents within the asthenosphere, which cause magma to rise towards the crust and then spread before cooling and sinking (Figure 9.3). This circulation of magma is the vehicle upon which the crustal plates move. The crust can be thought of as 'floating' on the more dense material of the asthenosphere. This is a continuous process, with new crust being formed along the line of constructive boundaries between plates (where plates move away from each other) and older crust being destroyed at destructive boundaries (where plates are moving towards each other).

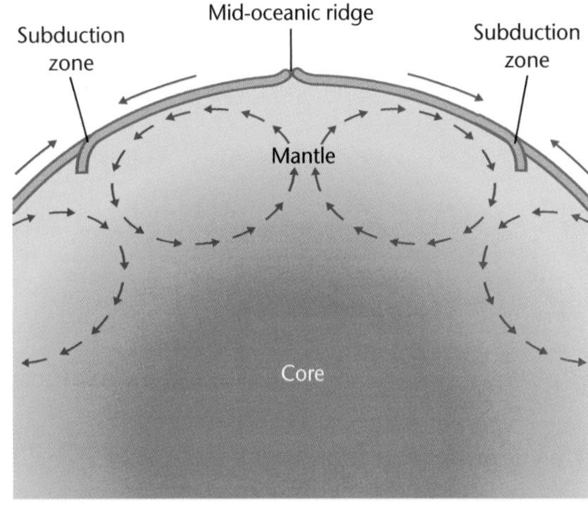

Figure 9.3 ***Convection currents and plate movement***

Features of plate margins

Constructive (divergent) margins

Where plates move apart in oceanic areas they produce mid-oceanic ridges. Where they move apart in continental crust they produce rift valleys. The space between the diverging plates is filled with basaltic lava upwelling from below. Constructive margins are therefore some of the youngest parts of the Earth's surface, where new crust is being continuously created.

Oceanic ridges

Oceanic ridges (Figure 9.4) are the longest continuous uplifted features on the surface of the planet, and have a total length of 60,000 km. In some parts they rise 3,000 m above the ocean floor. Their precise form appears to be influenced by the rate at which the plates separate:

- a slow rate (10–15 mm per year), as seen in parts of the mid-Atlantic ridge, produces a wide ridge axis (30–50 km) and a deep (3,000 m) central rift valley with inward-facing fault scarps
- an intermediate rate (50–90 mm per year), such as that on the Galapagos ridge (Pacific), produces a less well-marked rift (50–200 m deep) with a smoother outline
- a rapid rate (>90 mm per year), such as on the east Pacific rise, produces a smooth crest and no rift

Figure 9.4 ***Cross section of the mid-Atlantic ridge***

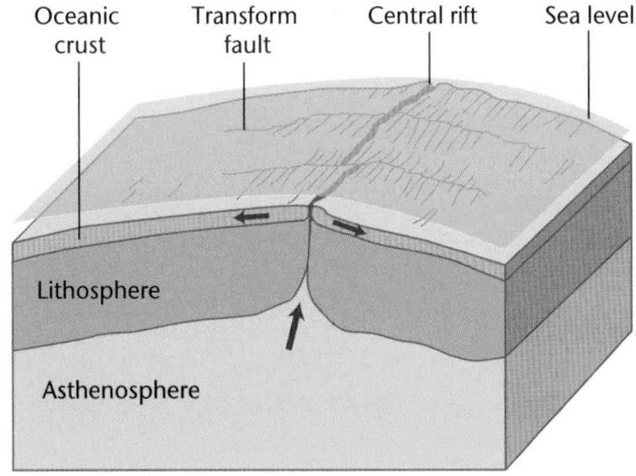

Volcanic activity also occurs along the ridge, forming submarine volcanoes, which sometimes rise above sea level, e.g. Surtsey to the south of Iceland (Iceland itself was formed in this way and is the largest feature produced above sea level on a divergent margin). These are volcanoes with fairly gentle sides due to the low viscosity of basaltic lava. Eruptions are frequent but relatively gentle (effusive).

As new crust forms and spreads, transform faults occur at right angles to the plate boundary. The parts of the spreading plates on either side of these faults may move at differing rates, leading to friction and ultimately to earthquakes. These tend to be shallow-focus earthquakes, originating near the surface.

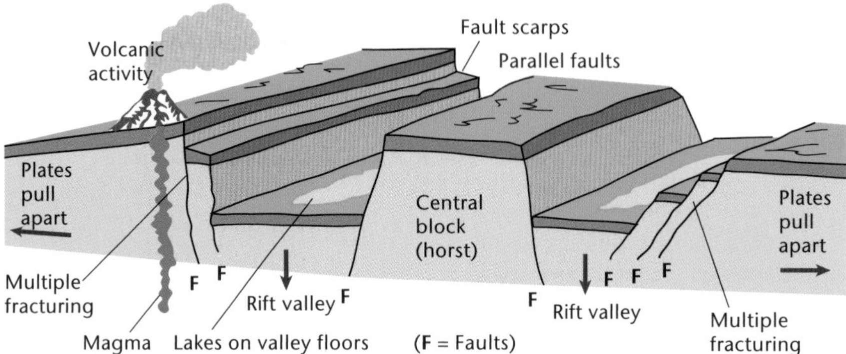

***Figure 9.5* Cross section of a rift valley**

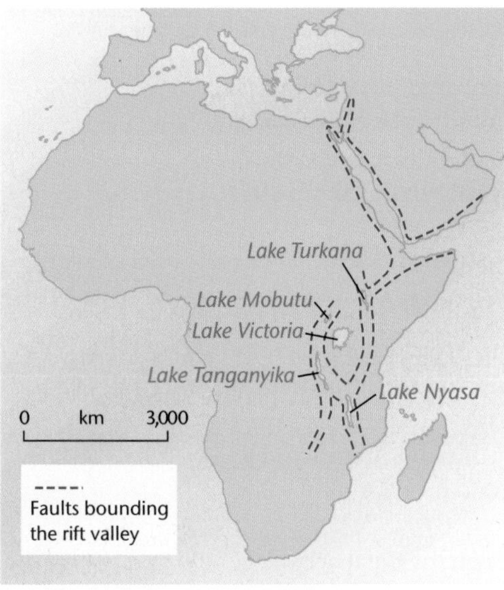

***Figure 9.6* The African rift valley**

Rift valleys

At constructive margins in continental areas, such as Africa, the brittle crust fractures as sections of it move apart. Areas of crust drop down between parallel faults to form **rift valleys** (Figure 9.5). The largest of these features is the African rift valley which extends 4,000 km from Mozambique to the Red Sea. From the Red Sea it extends north into Jordan, a total distance of 5,500 km (Figure 9.6). In some areas, the inward-facing scarps are 600 m above the valley floor and they are often marked by a series of parallel step faults.

The area is also associated with volcanic activity (for example the highest mountain in Africa, Mt Kilimanjaro, Photograph 9.1). The crust here is much thinner than in neighbouring areas, suggesting that tension in the lithosphere is thinning the plate as it

Corel

***Photograph 9.1* Mt Kilimanjaro, Tanzania, in the African rift valley area**

starts to split. The line of the African rift is thought to be an emergent plate boundary, the beginning of the formation of a new ocean as eastern Africa splits away from the rest of the continent.

Destructive (convergent) margins

There are two types of plates, so there are three different convergent situations:

- oceanic plate moves towards continental plate
- oceanic plate moves towards oceanic plate
- continental plate moves towards continental plate

Oceanic/continental convergence

Where oceanic and continental plates meet, the denser oceanic plate (see Table 9.1 on page 256) is forced under the lighter continental one. This process is known as **subduction**. The downwarping of the oceanic plate forms a very deep part of the ocean known as a **trench** (Figure 9.7). A good example of an ocean trench is off the western coast of South America where the Nazca plate is subducting under the South American plate, forming the Peru–Chile trench.

Sediments that have accumulated on the continental shelf on the margin of the land mass are deformed by folding and faulting. Along with the edge of the continental plate, these are uplifted to form **fold mountains** (Figure 9.7), such as the Andes along the Pacific side of South America. As the oceanic plate descends, the increase in pressure can trigger major earthquakes along the line of the subducting plate; these may be shallow-, intermediate- or deep-focus.

The further the rock descends, the hotter the surroundings become. This, together with the heat generated from friction, begins to melt oceanic plate into magma in a part of the subduction zone known as the Benioff zone. As it is less dense than the surrounding asthenosphere, this molten material begins to rise as plutons of magma. Eventually, these reach the surface and form volcanoes. The andesitic lava, which has a viscous nature (flows less easily), creates complex, composite, explosive volcanoes (contrast this to the basaltic emissions on

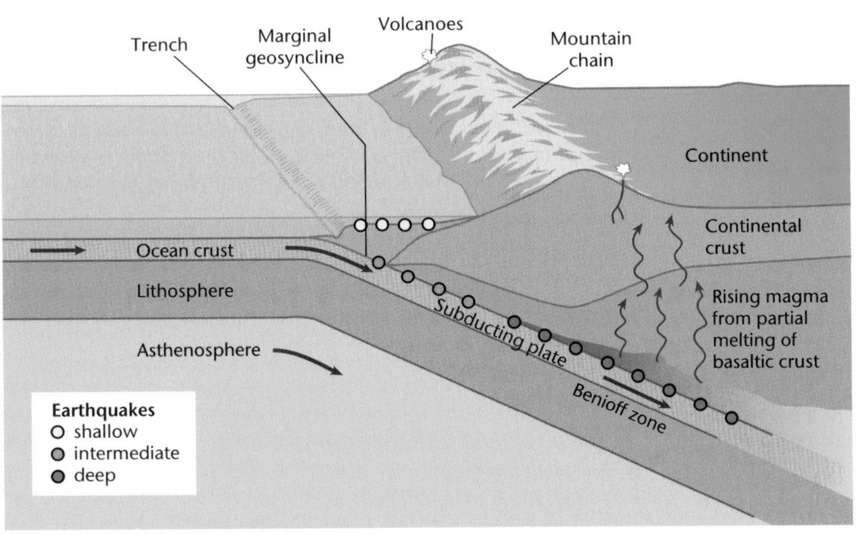

Figure 9.7 Cross section of oceanic/continental plate convergence at a destructive plate margin

constructive margins which tend to be gentle eruptions). If the eruptions take place offshore, a line of volcanic islands known as an **island arc** can appear, e.g. the West Indies.

Oceanic/oceanic convergence

Where oceanic plates meet, one is forced under the other and the processes involved with subduction begin. Ocean trenches and island arcs are the features associated with this interaction, as it takes place well offshore. A good example is

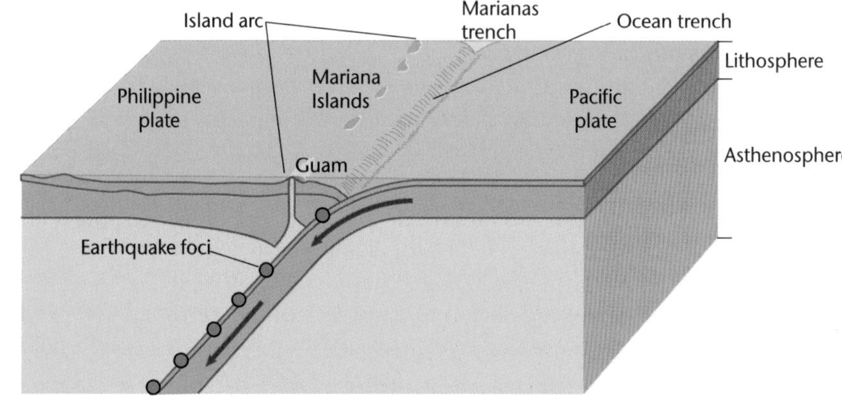

Figure 9.8 ***Cross section of oceanic/oceanic plate convergence at a destructive plate margin***

Table 9.2 ***Relationship of tectonic activity to plate margins***

Plate margin	Movement of plates	Tectonic features	Examples
Constructive	Divergent: two plates moving away from each other	New crust is formed from upwelling magma: mid-oceanic ridges, effusive ridge (shield) volcanoes, shallow focus earthquakes, median rift valleys	Mid-Atlantic ridge
		Continental rift valleys	East African rift valley
Destructive (1) Subduction	Convergent: two plates moving towards each other	(1a) Oceanic to oceanic: trenches, island arcs, explosive volcanoes, earthquakes (shallow, intermediate and deep)	On the margins of Pacific plate, with subduction under other, separate sections of the plate — Tonga trench
		(1b) Oceanic to continental: trenches, fold mountains, explosive volcanoes, earthquakes (shallow, intermediate and deep)	Andean type: Nazca plate subducting under South American plate
(2) Collision		(2) Continental to continental: fold mountains, shallow-focus earthquakes	Himalayan type: Indian plate colliding with Eurasian plate
Conservative	Two plates shearing past each other	Shallow-focus earthquakes	San Andreas fault: Pacific plate and North American plate
Not at plate boundaries	Hot spots: may be near the centre of a plate	Plume volcanoes	Hawaiian islands: Emperor seamount chain

on the western side of the Pacific Ocean where the Pacific plate is being subducted beneath the smaller Philippine plate. Here the ocean floor has been pulled down to form the very deep Marianas trench. A line of volcanic islands, including Guam and the Marianas, has been formed by upwelling magma from the Benioff zone (Figure 9.8).

Continental/continental convergence

The plates forming continental crust have a much lower density than the underlying layers, so there is not much subduction where they meet. Instead, as the plates move towards each other, their edges and the sediments between them are forced up into fold mountains. As there is little subduction, there is no volcanic activity, but the movement of the plates can trigger shallow-focus earthquakes. Material is also forced downwards to form deep mountain roots (Figure 9.9).

The best example of such a margin is where the Indo-Australian plate is being forced northwards into the Eurasian plate. The previous intervening ocean, known as the Sea of Tethys, has had its sediments forced upwards in large overfolds to form the Himalayas, an uplift that is continuing today. The Himalayan range of fold mountains, containing the highest mountain on the planet (Mt Everest 8,848 m), is up to 350 km wide and extends for 3,000 km (Photograph 9.2).

Figure 9.9 Cross section of continental/continental plate convergence (collision boundary)

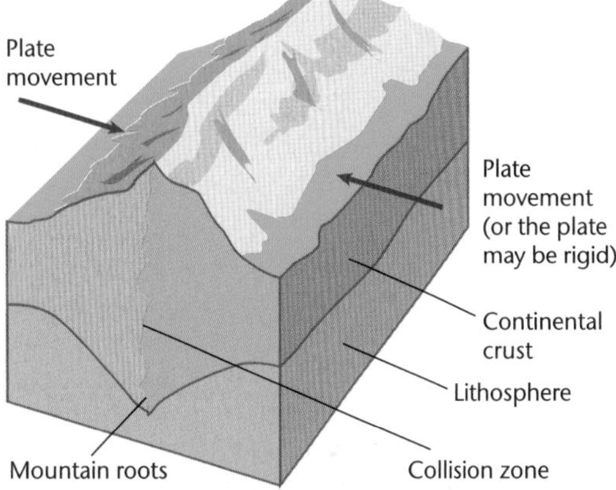

Corel

Photograph 9.2 The Annapurna range in the Himalayas has been formed at a convergent margin

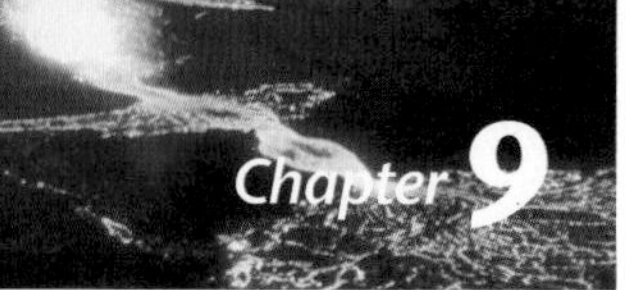

Conservative margins

Where two crustal plates slide past each other and the movement of the plates is parallel to the plate margin, there is no creation or destruction of crust. At these conservative margins (sometimes called passive) there is no subduction and therefore no volcanic activity.

The movement of the plates, however, creates stresses between the plate edges and, as sections of the plates rub past each other, the release of friction triggers shallow-focus earthquakes (e.g. San Francisco 1906 and 1989, Los Angeles 1994). These earthquakes occurred at the best-known example of a conservative margin — the San Andreas fault in California, where the Pacific and North American plates move parallel to each other (Figure 9.10). Both plates are moving in the same direction but not at the same speed. Stresses set up by this movement cause transform faults to develop, running at right angles to the main San Andreas fault.

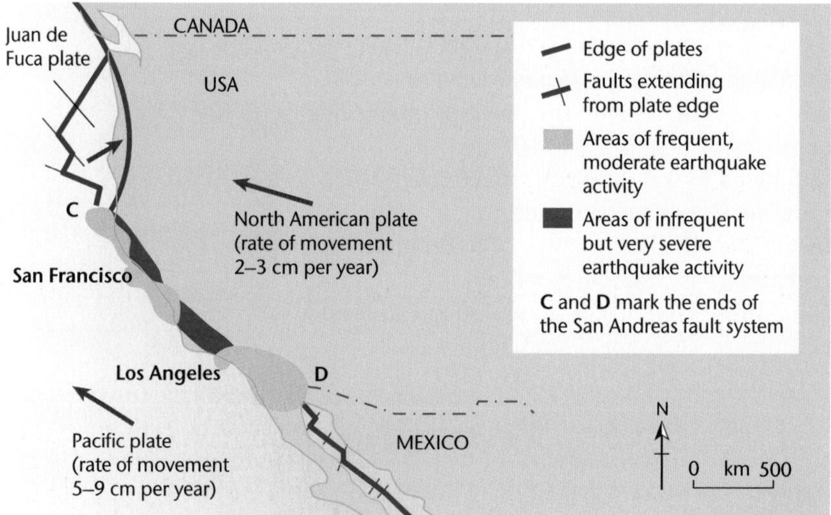

Figure 9.10 The San Andreas fault system: a conservative plate margin

Hot spots

Vulcanicity is normally associated with plate margins but, in the centre of the Pacific Ocean, we find the volcanic Hawaiian islands which are not connected with any plate boundary. It is believed that this volcanic area is caused by a localised **hot spot** within the Pacific plate. A concentration of radioactive elements inside the mantle may cause such a hot spot to develop. From this, a plume of magma rises to eat into the plate above. Where lava breaks through to the surface, active volcanoes occur above the hot spot.

The hot spot is stationary, so as the Pacific plate moves over it, a line of volcanoes is created. The one above the hot spot is active and the rest form a chain of islands of extinct volcanoes. The oldest volcanoes have put so much pressure on the crust that subsidence has occurred. This, together with marine erosion, has reduced these old volcanoes to seamounts below the level of the ocean. Figure 9.11 shows the line of the Hawaiian islands and their ages. From this evidence it is clear that the Pacific plate is moving northwest. This is further proof that the Earth's crust is moving, as originally suggested by Alfred Wegener.

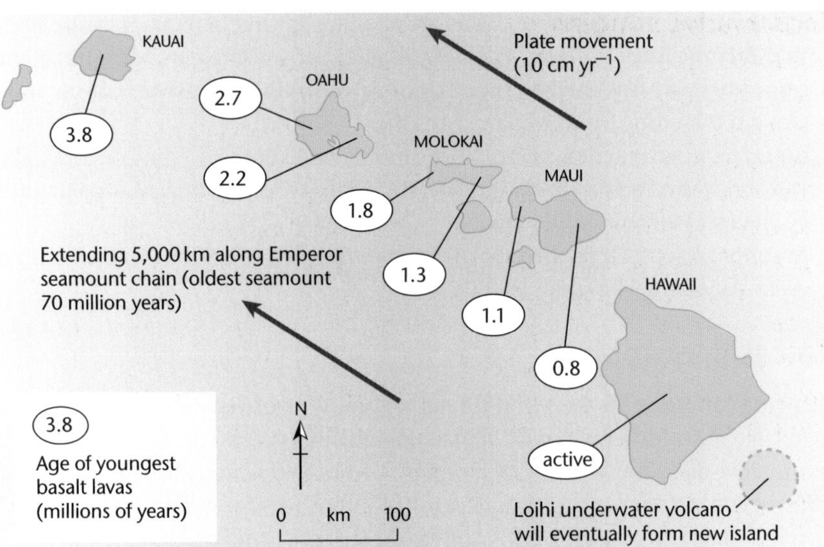

Figure 9.11
The Hawaiian hot spot

Volcanic activity

Distribution

Most volcanic activity is associated with plate tectonic processes and is mainly located along plate margins (Figure 9.12). Such activity is therefore found:

Figure 9.12
Global distribution of active volcanoes

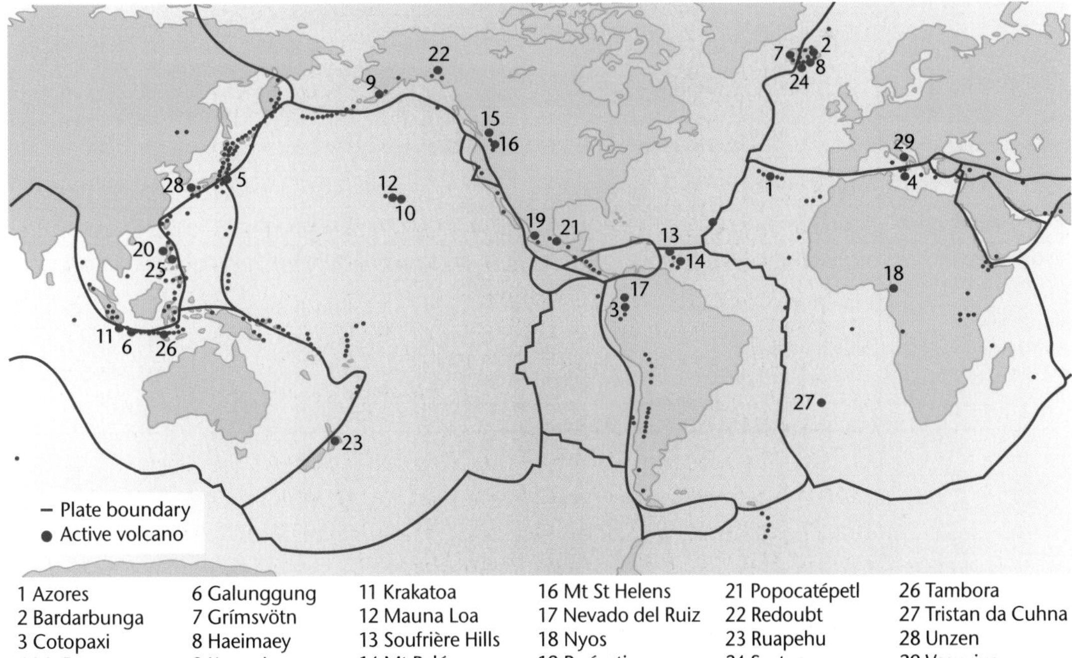

1 Azores
2 Bardarbunga
3 Cotopaxi
4 Mt Etna
5 Fujiyama
6 Galunggung
7 Grímsvötn
8 Haeimaey
9 Katmai
10 Kilauea
11 Krakatoa
12 Mauna Loa
13 Soufrière Hills
14 Mt Pelée
15 Mt Rainier
16 Mt St Helens
17 Nevado del Ruiz
18 Nyos
19 Parícutin
20 Pinatubo
21 Popocatépetl
22 Redoubt
23 Ruapehu
24 Surtsey
25 Taal
26 Tambora
27 Tristan da Cuhna
28 Unzen
29 Vesuvius

- along oceanic ridges where plates are moving apart. The best example is the mid-Atlantic ridge — Iceland represents a large area formed by volcanic activity
- associated with rift valleys. The African rift valley has a number of volcanoes along it including Mt Kenya and Mt Kilimanjaro
- on or near subduction zones. The line of volcanoes, or 'ring of fire', that surrounds the Pacific Ocean is associated with plate subduction. This tends to be the most violent of all activity
- over hot spots such as the one in the middle of the Pacific Ocean which has given rise to the Hawaiian islands

Volcanic eruptions

There are variations in the form, frequency and type of volcanic eruption. These are related to the different kinds of plate margin, emissions and lava. For example, constructive and destructive plate margins produce different types of lava, and this leads to different types and frequencies of eruption. How these different plate margins affect volcanic eruptions and landforms is summarised in Figure 9.13.

Figure 9.13 The effect of different plate margins on volcanic eruptions and landforms

	Constructive plate margins	Destructive plate margins
Plate margin	Movement of plate ← → Movement of plate Magma	Continental crust → ← Movement of plate Magma Oceanic plate Subduction zone Mantle
Type of magma	Basaltic Basalt — Andesite	Acidic Rhyolite
Lava characteristics	Runny — Increasing viscosity Low ← Silica	Slow flowing — very viscous } Lava Silica → High
Type of eruption	Little violence: gases easily escape	Potentially explosive: lava shatters into pieces
Materials erupted	Mainly lava	Lava bombs, ash, dust
Frequency of eruption time	Regular and can be continuous	From time to time: long dormant periods
Form of the volcano	Lava plateau Shield volcano Lava only	Acid lava dome Composite cone Column of gas and finer fragments Layers of lava/ash

Intrusive volcanic landforms

When magma is forced to the surface, only a small amount of the mass actually reaches that level. Most of the magma is **intruded** into the crust where it solidifies into a range of features. These are often exposed at the surface by later erosion.

Batholiths are formed deep below the surface when large masses of magma cool and solidify. As the magma cools slowly, large crystals are formed in the rock (e.g. granite). Batholiths are often dome-shaped and exposed by later erosion. This is the case on Dartmoor and the Isle of Arran (Scotland). Batholiths can be several hundreds of kilometres in diameter. The area surrounding the batholith is altered by the heat and pressure of the intrusion to form a **metamorphic aureole** (limestone, for example, can be transformed into marble). Batholiths are unaffected by the characteristics and structure of existing rock. Sometimes smaller injections of magma form a lens shape that is intruded between layers of rock. This then forces the overlying strata to arch upwards, forming a dome. This feature is known as a **laccolith,** and it may be exposed by later weathering and erosion to form a small range of hills, for example the Eildon Hills on the Scottish Borders.

Dykes are vertical intrusions with horizontal cooling cracks. They cut across the bedding planes of the rocks into which they have been intruded. Dykes often occur in groups where they are known as **dyke swarms**. Many Scottish islands, such as Mull and Skye, have clusters of dykes, all associated with one intrusive event (Figure 9.14).

Sills are horizontal intrusions along the lines of bedding planes. Sills have vertical cooling cracks. Examples include the Great Whin Sill (which carries part of Hadrian's Wall) and Drumadoon on the Isle of Arran. Both sills and dykes are commonly made up of **dolerite**.

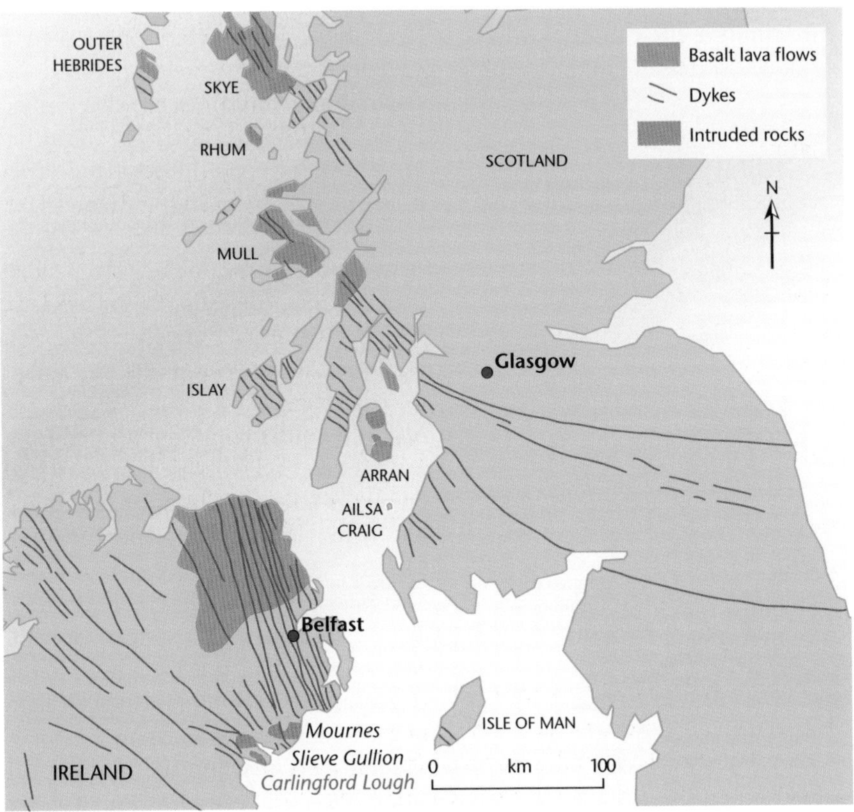

Figure 9.14 Dykes and lava flows in Scotland and Ireland

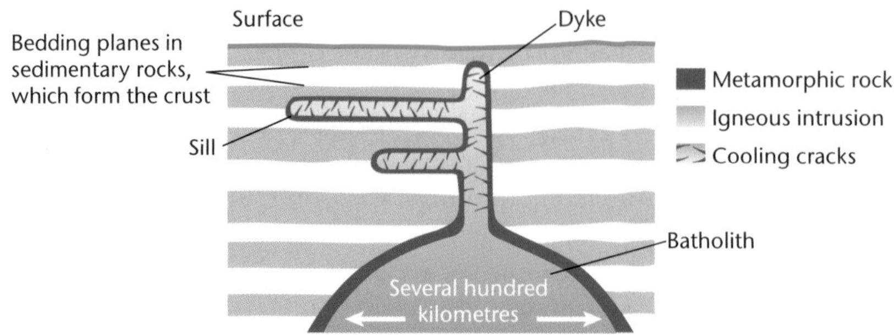

Figure 9.15 Intrusive vulcanicity

Extrusive volcanic landforms

Extrusive vulcanicity involves two forms of lava:

- **Basaltic lava** is formed from magma that is low in silica. This makes for a more fluid magma that allows gas bubbles to expand on the way up to the surface, so preventing sudden explosive activity.
- **Andesitic** and **rhyolitic** lavas are formed from silica-rich (acid) magma that is very viscous. This often solidifies before reaching the surface, leading to a build-up of pressure and, ultimately, to a violent explosion.

The main types of extrusive volcanic landforms are as follows:

- **Lava plateaux** are formed from fissure eruptions. The extensive lava flows are basaltic in nature, so the lava flows great distances. A good example is the Antrim lava plateau in Northern Ireland, the edge of which can be seen at Giant's Causeway. Lava plateaux are generally flat and featureless.
- **Basic/shield volcanoes** are also formed from free-flowing lava. The resulting volcanoes have gentle sides and cover a large area, for example Mauna Loa, Hawaii.
- **Acid/dome volcanoes** are steep-sided convex cones, consisting of viscous lava, which is probably rhyolite. The best examples can be seen in the Puy region of central France.
- **Ash and cinder cones** are formed from ash, cinders and volcanic bombs ejected from the crater. The sides are steep and symmetrical, for example Parícutin, Mexico.
- **Composite cones** are the classic pyramid-shaped volcanoes, consisting of layers of ash and lava, which is usually andesitic (Figure 9.17). Examples include Mt Etna on Sicily, and Mt Fuji in Japan.
- **Calderas** occur when the build-up of gases becomes extreme and a huge

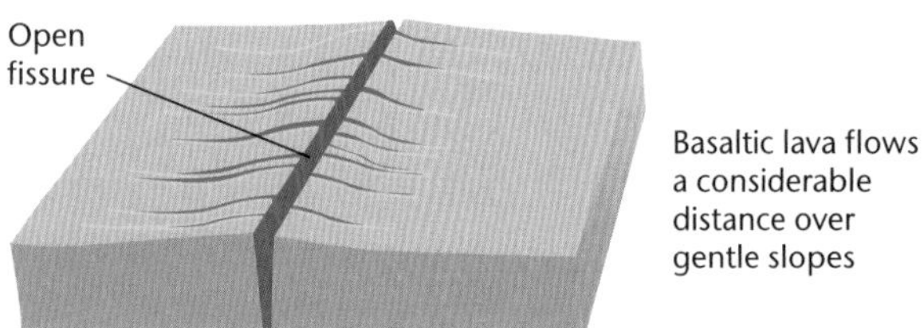

Figure 9.16 Fissure eruption

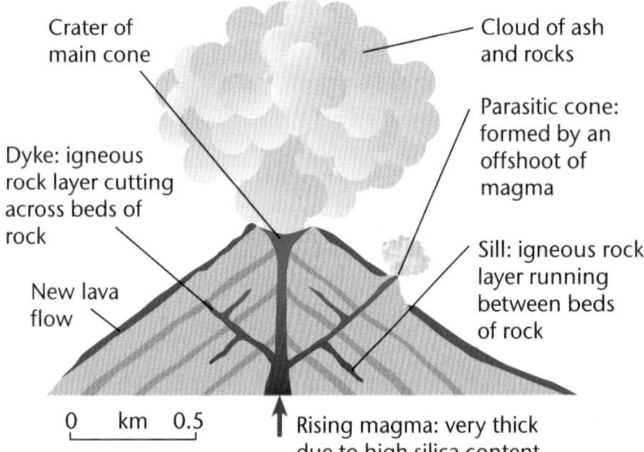

Figure 9.17 A composite volcano

explosion removes the summit of the cone, leaving an opening several kilometres in diameter. The caldera may become flooded by the sea, or a lake may form within it. Examples include Krakatoa in Indonesia and Santorini in Greece.

The nature of volcanic eruptions

Vulcanologists have traditionally classified volcanoes according to the nature of the eruption (Figure 9.18). This classification is based on the degree of violence of the explosion, which is a consequence of the pressure and amount of gas in the magma.

Minor volcanic forms

Minor volcanic forms include:

- **solfatara** — small volcanic areas without cones, produced by gases (mainly sulphurous) escaping to the surface, for example around the Bay of Naples in Italy
- **geysers** — these occur when water, heated by volcanic activity, explodes onto the surface, for example Old Faithful, Yellowstone National Park, USA
- **hot springs/boiling mud** — sometimes the water, heated below, does not explode onto the surface. If this water mixes with surface deposits, boiling mud is formed. Such features are very common in Iceland. There are hot springs at Bath in the west of England

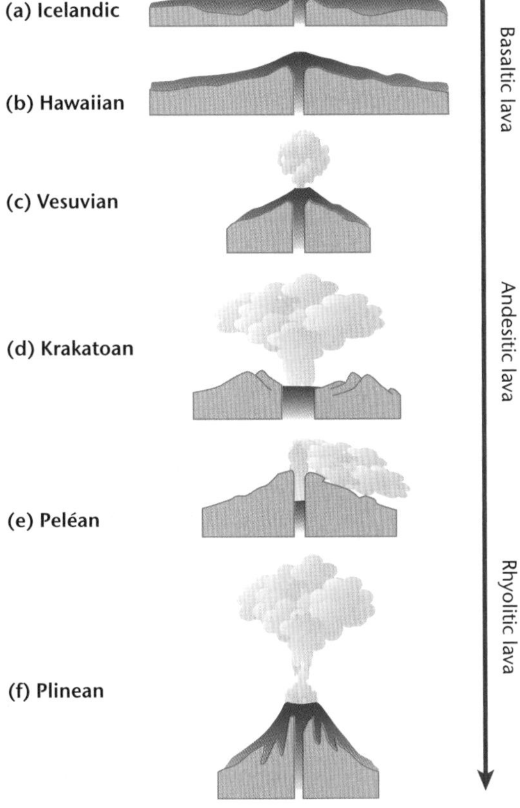

Figure 9.18 Forms of volcanic eruption

Intrusive and extrusive volcanic activity in the UK

Apart from hot springs, the UK has no current volcanic activity. However, there is much geological evidence of such activity, which occurred during the mountain-building periods of the Caledonian, Hercynian and Alpine orogenies (Figure 9.19).

- **Granites** and other examples of **intruded rocks** occur across the Grampians in Scotland, in Ireland, and particularly in the southwest of England where the top of an exposed batholith is seen in areas such as Dartmoor and Bodmin Moor. Here, weathering and erosion have combined to give a distinctive landscape of upland plateaux capped by rock outcrops, which are known as **tors**.
- **Dykes** and **sills** are also common. The dyke 'swarms' that radiate across the Isle of Arran in Scotland contain around 500 such features in a 20 km stretch of coastline. Dykes generally occur as small ridges in the landscape because they are more resistant than the surrounding rocks. The Great Whin Sill runs across

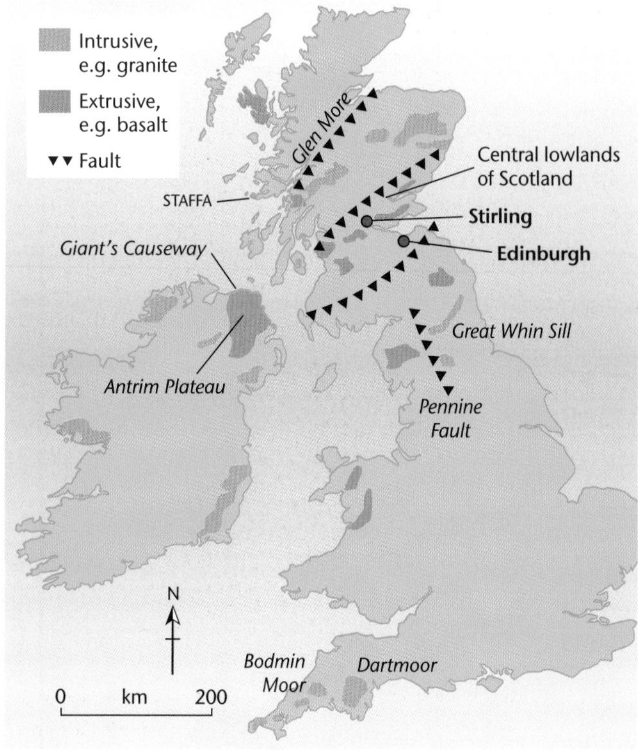

Figure 9.19 Examples of intrusive and extrusive volcanic activity in the UK

large distances in the north of England, forming an upstanding cliff-like feature. Many rivers produce high waterfalls as they plunge over it, for example High Force and Cauldron Snout in the Tees valley in the Pennines. It is also the defensive base for man-made features such as Hadrian's Wall and Bamburgh Castle.

- **Basaltic flows** can be seen where the Antrim lava plateau formed in Northern Ireland. When the lava cooled, vertical cracks in the flow resulted in hexagonal columns. These are exposed at the coast — the Giant's Causeway. The same volcanic feature can be seen in Fingal's Cave on the Isle of Staffa in Scotland.
- A **volcanic plug** from a long-extinct volcano (active over 300 million years ago) forms the site of Edinburgh Castle. Stirling Castle is also built on a volcanic plug.

Earthquakes

Causes

As the crust of the Earth is mobile, there tends to be a slow build up of stress within the rocks. When this pressure is suddenly released, parts of the surface experience an intense shaking motion that lasts for just a few seconds. This is an earthquake. The point at which this pressure release occurs within the crust is known as the **focus**, and the point immediately above that on the Earth's surface is called the **epicentre** (Figure 9.20). The depth of the focus is significant and three broad categories of earthquake are recognised:

- shallow-focus (0–70 km deep): these tend to cause the greatest damage and account for 75% of all the earthquake energy released
- intermediate-focus (70–300 km deep)
- deep-focus (300–700 km deep)

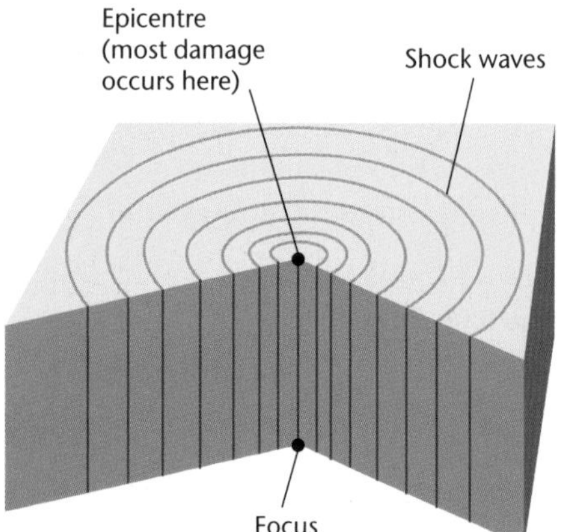

Figure 9.20 The focus and epicentre of an earthquake

Seismic waves radiate from the focus rather like the ripples in water when a rock is thrown into a pond. There are three main types of seismic wave, each travelling at different speeds:

- primary (P) waves travel fastest and are compressional, vibrating in the direction that they are travelling
- secondary (S) waves travel at half the speed of P waves and shear rock by vibrating at right angles to the direction of travel
- surface waves travel slowest and near to the ground surface. Some surface waves shake the ground at right angles to the direction of wave movement and some have a rolling motion that produces vertical ground movement

P and S waves travel through the interior of the Earth and are recorded on a seismograph. Studying earthquakes and the seismic waves they generate has made it possible to build up a picture of the interior of the Earth.

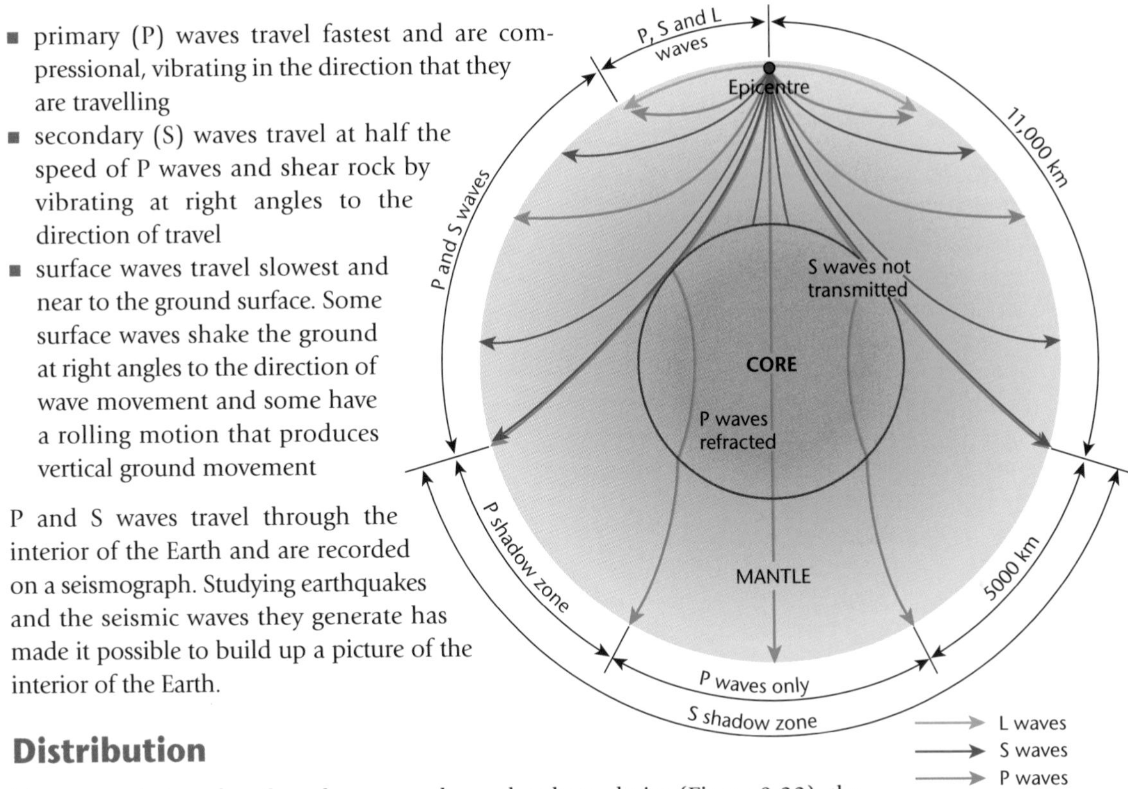

Figure 9.21
Seismic waves

Distribution

The vast majority of earthquakes occur along plate boundaries (Figure 9.22), the most powerful being associated with destructive margins. At conservative margins, the boundary is marked by a fault, movement along which produces the earthquake. Perhaps the most famous of these is the San Andreas fault in California which represents the boundary between the North American and

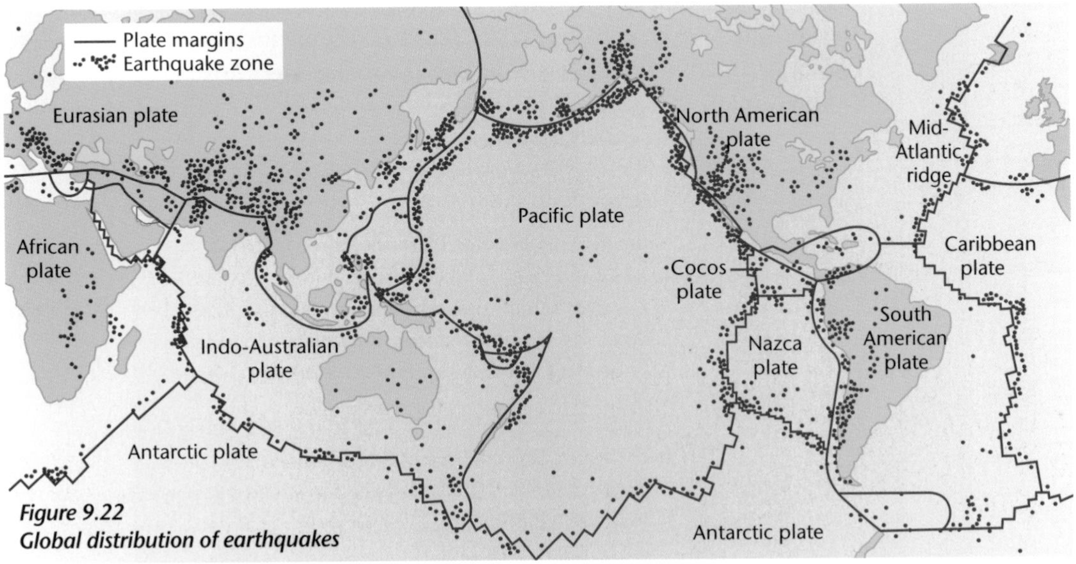

Figure 9.22
Global distribution of earthquakes

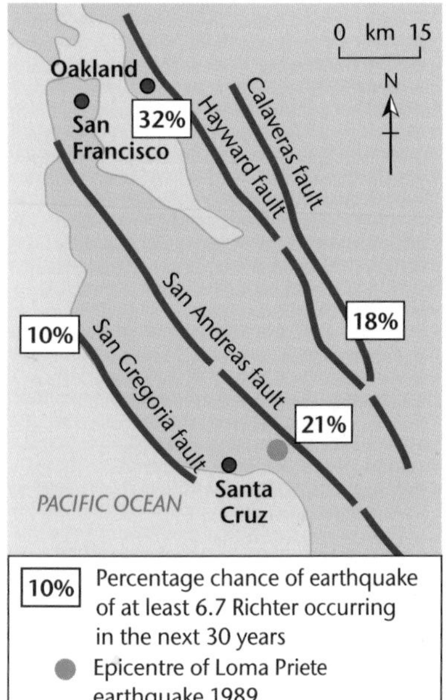

Figure 9.23 Earthquake probability in the San Francisco area

Pacific plates. In reality, the San Andreas system consists of a broad complex zone in which there are a number of fractures of the crust (Figure 9.23).

Some earthquakes occur away from plate boundaries and are associated with the reactivation of old fault lines. An example is the event that occurred on 23 September 2002 in the UK Midlands. This earthquake measured 4.8 on the Richter scale, and the epicentre was located in Dudley, west of Birmingham. It is believed that the cause was movement along an old fault line known as the Malvern lineament.

It has been suggested that human activity could be the cause of some minor earthquakes. Examples are the building of large reservoirs in which the water puts pressure on the surface rocks, or subsidence of deep mine workings.

Magnitude and frequency

The magnitude of earthquakes is measured on two scales. The **Richter** scale (Table 9.3) is a logarithmic scale — an event measured at 7 on the scale has an amplitude of seismic waves ten times greater than one measured at 6 on the scale. The energy release is proportional to the magnitude, so that for each unit increase in the scale, the energy released increases by approximately 30 times.

The largest event ever recorded was measured at 8.9 on the scale. The earthquake in Dudley described above, at 4.8 on the scale, was large for the UK but small compared to major earthquakes such as the 1999 Turkish earthquake which measured 7.4 on the Richter scale. This earthquake killed more than 14,000 people, injured 25,000 and completely destroyed over 20,000 buildings.

The **Mercalli** scale measures the intensity of the event and its impact. It is a 12-point scale that runs from Level I (detected by seismometers but felt by very few people — approximately equivalent to 2 on the Richter scale) to Level XII (total destruction with the ground seen to shake — approximately 8.5 on the Richter scale).

Table 9.3 The Richter scale

Number (logarithmic)	Effects
1–3	Normally only detected by seismographs, not felt
4	Faint tremor causing little damage
5	Widely felt, some structural damage near epicentre
6	Distinct shaking, less well-constructed buildings collapse
7	Major earthquake causing serious damage (e.g. Kobe 1995, Turkey 1999)
8	Great earthquake causing massive destruction and loss of life (e.g. Mexico City 1985, San Francisco 1906)
9–10	Very rare great earthquake causing major damage over a large region. Ground seen to shake

Seismic records enable earthquake frequency to be observed, but these records only date back to 1848 when an instrument capable of recording seismic waves was first developed.

Weathering and mass movement

Weathering

Weathering is the decay or decomposition of rocks in situ by physical or chemical action. There is no movement of material involved. Most forms of weathering involve elements of the weather, such as water and frost, and chemicals in the atmosphere. Weathering can also result from the activity of plants and animals, for example the physical effects of tree roots or the action of organic acids.

It is important to distinguish weathering from **erosion**. Erosion is carried out by the mobile forces of water, ice and wind and causes the breakdown of rock *and* its removal. Weathered material may be transported immediately after weathering has taken place, as would happen, for example, high on a cliff face due to the effect of gravity. Other transportation, however, occurs by a different force (water, ice or wind) from that which caused the weathering.

Weathering, erosion, and transportation work together to remove and lower the landscape. The term for this is **denudation**. Weathering is responsible for the early stages of denudation in which a rock surface is broken down to produce loose debris, known as **regolith**. Mass movements transport the pieces of rock and other debris caused by weathering until an agent of erosion picks them up. The agent of erosion then transports this debris to the sea, often using it as a tool for further erosion. This exposes fresh rock surfaces for weathering, and so the cycle continues.

Mechanical (physical) weathering

Mechanical weathering involves the breakdown of rocks without chemical change.

Frost shattering (freeze–thaw action) is the disintegration of rock brought about by the stresses caused by water freezing in cracks. When water freezes, it increases in volume by about 9%, which puts pressure on the rock. When it melts, this pressure is released. If an exposed rock surface goes through many cycles of freeze and thaw, joints and pores are gradually enlarged, eventually leading to the shattering of the rock. The products of this type of weathering are:

- **screes** — angular fragments of rock that collect at the foot of a slope
- **blockfields** — rock-strewn areas (**felsenmeers**) produced by the same weathering process operating on flatter terrain

Insolation weathering is the breakdown of rocks as a result of successive changes in volume brought about by heating and cooling. As rock is a poor conductor of heat, only the outermost layers respond to temperature changes. This sets up stress in the rock. Eventually the outer layers break away in a process known as

exfoliation. Many rocks contain different minerals that expand and contract at different rates, leading to the granular disintegration of the rock surface. Recent research has suggested that the presence of water contributes to the amount of disintegration caused by insolation. Studies of ancient buildings in Egypt have shown that there is little sign of decay unless they are located close to the Nile.

Pressure release occurs when overlying material is removed and a rock surface is exposed. The removal of pressure that results often leads to the expansion of the previously stressed rock, causing joints to open and surfaces to crack. Other agents of weathering are then able to exploit these weaknesses. This also produces a form of exfoliation.

Salt weathering is another example of a process in which rock is broken up by pressure exerted on it from within the rock structure. If water within the rock becomes saturated with salt, some of the salt crystallises and begins to exert pressure on the rock. As with freeze–thaw weathering, the process repeats over time. This type of weathering is most common in arid areas and along coasts.

Chemical weathering

Chemical weathering is caused by a reaction between the rock and the air, water and other solutions with which it comes into contact.

Solution occurs when soluble minerals dissolve in water. Only a few minerals will dissolve in pure water but many more will dissolve in a weak acid. If carbon dioxide is added to rainwater it produces a weak carbonic acid, which will dissolve some kinds of rock. Calcium carbonate will dissolve in carbonic acid, so limestone, which contsists mostly of calcium carbonate, is prone to higher levels of solution than other rocks. The dissolving of rocks containing calcium carbonate is known as **carbonation**.

Hydrolysis occurs when water reacts with minerals in the rock and causes them to break down. It is a common process because the minerals that are vulnerable to hydrolysis, including silicates such as feldspar, are found in many types of granite. Weak acid rainwater causes the feldspar to be converted into a clay called kaolin, and the whole rock gradually disintegrates. Chemically, it is the hydrogen ions in water that react with the metal cations in the mineral structure. This causes a complex series of changes that ultimately converts the silicate mineral into a clay mineral.

Hydration is the chemical equivalent of saturating a sponge. Some minerals absorb water into their structure and as a result expand. If these volume changes are repeated over time they make the rock vulnerable to mechanical failure, for example cracking or granular disintegration. Hydration also assists other forms of chemical weathering by introducing water throughout the crystal structure. The mineral anhydrite, for example, is converted into gypsum by hydration.

Oxidation occurs when oxygen dissolved in water reacts with certain minerals, particularly those containing iron. This chemical conversion weakens the mineral bonding and makes it more vulnerable to other weathering processes. Oxidation often results in colour change and may be the explanation for reddish-brown tinges on exposed rock faces or soils. Oxidation can also render a mineral more vulnerable to other forms of chemical weathering.

Biological weathering

Biological weathering occurs when living organisms bring about physical and chemical weathering. Plant roots seek out weaknesses in rocks, gradually prising them apart. Burrowing animals can play a similar role. The presence of organic matter can produce acids that promote chemical weathering, particularly of calcium-based rocks.

Factors that affect weathering

Climate is one of the most important factors to affect weathering. This is not surprising, given that virtually every weathering process requires either the presence of water or a change in temperature (or both) to work effectively. Chemical weathering is most intense in warm, wet climates; physical weathering is particularly active in cold climates (Figure 9.24).

Geology (rock characteristics and structure) has an important impact on weathering because the rate of chemical weathering is affected by the chemical composition of the rock. Some minerals are more prone to chemical change than others. Joints and bedding planes promote weathering as they enable water and roots to penetrate deep into the rock.

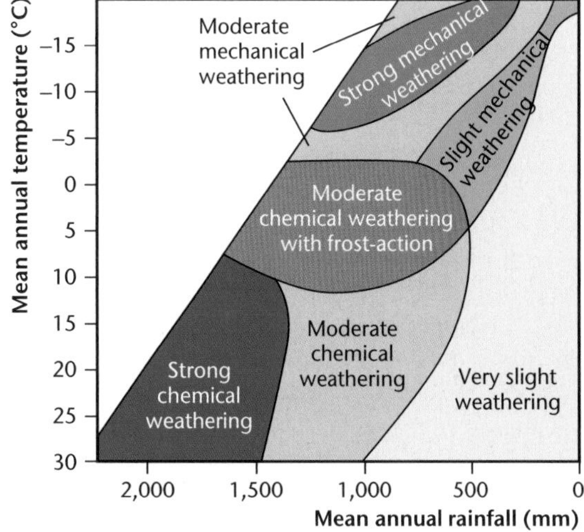

Figure 9.24 The relationship between weathering and climate

Soil depth and nature is important because it can have a significant impact on the amount of weathering that affects the underlying rock.

Vegetation can promote weathering. Organic acids from plants can speed up hydrolysis and plant roots can prise apart jointed rocks. Some forms of vegetation, such as moss, cling to rocks, holding water in contact with them and encouraging chemical weathering.

Topography can be a factor in weathering because transport is necessary to allow the weathering processes to access new material. If the slope is too gentle, weathered material may accumulate in situ and prevent this access. **Altitude** and **aspect** also have an impact on the type and amount of weathering that occurs.

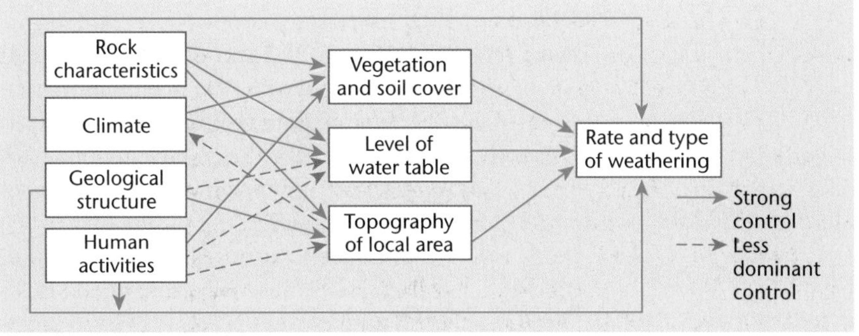

Figure 9.25 Factors affecting weathering

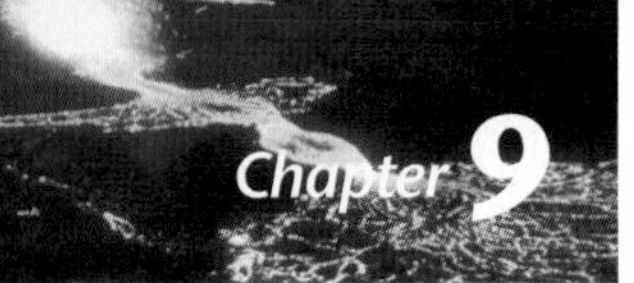

The role of people in weathering

People have a number of influences on weathering and are, in turn, affected by it. The influence of people includes the following:

- **Emissions of carbon dioxide and sulphur dioxide** produce carbonic and sulphuric acids when dissolved in rainwater. This has had an enormous effect upon certain exposed rock surfaces (for example, limestone) and has damaged buildings constructed from such rocks.
- **Export of pollution** has occurred, for example acid pollution from the UK has caused acid rain in Scandinavia which has led to building decay and increased soil acidification.
- The **removal of vegetation** can have a serious effect, particularly in the tropics, where it can expose the surface of the land to rapid chemical weathering.

All these effects can impact upon people. Chemical weathering can damage buildings, which then require cleaning and expensive restoration. For example, St Paul's Cathedral in London has had to have its Portland stone cleaned and occasionally replaced. In Egypt, atmospheric pollution from Cairo has drifted into the deserts and damaged many monuments of the ancient world, including the pyramids and the Sphinx.

Mass movement

Mass movement is the downhill movement of surface material under the influence of gravity. Mass movement may be assisted by the added buoyancy provided by water that has entered the material through precipitation or snowmelt. There are several classifications of mass movement. One of the most straightforward is shown in Figure 9.26.

Slopes are a part of the evolution of the landscape, responding to natural factors such as rock type, vegetation and climate, and eventually achieving a state of **equilibrium**. If conditions change, either naturally or through human intervention, the state of equilibrium will be lost and an unstable slope will be produced. The profile of this slope will change in order to achieve a new equilibrium. Some mass movements are rapid, spontaneous responses to slope failure, while others are continuous processes occurring over longer periods of time. There are three main types of mass movement: heave, flow and slide.

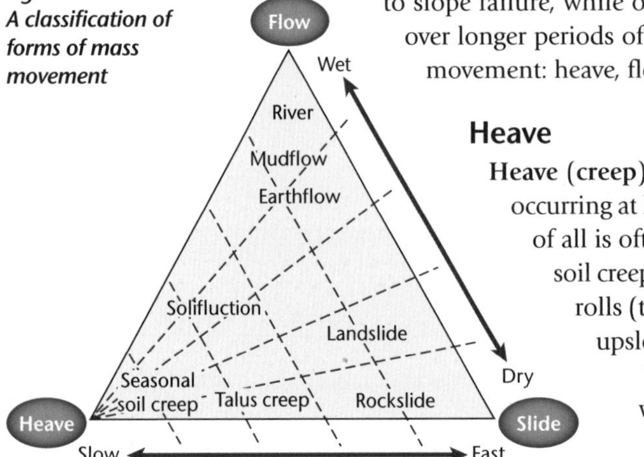

Figure 9.26 A classification of forms of mass movement

Heave

Heave (creep) is the slowest form of mass movement, occurring at less than 1 cm yr^{-1}. The slowest movement of all is often referred to as **soil creep**. The results of soil creep include leaning trees and fence posts, turf rolls (terracettes) and the piling up of soil on the upslope sides of walls.

The expansion and contraction of water within soil is the main cause of soil creep. Wetting causes the soil to expand and to move downslope under the influence of gravity. Frost-heaving in soils forces particles upward. When the ice melts, the particles drop downhill, also under the influence of gravity. It is this process that explains the high rates of soil creep in semi-arid regions with cold winters. Creep is also involved in the formation of stone polygons and stripes in periglacial areas (pages 310–311).

In periglacial environments, it is possible for the surface to become saturated, because water is unable to penetrate the underlying permafrost and temperatures are too low for much evaporation to occur. Under such circumstances, the downhill movement (**solifluction**) is considerably faster than soil creep. It is sufficiently fast for some people to classify solifluction as a flow. Rounded domes of rock and soil that have been moved downhill by this process are common in periglacial areas and in places like the British Isles that have been affected by periglaciation in the past. They are called **solifluction lobes**.

Flow

Flow takes place when the slope material is at its wettest. Flows occur in three main forms.

Earthflows occur when the regolith on steeper slopes becomes saturated and slowly flows downhill. They often flow down a distinct channel and quickly lose speed when reaching a flat surface. For this reason, they often form distinctive lobes when they arrive on a valley floor.

Mudflows are much faster, often moving at over 1 km h^{-1}. They occur when the regolith becomes saturated very quickly, either by heavy precipitation or by rapidly melting ice and snow — for example after a volcanic eruption. Up to 60% of the weight of a mudflow can be water. Their speed of movement means they have the potential to make significant alterations to the landscape. Volcanic eruptions are capable of producing huge mudflows known as **lahars** (for example the mudflow that occurred after the eruption of Mt Pinatubo in the Philippines, 1991).

Debris flows involve the rapid movement of relatively coarse material. They often occur in mountainous regions where surfaces may consist of debris unconsolidated by layers of vegetation. Debris flows tend to follow existing channels and can do enormous damage if they come into contact with human activity.

Slide

Many slides are a dry-mass movement, although water may be a factor in some types. A slide does not involve any internal deformation because it moves as one mass along a slip plane. Slides are promoted by a number of factors that include rock type, permeability, prolonged rainfall, vegetation removal, building on slopes and undercutting (Figure 9.27).

Figure 9.27 Factors that promote slides

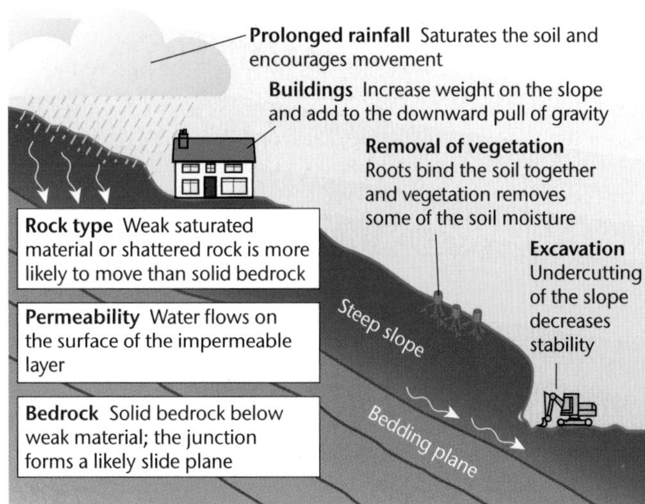

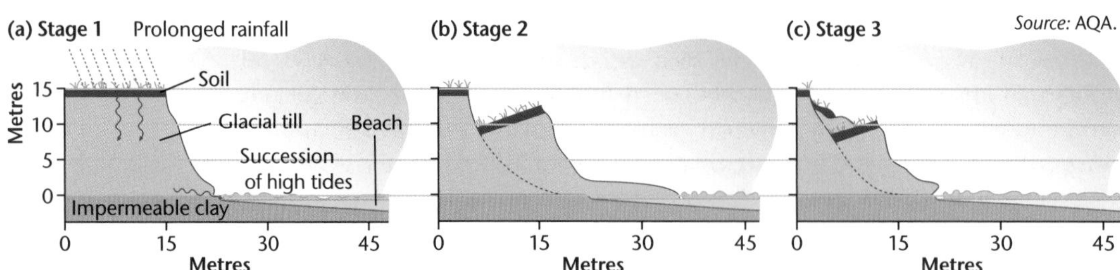

Figure 9.28 Rotational slumping

A rotational slide, or slump, produces an upper rotational slip plane, which is quite often lubricated by rainfall (Figure 9.28). This type of movement is often triggered when the base of a slope is undermined by a river or the sea. Slumps are a common feature of the British coast, particularly where glacial deposits form the coastal area, for example in east Yorkshire and north Norfolk. Figure 9.28 shows a typical rotational slump where glacial deposits form cliffs on top of an impermeable clay layer.

Falls are generated on the steepest slopes, which allow debris to fall through the air before accumulating at the base of the slope or cliff. Falls occur when the weathering processes acting on a cliff-face have done sufficient damage to allow a block of rock to become detached and fall to the base. Here it will be removed by river, sea or ice, or remain as scree.

Avalanches can consist of either snow or rock, or both. A snow avalanche is a sudden and rapid movement down a slope. For the snow to begin to move, the slope has to be at least 25°. One cause of an avalanche is heavy snowfall on top of previous layers of snow and ice. As layers of snow build up, it is possible for a weak layer to develop with the thawing and refreezing of the snow. Avalanches can also result from rapid thawing, which destabilises the snowfields.

Geomorphological processes and hazards: impact and response

Impacts on the natural world

Geomorphological processes have a number of impacts on the natural world.

Landscape

Volcanic activity has a major effect upon the landscape. Volcanoes and other forms of extrusive activity alter the landscape through violent volcanic action, pyroclastic and lava flows, and lahars. Although an **earthquake** can be a very violent event, it will only have a small-scale impact on the physical landscape, for example cracks opening up in the ground and small fault scarps being formed. Many forms of **mass movement** alter the landscape, but only very slowly, as is the case with soil creep. Landslides, however, can make a dramatic alteration to a slope.

Vegetation

Volcanic eruptions destroy the vegetation cover. However, once the activity is over, pioneer plants (for example mosses and lichens) begin to colonise the new surface. They are the first stage in a plant succession known as a **lithosere**. If uninterrupted by further eruptions or human activity, the succession will eventually lead to the return of the climatic climax vegetation.

Global effects

Large-scale volcanic eruptions can put so much fine debris into the atmosphere that incoming solar radiation is affected, leading to a reduction in global temperatures.

Impacts on human activity

Responses to hazards

Response to a hazard can be made at both a collective and an individual level. It very much depends upon how people or organisations perceive the hazard and this depends on factors such as past experience, values, personality and expectations. The response is influenced not only by perception but also by the economic ability to take various courses of action and the technological ability to carry them out.

The way in which hazards are perceived can be classified as follows:

- **Fatalism** — the acceptance that hazards are natural events which are part of living. Some communities go as far as saying that they are 'God's will'. Losses are accepted as inevitable and people remain in the area.
- **Adaptation** — people see that they can prepare for, and therefore survive, a hazard event by prediction, prevention and/or protection, depending upon the type of hazard and the economic and technological circumstances of the area.
- **Fear** — people feel so vulnerable to the event that they are no longer able to face living in the area and move away to regions perceived to be unaffected by the hazard.

Management of hazards takes a number of forms:

- **Prediction** — it is possible to give warnings of some hazards. Action can then be taken to reduce their impact. Improved monitoring, information and communications technology have made the prediction of hazards and the issuing of warnings more useful in recent years.
- **Prevention** — the ideal form of management is to prevent the occurrence of the hazard event. For most hazards this is entirely unrealistic, and the best that can be achieved is some form of control, often through modification of the environment.
- **Protection** — the aim is to protect people and property from the impact of the hazard, but protection can also take the form of insuring against losses (particularly in MEDCs) and the supply of aid (usually in LEDCs). In MEDCs, areas affected by hazard events are able to draw on central government funds for protection and relief.

Attempts to manage hazards must be evaluated in terms of their success in prediction, protection and prevention. Successful schemes, for example, have included the use of dynamite to divert lava flows on the slopes of Mt Etna in Italy, and pouring sea water on lava fronts in Iceland to solidify the flow. On the other hand, the Japanese felt they were well-prepared for earthquakes and yet the Kobe earthquake in 1995 left more than 100,000 buildings damaged and over 6,000 people dead (with 35,000 injured).

Volcanic activity

A volcanic event can have a range of impacts, affecting the area immediately around the volcano or the entire planet. Effects can be categorised into primary and secondary. **Primary** effects consist of:

- **tephra** — solid material of varying grain size, from volcanic bombs to ash particles, ejected into the atmosphere
- **pyroclastic flows** — very hot (800 °C), gas-charged, high-velocity flows made up of a mixture of gases and tephra
- **lava flows**
- **volcanic gases** — including carbon dioxide, carbon monoxide, hydrogen sulphide, sulphur dioxide and chlorine. Emissions of carbon dioxide from Lake Nyos in Cameroon in 1986 suffocated 1,700 people

Secondary effects include:

- **lahars** — volcanic mud flows such as those that devastated the Colombian town of Armero after the eruption of Nevado del Ruiz in November 1985
- **flooding** — melting of glaciers and ice caps such as the Grímsvötn glacial burst on Iceland in November 1996
- **tsunamis** — giant sea waves generated after violent caldera-forming events such as that which occurred on Krakatoa in 1883 — the tsunamis from this eruption are believed to have drowned 36,000 people
- **volcanic landslides**
- **climatic change** — the ejection of vast amounts of volcanic debris into the atmosphere can reduce global temperatures and is believed to have been an agent in past climatic change

Volcanic effects become a hazard when they impact upon the human and built environments, killing and injuring people, burying and collapsing buildings, destroying the infrastructure and bringing agricultural activities to a halt.

Management

Prediction

It is easy to locate volcanoes, but it is very difficult to predict exactly when activity will take place, particularly a major eruption. The Colombian volcano, Nevado del Ruiz, came to life in late 1984 with small-scale activity. Vulcanologists knew the danger a major eruption could pose to the surrounding area, but were unable to predict when the major event would take place. Small-scale volcanic activity continued for several months and people were not prepared to evacuate their homes on the basis of this threat. When the violent eruption came on 13 November 1985, almost all the population had remained in the area.

Case study Soufrière Hills, Montserrat, 1995–97

During and after the eruption of the Soufrière Hills volcano (Figure 9.29), the British government had to provide, or assist in, the following, as Montserrat was still a dependent territory:

- evacuation of 7,000 of the island's 11,000 population to neighbouring islands such as Antigua, or resettlement in the UK, and financial help with all resettlement
- resettlement of some of the population from the volcanic south to the 'safer' north of the island
- setting up of temporary shelters in the north
- re-establishment of air and sea links with the island
- building of new permanent housing
- moving the capital from Plymouth (now destroyed) to Salem
- providing farming areas for those resettled in the north

The British government spent over £100 million in total on mitigating the effects of the eruption and on a 3-year development plan for the island.

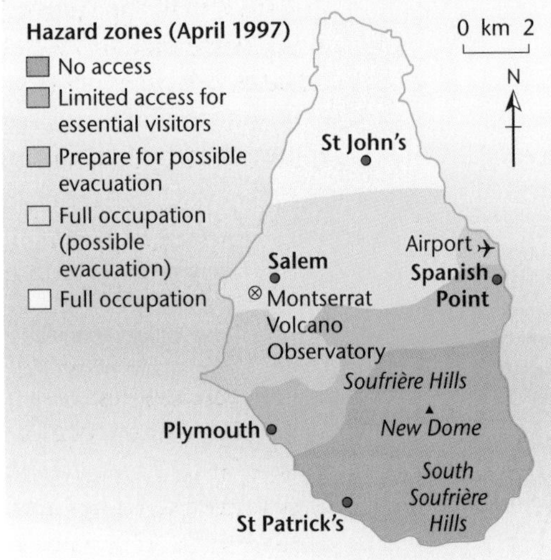

Figure 9.29 Montserrat: danger zones

Photograph 9.3 The former capital of Montserrat, Plymouth, covered by dust and ashes from the Soufrière Hills volcano, August 1997

Devastating lahars, resulting from melting snow and ice, swept down the valleys, killing over 20,000 people.

A study of the previous eruption history of a volcano is important in prediction, along with an understanding of the type of activity produced. At present, research is being conducted to see if it is possible to predict the time of an eruption accurately using the shock waves that are produced as magma approaches the surface, expanding cracks and breaking through other areas of rock. There was some success in predicting the recent eruption (2000) of Popocatépetl in Mexico, but it remains to be seen if such techniques can be applied to all volcanoes.

Protection

With volcanic activity, protection means preparing for the event. Monitoring of the volcano may suggest a time when the area under threat should be evacuated. Such monitoring includes observations of land swelling, earthquake activity, changes in groundwater level and chemical composition, emission of gases, magnetic field studies and the shock wave analysis mentioned above. Several governments of countries in volcanic areas have made risk assessments and from them produced a series of alert levels to warn the public. In New Zealand the government has produced a five-stage table that includes the following:

1 Signs of volcanic activity. No significant volcanic threat.
2 Indications of intrusive processes. Local eruption threat.
3 Increasing intrusive trends indicate real possibility of hazardous eruption.
4 Large-scale eruption now appears imminent.
5 Destruction within the permanent danger zone (as identified). Significant risk over a wider area.

Geological studies of the nature and extent of deposits from former eruptions and associated ashfalls, lahars and floods may also provide evidence for hazard assessment. Figure 9.30 shows the hazards posed by Mt Rainier (Cascade Range, USA), one of the most studied volcanoes in North America.

Following assessments, it is possible to identify the areas at greatest risk, and land-use planning can be applied to avoid building in such places.

Figure 9.30 Risk assessment of the Mt Rainier area

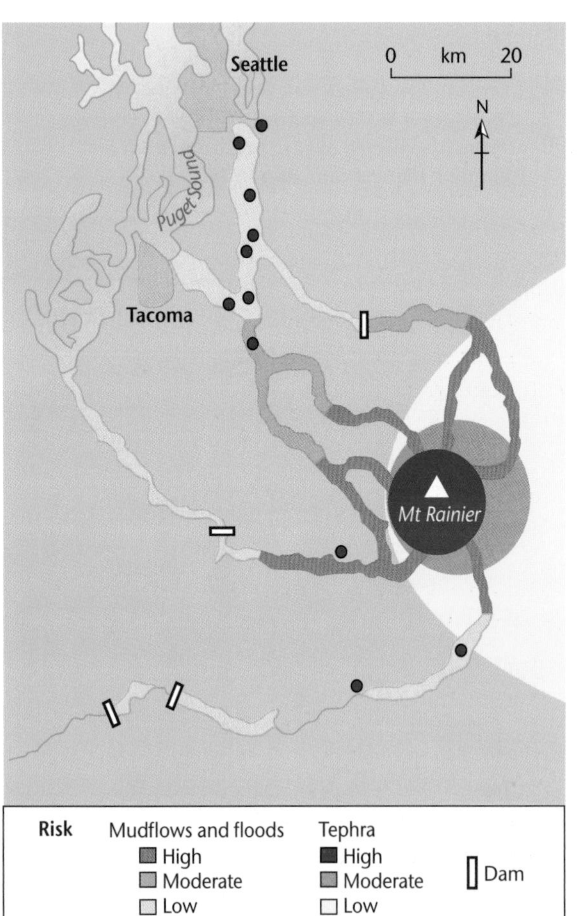

Once the lava has started to flow, it is possible, in certain circumstances, to divert it from the built environment by:

- digging trenches (Mt Etna, Sicily)
- explosive activity (Mt Etna, 1983)
- artificial barriers, which also protect against lahars (Hawaiian islands)
- pouring water on the lava front (Haeimaey, Iceland, 1973)

Foreign aid to LEDCs suffering volcanic eruptions may be required for considerable periods of time as volcanic events can be prolonged and devastating to the local economy. Such aid is needed for monitoring, evacuation, emergency shelters and food, long-term resettlement of the population and restoration of the economic base and the area's infrastructure (see case study on Montserrat, page 279).

Earthquakes

The initial effect of an earthquake is **ground shaking**. The severity of this will depend upon the magnitude of the earthquake, the distance from the epicentre and the local geological conditions. In the Mexico City earthquake of 1985, for example, the seismic waves that devastated the city were amplified several times by the ancient lake sediments upon which the city is built.

Secondary effects are as follows:

- **soil liquefaction** — soils with a high water content lose their mechanical strength when violently shaken, and start to behave like a fluid
- **landslides/avalanches** — slope failure as a result of ground shaking
- **effects on people and the built environment** — collapsing buildings; destruction of road systems and other forms of communications; destruction of service provision such as gas, water and electricity; fires resulting from ruptured gas pipes and collapsed electricity transmission systems; flooding; disease; food shortages; disruption to the local economy. Some of the effects on the human environment are short term; others occur over a longer period and will depend to a large extent on the ability of the area to recover
- **tsunamis** — giant sea waves (tsunami means 'harbour wave' in Japanese) generated mainly by shallow-focus underwater earthquakes; they can also be caused by volcanic eruptions, underwater debris slides and large landslides into the sea. They travel quickly over the ocean (possibly in excess of 700 km h^{-1}) as shallow waves with very long wavelengths (about 100 km). When they enter shallow water they increase rapidly in height, reaching in excess of 25 m. A tsunami event may consist of a number of waves — the largest not necessarily being the first. The wave washes boats and wooden coastal structures inland and the backwash may carry them out to sea. People are drowned or injured by the event as both the water itself and the debris it contains are hazards. Depending on the coastal geography, tsunamis can have an effect at least 500–600 m inland and in some circumstances even further. Around 90% of tsunamis are generated within the Pacific basin as result of the tectonic activity around its edges (see case study, page 283)

Case study Northridge, Los Angeles, 1994

There have been five earthquakes in the Los Angeles area since 1933 that measured at least 5.8 on the Richter scale (Figure 9.31). They were:

- 1933 Long Beach, 6.4 Richter, 120 people died
- 1987 Whittier Narrows, 5.9 Richter, 8 people died
- 1971 San Fernando, 6.6 Richter, 65 people died
- 1991 Sierra Madre, 5.8 Richter, 2 people died
- 1994 Northridge, 6.7 Richter, 57 people died

The Northridge earthquake occurred at 4.30 a.m. on Monday 17 January 1994 and was the result of movement along a thrust fault, whose presence was not known to geologists. The focus of the earthquake was at a depth of 18.4 km. The low death toll has been attributed to the fact that the earthquake occurred in the early morning. If it had happened several hours later, far more people would have been away from their homes, many of them on the roads of the area.

The main effects of the earthquake were:

- 57 people killed, over 1,500 seriously injured
- 12,500 structures suffered moderate to serious damage
- 11 major roads were seriously damaged (Photograph 9.4) and had to close; roads were damaged up to 32 km from the epicentre
- over 11,000 landslides were triggered
- 20,000 people were immediately made homeless
- several days after the event 9,000 premises had no electricity, 20,000 had no gas, 48,500 had little or no water
- nearly 6,000 aftershocks were felt in the days following the event, causing damage to already weakened buildings
- the cost of the damage exceeded $30 billion
- around 700,000 applications were made to federal and state assistance programmes for financial help

Topfoto

Photograph 9.4 Damage caused by the Northridge earthquake, Los Angeles

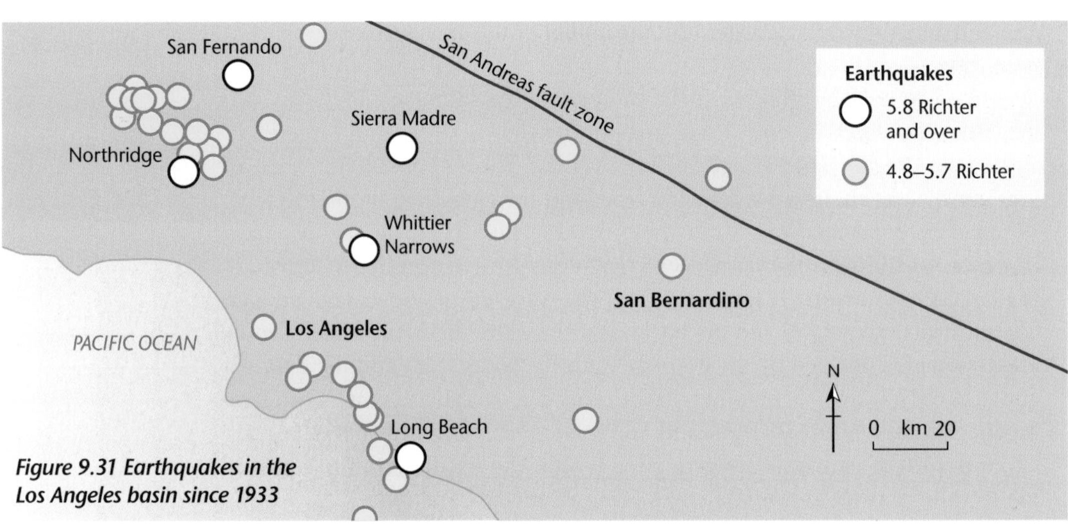

Figure 9.31 Earthquakes in the Los Angeles basin since 1933

Case study The Indian Ocean tsunami, 26 December 2004

Pressure had been building up for some time where the Indo-Australian plate subducts beneath the Eurasian plate south of Myanmar, and on Boxing Day 2004 there was a slippage along the plate edge some 25 km beneath the Indian Ocean. A section of sea bed on the Eurasian side of the fault rose several metres, generating a powerful earthquake which measured about 9.0 on the modified Richter scale. This makes it one of the biggest earthquakes ever recorded.

The epicentre of this earthquake was just off the northwestern tip of the island of Sumatra (see Figure 9.32). The earthquake triggered a tsunami that raced across the Indian Ocean, devastating islands (the Maldives, and the Andaman and Nicobar Islands) and the coastlines of the countries bordering the ocean, particularly Indonesia (Sumatra), Malaysia, Thailand, Myanmar, India and Sri Lanka. In some places the wall of water that came ashore was over 25 m in height. In the Pacific basin tsunami warning systems are in place but in the Indian Ocean no such system had been set up. The populations of these countries had no idea of what was about to arrive.

The main effects of the tsunami were:

- an estimated 300,000 people were killed by the waves
- tens of thousands of people were injured by the force of the waves and the debris that they carried
- many of these coastal areas, particularly in Thailand, Sri Lanka and the Maldives, are popular tourist destinations, so many hundreds of the dead and missing were from Europe — tourist figures were high as these areas are popular winter destinations, especially over the Christmas holiday
- whole towns and villages were swept away, particularly in northern Sumatra, the nearest land to the epicentre — it has been estimated that over 1,500 villages were destroyed in this area alone
- destruction of property resulted in millions of people being made homeless
- there was massive damage to the tourist infrastructure, particularly hotels, bars, restaurants and shops

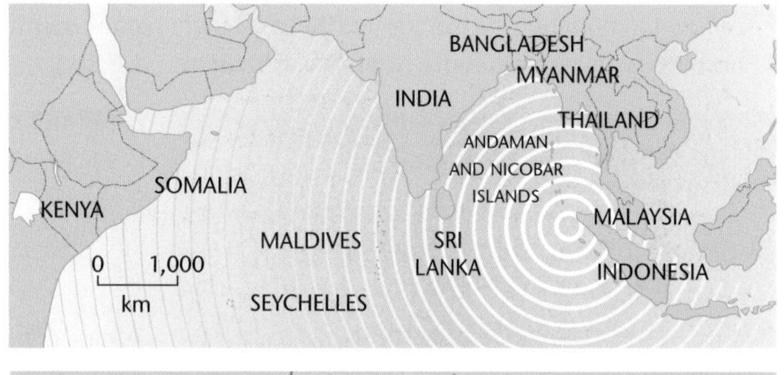

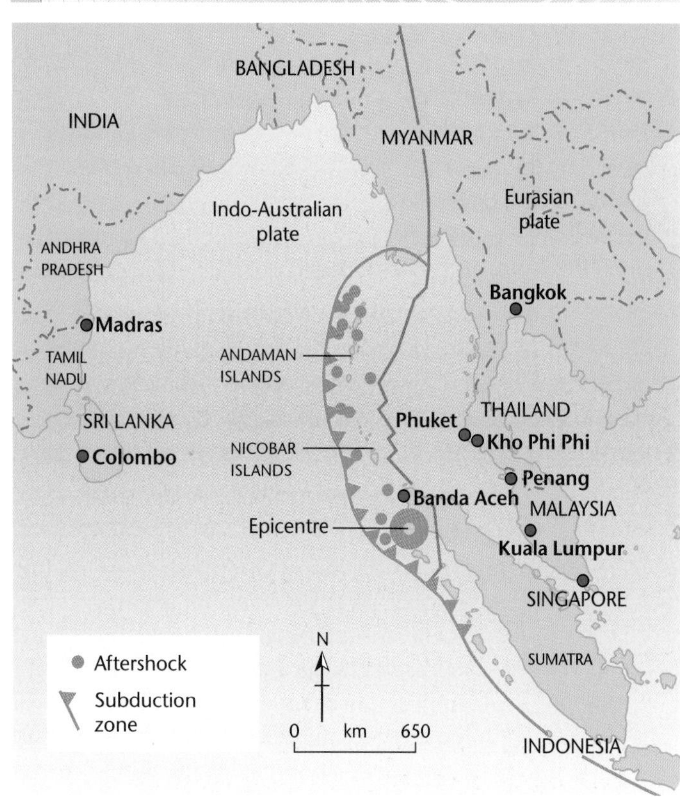

Figure 9.32 The area affected by the Indian Ocean tsunami

- there was widespread damage to coastal communications, particularly bridges and railway lines — in one instance in Sri Lanka, a train was swept off the tracks resulting in over 1,000 deaths
- damage to the economies of these coastal areas, particularly agriculture and fishing, left hundreds of thousands of people unable to feed themselves — the damage was so severe in places that coastal economies will be seriously affected for many years
- many hospitals and clinics were washed away or damaged, so a great deal of medical aid had to be brought in from outside the affected areas
- despite the enormous human cost, the insurance industry estimated that the disaster could cost it less than $5 billion

On the western side of the Indian Ocean, countries did receive a warning of what was to come and were able to take action. Kenya, for example, reacted quickly, moving thousands of tourists off beaches to safety.

One positive result of this tsunami is that a warning system is to be set up among the countries that border the Indian Ocean. This would have been of little use in northern Sumatra as the area was so close to the epicentre of the earthquake, but other countries would have benefited from some warning.

Photograph 9.5 Devastation caused by the tsunami: a lone mosque left standing in a flattened village in Aceh, Sumatra

TopFoto

Management

Prediction

The prediction of earthquakes is very difficult. Regions at risk can be identified through plate tectonics, but attempts to predict earthquakes a few hours before the event are unreliable. Such prediction is based upon monitoring groundwater levels, release of radon gas and unusual animal behaviour. Fault lines such as the San Andreas can be monitored and local magnetic fields can be measured. Areas can also be mapped on the basis of geological information and studies of ground stability. These can help to predict the impact of earthquakes and can be used to produce a hazard zone map that can be acted upon by local and even national planners.

Close studies of fault lines can sometimes indicate the point along the fault where the next earthquake might be due. A study of the pattern of events along the San Andreas fault between 1969 and 1989 revealed the existence of a 'seismic gap' in the area of Loma Prieta. This area suffered an earthquake in October 1989 which measured 7.1 on the Richter scale and was the worst to hit the San Francisco region since 1906. In total, 63 people died and more than 3,700 were seriously injured. Because of the seismic survey, this event was not entirely unexpected, but, like all earthquakes, it was not possible to predict it precisely. Such a system, however, would not work for events such as the one at Northridge, which took place on an unknown fault line.

Prevention

Trying to prevent an earthquake is thought by most people to be impossible. This, however, has not stopped studies into the feasibility of schemes to keep the plates sliding past each other, rather than 'sticking' and then releasing, which is the main cause of earthquakes. Suggestions so far for lubricating this movement have focused on water and oil. Some people have even gone as far as to suggest nuclear explosions at depth!

Protection

Since earthquakes strike suddenly, violently and without warning, preparation cannot be put off until the event. Being prepared for an earthquake involves everyone from civil authorities to individuals. In the USA, the Federal Emergency Management Agency's earthquake program has the following objectives:

- to promote understanding of earthquakes and their effects
- to work better to identify earthquake risk
- to improve earthquake-resistant design and construction techniques
- to encourage the use of earthquake-safe policies and planning practices

Protection therefore means preparing for the event by modifying the human and built environments to decrease vulnerability. It also includes attempts to modify the loss by insurance and aid. Some of the means of protection are described below.

Hazard-resistant structures

Buildings can be designed to be aseismic or earthquake-resistant. There are three main ways of doing this:

- putting a large concrete weight on the top of a building which will move, with the aid of a computer program, in the opposite direction to the force of the earthquake to counteract stress
- building large rubber shock absorbers into the foundations to allow some movement in the building
- adding cross-bracing to the structure to hold it together when it shakes

Older buildings and structures such as elevated motorways can be **retro-fitted** with such devices to make them more earthquake-proof. A comparison between the 1989 Loma Prieta earthquake in California (7.1 Richter) and the 1988 event in Armenia (6.9 Richter) shows the effects of different types of building structures. In California, with its earthquake-proof buildings, there were only 63 deaths, whereas in Armenia more than 25,000 people died, many inside buildings that collapsed as a result of soft foundations and no earthquake-proofing features. In the town of Leninakan, for example, over 90% of the modern 9–12 storey buildings with pre-cast concrete frames were destroyed.

Education

Education is an important way of minimising loss of life in the event of an earthquake. Instructions issued by the authorities explain how to prepare for an earthquake by securing homes, appliances and heavy furniture, and getting together earthquake kits. Schools, offices and factories may have earthquake 'drills'. Government offices and many companies in Japan observe Disaster Prevention Day (1 September) which marks the anniversary of the Tokyo earthquake.

Following the Loma Prieta earthquake (1989), the American Red Cross issued a list of supplies that people should keep at hand in case of an earthquake. These included:

- water: at least 3 days' supply for all persons and pets in the house
- a whole range of foodstuffs, particularly canned and high-energy foods
- clothing and bedding
- first-aid kit
- tools and supplies, to include radio, torch, batteries, can opener, matches, toilet paper, small fire extinguisher, pliers, aluminium foil

Figure 9.33 shows the instructions issued by the metropolitan government of Tokyo advising people what to do if an earthquake occurs in the city.

Fire prevention

'Smart meters' have been developed which can cut off the gas if an earthquake of sufficient magnitude occurs. In Tokyo, the gas company has a network transmitting seismic information to a computer which informs employees where to switch off major pipelines, reducing the number of fires.

Emergency services

Use of the emergency services in the event of an earthquake requires careful organisation and planning. Heavy lifting gear needs to be available. Civilians must be given first-aid training as trained medical personnel can take some time to arrive. Much of the preparation in California involves the establishment of computer programs that will identify which areas the emergency services should be sent to first.

Land-use planning

The most hazardous areas in the event of an earthquake can be identified and then regulated. Certain types of buildings such as schools and hospitals should be built in areas of low risk. It is also important to have sufficient open space, as this forms a safe area away from fires and aftershock damage to buildings.

Insurance and aid

In MEDCs, people are urged to take out insurance to cover their losses. This can be very expensive for individuals. Only 7% of the people affected by the Kobe earthquake in Japan (1995) were covered by earthquake insurance.

Most aid to LEDCs has been emergency aid in the few days after the event — providing medical services, tents, water purification equipment, and search and rescue equipment. Aid over the longer term, to reconstruct the built environment and redevelop the economy, is much less readily available.

Figure 9.33

Tokyo Metropolitan Government

What to do if a big earthquake hits

The worst shake is over in about a minute, so keep calm and do the following:

1 Quickly turn off all stoves and heaters. Put out fires that may break out. Do not become flustered by the sight of flames, and act quickly to put out the fire.
2 Get under a table or desk to protect yourself.
3 Do not run outdoors where you are liable to be hit by falling objects.
4 Open the door for an emergency exit. Door frames are liable to spring in a big quake and hold the door so tight it cannot be opened.
5 If you are outdoors keep away from narrow alleys, concrete block walls and embankments, and take temporary refuge in an open area.
6 During evacuation from department stores or theatres do not panic. Do as directed by the attendant in charge.
7 If driving in the street, move the car to the left and stop. Driving will be banned in restricted areas.
8 Evacuate to a designated safety evacuation area if a big fire or other danger approaches.
9 Walk to emergency evacuation areas. Take the minimum of personal belongings.
10 Do not be moved by rumours. Listen to local news over the radio.

Landslides and avalanches

A **landslide** can be a small event such as a localised cliff collapse or it can involve large-scale catastrophic movement of whole sections of mountainside. Southern Italy has areas that are highly susceptible to landslides. There are several factors that have contributed to this including:

- the mountainous nature of much of the terrain
- weak sedimentary rocks
- summer drought followed by torrential downpours
- extensive deforestation that has reduced the forest cover from around 90% to less than 30%

There is also widespread poverty in the region, which has made many people more vulnerable to hazards. On 6 May 1998 there was a series of devastating mudflows that affected the area east of Naples and Mt Vesuvius. Several villages and towns were hit. The main centre to be affected was the town of Sarno, where a wall of mud, at least 2 m high, swept through the middle of the urban area. These slides, which killed over 100 people, followed days of very heavy rainfall on slopes that had seen continuous tree removal in the years preceding the event. One authority on the area described the main cause as 'wild urbanisation in a high-risk zone'.

Most **avalanches** are small and/or remote from the built environment and so do not constitute a hazard. However, as settlement has expanded into mountainous regions, and winter sports and tourism have grown, people are becoming increasingly vulnerable to avalanches. Infrastructure, such as transport routes and power lines, is also at risk. Death and injury from avalanches are the result of impacts, suffocation, inhalation of powdery snow, hypothermia, frostbite and shock. Buildings and structures are at risk from impact and pressure that can move reinforced concrete structures.

There are certain times of year when avalanches are more frequent. In the French Alps, for example, three-quarters of all avalanches occur between January and March.

Management

There are a number of approaches that can be used to manage landslides.

- Engineering techniques can be used to make a slope more stable, for example:
  - drainage on the slope
  - terracing (benching)
  - stabilising the base of the slope
  - stabilising by driving anchors into rock strata.
- Forecasting, warning and evacuation are possible because many movements give warning signs beforehand, for example bulging walls and minor slumps. Education of the public is necessary if this strategy is to work.
- Hazard-mapping can be used to restrict development on potentially vulnerable slopes. However, this may reduce land values in areas that have been developed.

There are a number of ways in which the threat of avalanches can be reduced or removed.

- Controlled explosions can be used to lessen the risk of a major event by reducing the size of the snow pack.
- Risk management strategies can involve mapping avalanche paths and attempting to control human activities. At times of high risk, certain ski areas and roads may be closed.
- Engineering solutions can involve keeping the snow on the mountainside or trying to deflect it once it has moved. Methods include:
  - fences to trap the snow on the upper slopes
  - deflection structures to protect buildings and pylons
  - avalanche sheds to protect transport links — the avalanche passes over the top
  - afforestation — trees will slow down the movement of snow.

Positive impacts of volcanic activity on people

Volcanic activity has a number of beneficial aspects.

Geothermal power produced by the heat generated by volcanic activity is harnessed by a number of countries, including the USA, New Zealand, Italy and Iceland. In Iceland, the hot water from this source is used directly to heat buildings and greenhouses, which enables the country to be self-sufficient in many foodstuffs, despite its northerly latitude.

Mineral rich **volcanic soils** formed from the weathering of lava and ash have attracted many farmers to work on the lower slopes of volcanoes such as Mt Etna (Sicily) despite the ever-present danger of further eruptions and lava flows. In the Philippines, 4,000 people live on an island in Lake Taal, which they share with Mt Taal, one of the world's deadliest volcanoes.

Volcanic rocks are hard and make good building materials and aggregate for road building. There is also a market for pumice, a light porous lava, which has a number of uses including stain removal.

Volcanic areas attract **tourism** (Photograph 9.6). Many tourists are drawn to Mt Etna, particularly when it is smoking, although most do not reach the summit as it requires a cable car and a strenuous walk. On the other hand, large numbers climb to the rim of the crater of Mt Vesuvius, as there is a car park not far below the summit. Hot springs, mud volcanoes, gas emissions and geysers are also tourist attractions. At Solfatera, on the Bay of Naples, it is possible to take a guided tour of the gas emissions and areas of boiling mud.

Mineralisation is associated with igneous activity. Minerals found include tin, copper, silver and zinc. They have been important in the economies of some of the countries where they are mined, for example copper in Chile and tin in Bolivia. Concentrations of sulphur can also be exploited.

Jane Buekett

Photograph 9.6 Tourists watch the eruption of Pohutu Geyser, Rotorua, New Zealand

Chapter 10

Cold environments and human activity

Cold environments

The tundra and polar climates

The main features of the **tundra** climate are:

- long and bitterly cold winters with temperatures averaging −20 °C
- brief, mild summers with temperatures rarely above 5 °C
- at least 8 months of the year when the temperature remains below 0 °C
- small amounts of precipitation, less than 300 mm per year, most of which falls as snow
- frequent strong winds that increase the wind chill

Key terms

Fluvioglacial (glacifluvial) Processes and landforms associated with the action of glacial meltwater.

Glacier A tongue-shaped mass of ice moving slowly down a valley.

Ice ages The common term for the period when there were major cold phases known as glacials, and ice sheets covered large areas of the world. The last ice age lasted from about 2 million years ago to about 10,000 BP (before present). It was also known as the Quaternary glaciation. During the Quaternary there were many episodes of glaciation, the last major period beginning around 120,000 BP and reaching its maximum in 18,000 BP. At that time about 30% of the Earth's surface was covered by ice, compared with 10% today.

Ice sheet A body of ice covering an area of at least 50,000 km^2. Ice sheets are dome-shaped and the ice flows outward from the centre. Today, ice sheets cover Antarctica and Greenland, with smaller sheets (ice caps) covering areas of Iceland, Spitsbergen and Norway. Major ice sheets can be up to 2,000 m thick today; those that occurred at the maximum extent of the Quaternary glaciation could have been up to twice that thickness. The Quaternary ice sheets covered substantial areas of northern North America and Europe.

Periglacial Processes and landforms associated with the fringe of, or the area near to, an ice sheet or glacier.

Tundra A climatic and vegetation type found in the most northerly parts of Eurasia and North America. Tundra-like environments also occur above the tree line in mountainous areas such as the Alps, Rockies, Andes and Himalayas. The main differences between mountain and Arctic tundra are that the sun is higher in the sky in mountain tundra areas, giving warmer conditions and that permafrost is generally absent from these areas. During the Quaternary glaciation, when the ice sheets were more extensive, tundra climate affected large areas of central North America and Europe, including the British Isles. At present, tundra occupies around 25% of the Earth's surface.

The **polar** climate of the ice sheet in the interior of Antarctica is characterised by:

- mean monthly temperatures below freezing all year
- extreme cold in winter with monthly average temperatures below –50°C
- precipitation below 150 mm per year, with all of it falling as snow (at the south pole, precipitation is around 50 mm per year)
- strong winds blowing outwards from the interior of the continent. Winds of over 200 km h^{-1} have been recorded. There is therefore, a substantial wind chill factor. The winds also whip up the powdery snow to create frequent blizzards and white-outs

The causes of these climates are as follows.

The low level of insolation. In summer the sun remains at a low level in the sky even though there is a period of continuous sunlight during which it never sets. The incoming rays strike the Earth's surface obliquely, which means that there is a wide surface area to heat (Figure 10.1). In addition, the longer passage through the atmosphere allows for increased absorption, scattering and reflection of radiation. Therefore, less insolation reaches the surface than is the case in areas of lower latitude.

In mid-summer, there is continuous insolation for a period, which is why these areas are termed 'the land of the midnight sun'. The high daily input of solar radiation with a small diurnal temperature range makes the days seem pleasantly warm. This, however, only ensures that temperatures in tundra areas rise above 0°C for 3 months of the year at most. In winter, there is a corresponding period when there is no incoming solar radiation as the sun does not appear above the horizon. Temperatures fall throughout the winter period, which can last upwards of 6 months.

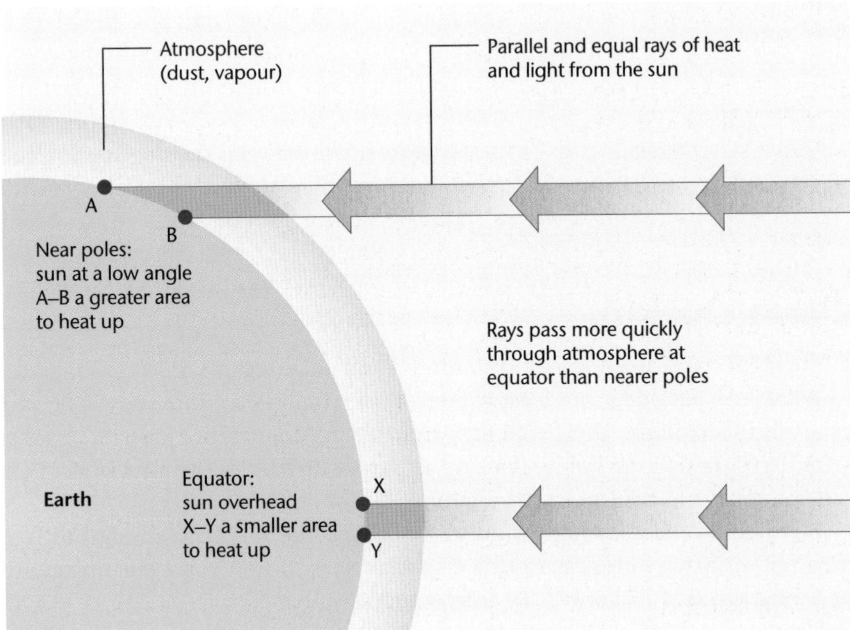

Figure 10.1 The effects of latitude on insolation

Snow surfaces have a high **albedo** of around 0.8. Where there is continuous snow cover, such as in Antarctica and Greenland, much of the incoming solar radiation is reflected off the snow surface. This further reduces the amount that can actually contribute to the warming of the atmosphere.

The Antarctic plateau is at a high **altitude**. The thinner air is unable to hold heat, which radiates back into space more readily than at sea level.

The **high-pressure** systems of polar regions mean that frontal systems rarely penetrate these areas, giving low levels of precipitation. The high pressure is most persistent over Antarctica, where the cooling of air in contact with frozen surfaces causes the air to become denser and sink.

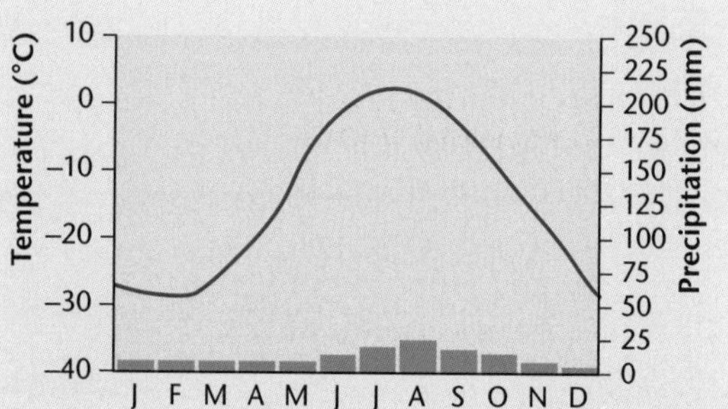

Figure 10.2 The tundra climate: Barrow, Alaska

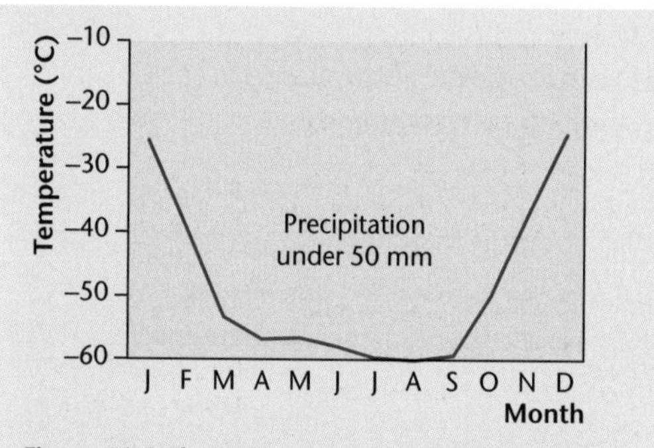

Figure 10.3 The polar climate: Amundsen–Scott base, south pole

The **coolness of the air** is another factor in low precipitation. Air that is below freezing, particularly air at the very low temperatures of polar regions, can only hold small amounts of water vapour. Even when precipitation occurs, nothing more than a very light powdery snow emerges from the clouds.

In the southern hemisphere strong winds circle the planet as part of the **westerly wind belt**. There are few land areas to hinder the movement, so winds blow strongly south of 50° latitude.

Regions such as Antarctica also generate strong downslope winds. Such **katabatic winds** occur when masses of cold, dense air flow down valleys and off upland areas. In Antarctica, the combination of the large landmass, the plateau and the very cold temperatures means that there is a real difference in conditions between the interior and the coastal areas. Strong katabatic movements occur between the interior and the coast, because there are few physical obstacles to reduce the wind speed. Such winds often exceed 200 km h^{-1}.

Climatic hazards

The climatic hazards associated with tundra and polar regions are as follows.

With short summers and long winters, these climates are **intensely cold** and generally inhospitable. There is a long period when the sun is not present. In polar areas, temperatures are below freezing all year, which accounts for the fact that Antarctica has no indigenous population.

Wind chill caused by high wind speeds makes the very cold conditions feel even colder. Strong winds can cause a considerable reduction in body temperature. At a wind speed of 25 km h^{-1}, air at freezing point feels like −12 °C; air at −15 °C feels more like −35 °C. At 50 km h^{-1}, an air temperature of −15 °C feels like −42 °C.

The faster the wind, the faster heat escapes from the body and the greater the risk of frostbite and hypothermia. This can lead to disorientation, unconsciousness and even death. The skin can actually freeze, causing frostbite as ice crystals form and damage tissue. In serious cases, the affected areas have to be amputated. Winds also whip up the snow into blizzards.

Low precipitation means trees cannot grow fully and agriculture is impossible. There is also insufficient water for people to carry out a normal life. Other features of the climate such as low temperatures, very short summers, strong winds and frozen ground mean that the areas are inhospitable for human settlement.

Glacial and periglacial processes and landforms

Ice formation and movement

When a climate starts to become colder, more precipitation in winter falls as snow. Summers also begin to shorten, so there is less time for the winter snow to melt. At first, this leads to permanent snow cover in upland areas, the lower edge of which is known as the **snow line**. As the climate continues to deteriorate, the snow line moves down the slope.

At present, the snow line is at sea level in Greenland but at 6,000 m on the equator. There is no permanent snow cover in the British Isles, so there is no snow line, but scientists estimate that if the Scottish mountains were 200–250 m higher, there would be. In the northern hemisphere, the snow line is found at a higher altitude on south-facing slopes than on those that face north, as the south-facing slopes receive more insolation (Figure 10.4).

Snow initially falls as flakes, which have an open, feathery structure that traps air. As the snow accumulates, compression by the upper layers gradually turns the lower snow into a more compact form known as **firn** or **neve**. Meltwater seeps into the gaps and then freezes, further compacting the mass. As more snow falls, air is progressively squeezed out of the lower snow by the weight of the upper layers and after a period of some years (most experts put it between 20 and 40), a mass of solid ice develops. Where there is no summer melting, this process takes longer. During this period, the mass changes colour from white, indicating the presence of air, to a bluish colour, indicating that the air has been largely expelled. This is the ice that begins to flow downhill as a glacier.

Figure 10.4 The snow line in the northern hemisphere

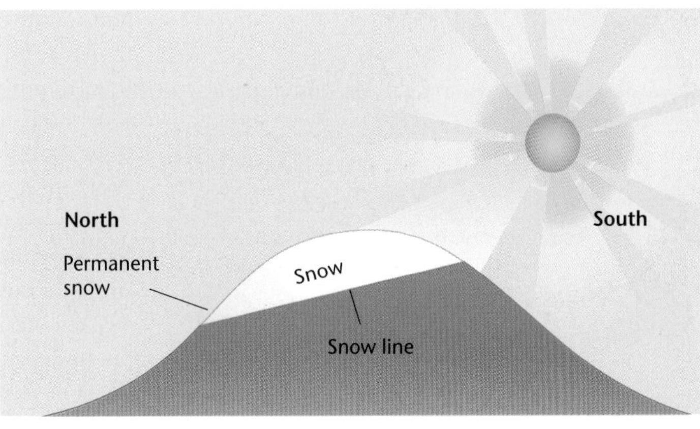

IGNS

Photograph 10.1 Franz-Joseph glacier in New Zealand

There are two types of glacier — temperate and polar. The characteristics of each affect ice movement and glacial processes.

Temperate (alpine) glaciers melt in summer, releasing huge amounts of meltwater. This acts as a lubricant, reducing friction. Temperate glaciers move by basal flow, extending/compressing flow, creep and surges. This type of glacier is more likely to erode, transport and deposit material.

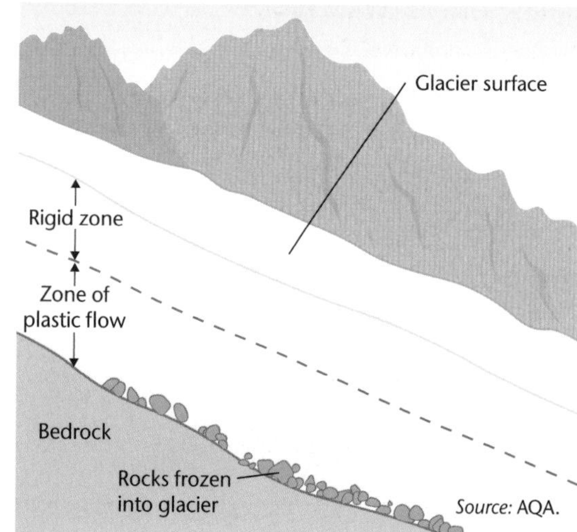

Figure 10.5 Zones within a glacier

Polar glaciers occur in areas where the temperature is permanently below 0°C, and therefore no melting occurs. Movement is slower than in temperate glaciers as they are frozen to their beds and thus move mainly by internal flow. Much less erosion, transportation and deposition occurs.

As ice moves downhill it does not always behave in the same way. It has great rigidity and strength, but under steady pressure it behaves as a plastic (mouldable) body. In contrast, when put under sudden compression or tension, it will break or shear apart. This gives two zones within the glacier (Figure 10.5):

- the upper zone where the ice is brittle, breaking apart to form crevasses
- the lower zone which has steady pressure. Here meltwater resulting from that pressure and from friction with the bedrock allows a more rapid, plastic flow. At depth in the glacier the melting point of the ice is raised slightly by the increased pressure. Basal ice is therefore more likely to melt at temperatures close to 0°C (pressure melting point)

Ice movement is generally very complex, and several types of movement can be identified. The main types are:

- **Compressing flow** which occurs where there is a reduction in the gradient of the valley floor leading to ice deceleration and a thickening of the ice mass. At such points ice erosion is at its maximum (Figure 10.6).
- **Extending flow** which occurs when the valley gradient becomes steeper. The ice accelerates and becomes thinner, leading to reduced erosion (Figure 10.6).
- **Basal flow (sliding/slippage)** — as the glacier moves over the bedrock, there is friction. The lower ice is also under a great deal of pressure and this, combined with the friction, results in some melting. The resulting meltwater acts as a lubricant, enabling the ice to flow more rapidly.
- **Surges** occur from time to time when an excessive build-up of meltwater under the glacier leads to the ice moving rapidly forward, perhaps by as much as 250–300 m in one day. Such surges represent a hazard to people living in the glacial valley below the **snout**.
- **Internal flow** occurs when ice crystals orientate themselves in the direction of the glacier's movement and slide past each other. As surface ice moves faster, crevasses develop. Internal flow is the main feature of the flow of polar glaciers as, without the presence of meltwater, they tend to be frozen to their beds.
- **Creep** occurs when stress builds up within a glacier, allowing the ice to behave like plastic and flow. It occurs particularly when obstacles are met.
- **Rotational flow** occurs within the corrie (cirque), the birthplace of many glaciers. Here ice moving downhill can pivot about a point, producing a rotational movement. This, combined with increased pressure within the rock hollow, leads to greater erosion and an over-deepening of the corrie floor.

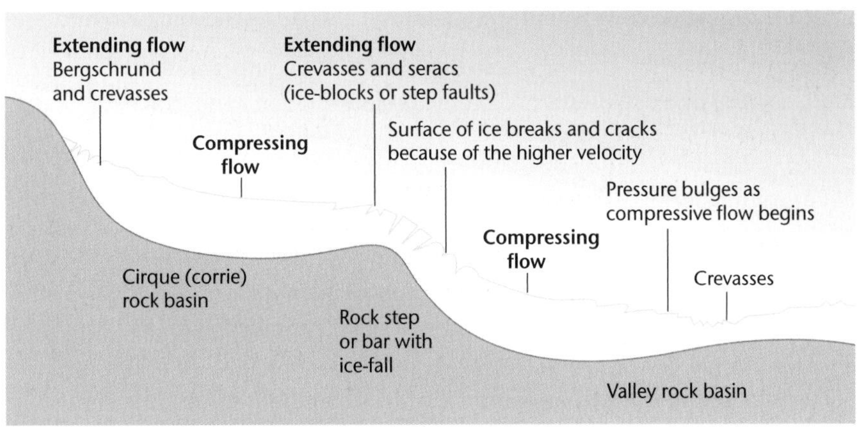

Figure 10.6 Extending and compressing flow

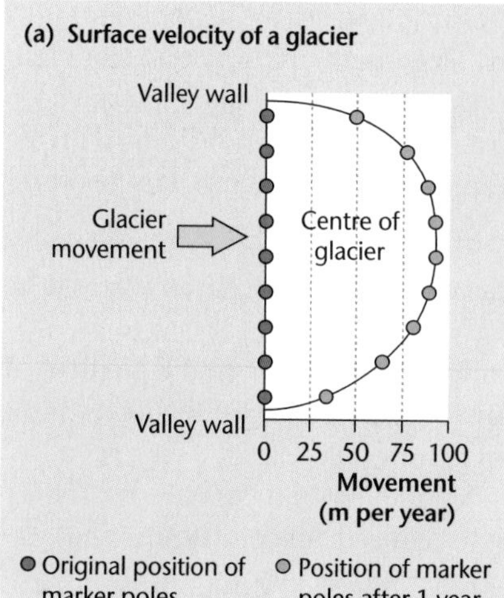

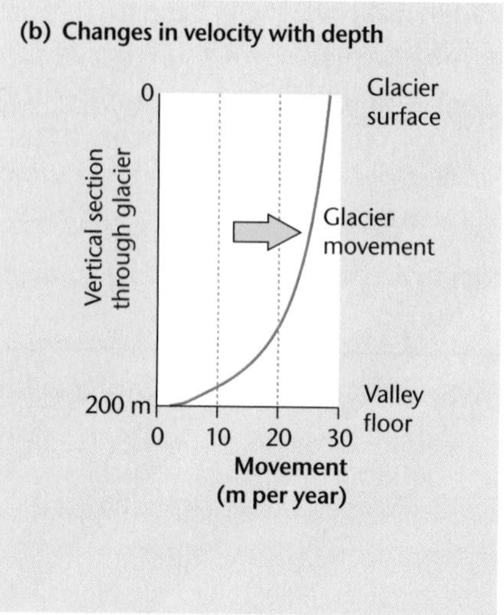

Figure 10.7 Differential rates of flow within a glacier

Within a glacier there are different rates of movement. The sides and base of the glacier move at a slower rate than the centre surface ice (Figure 10.7). As a result, the ice cracks, producing crevasses on the surface. These also occur where extending flow speeds up the flow of ice and where the valley widens or the glacier flows from a valley on to a plain (piedmont glacier).

Glacial budgets

A glacier can be viewed as a system with inputs, stores, transfers and outputs:

- **inputs** are precipitation in the form of snow and ice, and avalanches which add snow, ice and debris from the valley side
- **storage** is represented by the glacier itself
- **transfer (throughput)** is the way that the ice moves (the various types of flow are described above)
- **outputs** are water vapour (from evaporation of water on the ice surface and sublimation — the direct change of state from ice to water vapour), calving (the formation of icebergs), and water in liquid form from **ablation** (melting). The debris deposited at the snout (moraine) can also be considered an output

The upper part of the glacier, where inputs exceed outputs and therefore where more mass is gained than lost over a year, is known as the **zone of accumulation**; the lower part, where outputs exceed inputs, and where mass is lost rather than gained, is known as the **zone of ablation**. Between the two zones is the line of **equilibrium** which separates net loss from net gain and represents the snow line on the glacier (Figure 10.8). A glacier that is characterised by large volumes of gains and losses will discharge a large volume of ice through its equilibrium line to replace mass lost at the snout and will therefore have a high erosive capacity.

The **net balance** is the difference between the total accumulation and the total ablation during 1 year (Figure 10.9). In temperate glaciers, there is a negative balance in summer when ablation exceeds accumulation, and the reverse in

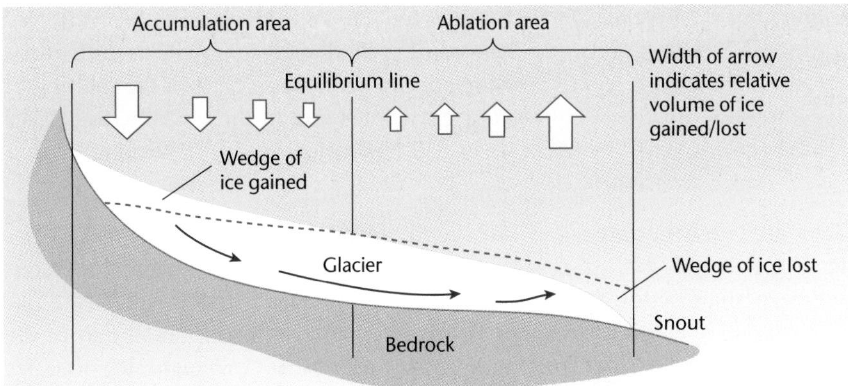

Figure 10.8 Glacier budget

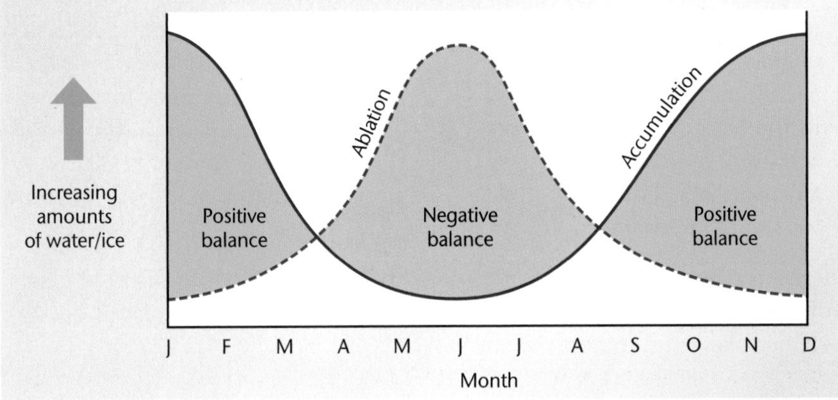

Figure 10.9 Net balance in a northern hemisphere temperate glacier

winter. If the summer and winter budgets cancel each other out, the glacier appears to be stationary. In other words, the snout of the glacier remains in the same position, although ice is still advancing down the valley from the zone of accumulation into the zone of ablation.

If the 'supply' begins to exceed the losses, then the snout moves down the valley. This is known as glacial **advance**. When the reverse is true, the glacier begins to shrink in size and the snout moves its position up the valley. This is called glacial **retreat**. Even though the *position* of the snout is moving backwards (retreating), ice continues to move down from the upper parts of the system.

Glacial erosion

Glacial erosion tends to occur in upland regions and is carried out by two main processes:

- **Abrasion** occurs where the material the glacier is carrying rubs away at the valley floor and sides. It can be likened to the effect of sandpaper or a giant file. The coarser material may leave scratches on the rock known as **striations**; the finer debris smoothes and polishes rock surfaces. The debris involved in abrasion is often worn down by the process into a very fine material known as **rock flour**.

- **Plucking** involves the glacier freezing onto and into rock outcrops. As the ice moves forward, it pulls away masses of rock. Plucking is mainly found at the base of the glacier where pressure and friction often result in the melting of the ice. It is also marked in well-jointed rocks and in those where the surface has been weakened by freeze–thaw action (frost shattering). Plucking leaves a very jagged landscape.

There are two other processes associated with glacial action that produce the debris glaciers use in their erosive action. Both of these are weathering processes:

- **Freeze–thaw action/frost shattering** occurs in areas where temperatures rise during the day but drop below freezing at night for a substantial part of the winter. Water which enters cracks in the rocks freezes overnight. Ice occupies more space than water (just under 10% more) and therefore exerts pressure on the crack. As the process continues, the crack widens, and eventually pieces of rock break off (Photograph 10.2). On steep slopes this leads to the collection of material at the base, known as **scree**. In a glacial valley, much of this material falls from the valley side onto the edges of the glacier and some finds its way to the base of the ice via the numerous crevasses which cross the glacier's surface.
- **Nivation** is a series of processes that operate underneath a patch of snow, leading to the disintegration of the rock surface (see page 310 for details).

There are a number of major landforms which are mainly produced by glacial erosion. These include corries (cirques), arêtes, pyramidal peaks, glacial troughs, hanging valleys and truncated spurs.

Alan Young

Photograph 10.2 Frost-shattering: a limestone boulder in County Clare, Ireland, shattered into several pieces by freeze–thaw action

Corries and associated landforms

A **corrie** is an armchair-shaped rock hollow, with a steep back wall and an over-deepened basin with a rock lip. It often contains a small lake (or tarn). In the British Isles, corries are mainly found on north, northeast and east-facing slopes where reduced insolation allows more accumulation of snow.

If several corries develop in a highland region, they will jointly produce other erosional features. When two corries lie back to back or alongside each other, enlargement will often leave a narrow, steep-sided ridge between the two hollows, called an **arête**. An example is Striding Edge on Helvellyn in the Lake District. If more than two corries develop on a mountain, the central mass will survive as a **pyramidal peak**, which often takes on a very sharp appearance due to frost shattering (Figure 10.10). An example is the Matterhorn in the Alps.

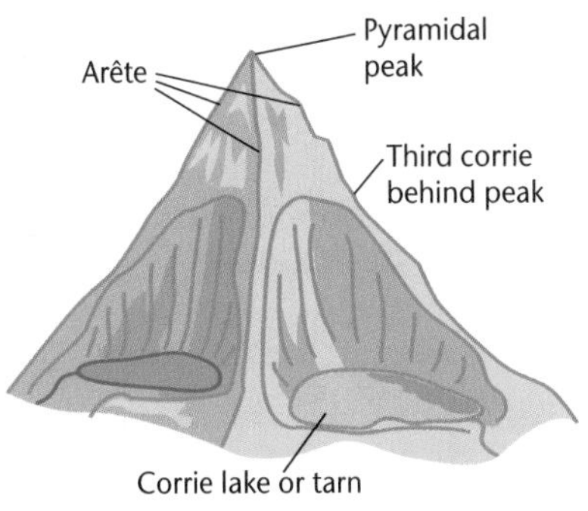

Figure 10.10 Arêtes and pyramidal peaks

Corrie formation is the result of several interacting processes (see Figure 10.11). The original process is believed to be **nivation** which acts upon a shallow, preglacial hollow and enlarges it into an embryo corrie (this may take a long time and be spread across several glacial periods within an ice age). As the hollow grows, the snow becomes thicker and is increasingly compressed to form firn and then ice. The back wall becomes steeper through the action of **plucking**. The **rotational movement** of the ice, together with the debris supplied by plucking and frost shattering on the back wall, abrades the floor of the hollow which over-deepens the corrie.

As the hollow deepens, the thinner ice at its edge does not produce the same amount of downcutting and a rock lip develops on the threshold of the feature. Some thresholds have their height increased by morainic deposits formed when the glacier's snout was in that position. After the last ice has melted, the corrie fills with meltwater and rainwater to form a small lake (tarn).

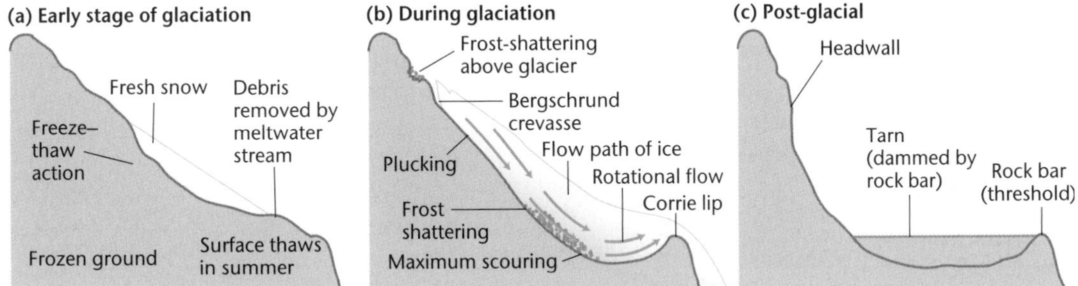

Figure 10.11 The formation of a corrie

Glacial troughs and associated landforms

Glaciers flow down pre-existing river valleys as they move from upland areas. They straighten, widen and deepen these valleys, changing the original V-shaped river feature into the U-shape typical of glacial erosion. The action of ice, combined with huge amounts of meltwater and sub-glacial debris, has a far greater erosive power than that of water.

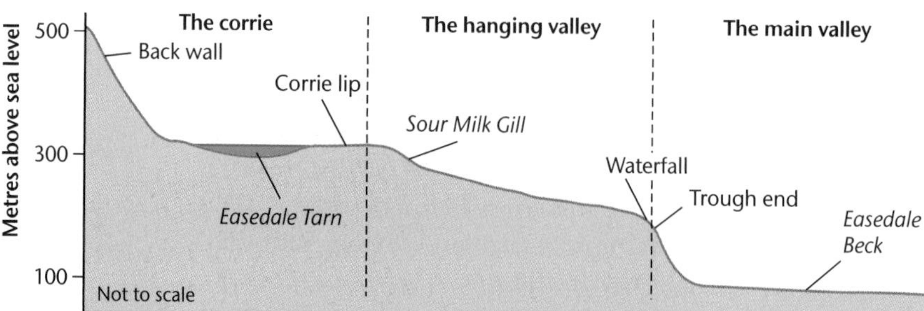

Figure 10.12 The long profile of a glacial valley: Easedale, Lake District

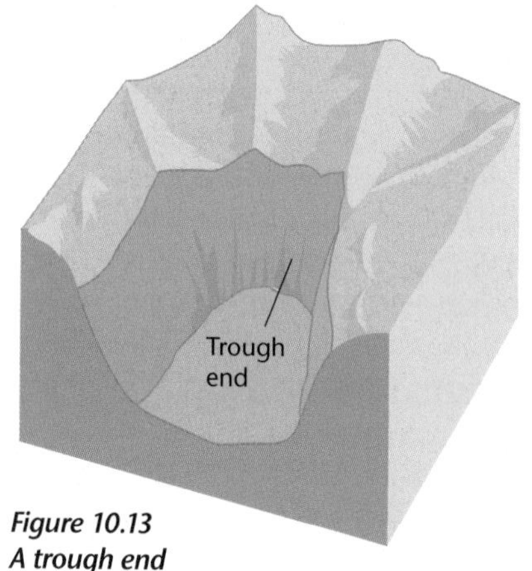

Figure 10.13 A trough end

As both extending and compressing flow are present, the amount of erosion varies down the valley. Where compressing flow is present, the glacier will over-deepen parts of the valley floor, leading to the formation of **rock basins**. It is also suggested that over-deepening is caused by increased erosion at the confluence of glaciers, areas of weaker rocks or zones of well-jointed rocks.

The major features of glacial troughs are:

- usually fairly straight with a wide base and steep sides — a U-shape
- stepped long-profile with alternating steps and rock basins
- some glacial valleys end abruptly at their heads in a steep wall, known as a **trough end**, above which lie a number of corries (Figures 10.12 and 10.13)
- rock basins filled with **ribbon lakes**, e.g. Wast Water in the Lake District
- over-deepening below the present sea-level — this led to the formation of **fjords** when sea-levels rose after the ice ages and submerged the lower parts of glacial valleys, for example on the coasts of Norway and southwest New Zealand (Milford Sound)
- **hanging valleys** on the side of the main valley (e.g. the valley of Church Beck which flows down into Coniston Water in the Lake District). These are either pre-existing tributary river valleys which were not glaciated, or tributary glacial valleys (Figure 10.14, Photograph 10.3). In tributary glacial valleys there would have been less ice and therefore less erosion than in the main valley. The tributary valley floor was therefore left higher than that of the main valley when the ice retreated.

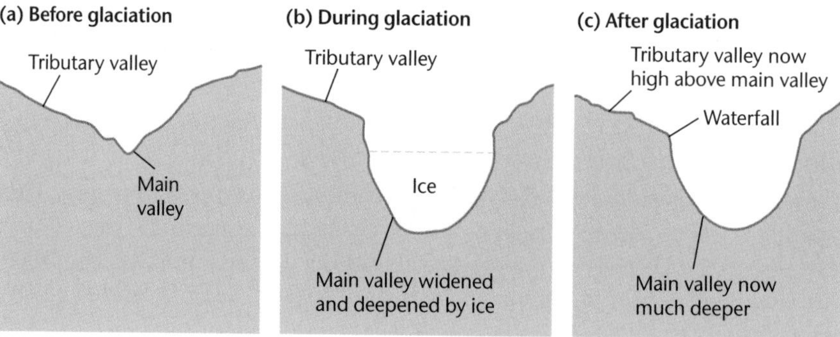

Figure 10.14 The formation of a hanging valley

Photograph 10.3 Lady Bowen waterfall in Milford Sound, New Zealand, is a hanging valley

- areas of land projecting from the river-valley side (spurs) have been removed by the glacier, producing **truncated spurs**
- small areas of rock on the valley floor are not always completely removed and this leaves **roches moutonnées**. These have an upstream side polished by abrasion and a downstream side made jagged by plucking (Figure 10.15)
- after ice retreat, many glacial troughs were filled with **shallow lakes** which were later infilled, and their sides were modified by frost shattering and the development of screes which altered the glacial U-shape (e.g. Great Langdale, Lake District) (Figure 10.16)

Glacial transportation and deposition

As well as eroding the rock over which it is flowing, a valley glacier is also capable of transporting large amounts of debris. Some of this may be derived from rockfalls on the valley side. It is then transported on the

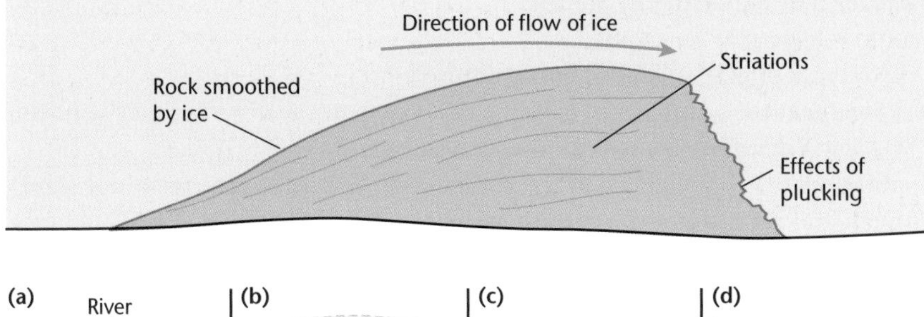

Figure 10.15 Formation of a roche moutonnée

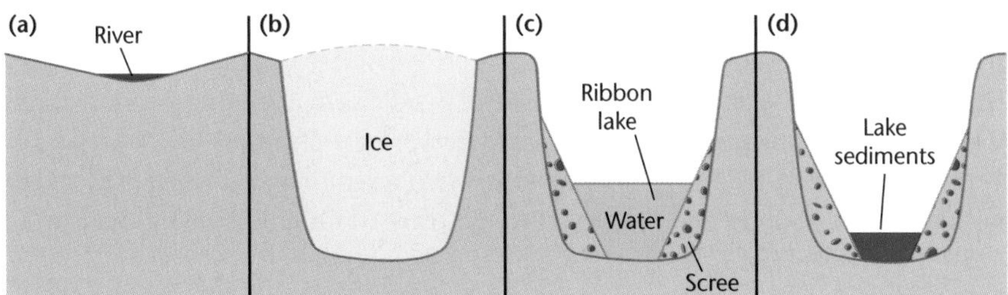

Figure 10.16 Formation of a glacial valley

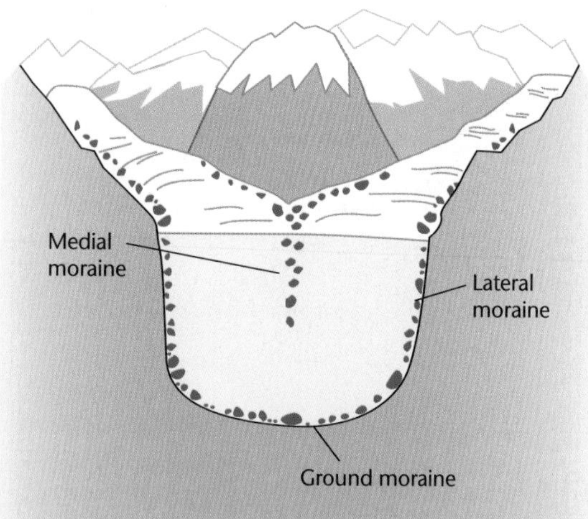

Figure 10.17 ***Transport of debris within a glacier***

surface of the glacier (**supraglacial** debris) or buried within the ice (**englacial**). Material found at the base of the glacier is known as **subglacial** and may include rock fragments that have fallen down crevasses and material eroded at the base. Another way of describing the material carried by the glacier is shown in Figure 10.17. Strictly speaking, **moraine** applies to a type of landform, but many textbooks now use the term in this way.

The huge amounts of material carried down by a glacier will eventually be deposited. The bulk of this will be the debris released by the melting of the ice at the snout. It is also possible for the ice to become overloaded with material, reducing its capacity. This may occur near to the snout, as the glacier melts, or in areas where the glacier changes between compressing and extending flow. Material that is deposited directly by the ice is known as **till** or **boulder clay**, although the latter term tends not to be used today.

Till is used to describe an unsorted mixture of rocks, clay and sand that was mainly transported as supraglacial or englacial debris and deposited when the ice melted. Individual stones tend to be angular to sub-angular, unlike river and beach material which is rounded. Till reflects the character of the rocks over which the ice has passed. In the till of south Lancashire, for example, it is possible to find rocks from the Lake District (e.g. Shap granite) and southern Scotland (e.g. riebeckite from Ailsa Craig in the Firth of Clyde). In the till of East Anglia, there are pieces of granite from southern Norway. This indicates not only the passage of the ice but the fact that the sea level must have been considerably lower to allow ice to move over the area that later became the North Sea.

Sometimes it is possible to find a large block of rock that has been moved from one area and deposited in another which has a very different geology. Such a feature is known as an **erratic**.

Two types of glacial deposit are recognised:

- **lodgement till** — subglacial material that was deposited by the actively moving glacier. A **drumlin** is a typical feature formed from this material
- **ablation till** — produced at the snout when the ice melts. **Terminal (end)**, **push** and **recessional moraines** are typical features produced from ablation till

Drumlins

The term drumlin is derived from the Gaelic word *druim*, meaning a rounded hill (Figure 10.18, Photograph 10.4). The main features of drumlins are:

- they are smooth, oval-shaped small hills, often resembling the top half of an egg
- they can be as long as 1.5 km (although most are much smaller) and up to 50–60 m in height
- they have a steep end known as the **stoss** and a gently sloping end, the **lee**

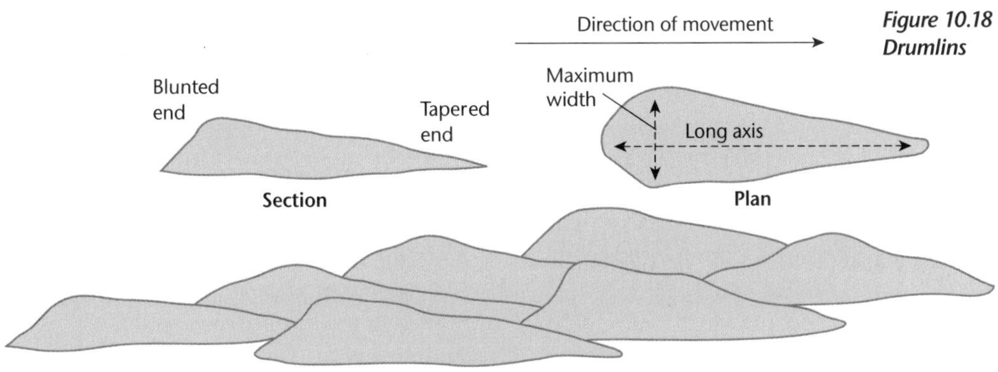

***Figure 10.18* Drumlins**

***Photograph 10.4* Risebrigg Hill in North Yorkshire is a drumlin, lying within a swarm of drumlins known as the Hills of Elslack**

- they are elongated in the direction of ice advance with the stoss at the upstream end and the lee at the downstream end
- they are often found in groups known as **swarms** and, given their shape, this is sometimes referred to as a 'basket of eggs topography'
- they are formed from unsorted till
- they are found on lowland plains such as the central lowlands of Scotland. A well-known swarm is at Hellifield in the Ribble Valley. Many are found at the lower end of glacial valleys

There is some controversy over the origin of drumlins, which are formed underneath the ice. The most widely-held view is that they are the result of the ice being overloaded with debris. This reduces its capacity to carry and deposition occurs at its base. Once this material has been deposited it is then streamlined by further ice advance. There could also be pre-existing sediment (older till from a previous glacial advance, for example) that is caught up in the streamlining process.

Moraines

Moraines are lines, or a series of mounds of material, mainly running across glacial valleys. The main type is the terminal or end moraine which is found at the snout of the glacier. **Terminal moraines** show the following features:

- they consist of a ridge of material (or several mounds) stretching across a glacial valley
- they are elongated at right angles to the direction of ice advance
- they are often steep-sided, particularly the ice-contact side, and reach heights of 50–60 m
- they are often crescent-shaped, moulded to the form of the snout
- they are formed from *unsorted* ablation material

Terminal moraines are formed when the ice melts and the material it has been carrying is deposited. This is why they contain a range of unsorted material, from clay to boulders.

Figure 10.19 Moraines

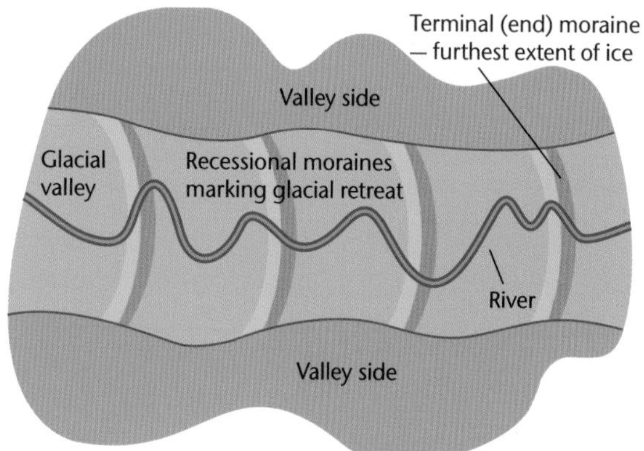

As the glacier retreats, it is possible for a series of moraines to be formed along the valley, marking points where the retreat halted for some time. These are known as **recessional moraines** (Figure 10.19).

If the climate cools for some time, leading to a glacial advance, previously deposited moraine may be shunted up into a mound known as a **push moraine**. Such features are recognised by the orientation of individual pieces of rock which may have been pushed upwards from their original horizontal position.

Fluvioglacial deposition

The melting of ice produces a great deal of water which has the capacity to carry much debris. As the water often flows under considerable pressure, it has a high velocity and is very turbulent. It can therefore pick up and transport a larger amount of material than a normal river of similar size. It is now believed that this water, with its load, is responsible for the creation of subglacial valleys that are often deep and riddled with potholes.

When the meltwater discharge decreases, the resultant loss of energy causes the material being carried by the meltwater to be deposited. As with all water deposition, the heavier particles will be dropped first, resulting in sorting of the material. Deposits may also be found in layers (stratified) as a result of seasonal variations in the meltwater flow. The main features produced by fluvioglacial deposition are eskers, kames and the outwash plain (Figure 10.20). Lakes on the outwash plain may have layered deposits in them called varves.

Eskers

Eskers have the following main features:

- they are long ridges of material running in the direction of ice advance

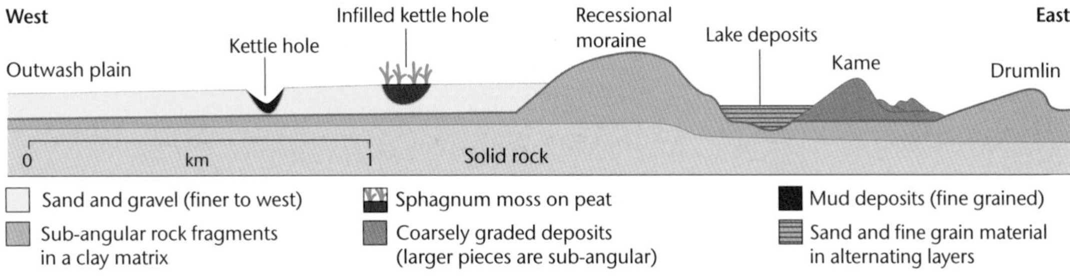

Figure 10.20 Features of lowland glaciation

- they have a sinuous (winding) form, 5–20 m high
- they consist of sorted coarse material, usually coarse sands and gravel
- they are often stratified (layered)

Eskers are believed to be deposits made by subglacial streams. The channel of the stream will be restricted by ice walls, so there is considerable hydrostatic pressure which enables a large load to be carried and also allows the stream to flow uphill for short distances. This accounts for the fact that some eskers run up gentle gradients. The bed of the channel builds up above the surrounding land, and a ridge is left when the glacier retreats during deglaciation. In some areas, the ridge of an esker is combined with mounds of material, possibly kames (see below). Such a feature is known as a **beaded esker**.

Kames

Kames are mounds of fluvioglacial material (sorted, and often stratified, coarse sands and gravel). They are deltaic deposits left when meltwater flows into a lake dammed up in front of the glacial snout by recessional moraine deposits. When the ice retreats further, the delta kame often collapses. Kame terraces are frequently found along the side of a glacial valley and are the deposits of meltwater streams flowing between the ice and the valley side.

Outwash plains (sandur)

Outwash plains are found in front of the glacier's snout and are deposited by the meltwater streams issuing from the ice. They consist of material that was brought down by the glacier and then picked up, sorted and dropped by running water beyond the position of the ice front. The coarsest material travels the shortest distance and is therefore found near to the glacier; the fine material, such as clay, is carried some distance across the plain before being deposited. The deposits are also layered vertically, which reflects the seasonal flow of meltwater streams.

Meltwater streams that cross the outwash plain are **braided.** This happens as the channels become choked with coarse material because of marked seasonal variations in discharge. On the outwash plain there is often a series of small depressions filled with lakes or marshes. These are known as **kettle holes**. It is believed that they are formed when blocks of ice, washed onto the plain, melt and leave a gap in the sediments. Such holes then fill with water to form small lakes. Aquatic plants become established in the lakes and this leads over time to the development of a marshy area and then peat.

Figure 10.21 Varves

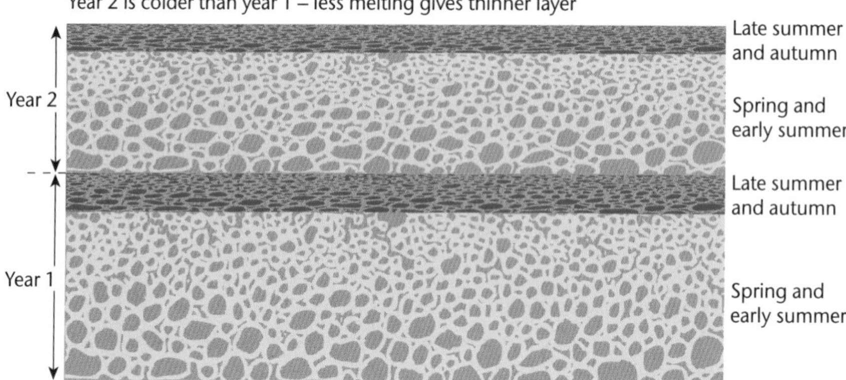

Lakes on the fringe of the ice are filled with deposits that show a distinct layering. A layer of silt lying on top of a layer of sand (Figure 10.21) represents 1 year's deposition in the lake and is known as a **varve**. The coarser, lighter layer is the spring and summer deposition when meltwater is at its peak and the meltwater streams are carrying maximum load. The thinner, darker-coloured and finer silt settles during autumn and through the winter as stream discharge decreases and the very fine sediment in the lake settles to the bottom. Varves are a good indicator of the age of lake sediments and of past climates as the thickness of each varve indicates warmer and colder periods.

Drainage diversion

Where ice sheets and glaciers exist it is possible for them to divert the course of the existing drainage systems (rivers and valleys). This happens as a result of direct glacial intervention (watershed breaching) or through erosion by meltwater.

Watershed breaching

Watershed breaching describes the situation where the glacier itself has been responsible for producing a new course for a river. One way in which this may happen is shown in Figure 10.22.

- **Stage 1** Two rivers flow in parallel valleys. On the watershed, there is a lower area known as a col.

Figure 10.22 Watershed breaching

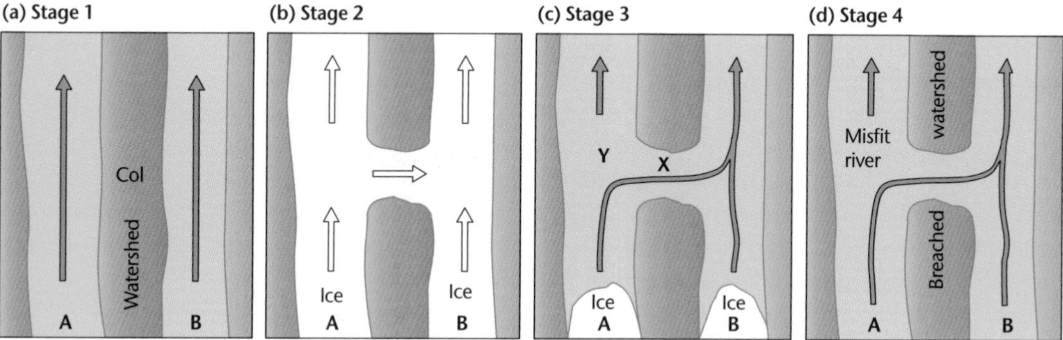

- **Stage 2** During glaciation, valley glaciers occupy both valleys but the glacier in valley A is of such a large volume that pressure forces some of the ice over the col into valley B, cutting a side valley in the process.
- **Stage 3** On deglaciation, meltwater from glacier A runs down the valley. If point X has been cut lower than point Y (there may also be glacial debris at point Y), then the meltwater will run through the valley at X and join the meltwater from glacier B.
- **Stage 4** The new drainage pattern of the area is left. If, of course, point X had *not* been cut lower than point Y, then the drainage would have resumed its pre-glacial pattern as in stage 1.

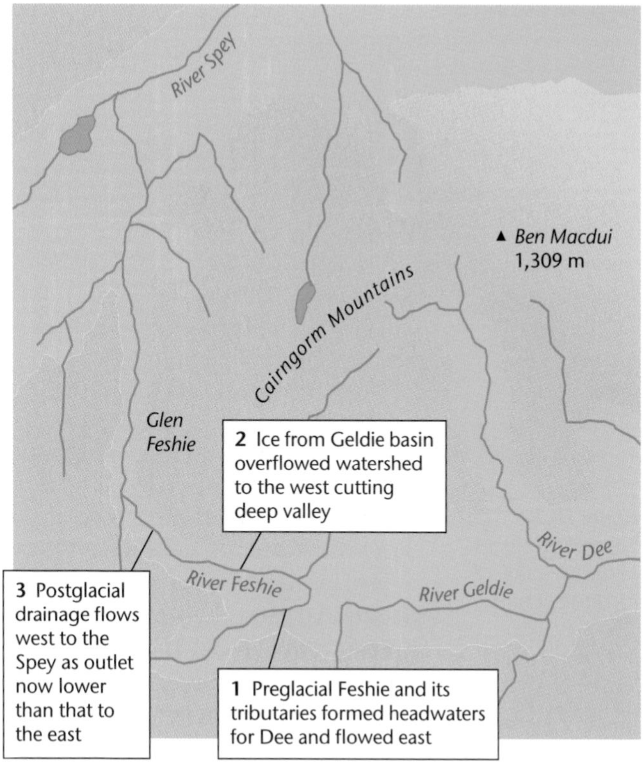

An example of watershed breaching causing a reversal of the preglacial drainage occurs in the Cairngorm Mountains in Scotland. The River Feshie and its tributaries formed part of the headwaters of the River Dee system that flowed towards the east. During the Quaternary glaciation large amounts of ice built up in the Geldie basin and some ice eventually overflowed the watershed, cutting a valley across it towards the west. This ice also overdeepened the existing valley on the northwestern side of the mountains. After the ice retreated this outlet to the northwest was lower than that to the east. The previous upper tributaries of the Geldie therefore joined and flowed west as the River Feshie to join the Spey system (Figure 10.23).

***Figure 10.23* Map of the present-day southwest Cairngorms showing where watershed breaching occurred**

Proglacial lakes and overflow channels

As has already been stated, glacial meltwater has great erosive power because of its volume and the large amounts of debris it contains. During deglaciation, lakes develop on the edges of the ice, some occupying large areas. Overflows from these lakes which cross the lowest points of watersheds will create new valleys. When the ice damming these meltwater lakes totally melts, many of the new valleys are left dry, as drainage patterns revert to the preglacial stage. In certain cases, however, the postglacial drainage adopts them, giving rise to new drainage patterns.

Large meltwater lakes of this kind occurred in the English Midlands (Lake Harrison), the Vale of Pickering in North Yorkshire (Lake Pickering) and the Welsh borders (Lake Lapworth, Figure 10.24) at the end of the last glaciation. The River Thames is thought to have followed a much more northerly course

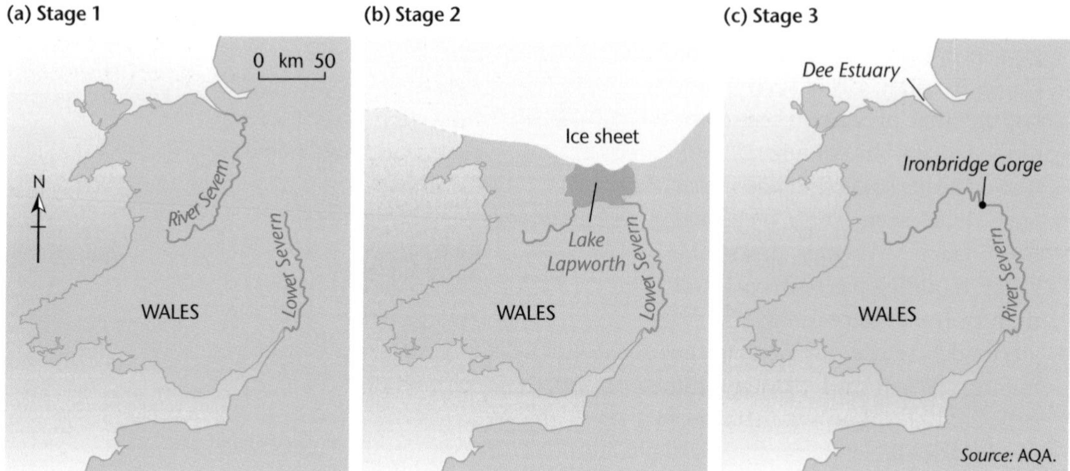

Figure 10.24 Theoretical stages in the diversion of the River Severn

before the Quaternary glaciation — its modern course was formed when ice filled the northern part of its basin and forced it to take a different route.

The River Severn is also believed to have been diverted during the last glaciation. Figure 10.24 shows the stages of this process.

- **Stage 1 Pre-glacial** The River Severn flowed northwards to enter the Irish Sea in what is now the estuary of the River Dee. The present Lower Severn was a shorter river flowing from the Welsh borderlands to the Bristol Channel.
- **Stage 2 The last ice age** Ice coming down from the north blocked the River Severn valley to the north. The water from the blocked river formed a huge proglacial lake known as Lake Lapworth. The lake eventually overflowed the watershed to the south to join the original Lower Severn. In the process it cut through a solid rock area, creating the gorge at Ironbridge.
- **Stage 3 Deglaciation and the postglacial period** As the ice retreated to the north, the way should have been left open for the two rivers to return to the preglacial situation. The route north, however, was blocked with glacial deposits, and as the Ironbridge Gorge had been cut very deep (lower than the exit to the north), the new drainage adopted this rather than its former route. The River Severn now flows from central Wales to the Bristol Channel.

Periglacial processes and associated landforms

Periglacial areas are those which, although not actually glaciated, are exposed to very cold conditions with intense frost action and the development of permanently frozen ground or permafrost. At present, areas such as the tundra of northern Russia, Alaska and northern Canada, together with high mountainous areas such as the Alps, experience a periglacial climate. In the past, however, as ice sheets and glaciers spread, many areas which are now temperate were subject to such conditions.

The climate of periglacial regions is marked by persistently low temperatures. Summers are short but temperatures can sometimes reach above 15°C. In winter, the temperature remains well below zero and in some areas may fall below –50°C at times.

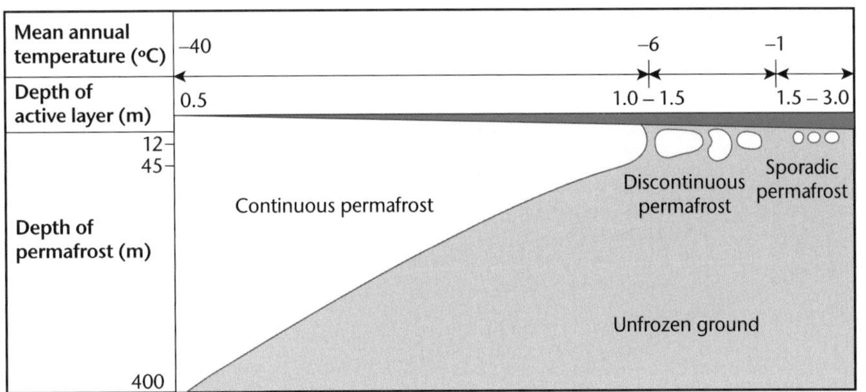

Figure 10.25 Variations in the depth of permafrost

Permafrost

Where subsoil temperatures remain below zero for at least 2 consecutive years, permafrost will occur. Today, it is estimated that permafrost covers around a quarter of the Earth's surface. When summer temperatures rise above freezing, the surface layer thaws from the surface downwards to form an **active layer**. The thickness of this layer depends upon local conditions, but may extend to 4 m. As the ice in this layer melts, large volumes of water are released. This water is unable to drain through the permafrost layer and, as low temperatures do not encourage much evaporation, the surface becomes very wet. On slopes as gentle as 2°, saturation of this upper layer encourages soil movement downslope, a periglacial process known as **solifluction** (see below).

There are three kinds of permafrost (Figure 10.25):

- **Continuous permafrost** is found in the coldest regions, reaching deep into the surface layers. In Siberia today, it is estimated that the permafrost can reach down over 1,500 m. In the very coldest areas, there is hardly any melting of the uppermost layer.
- **Discontinuous permafrost** occurs in regions that are slightly warmer, where the ground is not frozen to such great depths. On average the frozen area will extend 20–30 m below the ground surface, although it can reach 45 m. There are also gaps in the permafrost under rivers, lakes and near the sea.
- **Sporadic permafrost** is found where mean annual temperatures are around or just below freezing point. In these places, permafrost occurs only in isolated spots where the local climate is cold enough to prevent complete thawing of the soil during the summer.

Periglacial processes

There is a clear link between the landforms of periglacial regions and the processes that form them. The main processes are described below.

Freeze–thaw action (frost shattering)

This process has already been described above because it provides a great deal of the erosive material in glaciers. In periglacial areas, **screes** develop at the foot of slopes as a result of frost shattering. On relatively flat areas, extensive spreads of angular

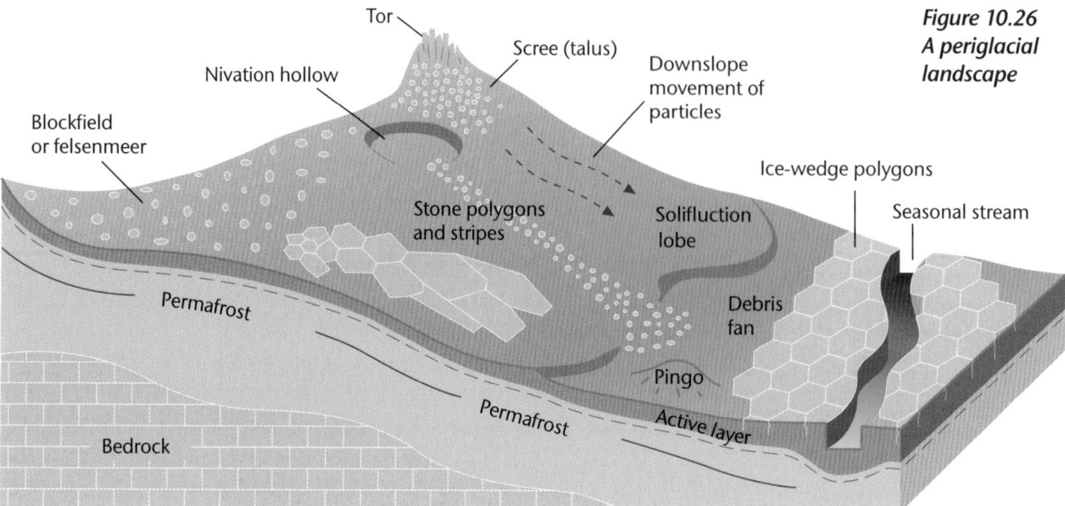

Figure 10.26* *A periglacial landscape

boulders are left, which are known as **blockfield** or **felsenmeer** (sea of rocks) (Figure 10.26).

Nivation

Nivation takes place beneath patches of snow in hollows, particularly on north- and east-facing slopes. Freeze–thaw action and possibly chemical weathering, operating under the snow, cause the underlying rock to disintegrate. As some of the snow melts in spring, the weathered particles are moved downslope by the meltwater and also by solifluction (see below). Over some period of time, this leads to the formation of **nivation hollows** which, when enlarged, can be the beginnings of a corrie (cirque).

Solifluction

When the active layer thaws in summer, excessive lubrication reduces the friction between soil particles. Even on slopes as shallow as 2°, parts of the active layer then begin to move downslope. This leads to **solifluction sheets** or **lobes** — rounded, tongue-like features often forming terraces on the sides of valleys. Solifluction was widespread in southern Britain during the Quaternary ice age, and such deposits are often known here as **head.**

Frost heave

As the active layer starts to refreeze, ice crystals begin to develop. They increase the volume of the soil and cause an upward expansion of the soil surface. Frost heave is most significant in fine-grained material and, as it is uneven, it forms small domes on the surface.

Within the fine-grained material there are stones which, because of their lower specific heat capacity, heat up and cool faster than the surrounding finer material. Cold penetrating from the surface passes through the stones faster than through the surrounding material. This means that the soil immediately beneath a stone is likely to freeze and expand before the other material, pushing the stone upwards until it reaches the surface. On small domes, the larger stones move outwards, effectively sorting the material which, when viewed from above, takes on a pattern. This **patterned ground** on gentler slopes takes the form of **stone polygons**, but where the ground is steeper (slopes exceeding 6°), the stones move downhill to form **stone stripes** (Figure 10.27).

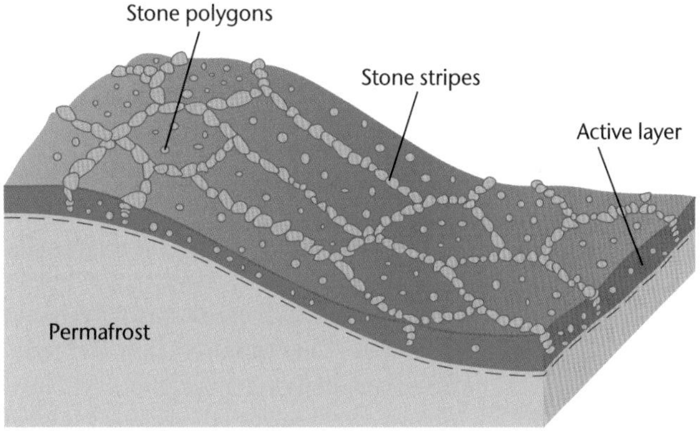

Figure 10.27 Stone polygons and stripes

Groundwater freezing

Where the permafrost is thin or discontinuous, water is able to seep into the upper layers of the ground and then freeze. The expansion of this ice causes the overlying sediments to heave upwards into a dome-shaped feature known as a **pingo** which may rise as high as 50 m. This type of pingo is referred to as an open-system or East Greenland type.

In low-lying areas with continuous permafrost on the site of small lakes, groundwater can be trapped by freezing from above and the permafrost beneath. As this water freezes, it will expand, pushing up the overlying sediments into a closed-system pingo or Mackenzie type. It is named after the Mackenzie delta in northern Canada where over 1,000 pingos have been recorded. Sometimes the surface of a pingo will collapse, leaving a hollow that is filled with meltwater.

Ground contraction

The refreezing of the active layer during winter causes the soil to contract. Cracks open up on the surface in a similar way to cracks on the beds of dried-up lakes. During melting the following summer, the cracks open again and fill with meltwater. As the meltwater contains fine sediment, this also begins to fill the crack. The process occurs repeatedly through the cycle of winter and summer, widening and deepening the crack to form an **ice wedge** which eventually, over a period of hundreds of years, can become at least 1 m wide and 2–3 m deep (Figure 10.28). The cracking produces a pattern on the surface which, when viewed from above, is similar to the polygons produced by frost heaving. These are therefore known as **ice-wedge polygons**.

Figure 10.28 The formation of ice wedges

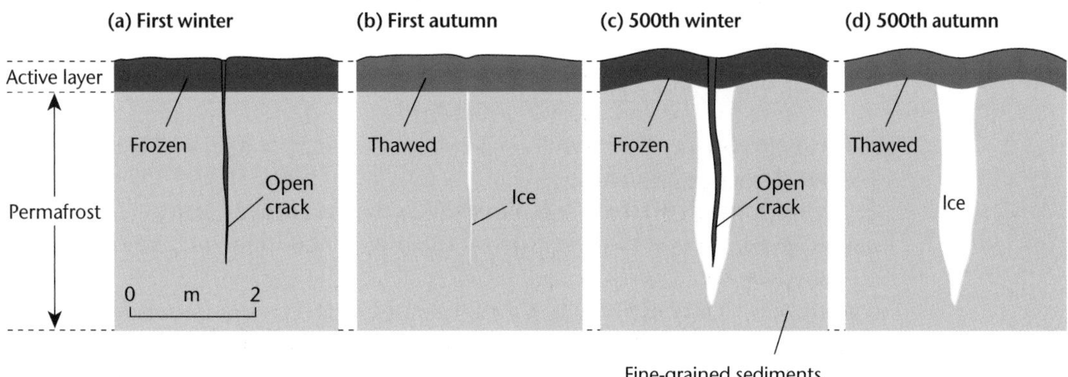

Water and wind action

Owing to the open and sparsely vegetated periglacial landscape, rates of erosion caused by water and wind can be high.

Water erosion is highly seasonal, occurring mainly in spring and summer when the active layer melts. This can cause short periods of very high discharge in rivers, bringing about far more fluvial erosion than would be expected given the relatively low mean precipitation. Drainage is typically **braided** because of the high amount of debris being carried by meltwater streams.

Unobstructed **winds** blowing across periglacial landscapes can reach high velocities. They cause erosion through abrasion and dislodge the fine unconsolidated materials that cover the area. The effects of erosion can be seen in grooved and polished rock surfaces and in stones shaped by the wind, known as **ventifacts**. The fine material of the outwash plain is picked up by the wind and carried long distances to be deposited elsewhere as extensive areas of **loess**. Loess is found in many parts of North America and Eurasia, south of the boundary of the Pleistocene ice sheets. In England, loess deposits, rarely more than 2 m in depth, cover parts of East Anglia and the London Basin where they are known as brick-earth deposits. In China, loess deposits are widespread and in places reach depths of over 300 m.

Biomes and ecosystems

The tundra biome

The tundra biome extends across the northern regions of Alaska, Canada, Scandinavia and Russia. Small areas can also be found in the extreme southerly areas of the southern hemisphere on islands such as South Georgia and on the very fringes of Antarctica.

The tundra area has many features that make plant growth difficult, including:

- low levels of insolation, with many months of permanent night
- a very short growing season of no more than 50–60 days
- low levels of precipitation, with soil moisture being frozen for most of the year
- waterlogged soils through the short summer when marshy conditions often predominate — the thawed water is unable to penetrate the ground because of the permafrost and temperatures are too low to allow much evaporation
- strong, desiccating winds
- permafrost at a variable depth

The main features of the tundra vegetation (Photograph 10.5) are that:

- net primary productivity is very low, varying between 50 and 150 g m^{-2} yr^{-1}. Only in scrub deserts and semi-deserts is the productivity lower
- it has the fewest plant species of any biome and, therefore, low biological diversity
- there is an absence of fully-grown trees (the name 'tundra' is an Inuit word for treeless plain). Some trees produce dwarf varieties, for example the dwarf willow

Photograph 10.5 Autumn tundra vegetation in Yukon, Northern Canada

- the lack of nitrogen-fixing plants limits fertility and the cold, wet conditions reduce the rate of decomposition
- there are five types of dominant plant, each occupying its own specialised niche: lichens, mosses, grasses, cushion plants and low shrubs. The environments in which these are typically found are shown in Figure 10.29. Mosses and lichens form a well-defined ground layer. Lichens are pioneer plants. They colonise bare areas, which is the first stage in the development of a lithosere. Lichens have no roots and are able to absorb water and nutrients directly into their foliage. Together with mosses, they initiate soil formation.
- most flowering plants are perennials — they flower year after year. They have hardy seeds armoured in a thick seed case

Figure 10.29 Small-scale variations in tundra vegetation

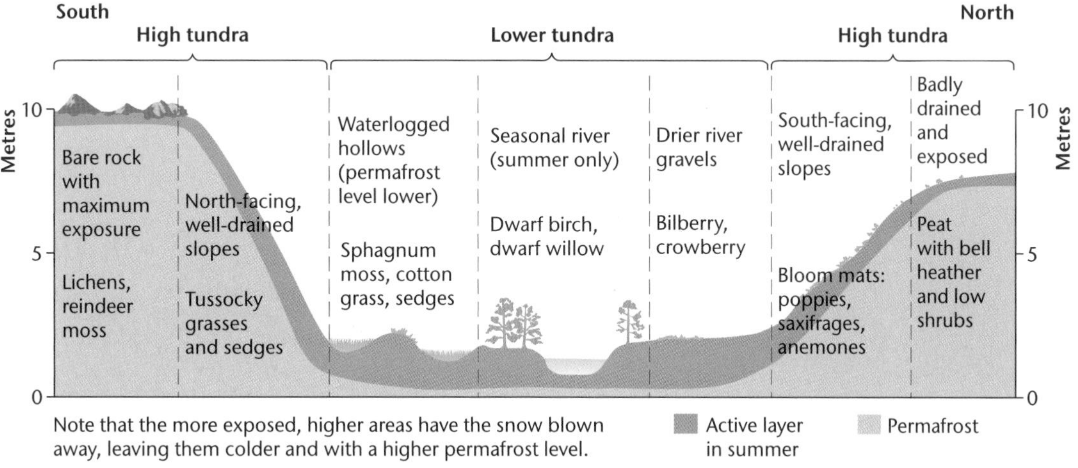

Tundra plants have to overcome the restrictions imposed by the environment. To cope with such difficulties, plants have adopted some of the following features:

- **ground hugging** — avoids the cold, desiccating wind and takes advantage of any warmth close to the ground
- **slow growth rates**
- **shallow roots** — because of the presence of permafrost
- **ability to photosynthesise** at extremely low temperatures and under a shallow covering of snow
- **reduced transpiration** due to small leaves and thick cuticles. Leaf hairs may trap warm air close to the leaf surface
- **low albedo** of plant surfaces — they can absorb more insolation than the surrounding surfaces
- **perennial plants** — can store food from year to year

The biome's low primary production only supports a small number of animal species; fewer than 50 species are considered to be residents. There is a marked variation in numbers between winter and summer because many species migrate to the boreal forests in search of food. This is particularly the case with the large herbivores, such as reindeer and caribou. Many tundra plants, such as mosses and lichens, have a high sugar content, enabling large herbivores to build up body weight in the summer to support themselves through the long winter. Many smaller herbivores, such as lemmings and arctic hares, hibernate during the winter, living underground insulated by the snow cover above them. Insect life abounds in the area.

The food chain on the land is short. The plants make insect and animal life possible, with small herbivores being the most common animals. They represent the food supply for the small carnivores such as the snowy owl and the arctic fox. At the top of the tundra food chain are bears, particularly the polar bear.

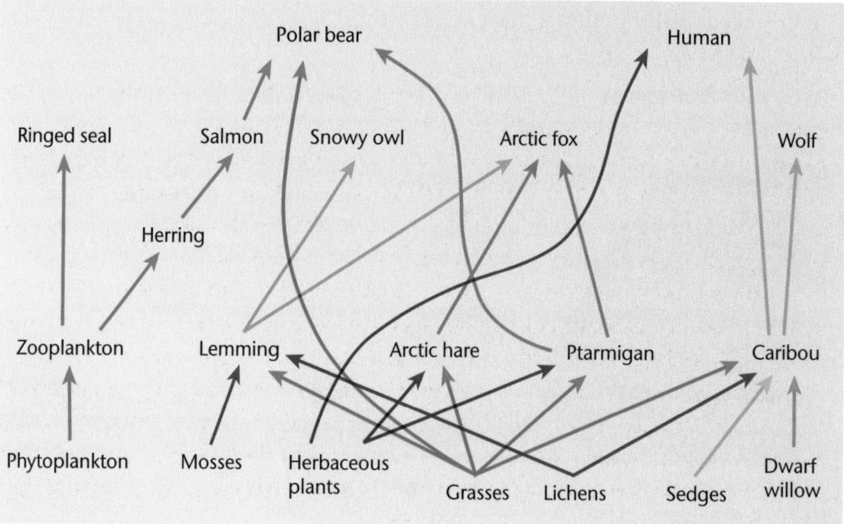

Figure 10.30
A tundra food web

Tundra soils

A distinctive soil type has developed underneath tundra areas. Its major features are:

- a lack of clearly differentiated horizons
- a thin surface organic layer which is often formed from very acidic humus (mor)
- a uniform blue-grey colour
- it is waterlogged in summer
- it is gleyed

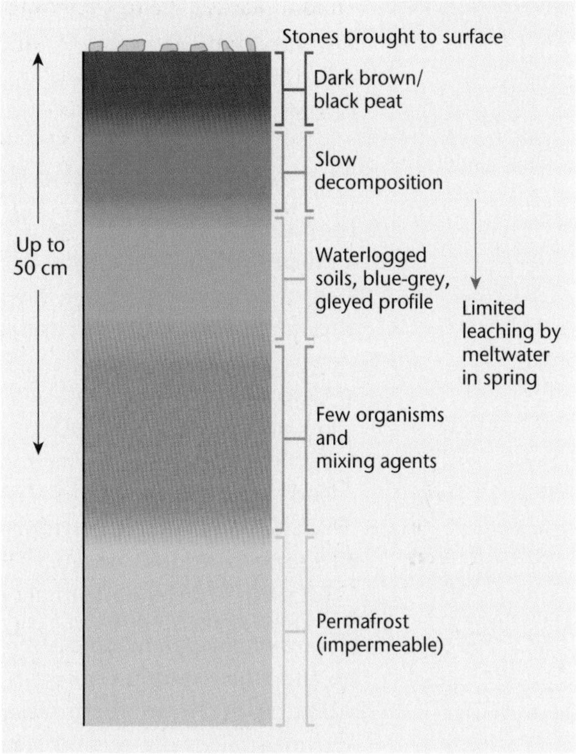

Most tundra soils are gleyed as a result of the area being waterlogged through the summer. Drainage is impossible because of the underlying permafrost and water is retained in the upper layers. Evaporation, which would otherwise remove the water, occurs at a very slow rate. Under such conditions, iron compounds are reduced to their ferrous form, which is grey (as opposed to ferric compounds, which are red-brown).

Surface litter is restricted by the limited tundra vegetation. The slow rate of decay of the vegetation due to the climate and the presence of only a few soil organisms also means there are limited amounts of organic matter in the soil. Soil organisms normally act as mixing agents and as there are few organisms available to carry out this work the soil horizons are poorly differentiated. The freezing of the soil in autumn leads to it being churned and the horizons becoming further distorted.

Where the soil overlies bedrock, frost-heave raises fragments to the surface, giving rise to typical periglacial features on the surface.

Stones brought to surface
Dark brown/ black peat
Slow decomposition
Up to 50 cm
Waterlogged soils, blue-grey, gleyed profile
Limited leaching by meltwater in spring
Few organisms and mixing agents
Permafrost (impermeable)

Figure 10.31 Tundra soil profile

A fragile environment

The tundra, because of its climate and limited productivity, is considered to be a fragile environment. There are a number of reasons for this.

The slow rate of plant growth means that any disruption to the ecosystem takes a long time to be corrected. Some scientists estimate that it could take over 50 years to return an area of tundra to its former state after interference. (It can take this length of time before tyre tracks are completely revegetated.) The low productivity and limited species diversity mean that the plants are very specialised and any disruption causes difficulty when it comes to regeneration. In such circumstances, species have great difficulty in adapting to a changed environment.

Wide fluctuations occur in the amount of energy held in each trophic level of food chains because population numbers change rapidly. For example, variations in the numbers of lemmings and arctic hares, both of which are liable to short-term and long-term fluctuations, have consequences for the populations of their predators, such as arctic foxes and snowy owls.

Disruption to the functioning of the biome has long-term implications. This is why there has been so much concern over the proposed exploitation of resources such as the oil reserves of north Alaska that fall within the Arctic National Wildlife Refuge.

The ecosystem of the Southern Ocean

The Southern Ocean is an area of sea that borders Antarctica. It comprises the southern parts of the Atlantic, Pacific and Indian Oceans. The biological productivity of the Southern Ocean, based upon measures of the size of standing crop of phytoplankton and its yield, is the highest of any marine area in the world. There are several reasons for this:

- **Cold sea water** has an advantage over warmer water in that it can hold larger quantities of dissolved gases such as oxygen and carbon dioxide.
- **Turbulent waters**, resulting from upwelling currents, strong surface movements and regular storms, keep the nutrients and minerals in suspension where they can be utilised by the phytoplankton.
- Almost **continual photosynthesis** during the long daylight hours of the southern hemisphere summer enables the growth of the phytoplankton.

Blooms of phytoplankton occur from October onwards, after the break up of the ice and when sunlight becomes continuous. Phytoplankton are the primary producers in the Southern Ocean and represent the base of the food chain. Above them, in the second stage, are zooplankton. There are a number of species, but zooplankton are dominated by the shrimp-like **krill** (about 5 cm long), which feed directly on the phytoplankton. Krill form in dense swarms — so much so that the ocean often takes on a pink colour. Predators are easily able to feed on them and krill are the main food supply for fish, penguins, albatrosses, some seals and whales (baleen whales — those without teeth). They are also an important food supply for other aquatic birds and mammals and the main food of squid, which are abundant in these waters. Squid form another link in the food chain, being an important food supply for larger fishes, sea birds, seals and the toothed whales.

Figure 10.32 The Southern Ocean food web

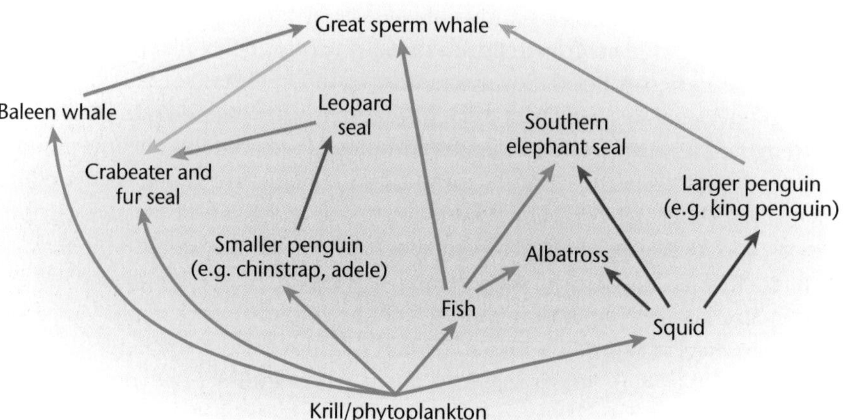

The Southern Ocean is home to vast numbers of birds but species diversity is low. There are fewer than 50 species regularly present in this area (there are over 8,000 species of bird in the world). Penguins, petrels and albatrosses are the dominant species. For example, there are an estimated 100 million penguins nesting in the Antarctic region. The ocean is also home to a variety of seals, including leopard, elephant, crabeater and fur seals.

Human activity, economic processes and resource management

Local economies of the indigenous population

The traditional economic activity of the indigenous population of the tundra was hunting and fishing. In the north of North America, the main activity of the **Inuit** was hunting seals, which provided them with meat, oil and skins. Fishing (including whales) was also a major activity. Some groups occasionally hunted polar bears and smaller mammals. Mobility was a key to their continued existence. Sledges were pulled by teams of dogs over the icy areas; kayaks, and sometimes larger boats, were used on water. The number of Inuit was always small in terms of the vast area in which they lived, so very little pressure was put on the environment, which remained relatively undisturbed.

In the north of Europe, the **Lapps** followed the seasonal movements of the herds of wild reindeer that provided them with most of the food and materials that they needed. Fishing was used to supplement their diet. Reindeer spend the winter period in the boreal forests living on tree mosses and bark. They move back into the tundra during the summer. Like the Inuit, the Lapps lived in an environment that provided all that they needed but which could only support a low-density population.

Bryan and Cherry Alexander

Photograph 10.6 An Inuit hunter in fox furs with a fish spear, Igloolik, Nunavut, Canada

Both Inuit and Lapps developed strategies to survive in a difficult natural environment. The ways of life that they adopted were totally **sustainable**.

Resource exploitation by newcomers

From the seventeenth century onwards, the resources of tundra areas began to be exploited by outsiders. The major forms of economic activity that occurred included sealing, whaling, trapping for fur, and mining, particularly for gold. Mining led to the establishment of permanent settlements whereas the other activities tended to be temporary or seasonal.

In the last 100 years or so, exploitation of the tundra has been on a much larger scale and has had a dramatic impact on the lifestyle of the indigenous populations. Activities include mining (particularly for oil), production of hydroelectric power (HEP), fishing, and, latterly, tourism. Military, strategic and geopolitical concerns have given these areas increasing importance, particularly in Alaska and northern Russia. Strategic interest in the northern areas of North America dates back to the Second World War. With the threat of Japanese invasion, the USA constructed the Alaska Highway, which runs northwest from Dawson Creek in Canada to Fairbanks in Alaska. The purpose was to carry heavy weapons to the north. The rise of the USSR after the Second World War, and the beginning of the Cold War, increased the strategic significance of Alaska and northern Canada. Such is the involvement of the armed forces that military personnel have, at times, made up at least 25% of the population of Alaska. Numerous roads, air-force bases, radar and early warning stations have been built. However, the military presence has led to little permanent settlement beyond the main bases, which are maintained from outside and are not dependent on local resources.

Human activities and the physical environment

The physical environment has an undoubted impact on human activities. In turn, human activities in such cold regions can have a great impact on the physical environment. The harsh conditions of cold environments present a challenge for human occupation and development. These conditions include:

- very low temperatures
- short summers and therefore short growing seasons
- low precipitation
- thin, stony, poorly-developed soils
- permafrost
- surface thaw in summer leading to waterlogging
- snow lying for long periods
- blizzards

Indigenous peoples have adapted their ways of life to cope with the climate and to make the most of the limited resources. Establishing permanent settlements and developing activities such as mining has required major technical advances, primarily because the permafrost creates a unique set of problems for construction work and engineering.

Problems are caused when vegetation is cleared from the ground surface. This reduces insulation and results, in summer, in the deepening of the active layer. Even minor disturbances, such as vehicle tracks, can greatly increase melting, because the vegetation is very slow to re-establish itself.

Buildings speed up this process by spreading heat into the ground. The thawing of ground ice leads to the development of **thermokarst**, a landscape of topographic depressions characterised by extensive areas of irregular, hummocky ground interspersed with waterlogged hollows. The damage caused by this form of ground subsidence can be seen in tilted and fractured older buildings and in damage to roads, railways and airfield runways.

In recent years, many new methods of construction have been employed to protect the permafrost and prevent subsidence. Although they are successful, these methods are more expensive than conventional construction, adding to the costs of living in the region, and continual maintenance is often necessary. Some of the methods include the following:

- Smaller buildings, such as houses, can be elevated above the ground on piles driven into the permafrost. The gap below the building allows air to circulate and remove heat that would otherwise be conducted into the ground.
- Larger structures can be built upon aggregate pads, which are layers of coarse sand and gravel, 1–2 m thick. This substitutes for the insulating effect of vegetation and also reduces the transfer of heat from building to ground. These pads can also be placed beneath roads, railways and landing strips as well as buildings.
- In large settlements **utilidors** (Figure 10.33) have been built. A utilidor is an insulated box, elevated above the ground, that carries water supplies, heating pipes and sewers between buildings. Pipes cannot be buried underground because of the damage that would be caused by freezing and thawing in the upper soil layers.

Apart from the production of thermokarst, human impacts on the physical environment include:

- hunting — over-exploitation
- transport — risks of spillages, road vehicles damaging ground
- tourism — vegetation removal, litter and waste not easily degraded
- general air pollution

These factors add to the effects of global warming, melting the snow and ice of the region.

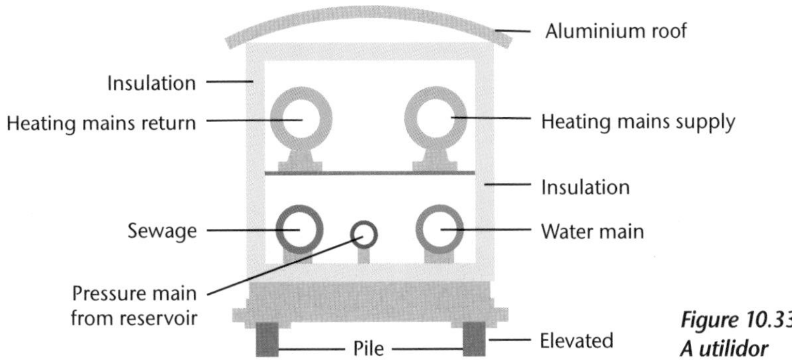

Figure 10.33 A utilidor

Case study The Trans-Alaskan oil pipeline

In 1968, vast deposits of oil were discovered on the North Slope of Alaska in the area of Prudhoe Bay. The removal of the oil after extraction from the ground was a major problem, because the presence of pack ice in the seas to the north meant that the oil could not be removed by tanker (two failed supertanker attempts were made). The alternative was to transport the oil by pipeline to the southern shores of Alaska, in particular to the ice-free port of Valdez. Lobbying by environmentalists at first prevented construction of the pipeline. They argued that the tundra environment should be protected. There were real concerns and uncertainties about the pipeline's design, route and ecological impact. It could not be buried in the ground because the warm oil would melt the permafrost. There were also concerns about earthquakes, avalanche hazards and animals crossing the pipeline.

For some of its length it crosses permafrost-free areas or regions where the permafrost sediment is coarse grained. Such surface deposits are free draining and less susceptible to subsidence on thawing and so the pipeline can be buried in the conventional way. For most of its length, though, the pipeline incorporates features designed to cope with the permafrost conditions:

- Where the pipeline crosses areas of fine-grained permafrost sediment (for over half of its length), it is **elevated above the ground** so that heat from the line is not conducted into the ground surface. If this happened thawing of the permafrost would cause subsidence.
- The elevated structure also allows the pipeline to **shift sideways** on its supports as an extra protection against damage caused by ground movement.

However, oil demand in the USA was increasing and exploitation of this, the biggest field in the country, was seen as essential, particularly as it would reduce dependence upon supplies from the politically unstable Middle East.

The Trans-Alaskan pipeline took over 5 years to design and 3 years to build. The environmental lobby ensured that the oil companies were not allowed to use the cheapest option. It has been estimated that the total cost of the operation was around $8 billion. The pipeline has a maximum daily throughput of 1.4 million barrels and the oil is pumped through at a temperature of 65°C.

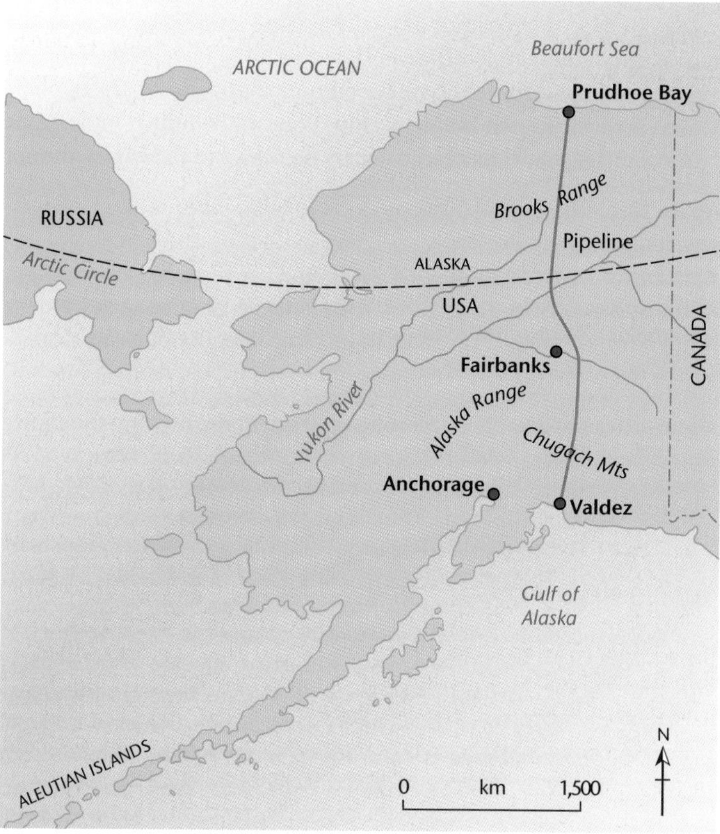

Figure 10.34 The route of the Trans-Alaskan oil pipeline

Bryan and Cherry Alexander

Photograph 10.7 The Trans-Alaskan oil pipeline

- The pilings are specially designed to **resist being jacked up** by successive years of frost heave.
- The line itself is built in a **zigzag pattern** so that it is able to adjust to ground movements caused by either temperature changes or earthquakes.
- The pipe is buried where it passes under roads, through avalanche sensitive areas and where it could block major caribou migration routes. Here, the pipe is covered by **thick insulation**. In a few areas (only 6.5 km of its length), **refrigeration units** have been installed to keep the ground frozen.

Case study Exploitation of the Southern Ocean

The discovery of the islands of the Southern Ocean in the eighteenth century led to the start of exploitation of the area. A number of economic activities have taken place in the region.

Sealing began in the eighteenth century on and around the island of South Georgia. By 1800, the fur seals of South Georgia were wiped out and interest then centred on the South Shetland Islands. Within 3 years, over 300,000 seals had been killed and the population had been virtually eradicated. This was exploitation at its worst, with no thought given to future development.

Whaling began in the nineteenth century. The main targets were blue and right whales; the main products, oil and whalebone (baleen). As the whale population of the North Atlantic became reduced by massive exploitation, the whalers turned their attention to the Southern Ocean. Whalers sailed from several countries in the northern hemisphere, particularly Norway, the USA and the UK.

Whaling was a highly profitable business and whaling stations were established on South Georgia and the South Shetlands. In 1904, the Norwegians developed Grytviken on South Georgia, which at its height employed over 300 people. The range of products increased to include meat meal, bonemeal, meat extract and, in later years, frozen whale meat. Grytviken was abandoned in 1965 because whale stocks were becoming seriously depleted and whaling was no longer commercially viable. The establishment of the International Whaling Convention in 1946 eventually led to an end to most whaling in 1985. Most, but not all, the whaling nations agreed to halt the slaughter, as stocks of many species were running dangerously low.

Fishing has now replaced whaling in the area. In the 1960s, Russian ships began to exploit the Southern Ocean for a number of fish species, including the Antarctic rock cod. Concerns have been expressed recently (see page 326) over the number of fish being taken, particularly fishing for krill by the Russians and Japanese. It is not clear how many krill can be taken without causing damage to the fragile ecosystem that they support.

Tourism also began in the region in the 1960s. Today, over 100,000 people visit every year (see Chapter 13). Penguin colonies are the prime tourist attraction. In order to prevent damage to ecologically fragile areas, a code has been drawn up by the International Association of Antarctic Tour Operators (IAATO). There are strict regulations to ensure safe, responsible and environmentally sensitive tourism.

Case study The Alpine region of Europe

The Alpine region of Europe is an area that still contains permanent snow and ice, with numerous glaciers flowing from the mountains. Glaciation was more extensive during the most recent ice ages and this has left a legacy of deeply gouged U-shaped valleys, steep slopes, lakes, high waterfalls and jagged peaks. At the highest level there is a tundra-type environment with cold winters. However, the height of the sun and the length of the summer season at this latitude give warm, and locally hot, summer days. The main economic activities of this region include the following:

- **Agriculture** — the warm summer conditions mean that a variety of crops can be grown in the valleys. In favourable sunny locations even fruits and vines can be cultivated. However, the main agricultural activity in Alpine regions is pastoral, with particular emphasis on dairy farming. Traditionally animals were taken to the high pastures in the summer when the snow had melted. The lower pastures and fields were used to grow hay or root crops. These provided the winter fodder (indoor feeding) for the animals,

Photograph 10.8 Alpine scenery

Corel

after they had been driven down the slopes in autumn. This seasonal migration is known as **transhumance**. It is now dying out in most regions — the Alpine pastures are being abandoned as young people seek employment in urban areas.

- **Processing industries** — the production of large quantities of milk that could not be consumed in the area in its liquid form, gave rise to processing industries that converted the milk into, for example, cheese and chocolate. Nestlé, a major milk-products company, is of Swiss origin.
- **Hydroelectric power (HEP)** — glacial lakes, steep slopes and fast-flowing rivers combine to give plentiful opportunities to produce HEP for industrial, domestic and transport uses.
- **Tourism** — this has replaced agriculture as the main source of income for many Alpine communities. Mountain railways and cable cars give tourists easy access to the higher Alpine areas — so much so that tourism has now become a year-round activity. In winter, the large amounts of snowfall and the steep slopes are used for winter sports; in summer, the stunning glacial scenery attracts many visitors. The Alpine area is fortunate in being surrounded by populated and affluent countries that do not have the same natural conditions for winter sports. However, the development of winter sports has led to severe environmental degradation. Deforestation of some areas in order to provide ski runs has destabilised slopes and increased the risk of avalanches and landslides.

Present problems and future issues

The increasing settlement and development of transport links in cold environments has had a great impact on the indigenous populations. The influx of relatively large numbers of people, and the infrastructure and economy they have brought has forced the traditional nomadic way of life to change. Many Inuit in North America are now sedentary and living in towns. For many this has not been a happy experience, with people living on benefits and suffering a range of health problems, including alcoholism. In addition, the ever-increasing exploitation of resources has placed pressure on the environment. Disagreement between different interest groups about how to use such regions has invariably brought them into conflict with each other.

Wilderness areas

Much of the Arctic tundra and Antarctica typify the common perception of wild and natural places. Their remoteness and the extremes of physical processes keep them inaccessible to mass tourism and the excesses of economic development. Conservationists believe wilderness areas have intrinsic value and possess outstanding qualities that are worth conserving for the future. Areas such as these have an aesthetic value for people seeking spiritual refreshment and contemplation. Scientifically, they are important because:

- there is a need to maintain the gene pool of wild organisms to ensure that genetic variety is maintained
- animal communities can be studied in their natural environment in such regions

- wilderness is a natural laboratory for the scientific study of ecosystems
- there is a need for pure natural systems to be used as a yardstick against which managed or mismanaged systems can be compared

There are good reasons for conserving wilderness regions, but they also often contain a range of exploitable resources. Pressure for the development of these resources comes from national and transnational groups that require both energy sources and raw materials to support industrial growth. Balancing developmental pressures against the need to conserve the essential values of wilderness is the increasingly difficult task of management. Sustainable development has an important role to play here but there is disagreement about how it may be successfully applied in many wilderness environments.

In 1964, the Wilderness Act in the USA designated a number of wilderness areas. The largest number of designated areas in any state is in Alaska, which instituted its own wilderness legislation, the National Interest Lands Conservation Act, in 1980.

Case study The Arctic National Wildlife Refuge, Alaska

According to the Arctic National Wildlife Refuge (ANWR) website, the refuge was set up to:

> preserve unique wildlife wilderness and recreational values; to conserve caribou herds, polar bears, grizzly bears, musk ox, wolves, wolverines, snow geese, peregrine falcons, other migratory birds and grayling; to fulfil international treaty obligations; to provide opportunities for continued subsistence uses; and to ensure necessary water quality and quantity.

However in recent years, the ANWR has come under increasing pressure from the oil industry to allow drilling on the coastal plain. For more than a decade this proposal, backed by the oil companies and supported by most Alaskan government officials, has drawn full-scale opposition from powerful environmental organisations representing millions of members throughout the USA.

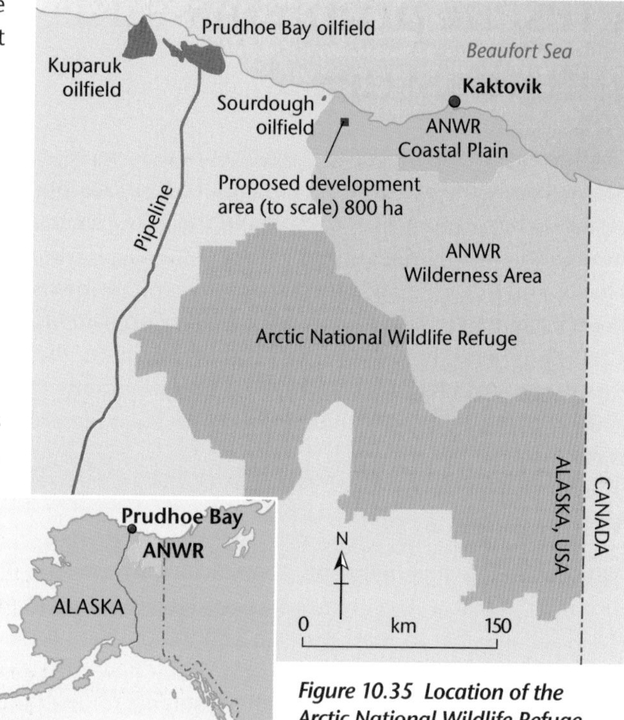

Figure 10.35 Location of the Arctic National Wildlife Refuge

The area's indigenous population is also actively involved in the debate. Their views are shaped by the nature of their relationship with the economy, the land, and its natural resources.

The arguments for oil drilling include the following:

- there could be a major oilfield underneath the coastal plain. Recent US Geological Survey reports indicate that there is a one-in-five chance of finding an oilfield that would yield, in its lifetime, over 5 billion barrels

- the North Slope of Alaska is in decline as an oil producer, with production now less than 1 million barrels a day — currently (2004) 16% of the USA's domestic production
- the USA now depends on imports for over 50% of its oil consumption (58% in 2004)
- revenues to the state and federal treasury would be enhanced by billions of dollars
- at least 250,000 jobs would be created (possibly as many as 500,000)
- at least 75% of the inhabitants of Alaska support the idea
- less than 1% of the total area of the ANWR would be considered for exploration
- those in favour of the scheme claim that the oil developments in the Prudhoe Bay area do not seem to have harmed the wildlife which can apparently coexist with petroleum development and production

The arguments against the proposed drilling include the following:

- the ANWR contains some of the last true remaining wilderness areas in the USA
- the coastal plain is the habitat of one of the largest herds of porcupine caribou in the world, with over 150,000 animals
- the area contains the calving grounds for the caribou
- the caribou herds are an important means of subsistence for the indigenous population, the Gwich'in Athabascan-speaking Indians
- the Gwich'in's opposition to drilling could seriously strain relations with non-native Alaskans who perceive their jobs and standard of living to be closely linked to continued production on the North Slope
- it would take 10 years to bring any ANWR oil onto the market
- opponents of the scheme claim that the area in and around Prudhoe Bay is over 2,000 km^2 of fragile tundra that has been turned into an industrial zone containing over 2,000 km of roads and pipes and more than 60 contaminated waste sites
- studies have shown that the oil is not concentrated into a single reservoir, but is spread across the coastal plain and would require a vast network of roads and pipelines that would fragment the habitat, disturbing and displacing wildlife

On 28 April 2005, the US House of Representatives passed a bill that paved the way for opening up the ANWR to oil drilling.

In December 2005, however, the bill was not ratified by the Senate. This meant that the ANWR was safe for at least another year, and possibly for the foreseeable future.

Case study Antarctica and the Southern Ocean

A number of issues have arisen in Antarctica over the past 50–60 years.

The issue of **sovereignty** was resolved in December 1959, when 12 nations signed up to the Antarctic Treaty. This formalised and guaranteed free access and research rights so that all countries could work together for the common causes of scientific research and exchange of ideas.

The treaty further stated that Antarctica should be used for peaceful purposes only, prohibiting activities of a military nature and subjecting all areas and stations to on-site inspection. The treaty prohibits nuclear explosions and the dumping of nuclear waste. In addition, the 1991 Protocol on Environmental Protection requires that comprehensive assessment and monitoring should be carried out to minimise human impacts on the fragile ecosystems of the region. This protocol also bans all mineral resource activity in Antarctica, including exploration of the continental shelf.

Following the exploitation of seals and whales, attention was turned in the 1960s to the rich **fish stocks** of the Southern Ocean. However, years of overfishing resulted, in 1982, in the signing of the Convention on the Conservation of Antarctic Marine Living Resources. This led to the closure of most fisheries to allow sustainable recovery to occur.

At present, fishing for krill is causing the most concern. Krill underpins the whole of the Southern Ocean food web and scientists do not know how much krill can be taken before the ecosystem is harmed.

As visitor levels increase in the area, **tourism** and its effects have become the latest issue. Important guidelines have been established by the International Association of Antarctic Tour Operators, which are followed by almost all companies operating in the area. Two successful parts of the guidelines are:

- the removal of waste (in the past visitors have left rubbish behind)
- minimising effects upon seals and penguins by avoiding feeding, touching or handling animals

Visitors have to live onboard the cruise ships, as the building of hotels in Antarctica is not allowed. An analysis of tourism in Antarctica appears in Chapter 13.

Case study The Lake District, UK

The Lake District is an area of old rocks (for example the Borrowdale volcanic series and Skiddaw slates) that was extensively glaciated during the most recent ice ages.

The height of the mountains ensured that for a time a small ice cap covered the central area. From this, valley glaciers flowed out in all directions. These glaciers widened and deepened the existing river valleys. During this process deep, steep-sided valleys and rock basins were created within the glacial troughs. These later filled with ribbon lakes. In the mountains, ice sharpened the relief and the glaciers created corries, which filled with water and became tarns.

The attractive mountain landscape and the numerous ribbon lakes offer a variety of recreational activities. The lakes and the areas immediately around them have attracted a large tourist industry. Before the beginning of mass tourism, the major occupation on the uplands was agriculture, particularly sheep farming, which was suited to the higher regions with their cool, damp climate, thin and acidic soils, and steep slopes.

Over 12 million people visit this region every year. This high level of tourism can lead to a conflict of interest with local residents and cause problems for the environment.

Some of the major issues are:

- **Traffic** — around 90% of the visitors to the Lake District arrive by car. At certain times, some towns (for example Bowness and Ambleside) are heavily congested. This gives rise to parking problems, noise and air pollution. Many roads away from the major centres are narrow and winding. They are unsuitable for modern traffic, particularly tourist buses. The Lake District Traffic Management Initiative has attempted to reduce this pressure by restricting parking, improving local transport, developing village traffic-calming schemes, and other methods to try to tailor traffic to the capacity of the existing roads.
- **Footpath erosion** — many popular routes have become severely eroded, with ugly scars dominating hillsides. The Lake District National Park Authority has begun to repair eroded footpaths and damaged dry-stone walls, and has attempted to attract visitors to less popular areas.
- **Second/holiday homes** — in some parts of the Lake District at least one in five of all properties is a second home or holiday cottage. The demand for such properties has forced house prices beyond the reach of most local people. The reduction in the permanent population of

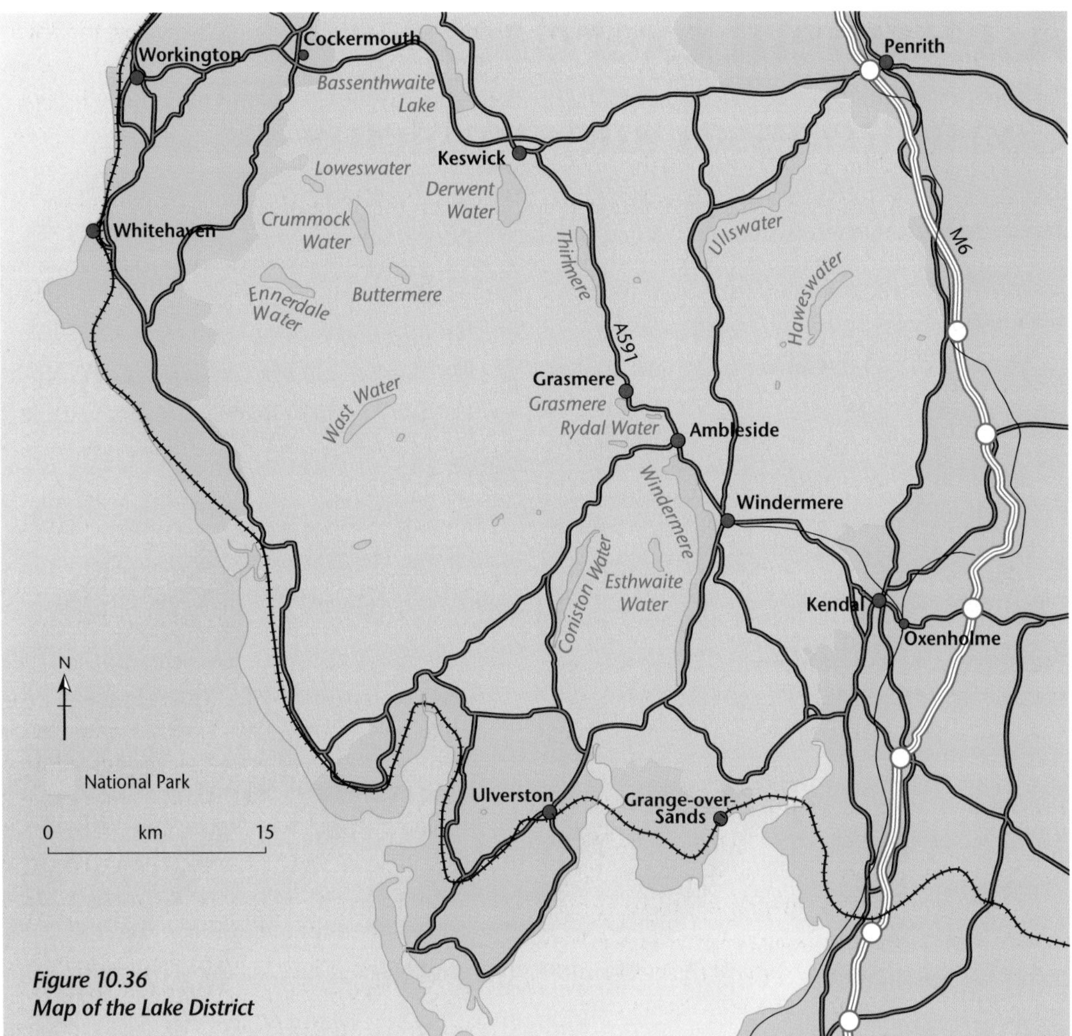

Figure 10.36
Map of the Lake District

many villages has led to the closure of services such as shops, pubs and post offices, because there are not enough people using them on a permanent basis. The Park Authority has tried to persuade the government to bring in legislation to prevent the buying of second homes, but this has proved difficult. One way forward could be the building of low-cost homes that would only be available for local residents to purchase.

- **Conflict** — a major area of conflict is that between people who want to protect the area and who want 'peace and quiet' and those who want to take part in activities such as speedboating, water-skiing, car rallying and mountain biking. Several years ago, the Park Authority restricted speedboating and water skiing to only one lake, Windermere. In 2005, further restrictions were made, lowering the speed limit on Windermere to the point at which water-skiing is impossible. There have been numerous protests, not only from water-sports enthusiasts and powerboat businesses, but also from other businesses in the Windermere area that have suffered from a reduction in visitor numbers. However, the Park Authority is adamant that the restrictions are here to stay.

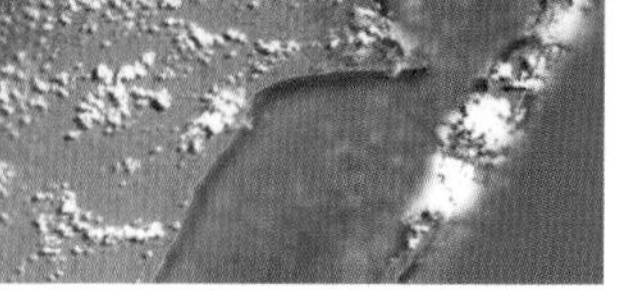

Assessment exercises

Coast processes and problems

1 Study Figure A, which is a map of Blakeney Point, a spit on the coast of north Norfolk.

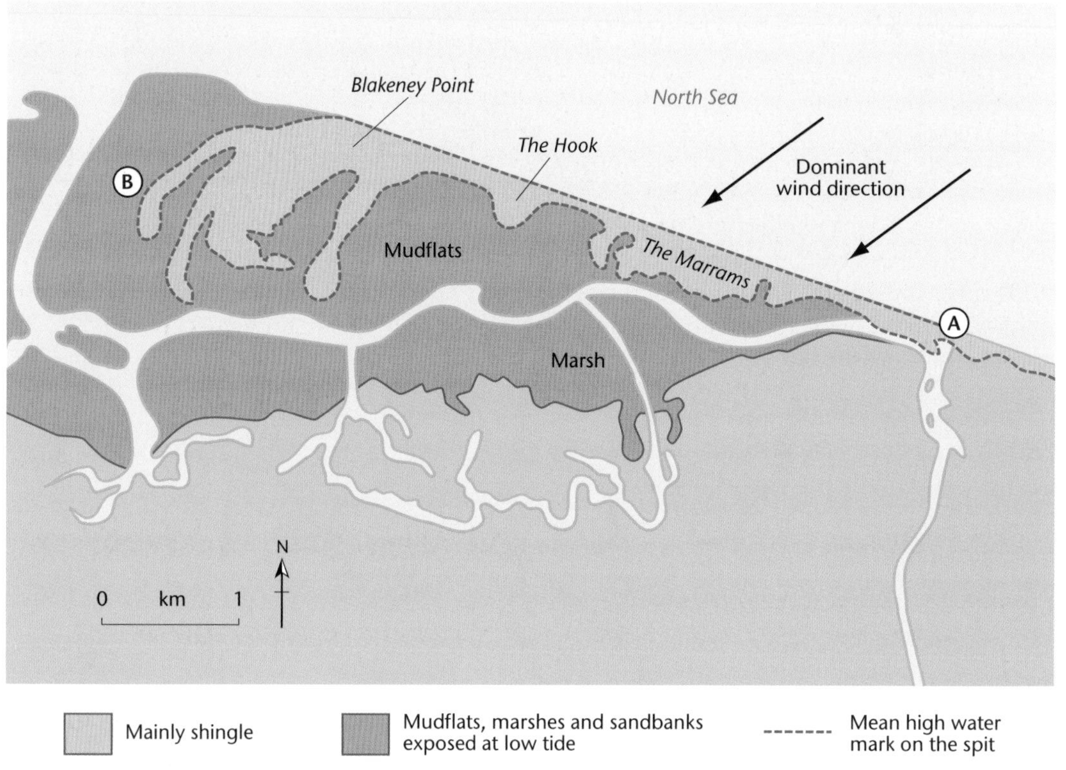

Figure A Map of Blakeney Point

a Describe the process of longshore drift that seems to be contributing to the development and extension of Blakeney Point between points A and B. (4 marks)

b Describe the evidence for the existence and direction of longshore drift that you would expect to find on this type of feature. (4 marks)

c With reference to an area that you have studied, outline strategies for managing the impact of longshore drift and comment on the success of such strategies. (7 marks)

(15 marks)

Geomorphological processes and hazards

1 Study Figure B that shows a simplified section across part of the oceanic crust.

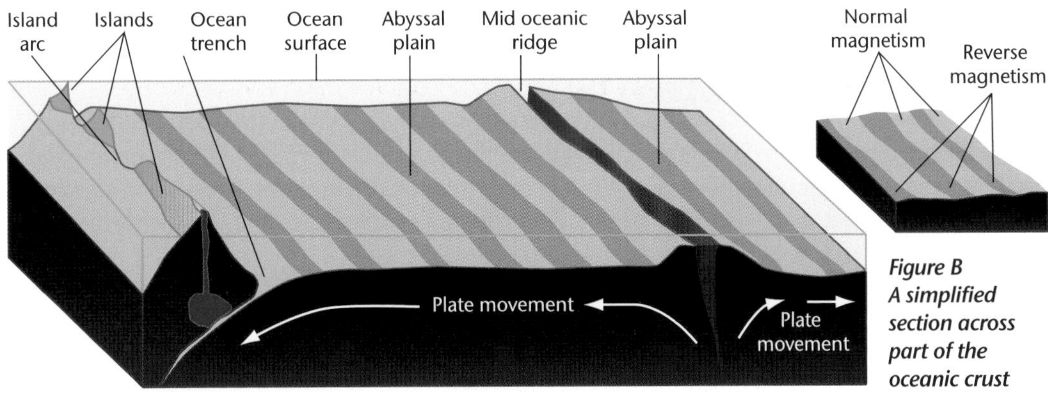

Figure B A simplified section across part of the oceanic crust

a Describe the characteristics of tectonic plates. (4 marks)

b How does the alternate banding of normal and reverse magnetism that occurs on the ocean crust support the theory of plate tectonics? (4 marks)

c To what extent does the theory of plate tectonics provide an explanation for the Earth's major surface features? (7 marks)

(15 marks)

Cold environments and human activity

1 Study Figure C, which shows the seasonal variations in the mass of a temperate valley glacier and the rates of ablation and accumulation that can be expected over a period of 1 year.

a Account for the seasonal variations in the mass of the glacier as shown in Figure C. (4 marks)

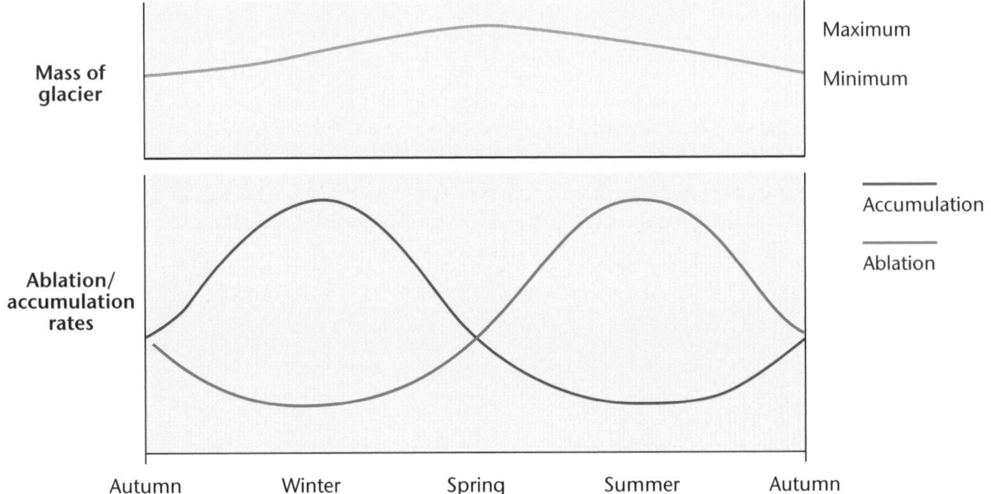

Figure C Seasonal variations in the mass of a temperate valley glacier and and annual expected ablation and accumulation rates

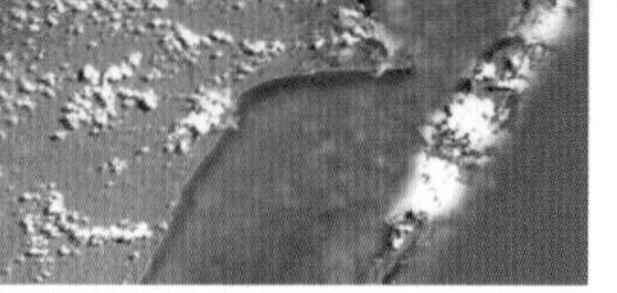

b Outline the factors that influence the rates of flow of a valley glacier. (4 marks)

c With reference to specific examples, contrast the nature and origin of one glacial landform with the nature and origin of one fluvioglacial landform. (7 marks)

(15 marks)

Synoptic questions

The following questions are all **synoptic** in nature. This means that in your response you are required to show your knowledge and understanding of different aspects of geography, the connections between these different aspects and, where relevant, human perspective upon geographical themes and issues.

1 Many models of climatic change predict a gradual and sustained increase in sea level over the twenty-first century. Examine how the geographical impact of such a rise might vary from place to place. *(30 marks)*

2 Why is effective coastal management more difficult to achieve in some parts of the world than in others? *(30 marks)*

3 The extent to which geomorphological processes represent hazards depends on when and where they are experienced. How far do you agree with this statement? *(30 marks)*

4 Discuss the following statement. Geomorphological hazards at a variety of scales should always be considered when planning the location of settlement and economic activity. *(30 marks)*

5 With reference to one or more specific cold environments that you have studied, discuss whether or not human activity has harmful and/or beneficial effects. *(30 marks)*

6 To what extent are cold environments fragile environments? How far does this affect their development? *(30 marks)*

A2

Module 5

Challenge and change in the human environment

Chapter 11

Population pressure and resource management

Patterns, trends and concepts

The growth of world population

In 1999, the world's population reached 6 billion. It has grown rapidly in the last 200 years, particularly since 1950. Natural increase peaked at 2.2% globally in the 1960s. Since then, falling birth rates have reduced this increase to 1.7%. However, the global population is still expanding by 80 million every year. Estimates suggest that by 2050 the global population will be 9 billion, with zero growth occurring only towards the end of the century.

Table 11.1 World population growth, 1800–2000

Year	Population (billions)
1800	1.1
1850	1.4
1900	1.8
1950	2.6
2000	6.1

The growth in world population has not taken place evenly. The populations of some continents have grown and continue to grow at faster rates than others. Europe, North America and Australasia have very low growth rates. In 1995, their share of the world's population was 20%. This is expected to fall to 12% by 2050. It is estimated that Europe's population will shrink by 90 million during this period.

Ron Giling/Still Pictures

Photograph 11.1 A crowded street in Calcutta. India could overtake China as the country with the most people in the next 50 years

Asia has a rapid, but declining, rate of population growth. Between 1995 and 2050, China, India and Pakistan will contribute most to world population growth. Indeed, it is estimated that by 2050, India will overtake China as the world's most populous country (Photograph 11.1). Another potential area of rapid population growth is sub-Saharan Africa, particularly Nigeria and the Democratic Republic of Congo.

Causes of population growth

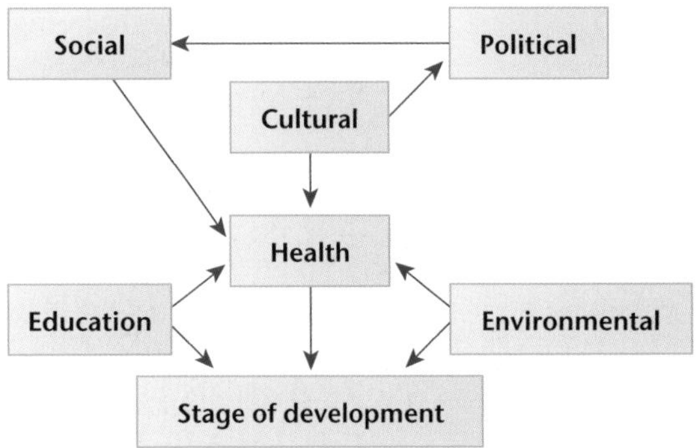

Figure 11.1 Causes of world population growth

Several different factors interrelate to cause growth in the world's population:

- **health** — the control of disease, birth control measures, infant mortality rates, diet and malnutrition, the numbers of doctors and nurses, sexual health, sanitation
- **education** — health education, the age at which compulsory schooling finishes, females in education, levels of tertiary education, literacy levels
- **social provision** — levels of care for the elderly, availability of radio and other forms of media, clean water supply
- **cultural factors** — religious attitudes to birth control, status gain from having children, the role of women in society, sexual morality
- **political factors** — taxation to support services, strength of the economy, impact of war and conflicts, access to healthcare and contraception
- **environmental factors** — frequency of hazards, environmental conditions that breed disease

All countries and regions of the world are dynamic and changing. They develop both economically and socially and this affects population change over time.

The fertility issue: explosion or implosion?

There are over 6.4 billion people in the world. In the late twentieth century, the population was doubling every 30 years — this was described as the 'population explosion'. Various predictions have been made about future population growth. In 1996, one study by Earthscan estimated that the world's population would peak at around 10.6 billion in 2080 and would then decline. The main reason for the slow down in population growth is that fertility rates are falling faster than had been expected.

Population growth in the LEDW

The fastest rates of population growth have been in the less economically developed world (LEDW). Consequently, the greatest falls in fertility rates are expected to take place there. The average growth rate in the LEDW is 1.8%. Except in Africa and the Middle East, where in almost 50 countries families of at least six children are the norm and the annual population growth is still over 2.5%, birth rates are now declining in the LEDW.

India is approaching China as the most populous country on Earth. Its population is close to 1 billion and is expected to overtake that of China by 2050. This assumes an annual population growth of around 0.9% per year for India compared with 0.4% a year for China. In the southern states of India, such as Tamil Nadu and Kerala, where literacy rates are high, fertility rates have fallen sharply. However, in the impoverished Hindi belt in the north, traditional attitudes prevail, ensuring large numbers of children. Nevertheless, in India as a whole, fertility has dropped more than 50% in the last 30 years.

Fertility rates are declining in a range of LEDCs from east Asia to the Caribbean, and throughout most of South America. Although traditional religious attitudes are usually seen as a barrier to low fertility, fertility in the Islamic world is now below replacement level, at fewer than 2.12 children per woman. Algeria, Tunisia, Iran and Turkey are all now in this category.

Population growth in the MEDW

In the MEDW, population growth has been slow for several decades. In some countries, for example Italy, Russia and Portugal, there has even been a small fall in the population — in Italy a population decrease of 4 million by 2020 is forecast. In the next 40 years, Germany could see its population drop by almost 20% and Japan by 25%. In Russia, President Putin has described the country's natural decrease as a 'national crisis'.

The fertility required to maintain the population level is 2.12 children per woman. There are already over 50 nations with fertility rates at or below this level. The United Nations (UN) predicts that by 2016 there will be 88 nations in this category — the 'Under 2.1 Club'. China is already a member of this 'club', although its population will not begin to decline until 2040 at the earliest. This is due to the time lag between reaching replacement-level fertility and actual population decline. Population growth in China will continue well into the twenty-first century.

There are very low fertility rates in many east European countries, for example Ukraine, Romania, Bulgaria, Belarus, Hungary, the Czech Republic and Latvia. Here economic collapse and uncertainty following the end of communist rule has made many women postpone or abandon having children.

Conversely, at 2.1, fertility in the USA is relatively high. Some writers suggest that this is because the American people are more religious and optimistic than those in most other rich nations, leading to a desire for more children. It is also thought that immigration will continue to be high in the USA. This gives a younger structure to the population, thereby increasing fertility.

As concern spreads about low fertility in the MEDW, governments are beginning to act. For example:

- the Japanese government has set aside £50 million to try to stop the fall in fertility. The money is being spent on encouraging people to have more children and on projects to assist this objective
- several European countries have put in place a series of incentives to increase birth rates, with considerable financial benefits being offered for a third child (Table 11.2).

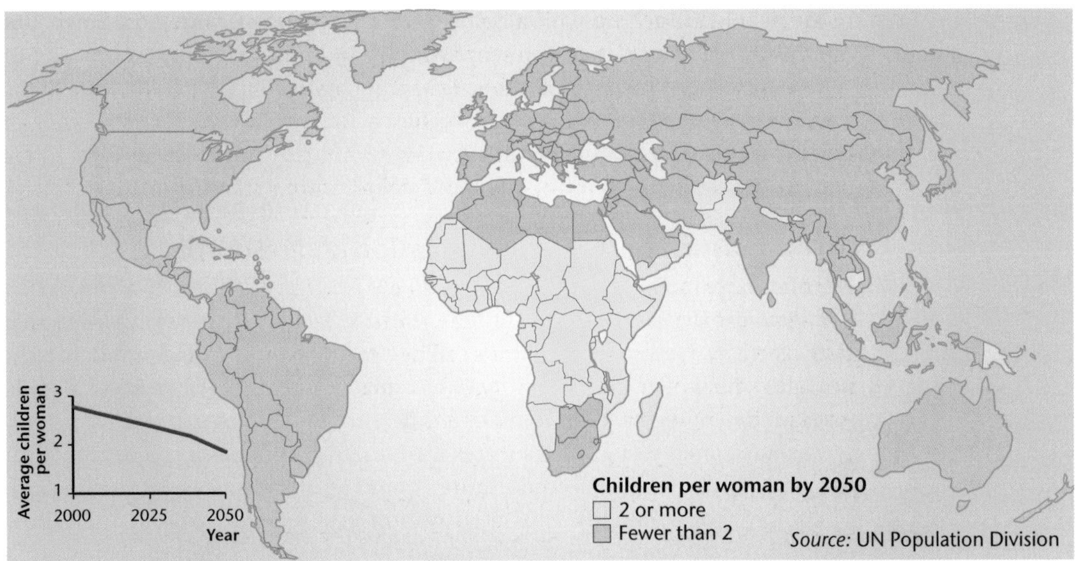

Figure 11.2 Global fertility decline

Country	Child benefit for mother with three children (£ per month)	Maternity and parental leave (weeks)	Percentage of working women aged 25–54 with no children	Percentage of working women aged 25–54 with two children	Birth rate
Germany	290	170	7.7	56	1.3
France	263	170	7.3	59	1.9
Sweden	226	78	8.2	82	1.6
Ireland	189	40	6.6	41	2
UK	170	52	8.0	62	1.6

Table 11.2 Incentives to increase fertility

Overpopulation, underpopulation and optimum population

Overpopulation exists when there are too many people in an area relative to the amount of resources and the level of technology locally available to maintain a high standard of living. It implies that, with no change in the level of technology or natural resources, a reduction in a population would result in a rise in living standards. The absolute number or density of people need not be high if the level of technology or natural resources is low. Overpopulation is characterised by low per capita income, high unemployment and underemployment, and outward migration.

Figure 11.3 The relationship between GDP and population

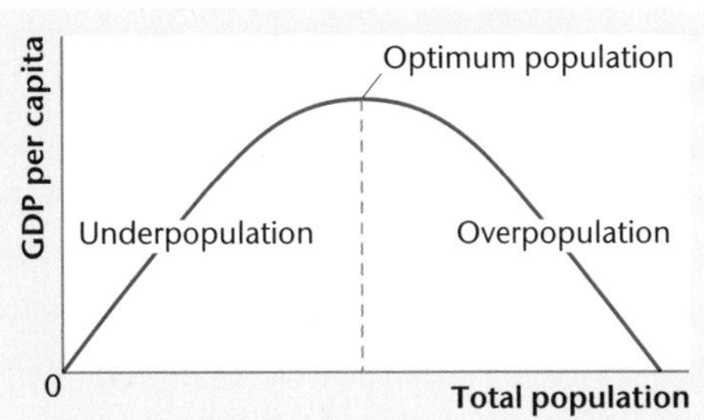

Underpopulation occurs when there are too few people in an area to use the resources efficiently for a given level of technology. In these circumstances an increase in population would mean a more effective use of resources and increased living standards for all of the people. Underpopulation is characterised by high per capita incomes (but not maximum incomes), low unemployment, and inward migration.

Optimum population is the theoretical population which, working with all the available resources, will produce the highest standard of living for the people of that area. This concept is dynamic — when technology improves, new resources become available which mean that more people can be supported.

An optimistic approach to population and resources

Ester Boserup, in *The Conditions of Agricultural Change: The Economics of Agrarian Change under Population Pressure* (1965), stated that environments have limits that restrict activity. However, these limits can be altered by the use of appropriate technologies which offer the possibility of resource development or creation. People have an underlying freedom to make a difference to their lives.

Boserup stated that food resources are created by population pressure. With demand, farm systems become more intensive, for example by making use of shorter fallow periods. She cited certain groups who reduced the fallow period from 20 years, to annual cropping with only 2–3 months fallow, to a system of multi-cropping in which the same plot bore two or three crops in the same year.

The pressure to change comes from the demand for increased food production. As the fallow period contracts, the farmer is compelled to adopt new strategies to maintain yields. Thus necessity is the mother of invention.

Evidence to support this approach

The following two changes in agricultural practice support this view:

- The increasing intensity of shifting cultivation systems in various parts of the world. These move from 'slash and burn' systems in areas of very low rural population density, to systems making use of irrigation in areas of higher rural population density. People are adapting to their changing circumstances by adopting more intensive forms of agriculture.
- The Green Revolution — the widespread introduction of high-yielding varieties of grains, along with the use of fertilisers and pesticides, water control and mechanisation. The increased yields from these processes allow more people to be fed.

More recently, other writers, notably Julian Simon and Bjørn Lomborg, have contributed to these optimistic views. They refer to a number of so-called environmental scares of recent years. In the 1960s it was pesticides, carcinogens and the population explosion. In the 1970s there was the oil crisis, the imminent failure of the world's food supply and the fear of nuclear power. In the 1980s the deserts were advancing, acid rain was killing trees, the ozone layer was thinning and the elephant was on the point of extinction. The 1990s brought retreating rainforests, falling sperm counts, new diseases such as ebola, and genetically modified crops.

They argue that the alarmists were wrong. In their opinion none of these predictions has been fulfilled — there has been no rise in cancer caused by pesticides, population growth has slowed, oil reserves have increased, food production per head has increased even in the poorer countries of the world, nuclear accidents have been rare, deserts have not advanced, acid rain has killed no forests, the elephant has never been in danger of extinction, sperm counts are not falling and rainforests are still 80% intact. They think people are being made to indulge in environmental guilt when technology should in fact be encouraged, to improve living standards throughout the world, rather than just for a rich minority.

A pessimistic approach to population and resources

In *An Essay on the Principle of Population as it Affects the Future Improvement of Society* (1798), Thomas Malthus suggested that the environment dominates or determines patterns of human life and behaviour. Our lives are constrained by physical, economic and social factors.

His argument was that the population increases faster than the supporting food resources. If each generation produces more children, population grows geometrically (1, 2, 4, 8 etc.) while food resources only develop arithmetically (1, 2, 3, 4 etc.) and cannot keep pace (Table 11.3). He believed the population/ resource balance was maintained by various checks:

- increased levels of misery through war, famine and disease
- increased levels of moral restraint such as celibacy and later marriages
- increased incidence of activities such as abortion, infanticide and sexual perversions

Time periods (25 year intervals)	1	2	3	4	5	6	7
Population	1	2	4	8	16	32	64
Food supply	1	2	3	4	5	6	7

Table 11.3 Changes in population and resources (food supply) over time

Malthus asserted that the power of a population to increase its numbers was greater than that of the Earth to sustain it. This view is still held by so-called neo-malthusians. For example, in 1972 the Club of Rome (an international team of economists and scientists) predicted in a book entitled *The Limits to Growth* that a sudden decline in population growth could occur within 100 years if present-day trends continued. They argued that environmental degradation and resource depletion were not only related to population growth, but were also a function of the technologies and consumption patterns of greater numbers of people. They suggested greater control and planning of both population and resource use to create more stability.

Evidence to support this approach

Neo-malthusians believe that a number of recent issues support their views:

- They believe the wars and famines in Ethiopia, Sudan and other countries of the Sahel region of Africa in recent decades suggest that population growth has outstripped food supplies. On a global scale, the Food and Agriculture Organization (FAO) suggests that over 800 million people are chronically malnourished, while 2 billion lack food security.
- Population growth accelerated rapidly in less economically developed countries (LEDCs) after their mortality rates began to fall. Rapid population growth impedes development and brings about a number of social and economic

problems. In recent decades, however, population growth has slowed. In 2000, the population growth rate was 1.4% per annum compared with 2.4% in 1960.

- Water scarcity is predicted to be a major resource issue this century. The UN predicts that by 2050, 4.2 billion people (45% of the world's population) will be living in areas that cannot provide the required 50 litres of water a day to meet basic needs.

One of the most prominent neo-malthusians in recent years has been the American writer Paul Ehrlich. In the 1960s he suggested that India should not receive Western emergency aid because of its environmental state at the time. He said then that 'sober analysis shows a hopeless imbalance between food production and population'. However, optimists have since pointed out that India now more than feeds its population due to the advances of the Green Revolution.

The most recent scare from the pessimists is global warming, and one of the key features of this is that it cannot be proven either right or wrong within our lifetime. In response to this threat, at the 1997 Kyoto conference on the environment, the industrialised countries agreed to cut their carbon dioxide emissions by 30% by 2010. In the UK this was to be achieved by a switch away from coal-fired power stations to alternative sources, increases in public transport and taxes on fuel consumption. However, the USA, under President Bush, has refused to comply with the agreement.

In 2002, at the World Summit on Sustainable Development held in Johannesburg, key issues were sustainable management of the global resource base, poverty eradication and better healthcare. The last two were seen as ways in which population growth could be reduced. Clearly, the population–resources debate continues.

Case study Niger famine, 2005

In 2005 drought and plagues of locusts caused severe food shortages in Niger, one of the poorest countries in the world. Aid agencies warned that 3.6 million people could be affected and a major appeal was launched in Britain.

This response to the images of starving children broadcast from the south of Niger in July 2005 was natural and humanitarian. But donor governments in the developed world with contingency funds to relieve situations like these had ignored all the warning signs. The UN's emergency relief coordinator, Jan Egeland, said: 'The majority of our activities in Africa are badly underfunded'.

There are sometimes bad years in Niger, but not since the great famine of 1973 had there been a cycle of three bad years in a row. There was a drought in 2004, followed by locusts ravaging the region. A second year of drought in 2005 turned farms to barren land, their distinctive ball-shaped storage silos empty.

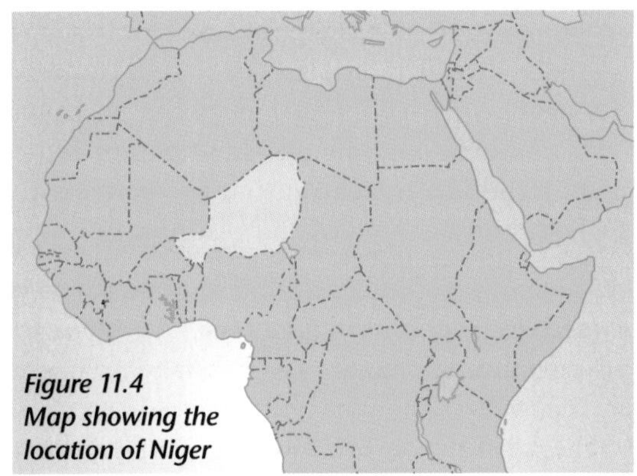

Figure 11.4 Map showing the location of Niger

In this harsh environment, people cope with hardship by selling animals, but the price of animals is depressed by so many people trying to sell them.

Men migrate in search of work, sometimes as far away as Libya and Algeria, and if conditions at home do not improve they cannot come back. There is a shortage of pasture for animals and nomads compete with farmers for scarce resources as they try to move their herds around.

In a normal year in Niger one in four children do not live to see a fifth birthday. Child mortality is highest around Maradi, the area where the worst famine images came from. The situation in 2005 in this area was much worse than normal because of an acute shortage of clean drinking water.

Aid agencies welcomed the attention and relief funding for Niger but were concerned that crises in other African countries were not being addressed. They warned, too, of the consequences of the continued failure to address the root causes of such disasters. A report by an American forecasting organisation stated: 'Without a similar commitment and prolonged attention to addressing the chronic issues that are at the heart of the current localised crisis in Niger, the same problems will recur again soon.'

Source: Adapted from a BBC website, July 2005.

Resource exploitation and management

Resources and reserves

A **resource** is defined as any aspect of the environment that can be used to meet human needs. Resources can be classed as either natural or human and as renewable, non-renewable or aesthetic.

Non-renewable resources (also known as finite, stock or capital resources) are those that have been built up, or have evolved, over geological time. They cannot be used without depleting the stock because their rate of formation is so slow as to be meaningless in terms of the human lifespan. There is no theoretical limit on the rate of use of a non-renewable resource — it depends on the capacity of society to exploit it. Non-renewable resources can be subdivided into:

- consumable (e.g. fossil fuels)
- recoverable (e.g. non-metallic resources such as sands and gravels)
- recyclable (e.g. metals, glass, paper)

Each of these subdivisions indicates the potential life cycle of that resource. Consumable resources cannot be used again; recoverable resources may change their physical and/or chemical nature and so may be re-used in a different form; recyclable resources by definition can be used again and have a constant life cycle.

Renewable resources (also known as flow or income resources) have a natural rate of availability. They yield a continuous flow that may be consumed in any given time period without endangering future consumption, as long as current use does not exceed net renewal during the same period. Renewable resources can be subdivided into:

- critical (e.g. sustainable resources of soil, forest and water in aquifers, which all require prudent management)
- non-critical (e.g. everlasting resources such as tides, waves, water, air and solar heat)

Renewability may not be automatic and certain resources may be depleted by heavy use or misuse. In such cases the life cycle of that resource is curtailed.

Aesthetic resources include natural and human landscapes.

Resource management is the control of the exploitation and use of resources in relation to the associated economic and environmental costs. A key element of this is the concept of **sustainable development**. This involves a carefully controlled system of resource management to ensure that the current level of exploitation does not compromise the ability of future generations to meet their own needs.

A **reserve** is the proportion of a resource which can be exploited under existing economic conditions and with available technology. Reserves can be classified as recoverable or speculative. **Recoverable reserves** are the amount of a mineral likely to be extracted for commercial use within a certain time period and at a certain level of technology. They can be:

- proven — known to exist
- probable — estimated on the basis of information and judgement
- possible — in unexplored extensions of established areas of production

Speculative reserves are deposits that may exist in a geological basin or terrain where no exploration has yet taken place but where the geological make-up of the Earth's crust is similar to that of regions that have yielded similar deposits.

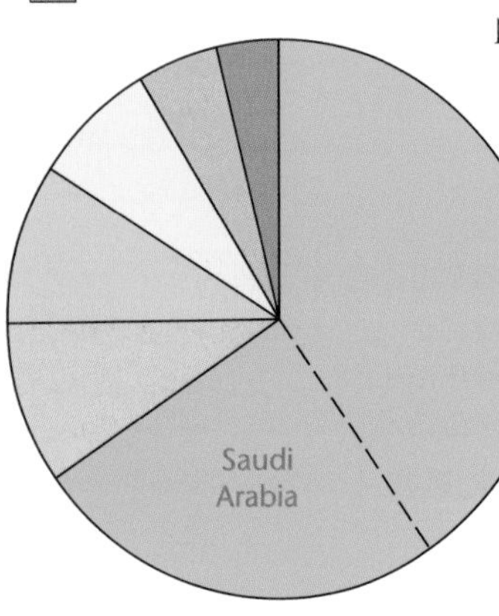

Note: Proved reserves are those that can be recovered under existing conditions.

Source: BP

Figure 11.5 Proved oil reserves, 2002

A non-renewable resource: oil

Background information

Most of the oil reserves in the world are in the Middle East, which is why the region is so politically important. Saudi Arabia alone possesses 25% of the world's proved reserves. The North Sea and Canada still have substantial reserves, but they would be very expensive to extract.

No-one knows how long oil reserves will last, but even the oil industry suspects that the world peak is now approaching. It says that at the moment it has 40 years of proved reserves. However, it also said that 30 years ago (Figure 11.6). In fact, this estimate has increased in recent years even as production has fallen. Cutting consumption would clearly preserve the oil supply.

The Middle East is the biggest oil producer, currently providing nearly one-third of the world's total. But Europe and Eurasia (mainly Russia and the UK) and North America are also big producers. The difference is that nearly all the oil produced in the Middle East is for export whereas Europe and the USA do not produce enough oil to meet their own needs and so have to import it. Western Europe and Japan are heavily dependent on oil imports because production cannot meet massive domestic demand. The USA is the world's largest per-capita oil consumer. However, it produces much of its own requirements. Producers in the Middle East, where oil is cheap, are also heavy users. Poorer countries consume much less oil per head (Figure 11.8).

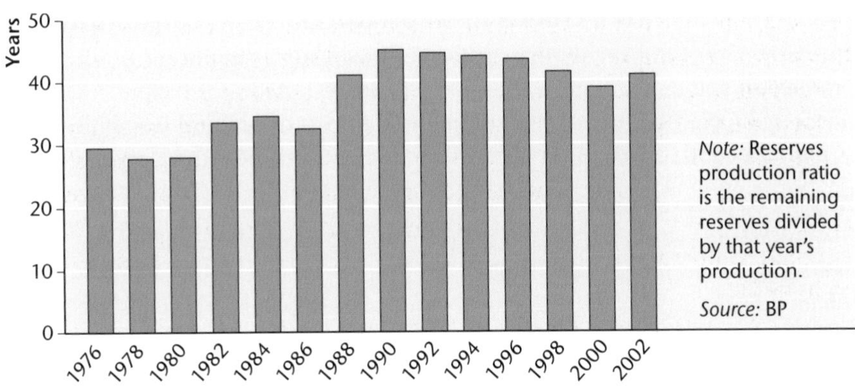

Figure 11.6
World reserves: production ratio

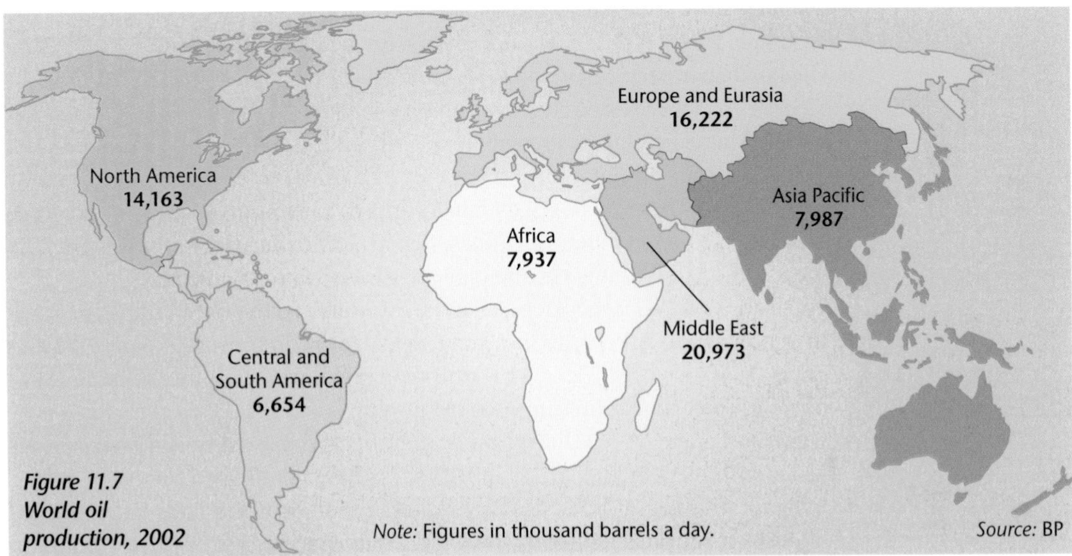

Figure 11.7
World oil production, 2002

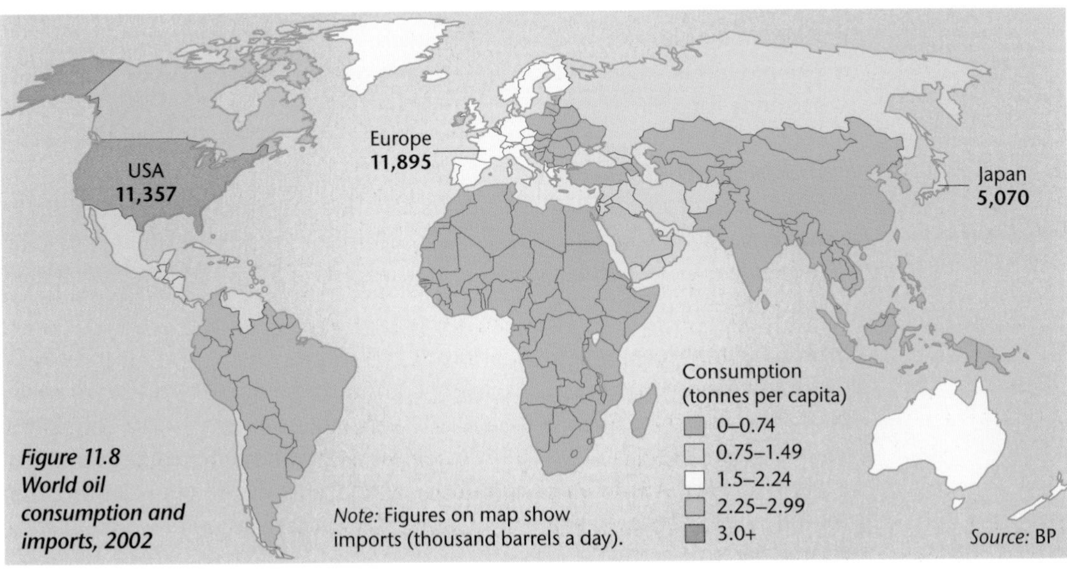

Figure 11.8
World oil consumption and imports, 2002

Twenty-first century trends in oil production and consumption

The early part of the twenty-first century has seen some significant trends in oil production and consumption. These trends are reflected in the rapid rise in oil prices that took place in 2005, accompanied by fears of political instability, risks of pollution and threats to the security of the industry across the globe.

Why are oil prices so high?

In oil-importing countries, rises in the price of oil and therefore energy can have a damaging economic impact. Higher fuel prices can cause unwelcome rises in inflation, can restrict economic growth and are unpopular with voters. Major oil exporters are divided between those, for example Saudi Arabia and Kuwait, that favour increasing output in an attempt to ease prices and those, such as Venezuela, that argue against conciliatory moves towards the big consumers, especially the USA.

In simple terms, global economic expansion is driving up the price of oil. There is a higher than expected demand in the industrialised countries and China's rapidly expanding economy has created a huge boost in demand. In the USA, demand has also risen. This is because of strengthening economic recovery and a greater need for higher grade crude oil suitable for processing into petrol for fuel-hungry sport utility vehicles (SUVs). These are popular with US drivers, a phenomenon that is spreading to consumers in western Europe. Chinese demand for oil has been increasing at 20% per year. Only Saudi Arabia has the capacity to respond to this increase.

There are, however, other factors that have influenced the rise in the price of oil:

- In recent years, oil companies have tried to become more efficient and to operate with lower stocks of crude oil than previously. This means there is less of a cushion against interruptions in supply.
- Terrorist threats in the Middle East from militants inspired by Al-Qaeda, ethnic tensions in Nigeria and strikes in Venezuela have all affected prices.
- In Saudi Arabia and Iraq, sabotage attacks on oil facilities have had a limited impact on supplies. However, they have raised questions over the long-term stability of the area. Any substantial attack on Saudi Arabian oil facilities would have a major impact on global oil markets.
- The producers' cartel OPEC (Organisation of Petroleum Exporting Countries) accounts for 50% of the world's crude oil exports. It attempts to keep prices roughly where it wants them by reducing or increasing supplies to the market, thereby preventing a fall in either price or demand.
- The actions of analysts and speculators have had a significant effect. Analysts in some major oil companies have made incorrect forecasts of demand, thereby lowering output. Speculators in the stock markets of the world have exacerbated price pressure in the market.

Environmental concerns

The continued rise in the consumption of oil means a predicted 60% rise in carbon dioxide emissions between 2004 and 2030, mostly from cars, trucks and power stations. More than two-thirds of the increase will come from developing countries, as a consequence of fast economic growth and a massive rise in car ownership. This rise will be in addition to that which has already taken place over the last 50 years (Figure 11.9).

Views still differ over the degree to which human activity has contributed to global warming. However, there is a growing international consensus that human-induced emissions of carbon dioxide and other gases, for example methane and nitrous oxide, are a major factor causing climate change. These emissions come from, among other sources, burning ever-greater quantities of oil, coal and gasoline. The gases trap the sun's energy in the atmosphere and cause what is known as the 'greenhouse effect'. Carbon dioxide occurs naturally and the greenhouse effect keeps temperatures on the planet at a level that makes it habitable, but current carbon dioxide levels are about 40% higher than they were before the Industrial Revolution.

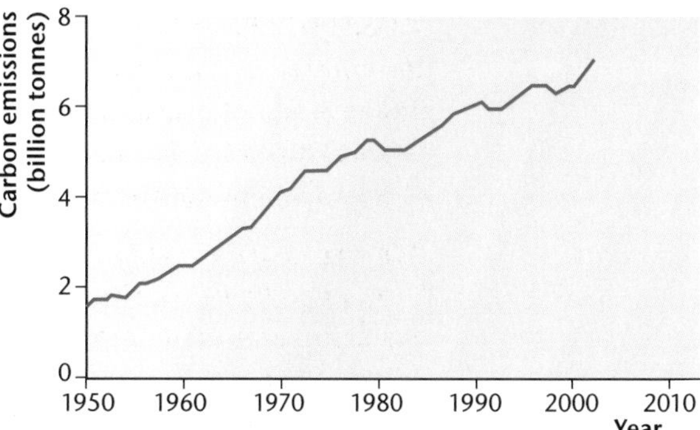

Figure 11.9 Carbon emissions from fossil fuel burning, 1950–2003

Most observers agree that the LEDW is more susceptible to the effects of climate change than the MEDW. This is because poorer countries do not always have the infrastructure and resources to counter the effects of climate change. It is not uncommon for single weather events, such as tropical cyclones and floods, to kill thousands of people in regions such as south Asia, southern China and Central America. In Africa the UN reports a 40–60% decrease in total water in the large catchment basins of Niger, Lake Chad and Senegal. In a continent already struggling with poverty and famine, these climate changes are a matter of life and death.

As the risks of man-made climate change became better known, the international community began to negotiate a treaty that would define mandatory limits for greenhouse gas emissions. The Kyoto Protocol, adopted in 1997, required that by 2008–12, developed countries should have reduced carbon dioxide emissions by 5% from 1990 levels. This was considered minimal because many scientists claimed that a 50% reduction would be needed to achieve climate stabilisation.

When the Kyoto Protocol was developed, poorer countries felt they needed to prioritise basic needs and that the rich countries should take responsibility for solving problems of which they had been the primary cause. Reductions in emissions for developing countries were, therefore, to be phased in over time; targets for richer countries were to be imposed sooner. At the insistence of the US government, several 'flexibility mechanisms' were added to the treaty to, in its view, spread the burden more evenly. These measures included trading carbon emission credits between nations, so that some could emit more if they helped others to emit less. Different countries were given different emission-reduction targets, for example 8% for the EU countries and 6% for Japan.

Although carbon dioxide emissions from developing countries such as China and India are rising rapidly, developed countries are still the biggest emitters. For example, the USA puts nearly 25% of global greenhouse gases into the atmosphere. The US decision to drop out of the Kyoto treaty in 2001 was therefore a major setback, which has been widely frowned upon by the international community. In leaving the treaty, the Bush administration claimed that it would take its own steps to reduce greenhouse gases. It was worried that meeting its target of a 7% reduction in emissions would affect economic growth.

US absence aside, the Kyoto Protocol came into force in February 2005, after Russia's accession to the treaty. The 150 countries that have ratified the treaty (as of May 2005) now need to meet legally-binding commitments to reduce carbon dioxide emissions. Because emissions in most countries have risen since 1990 — in some cases substantially — it will not be an easy task. The national statistics in many countries are quite sobering. However, a few countries in Europe have been gradually reducing emissions and some encouraging initiatives are taking place at regional and local levels.

A renewable resource: water

Environmental impacts

All life and virtually all human activities need water. It is the world's most essential resource. However, for about 80 countries, with 40% of the world's population, lack of water is a constant threat. The situation is worsening, with demand for water doubling every 20 years.

In those parts of the world where there is enough water, it is being wasted, mismanaged and polluted. In the poorest nations of the world, it is not just a question of lack of water — the limited available supplies are often polluted. The UN estimates that dirty water is responsible for 80% of disease in developing countries, resulting in the death of 10 million people each year. Every day, 25,000 children die from diseases caused by unsafe water. In 2001, 20% of the world's people had no access to clean drinking water, and over 40% did not have access to Western-style toilet facilities; a deplorable state of affairs for the third millennium. Scarcity of water has been labelled a 'sleeping tiger' in the world's environmental problems. It:

- threatens production of food supplies
- limits economic and social development
- creates the possibility of conflict between neighbouring countries in the same drainage basins

Water use varies considerably between continents. On average, North America uses 400 litres per person per day, Europe uses 200, Asia and South America use between 200 and 400. In contrast, sub-Saharan Africa uses just 10–20 litres per person per day. The rate of increase in the use of water is greater than the rate of population growth. In the past, increasing demand was largely satisfied by constructing new dams. For example, between 1950 and 1997 the number of large dams rose from 5,000 to over 38,000. However, most of the best sites have been utilised and environmental opposition now means that dam construction is more unlikely. It is not obvious where the water needed to meet future food needs will come from on a sustainable basis.

Examples of global stress on water supplies include:

- In central Asia, the diversion of the rivers Amu Darya and Syr Darya to irrigate cotton fields has resulted in the Aral Sea shrinking. It has lost over half its surface area, retreated by up to 60 km in places and lost 75% of its volume. As a result, evaporation is now lower and rainfall in the area is declining.
- Mexico City is sinking by as much as 40 cm a year due to overdrawn aquifers.

- Water tables are falling worldwide — in southeast England, northern China, the Punjab in India and throughout the Arabian peninsula (where it is estimated that groundwater supplies could be exhausted in 50 years).
- Related to this is the problem of salt-water intrusion, which is the movement of salt water into a fresh water aquifer. It is severe along the Mediterranean, Black Sea and Baltic coasts.
- The world's largest new dam project, the Three Gorges Dam in China, will displace over 2 million people. It has had much criticism from environmentalists.
- On a much smaller scale, the rapid growth in the number of golf courses in the Mediterranean is causing problems in areas such as the Costa del Sol in Spain. Much water is used to maintain high-quality greens. There is the additional problem that fertilisers and pesticides used on golf courses may enter groundwater supplies. Guidelines are now being produced for sustainable construction and management of courses. Regions such as Majorca insist on the use of recycled water for the irrigation of courses.

The exploitation of water resources has caused one significant environmental and management problem, that of pollution. **Pollution** refers to the presence or introduction of unwanted damaging loads or concentrations of materials into the water. In some areas, polluted water can still be used for industry or for agriculture, whereas the same water may not be of high enough quality for drinking. There is a wide range of sources of pollution and a large number of possible pollutants.

Nitrogen and phosphorus are two of the most common pollutants. Sources include industrial effluent, fertilisers, sewage effluent and detergents. They are removed from farmland by percolating water, through soil erosion and through the application of slurry on to the land. High levels of nitrogen and phosphorus are linked to the eutrophication of streams and lakes. The nutrient-rich waters encourage rapid growth of algae (blooms) which starve the water of oxygen.

Case study Pollution in Lake Balaton, Hungary

Lake Balaton in Hungary is the largest lake in central Europe. Eutrophication became a serious problem in the lake as a result of the increasing use of fertilisers in the area and inputs of phosphorus in sewage discharges from lakeside towns. Lake Balaton is a major tourist attraction in the summer months, when the lakeside population swells to 1 million. It is also a popular location for angling. Algal blooms became frequent in the most polluted western parts of the lake. There is now a pollution control programme in place involving sewage treatment and the use of reedbeds to naturally combat pollution. Other provisions for improving water quality in the lake include:

- the establishment of reservoirs on the major tributaries feeding the lake
- selected removal of phosphorus-rich lake sediment
- the control of wastes from large cattle-rearing units

Figure 11.10 Map showing the location of Lake Balaton

The demographic response

In recent decades there has been increasing concern about the imbalance between population growth and the resource base of the world. In particular, there have been worries about inequalities in economic growth, development and welfare between countries.

Indicators of imbalance

A number of indicators have been used to measure development and welfare.

Economic indicators: GNP and GDP

The simplest way to examine global inequality is to compare wealth, country by country. National wealth is usually measured by gross national product per person (GNP per capita). This is the total value of the goods and services produced by the people of a country, divided by its population. It is similar to gross domestic product per person (GDP per capita). However, GDP is based on goods and services produced within the country; GNP is based on goods and services produced by its population in the country and abroad. Both GNP and GDP are usually given in US dollars to make comparisons between countries easier. Geographers use GNP per capita to divide the world into two areas — the MEDW with high GNP per capita (the 'North') and the LEDW with low GNP per capita (the 'South'). The problem with this is that not all countries in the MEDW are rich and not all countries in the LEDW are poor.

Demographic and social indicators

In general, people in the richer MEDW enjoy a better quality of life than those in the poorer LEDW. However, a country's wealth does not paint the whole picture. To judge how developed a country really is, a number of other indicators are used. There is a wide range of such indicators, both demographic and social, including:

- birth rate
- death rate
- fertility rate
- infant mortality rate
- life expectancy
- access to drinking water
- children enrolled in primary school
- adult literacy
- number of people per doctor
- telephone ownership
- urban population

Each year, the Population Reference Bureau publishes details of many of these indicators in its *Population Data Sheet*. Details of some indicators for 20 selected countries (2004) are given in Table 11.4.

Country	Population (millions)	Birth rate (per 1,000)	Death rate (per 1,000)	Infant mortality rate (per 1,000 live births)	Fertility rate (children per woman)	Life expectancy (years)
Afghanistan	28.5	48	21	165	6.8	43
India	1,086.6	25	8	64	3.1	62
China	1,300.1	12	6	32	1.7	71
Bangladesh	141.3	30	9	66	3.3	60
Chad	9.5	49	16	103	6.6	49
Mali	13.4	50	17	123	7	48
Niger	12.4	55	20	123	8	45
Rwanda	8.4	40	21	107	5.8	40
Egypt	73.4	26	6	38	3.2	68
Uganda	26.1	47	17	88	6.9	45
Malaysia	25.6	26	4	11	3.3	73
Thailand	63.8	14	7	20	1.7	71
Mexico	106.2	25	5	25	2.8	75
Brazil	179.1	20	7	33	2.2	71
Russia	144.1	10	17	13	1.4	65
Germany	82.6	9	10	4.1	1.3	78
France	60.0	13	9	4.1	1.9	79
Japan	127.6	9	8	3.0	1.3	82
USA	293.8	14	8	6.7	2.0	77
UK	59.7	12	10	5.3	1.7	78

Table 11.4 Demographic indicators, 2004

Composite quality of life indicators

In recent decades, it has become widely accepted that development is a complex concept, encompassing the social, cultural, environmental and political factors that affect quality of life, as well as the economic conditions that influence wellbeing. Composite indices have been developed which measure a number of indicators.

The Physical Quality of Life Index

The Physical Quality of Life Index (PQLI) summarises infant mortality, life expectancy at 1 year and basic literacy on a 0–100 scale. The index enables researchers to rank countries, not by income but by changes in the quality of life in those countries. The developers of the index believed that the use by the World Bank of GNP as a basic indicator of human wellbeing was seriously flawed. The GNP ignores differences in prices and the distribution of income. It also fails to illuminate how efficiently income is spent. For instance in 1995, health expenditure per capita in the USA was the highest in the world but at least 22 countries had better infant and child mortality rates. The PQLI shows not how much has been spent but how effectively lives have improved.

One major finding in the initial use of this measure was the lack of congruence between GNP per capita and the PQLI. In 1995, the world average PQLI was 72. Industrialised countries in the MEDW tended to rank high in the index, but other countries with high incomes, particularly the very richest Middle Eastern oil producers, had PQLIs in the low 30s. Some very poor countries, for example Sri

Sean Sprague/Still Pictures

Photograph 11.2 Children at a school in southern Thailand. Enrolment in primary school is an important quality-of-life indicator

Lanka (PQLI of 82) and India (PQLI of 68), performed well, despite very low monetary incomes.

In 1960, 53% of the world's population lived in countries with PQLI averages of less than 50. By 1995, only 11% lived in countries with averages of less than 50. This means that during that 35-year period, the number of people in the under-50 PQLI group fell from 1.7 billion to 584 million.

Between 1960 and 1995, the PQLI values of the economically poorest countries — those with incomes under US$450 per capita in constant 1980 dollars — rose from 31 to 64. This was a faster improvement than that which occurred in the higher income countries. Sub-Saharan Africa had the world's worst PQLI performances in 1960 and in 1995. Yet between 1960 and 1995, the average PQLI of sub-Saharan Africa rose from 21 to 50, quite inconsistent with the economic indicators.

The Human Development Index

The Human Development Index (HDI) was devised by the UN in 1990. It measures three variables:

- life expectancy
- educational attainment (adult literacy and combined primary, secondary and tertiary enrolment)
- real GDP per capita

Real GDP per capita is the GDP per capita of a country converted into US dollars on the basis of the purchasing-power parity of the currency of the country. It is assessed by calculating the number of units of a currency required to purchase the same representative basket of goods and services that a US dollar would buy in the USA.

Table 11.5 shows a selected sample from the *Human Development Report* (2004) for 177 countries in the world. It includes the component parts of the HDI and highlights variations between the different indicators. The final column, showing

HDI rank	Country	Life expectancy, 2002 (years)	Educational attainment index	Real GDP per capita,2002 (US dollars)	HDI	Real GDP per capita rank minus HDI rank
1	Norway	79	0.99	36,600	0.956	1
2	Sweden	80	0.99	26,050	0.946	19
3	Australia	79	0.99	28,260	0.946	9
4	Canada	79	0.98	29,480	0.943	5
56	Bulgaria	71	0.91	7,130	0.796	10
57	Russia	67	0.95	8,230	0.795	3
58	Libya	73	0.87	7,570	0.794	6
59	Malaysia	73	0.83	9,120	0.793	-2
144	Democratic Republic of Congo	48	0.71	980	0.494	17
145	Lesotho	36	0.70	2420	0.493	-24
174	Mali	48	0.21	930	0.326	-11
175	Burkina Faso	46	0.16	1,100	0.302	-20
176	Niger	46	0.18	800	0.292	-8
177	Sierra Leone	34	0.39	520	0.273	-1

Table 11.5 Sample from the **Human Development Report**, *2004*

the difference between the key economic indicator of GDP per capita and the HDI rank, is important. A positive figure indicates that the HDI rank is higher than the GDP rank; a negative figure that it is lower.

Summary

In many ways, both PQLI and HDI measure poverty. In assessing the progress made in reducing global poverty, the *Human Development Report* (HDR) published by the UN notes that:

- in the past 50 years, poverty has fallen more than in the previous 500 years
- poverty has been reduced in some respects in almost all countries
- death rates of children in the LEDW have been cut by more than half since 1960
- malnutrition has declined by almost one-third since 1960
- since 1960, the proportion of children not in primary education has fallen from more than a half to less than a quarter

On the negative side, the HDR details that there are still substantial problems, including:

- more than one-quarter of all people living in the LEDW still live in poverty, with more than 1.3 billion living on less than $1 a day
- nearly 1 billion people are illiterate
- some 840 million people go hungry or face food insecurity
- more than 1.2 billion people lack access to safe drinking water
- women are disproportionately poor, with half a million women in the LEDW dying in childbirth each year

A development continuum?

Global inequalities are no accident of history. They have developed over hundreds of years. Rostow (an American economist) proposed a model that shows that all countries pass through the same historical stages of economic development and

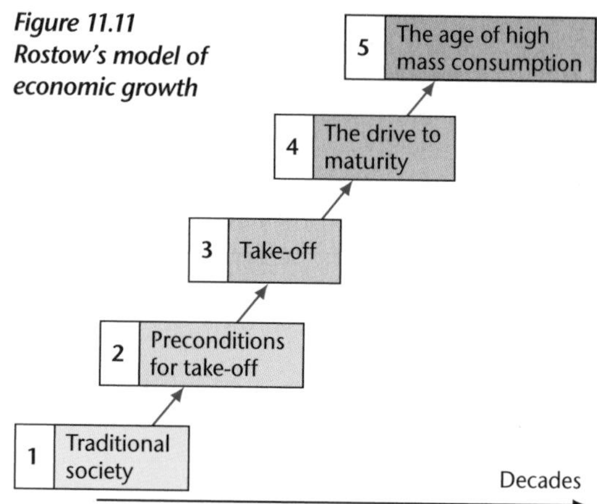

Figure 11.11 Rostow's model of economic growth

that developing countries are simply at an earlier stage in this progression.

There are five stages in the model:

- **Stage 1 Traditional society** The first stage is a subsistence economy based largely on agriculture, with limited technology and capital to process raw materials or to develop manufacturing industries. The UK was in this stage up to around the end of the seventeenth century.
- **Stage 2 Preconditions for take-off** With an injection of investment, agriculture has the possibility of becoming more commercialised. Extractive industries also begin to develop. Technological developments cause a growth in infrastructure, with the development of a transport system. A single industry begins to dominate the economy. This was the case in the UK around the middle of the eighteenth century.
- **Stage 3 Take-off** Manufacturing industries grow rapidly with growth concentrated in one or two regions. Improvements in the transport system continue, together with some progress in improving social conditions. Employment in agriculture declines with increased efficiency and a rise in manufacturing. Investment begins to rise to above 10% of GDP. The UK was in this stage in the early part of the nineteenth century.
- **Stage 4 The drive to maturity** This is a period of self-sustaining growth, with economic growth beginning to spread to all parts of the country. An increasing number of manufacturing industries develop and expand. All this is linked to increased urbanisation. The UK reached this stage in the middle of the nineteenth century.
- **Stage 5 The age of high mass consumption** At this stage there is massive expansion of tertiary services with a corresponding decline in manufacturing. The UK reached this stage in the middle of the twentieth century.

This model is now regarded as too simplistic and too heavily based on the experiences of countries in Europe and North America. Other economic theories have suggested that there are no obvious linear stages of development — it is more to do with capital growth through savings and government planning.

Population policies

A variety of social policies aimed at the control of population growth have been established around the world:

- Policies that aim to tackle the problem of rapid population growth by reducing fertility are known as **anti-natalist**. An example is the Chinese one-child policy (see case study, page 351). In most cases, the use of family-planning programmes forms the main strategy.
- For economic and political reasons, a few countries have **pro-natalist** policies designed to increase population. Examples include France after the Second

World War and Russia and Romania in the 1980s (see case study, page 352). These policies may be either voluntary or imposed on the people.

- Other countries try to manage population numbers by controlling immigration (e.g. Australia and the USA) or by encouraging emigration (e.g. the Philippines) or transmigration (e.g. Indonesia, see case study, page 354).
- Many countries that do not have population policies try to influence fertility indirectly through fiscal measures such as child allowances and tax concessions for young married couples.

Case study The Chinese one-child policy

One of the most documented population-control policies has been the Chinese one-child policy. During the second half of the twentieth century the Chinese government became concerned about population growth. There were two main reasons for this:

- the Chinese wanted to avoid a malthusian-type disaster in the future
- they realised that Chinese people could only have a rising living standard if the population was controlled

Chinese population policies have gone through a number of stages:

1950–59 The philosophy of the government under Chairman Mao was that 'a large population gives a strong nation'. The government encouraged people to have children for the good of the country. In 1959, there was a serious famine and 20 million people died.

1960–73 After the famine there was a population boom. The population increased by 55 million (equivalent to the population of the UK) every year. Nothing was done to reduce the spiralling birth rate.

1974–79 There was a policy change and people were encouraged to reduce the birth rate by the slogan '*wan-xi-shao*' (later, longer, fewer):

- later marriages
- longer gaps between children
- fewer children

1979–90 The *wan-xi-shao* policy did not work well and the population went on increasing. In 1979 the government introduced the one-child policy which set very strict limits on who was allowed to have children, and when. Strong pressure was put on women to use contraception. Special family-planning workers in every work-place, and 'granny police' in housing areas, were instructed to make sure women were practising contraception, and to report on any suspicious or unauthorised pregnancies. Enforced abortions and sterilisation became common. The policy was very successful in urban areas, but less so in rural areas where disobedience was more common. A disturbing effect of the policy was the practice of female infanticide. Couples wanted sons and so many baby girls were killed or 'disappeared'. The dominance of male babies also led to the spoilt 'little emperor' syndrome — the one child had no brothers or sisters and the attention of the extended family fell on him.

1990 onwards The one-child policy has been relaxed slightly. This is partly because it was so difficult to enforce, and because the Chinese government was concerned about the economic implications of a population in which there were far more older people than younger ones. In addition the revolution in global communication systems (the internet, satellite phones) has opened up the country to much greater social influence from the West. In more remote parts of the country the policy is still being encouraged. For example, the authorities in Guangdong, the state capital, ordered 20,000 abortions and sterilisations by the end of 2001 in the mountainous region of Huaiji.

Case study Pro-natalist policies in Romania, 1960s–1980s

Under Communist President Ceauşescu, the political system in Romania made long-range planning the basis of economic growth and demographic trends took on particular significance. As development proceeded, it became apparent that the country was approaching zero population growth, which worried a government that needed a growing workforce to support industrialisation. The government responded in 1966 by prohibiting abortion on demand and introducing other pro-natalist policies to increase birth rates.

Government policies in the 1960s

Men and women who remained childless after the age of 25, whether married or single, were liable for a special tax amounting to between 10 and 20% of their incomes. The government also made divorce much more difficult. By government decree, a marriage could be dissolved only in exceptional cases. The ruling was rigidly enforced. Only 28 divorces were allowed nationwide in 1967, compared with 26,000 the previous year.

Family allowances paid by the state were raised, with each additional child bringing a small increase. Monetary awards were granted to mothers, beginning with the birth of the third child. In addition, income tax for parents of three or more children was reduced by 30%.

Contraceptives were not manufactured in Romania and all legal importation of them was stopped, so birth control was difficult, and abortion was no longer available.

Not surprisingly, these policies had an immediate impact, and the number of live births rose from 274,000 in 1966 to 528,000 in 1967 — an increase of 93%. Legal abortions fell just as dramatically with only 52,000 performed in 1967, compared with more than 1 million in 1965. This success was due in part to the presence of police in hospitals to ensure that no illegal abortions were carried out.

The 1980s

The Ceauşescu regime took more aggressive steps in the 1980s. By 1983, the birth rate had fallen to 14.3 per 1,000, the rate of annual increase in population had dipped to 3.7 per 1,000 and the number of abortions (421,386) again exceeded the number of live births (321,489). Ceauşescu complained that only some 9% of the abortions performed had the necessary medical justification. In 1984, the legal age for marriage was lowered to 15 years for women and additional taxes were levied on childless individuals over 25 years of age. Doctors and nurses came under increasing pressure, especially after 1985, when 'demographic command units' were set up to ensure that all women were medically examined at their place of work. By 1985, to qualify for an abortion a woman had to have had five children, with all five still under her care, or be over 45 years of age.

Despite the extreme measures taken by the regime to combat the decline in fertility, there was only a slight increase in birth rates, from 14.4 per 1,000 in 1983 to 16 per 1,000 in 1985. After more than two decades of draconian anti-abortion regulation and expenditure on material incentives, Romanian birth rates were only a fraction higher than those in neighbouring countries.

The regime continued its crusade to raise birth rates, using a more subliminal approach. In 1986, mass media campaigns were launched, extolling the virtues of the large families of the past and of family life in general. Less subtle were the pronouncements that procreation was the patriotic duty and moral obligation of all citizens. The campaign called for competition among *judete* (counties) for the highest birth rates and even encouraged single women to have children, despite the fact that illegitimacy carried a considerable social stigma.

Following an uprising in 1989, Ceauşescu was arrested and executed, and his regime came to a dramatic end.

Examples of national policies

Thailand

In 1969, women in Thailand averaged 6.5 children each, 16% of the population used contraception and population growth was 3% a year. The government tried to reduce the birth rate through a nationwide family-planning programme that began in 1970. It included free contraception, trained family-planning specialists and government campaigns, especially among rural communities. By 1999, contraceptives were being used by 72% of people, women averaged 1.7 children and population growth was only 0.8% a year. The policy is community-based, rather than coercive.

For more information on population policies in Thailand, see page 115.

The Philippines

Opposition to birth control from the Roman Catholic Church (83% of the population are Catholic) has countered government encouragement of contraceptive use in the Philippines. In 1999, only 47% of the population used contraceptives and the population growth rate was 1.7% per year. Women now average 3.6 children each and the population is expected to double by 2027. The government is seeking to increase food production through the Green Revolution, while at the same time not discouraging the out-migration of labour to Singapore, Malaysia and the UK.

Migration controls and schemes

The causes and consequences of migration have been covered in Chapter 4. In some parts of the world, migration is a means by which populations can be managed, either by preventing people entering a country (e.g. immigration controls on the USA–Mexico border), or by seeking to move people from an over-populated area to an under-populated area (e.g. transmigration in Indonesia, see case study, page 354).

Immigration controls

The border between the USA and Mexico

The border between the USA and Mexico is the most closely monitored in the world. Every day, 800,000 people arrive in the USA from Mexico. In 2001, over 300 million two-way border crossings took place at 43 crossing points. In the same year there were over 19 million pedestrian crossings in Texas alone.

There are currently around 9,150 border patrol agents working along the 3,200 km border. After the events of 9/11, President Bush asked Congress to approve funding for an additional 280 border-patrol agents in 2002.

The US Immigration and Naturalization Service (INS) has four operations to apprehend unauthorised border crossers as part of its southwest border-control strategy: Operation Hold-the-Line in El Paso, Operation Gatekeeper in San Diego, Operation Rio Grande in El Paso and Operation Safeguard in Tucson. These operations use a combination of electronic detection devices and heat sensors, night vision telescopes, ground vehicles and aircraft, including Blackhawk helicopters.

Case study Transmigration in Indonesia

Transmigration is a scheme by which the Indonesian government provides transportation to a new settlement site in a less populated part of the country. In addition, a house and a farming plot are provided, together with basic infrastructure and a living allowance intended to support the transmigrant family, usually for the first 18 months.

Transmigration is not a new policy. It was begun under Dutch colonial rule during the early twentieth century and was taken over by the Indonesian government after independence. The three main goals of transmigration were:

- to move millions of Indonesians from the densely populated inner islands (Java, Bali, Madura) to the less densely populated outer islands, to achieve a more balanced demographic development
- to alleviate poverty, by providing land and new opportunities for poor landless settlers to generate income
- to exploit more effectively the potential of the outer islands

Objections to the policy

In the 1980s, transmigration increased dramatically and large numbers of people were resettled, mainly to Kalimantan, Sumatra, Sulawesi, Maluku and West Papua (Irian Jaya). Massive financial support from the World Bank and bilateral donors (other countries) helped to boost the programme. The expansion of the programme alerted environmental and human rights critics both inside and outside Indonesia who exposed transmigration as a development fraud and an environmental disaster. Important criticisms of the transmigration policy have included:

- Indonesia's outer islands contain 10% of the world's remaining rainforest and transmigration has led to loss of forest.
- Resettlement is political and intended to control the indigenous population of the outer islands (e.g. Irian Jaya, East Timor, Kalimantan).
- Transmigration has violated customary land rights and is aimed at the forced assimilation of indigenous people and forest dwellers.
- With average resettlement costs of US$7,000 per family in the mid-1980s, the programme has been an economic disaster, increasing Indonesia's national debt.
- Transmigration failed to reach its core goals. Rather than alleviating poverty, the programme redistributed poverty. Most transmigrants were actually worse off in their new locations because of inadequate planning and site preparation, poor access to markets and neglect of the soil and water necessary for a prosperous agricultural economy.
- Transmigration has made virtually no dent in the population pressure in Java.

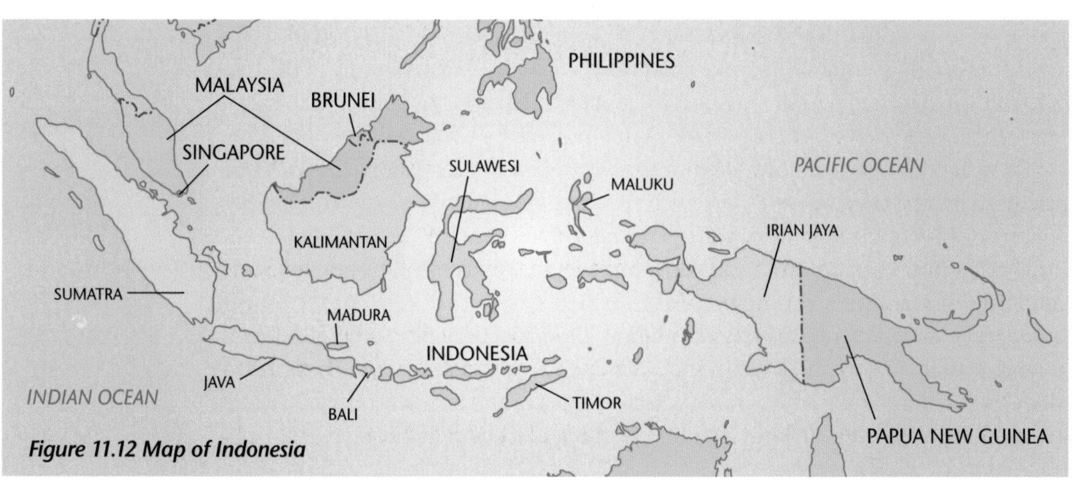

Figure 11.12 Map of Indonesia

Recent changes

The course of transmigration policies has changed dramatically over recent years. Foreign financial assistance switched to a new strategy to improve the existing resettlement projects. The financial crisis which hit Indonesia in mid-1997, and the struggle to rebuild the economy and transform the corrupt political system, have resulted in major changes in the transmigration programme.

Today the picture is both reassuring and alarming. On the positive side, the official transmigration programme appears to have been quietly dropped by the current government. Forced transmigration — so damaging to indigenous communities in receiving areas, and to those Javanese peasants who had to move out after losing their own lands to development — is no longer possible.

However, there is a real danger that transmigration in a new guise may take over where the old programme left off. Both the central government and the newly empowered local governments are relying on exploitation of natural resources — logging, mining, industrial timber and pulpwood plantations, oil palm, and industrial shrimp farming — to generate revenue. Large-scale commercial exploitation of these resources, aimed at export markets, is being actively encouraged by Indonesia's international creditors, led by the IMF and the World Bank. If this continues, the demand for labour in areas of low population will increase, fuelling a new migration — and possibly transmigration — boom.

Mark Edwards/Still Pictures

Photograph 11.3 Migrants from Java working on their new home in the former rainforest

In 2000, over 1.6 million immigrants were caught at the border, 100,000 more than in 1999. This number includes those who may have been caught several times.

Elsewhere in the world

Elsewhere in the world, policies that have been introduced to deal with the numbers of migrants include:

- limiting the number of migrant workers at source — for example by making it more difficult to satisfy visa requirements (prospective east European migrants to the UK require a business plan)
- insisting on pre-boarding arrangements — for example a return ticket
- preventing illegal crossings — for example sea patrols between Florida and Cuba
- returning ineligible **asylum seekers** immediately and requiring the carrier to pay for the return

- fast-track procedures to enable entry for genuine asylum seekers
- the use of holding bases in third countries where checks are made on visas — as used by Germany in collaboration with Bulgaria, Poland, Romania and the Czech Republic

The resource response: food surpluses in the MEDW

One of the main causes of food surpluses in the MEDW has been the Common Agricultural Policy (CAP) of the EU. Before the Second World War, Europe imported a lot of food from North America, Argentina, Australia and New Zealand. It was produced more cheaply there and European farmers could not compete. Following the war there were severe food shortages across the continent. When the European Economic Community (the forerunner of the current EU) was established in 1957, one of the main aims was to establish a common policy on agriculture and fishing in order to boost and maintain food production.

The Common Agricultural Policy

The basic aims of the CAP were:

- to increase agricultural productivity within member states
- to ensure a fair standard of living for farmers
- to stabilise agricultural markets within and between member states
- to ensure reasonable consumer prices
- to maintain employment in agricultural areas

These aims replaced existing national agricultural policies and they have often caused conflict between member states. Under the CAP, farmers were given guaranteed prices for their produce, known as the **intervention price**. If world prices fell below this, then the intervention price was paid to farmers, encouraging them to maximise production. This created **surpluses** in a range of products that were sometimes known as 'mountains' or 'lakes'. Over the last 40 years, products in surplus have included cereals, butter, beef, apples, oranges, tobacco and wine.

Agriculture provides only 5% of the EU's total income, but at one time 70% of its budget went on supporting agriculture. The net gainers from the CAP tended to be countries such as France and those in southern Europe with small, less efficient farms. The net losers tended to be those countries with a smaller agricultural sector but with efficient farms, such as the UK. By the mid-1980s it was accepted that the CAP had brought great benefits, such as close to self-sufficiency in food production, but it had also caused problems, including:

- the surplus production detailed above
- over-intensive farming, which was damaging the environment, especially the use of fertilisers
- growing tension between the EU and some of its main trading partners,

for example the USA, Australia and New Zealand, over the impact of EU-subsidised produce on world markets
- large, prosperous farmers benefiting more than the medium to small farmers — this has caused many to leave the land and migrate to urban areas

CAP reform

In 1992, radical reforms to the system were introduced, in which:
- the support for cereals, beef and sheep was reduced
- quotas were introduced, particularly in dairy farming
- there was to be an increase in set-aside policies
- environmentally sensitive farming was to be encouraged, decreasing the use of fertilisers and pesticides
- early retirement plans for farmers aged 55 and above were to be implemented

Although surpluses fell dramatically through the mid-1990s, several member governments were still not happy with the way in which the CAP operated. Germany, which was the CAP's main paymaster, was particularly anxious to reduce its net contributions. There was also the problem of accommodating the agricultural economies of those countries of central and eastern Europe that were intent on joining the EU.

Germany and the UK were aware that the CAP could not sustain this level of funding without financial problems. A move to curb open-ended production-based subsidies was inevitable, to prevent the collapse of the CAP. The other major factor driving reform was the need for the EU to comply with World Trade Organization (WTO) negotiations to work towards freer trade in food commodities. Import tariffs and export subsidies needed to be cut, and European farmers forced to rely more on world prices. Consumers in Europe should then benefit from a shift in emphasis from agricultural production to 'rural stewardship'.

These reforms, which were agreed in March 1999, did not go as far as many wanted. Some member states voted to reduce the level of changes, claiming that the effect on their agriculture and farming communities would be too great. In 2002, a new plan was put forward by the European Commission to switch funds gradually from intensive production to schemes that promote rural life, safer food, animal welfare and a greener environment. Farmers will no longer be subsidised on the basis of crop area or head of livestock, ending the incentive that led to over-production. It is intended that no farming operation will receive more than £200,000 per year, ending the anomaly by which 80% of CAP funds went to the big farmers, while the smallest producers received nothing.

These plans were adopted by EU farm ministers in June 2003. The new CAP is geared towards consumers and taxpayers, while giving EU farmers the freedom to produce what the market wants. In applying the new regulations in the UK in early 2005, the DEFRA website informed farmers that:

> The CAP reform will simplify arrangements for subsidy payments by replacing ten major CAP payment schemes with one new single payment. Farmers will have greater freedom to farm to the demands of the market, as subsidies will be decoupled from production. At the same time, environmentally friendly practices will be better acknowledged and rewarded.

Case study Rural development in Sicily, Italy

The EU rural development programme for Sicily aims to strengthen the competitiveness of its rural areas by encouraging development across the agricultural sector, while being compatible with the need to protect the landscape and the agricultural ecosystem. The total cost of the programme is €561 million. The programme complements the rural development measures included in the regional development programme for Sicily (Objective 1 of the Structural Funds).

The current situation

Some data about the current situation in Sicily are given in Table 11.6.

Figure 11.13
Location map of Sicily

Population	Approximately 5.3 million
Total agricultural area	1.84 million hectares (of which 51.6 % are less favoured areas)
Utilised agricultural area	1.52 million hectares
Number of holdings	330,000
Agricultural employment rate	Approximately 12.1%

Table 11.6
Sicily statistics

As the third most important agricultural region in Italy, Sicily is faced with various difficulties, including:

- the inadequate size of the average farm
- the ageing population
- rural–urban migration
- an inadequate water-supply system
- frequent fires
- the high cost of transport, because it is an island
- lack of diversification in production
- the low added-value of processed products
- an increase in competition for Mediterranean products
- problems in meeting the hygiene and health standards of the EU

Among the advantages of Sicily are:

- the attractions of the natural environment and climate, which favour the development of year-round tourism and agritourism
- the possibility of developing environmentally sound agriculture (in particular, organic production) and activities related to agriculture
- the growing demand for quality products, particularly fruit and vegetables
- the existence of animal husbandry that is well-adapted to the local conditions

Priority measures, 2000–06

The programme has four priorities.

Priority 1 Agrienvironment

This involves encouraging agricultural production and soil management techniques, while ensuring the economic viability of the holdings by awarding premiums for activities such as:

- integrated agriculture — for example rotating crops by alternating between a cereal and another crop, banning chemical weedkillers and reducing the use of nitrate and phosphate fertilisers by 25%
- organic arable and livestock farming, including the development of systems for extensive livestock farming (meadows and pastures)

- landscape conservation (hedges, copses and ponds), the preservation of traditional terrace cultivation and set-aside to create humid zones and scrub

Priority 2 Compensatory allowances in disadvantaged areas

The compensatory allowances given to farmers (in which priority is given by the EU to those who farm in mountainous areas and on the minor islands, such as Sicily) aim to maintain a viable rural community while encouraging environmentally sound production methods.

Priority 3 Arable land re-afforestation

Payments for the costs of re-afforestation and annual maintenance premiums are given for two types of re-afforestation — timber production and the creation of woodland. This measure aims to diversify the economic activities of the holdings while fighting soil erosion and damage.

Priority 4 Aid for early retirement

Payments are given for agricultural workers to encourage the younger generation to take over holdings.

Case study *Precision farming in Oxfordshire, UK*

Precision farming is a form of intensive arable farming that is thought to be more environmentally friendly than other methods. It uses the most modern technology to help farmers work with the natural environment, rather than against it. It depends on knowing the precise conditions in each part of each field. Each part then has to be farmed to gain the biggest yield for the smallest amounts of inputs (fertiliser and pesticides).

Precision farming both cuts costs and reduces damage to the environment — a win–win situation. By ensuring that fertilisers and pesticides are applied in just the right places, farmers reduce their inputs without reducing yields. Indeed, yields may be increased.

How does technology help the precision farmer?

Precision farming requires detailed information about each field. Modern technology allows the following to be used:

- satellite technology including GPS (global positioning systems) and infrared imaging
- sensors in a combine harvester to measure yields
- computers in the cabs of tractors and harvesters to collect data
- computers in farm offices to analyse data
- precision controls on seed and fertiliser spreaders, linked to computers in tractor cabs

How does precision farming operate?

- Farmers first need to learn more about the potential of the soil in each part of each field. Therefore, yield mapping at the time of harvest is the first step.
- Areas of soil that can be improved in a traditional way, for example by adding farmyard manure to improve soil structure, are tackled first.
- Areas that need targeted inputs, for example the liming of patches of acidic soil, are identified and dealt with.
- Land beside hedgerows that has a low yield (due to shade or the roots of the hedges taking some of the nutrients) can be left as an uncultivated strip and set-aside payments claimed from the EU.
- High inputs of fertilisers are concentrated in those areas known to have high yields, which are often in the main body of the field.
- By using satellite imagery, it is possible to identify areas with a high coverage of weeds. These can be targeted and sprayed early, ensuring the minimum amounts of chemicals are used.

The overall aim of precision farming is to produce food intensively, cheaply and with minimum damage to the environment.

Organic farming

Organic farming is expanding in the UK. To be recognised as organic, farmers must register with the Soil Association, which sets certain standards. Farmers have to be able to prove that they do not use any inputs of artificial chemicals (except those that are acceptable to the Soil Association) and have not done so for a certain number of years. Instead of artifical fertilisers, organic farmers use animal and green manures and mineral fertilisers such as fish- and bone-meal. Pesticides are not used either — farmers weed the fields instead of using herbicides, and use biological control instead of insecticides. The farming is still intensive, but it involves more crop rotation and more use of fallow periods than conventional farming practices. Once a farm achieves organic status it can charge a premium for food that is guaranteed free from artificial chemicals.

The advantages of organic farming are that:

- the increased organic matter in the soil enables it to retain more moisture during dry periods and allows better drainage during wet spells
- soil erosion or exhaustion are less likely, because as well as more organic matter, there are more soil fauna, such as earthworms
- it should be less harmful to the environment — for example eutrophication in rivers due to nitrate runoff is less likely
- it is kinder to wildlife because pesticides, which kill insects and birds, are not used
- it is less harmful to humans, both farm workers and consumers, because fewer chemicals are used

The disadvantages are that:

- yields can drop considerably in the initial period, compared with conventional farming
- weeds can increase and need to be controlled by hand labour
- wildlife can be present in excessive numbers — some organic farmers have problems with rabbits, badgers and birds of prey such as buzzards and hawks
- the produce is more expensive to buy than that from conventional farming

Case study The genetic modification of crops

The latest revolution in plant breeding is a result of genetic modification (GM) of seeds. All living things contain DNA, a complex molecule that holds a genetic code for each plant or animal. DNA contains the instructions, inherited from the previous generation, for building the new organism. Genetic modification involves taking some of the DNA from one species and adding it to that of another species. When a plant is genetically modified, one or more characteristics of the donor species are transferred to the new plant.

How GM works

Some examples of the methods by which new varieties can be developed include:

- Adding the appropriate genes of a herbicide-resistant weed to a wheat seed to produce a type of wheat that is not harmed by herbicides. A field of wheat can then be sprayed to kill all the weeds without affecting the crop.
- Adding the genes of a species resistant to a particular pest to soya bean seed, so that the plant is not damaged by that pest.

- Adding a gene from a plant that grows well in an arid environment to the DNA of a rice plant. This would produce a plant that could grow in drier areas than traditional types of rice plant.

Arguments in favour

Those in favour of GM crops claim that the newly-engineered crops could solve many food shortages around the world, and also reduce the input of chemicals into farming. Trials of GM soya beans and maize have done well in the USA. Much of the soya imported into the UK and used in animal feeds is GM.

China has also invested a great deal into research of GM rice and cotton crops. Rice is the staple diet for its huge population, and cotton is an essential raw material for its clothing industry. Such developments are therefore important both for feeding its population and for improving its level of development. It is no surprise therefore that there is little opposition to GM crops in China.

Arguments against

The same cannot be said for the UK. Trials have been conducted here since 1999, but they have been very controversial. Critics of GM have the following objections:

- the pollen from GM plants may pollinate nearby plants and crops, spreading the modifications in an uncontrolled way
- crops on organic farms might be contaminated by the pollen from GM crops, causing the farms to lose their organic status
- the long-term effects of GM on human health are unknown

Protestors have destroyed GM field trials in the UK because of these fears. Campaigners want GM crops to be banned completely and point to other agricultural innovations that have had serious health effects, such as BSE. On the other hand, some farmers and companies see a great opportunity to make profits from GM crops. The UK government is encouraging further testing in laboratories, along with carefully-controlled field trials. In the meantime, any GM crops that are sold to the public have to be clearly labelled.

The future

At a global scale, GM production is continuing in countries such as the USA and China. The international seed companies and food manufacturers are unlikely to be influenced by protestors in one country. Similarly, within a free-trade environment such as the EU, it will be increasingly difficult for governments to regulate the import of GM seeds or products.

In LEDCs, farmers may well face similar problems as those caused by the Green Revolution. GM seeds will only be available from the large seed companies, and it will not be possible to save seeds from one year to the next because many of the crops have been designed to produce infertile seeds. Poor farmers will not be able to compete with their richer neighbours.

Consequences of agricultural change in the UK

Only around 2% of the UK workforce is employed in farming. However, of the 88% of England that is classed as countryside, most is used for arable or pastoral farming. Farmers are, therefore, described as the 'custodians of the countryside'. They are charged with the responsibility of managing the environmental sustainability of the landscape. Changes in farming practices, some caused by diversification and environmental schemes from national and EU governments, have had a major impact on the rural landscape. Table 11.7 identifies a number of these changes and provides further detail of their impact on the landscape.

Table 11.7 Impacts on the landscape of changes in farming and agricultural practices

Change in farming practice or agricultural scheme	Impact on the landscape
Plant and animal breeding to produce higher yielding varieties	Some agricultural land has become redundant and available for other uses, e.g. afforestation of uplands
Use of large quantities of fertiliser, especially nitrates, to increase yields	Problems of increased pollution of watercourses; eutrophication
Use of pesticides (herbicides and insecticides) to reduce crop losses	Loss of biodiversity of herb meadows; killing of 'weeds' which include wild flowers; many improved pastures lack diversity
Improvements in farm technology (e.g. more effective driers and harvesters)	Removal of hedgerows to create larger fields for use of large machinery; increased arable farming has led to massive soil erosion as cover is removed
From 1988, set-aside payments from the EU	Reduction in the cropping area, allowing land to be used to create more natural areas
Introduction of new crops	Fields of industrial crops, e.g. oilseed rape (yellow), linseed (blue) and burdock (purple)
From 1989, the Farm Woodland Scheme	Encourages the planting of broad-leaved woodland on land currently used for agriculture, to enhance the landscape and provide new habitats to increase biodiversity
The Countryside Stewardship Scheme (1991)	Aims to restore and conserve traditional landscapes and wildlife habitats, such as traditional drystone walls and hay meadows
The Moorland Scheme (1995)	Protects heather moorland by paying farmers to reduce sheep-stocking densities
The Farm and Conservation Grant Scheme (1995)	Provides grants for planting hedgerows or establishing shelterbelts on farms
The England Rural Development Programme (2000)	A 7-year programme that further supports the above schemes; encourages farm diversification including tourist and craft activities on farms; provides grants to support farm businesses; provides training to improve expertise of farm and forestry workers

The resource response: food shortages in the LEDW

Problems of traditional farming systems

In the LEDW, changes in traditional farming systems have been largely brought about by population changes and migration to urban areas. In most rural areas there is continued high population growth, with many people living below the poverty line. This is particularly true in sub-Saharan Africa, where most of the world's poorest countries are concentrated. A vicious cycle of decline sets in that is hard to break (Figure 11.14). In some southern African countries the development of HIV/AIDS has had an enormous impact, with many rural areas in terminal decline (Figure 11.15).

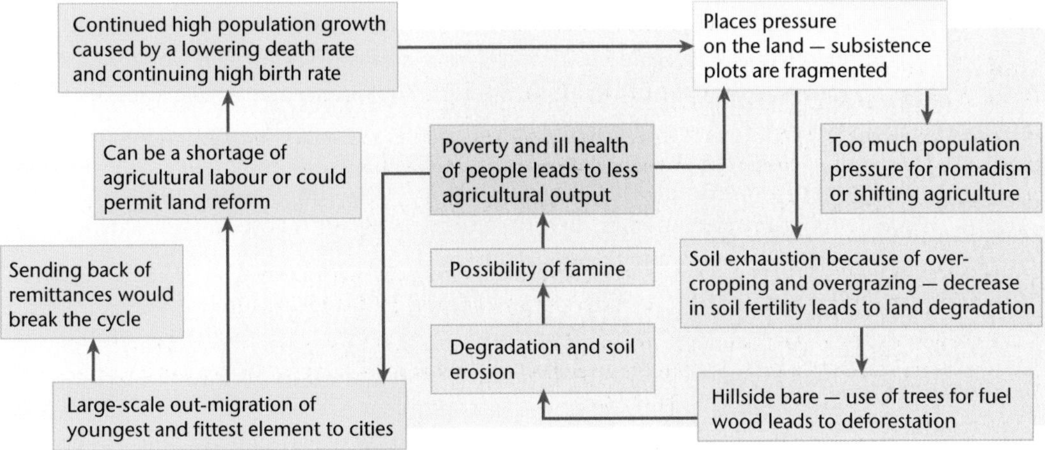

Figure 11.14 The cycle of rural decline

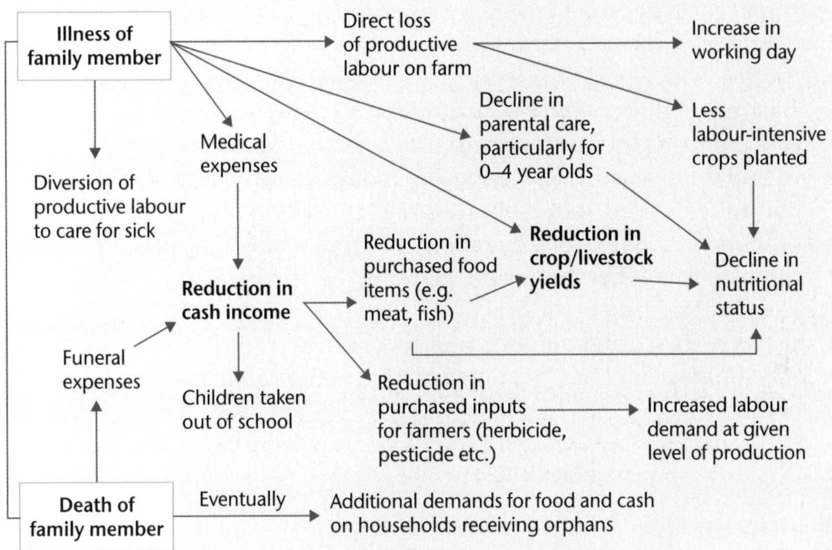

Figure 11.15 Effects of AIDS on families in Africa

To the above can be added political pressures, including:

- the demand to grow large quantities of **cash crops** for export at the expense of maintaining the supplies of food for subsistence, for example in Zimbabwe and Brazil (see case study, page 366)
- the demand to make money from enterprises such as mining (New Guinea) or building a mega-dam (India) or from mass tourism (Dominican Republic)
- **political instability** brought about by civil war, with vast areas of a country destroyed or land-mined and millions of people killed (Rwanda/Burundi)

Additionally, rapid **rural–urban migration** has had a major effect on rural areas. The benefits of this migration include relieving population pressure and possibly allowing land reform to take place. It halts excessive fragmentation of plots as they are passed down through the generations. Those who migrate may return for key harvest seasons and bring with them, or send, remittances from their new jobs.

These payments can provide new facilities or new enterprises in villages, as has happened in Bangladesh. However, as it is mostly young men who migrate, there can be a shortage of labour to work the subsistence farms. The farm work is left to the very young or the very old.

As urbanisation occurs, there is increasing urban sprawl and pressure on the land, for example at Giza, near Cairo. Also, the growing urban areas place enormous demands on their rural hinterlands for fuelwood (for charcoal), food and water and waste disposal sites.

The Green Revolution

The package of agricultural improvements known as the Green Revolution has been seen as the answer to the food problem in many parts of the LEDW. India was one of the first countries to benefit, when a high-yielding variety seed programme (HVP) commenced in 1966. In terms of production it was the turning point for Indian agriculture, which had virtually reached stagnation. The HVP introduced new hybrid varieties of five cereals — wheat, rice, maize, sorghum and millet. With the exception of rice, they were drought-resistant. All were responsive to fertilisers and had a shorter growing season than the traditional varieties they replaced. Advantages of the Green Revolution are that:

- yields of the new varieties are two to four times greater than those of traditional varieties
- the shorter growing season has allowed the introduction of an extra crop
- farming incomes have increased, allowing the purchase of machinery, better seeds, fertilisers and pesticides
- the diet of rural communities is now more varied
- local infrastructure has been upgraded to accommodate a stronger market approach
- employment has been created in industries supplying farms with inputs
- areas under irrigation have increased in number

Disadvantages of the Green Revolution are that:

- high inputs of fertiliser and pesticide are required to optimise production, which is costly in both economic and environmental terms
- in some areas, rural debt has risen sharply as farmers borrow money to pay for these inputs
- high-yielding varieties (HYVs) require more weed control and are often more susceptible to pests and disease
- middle- and high-income farmers have often benefited much more than those on low incomes, thus widening the income gap in rural communities
- increased rural–urban migration has often been the result
- mechanisation has increased rural unemployment
- some HYVs have inferior tastes
- salinisation (soils becoming increasingly saline) has increased along with the expansion of irrigation
- the dependence of nations on **transnationals** (which supply the seeds, the fertiliser, the pesticides, the machinery and the markets) has increased significantly

Recent concerns

In recent years, a much greater concern has arisen about the Green Revolution. In the 1990s, nutritionists noticed that even in countries where average food intake had risen, incapacitating diseases associated with mineral and vitamin deficiencies remained commonplace and in some cases had actually increased. A UN report linked some of these deficiencies to the increased consumption of Green Revolution crops. It seems that the HYV crops are usually low in minerals and vitamins. The new crops have displaced the local fruits, vegetables and legumes that traditionally supplied vitamins and minerals in people's diets. Therefore, the diet of many people in the LEDW is now extremely low in zinc, iron, iodine and vitamin A. This threatens to lock people into a cycle of ill-health, low productivity and underdevelopment. The International Food Policy Research Institute has suggested that there should be an effort to breed new crop strains for the LEDW that are both high-yielding and rich in vitamins and nutrients. The issue here is that in order to do this, scientists may enter the uncertain world of genetically modified crops (see case study, page 360).

Case study Farming in Bangladesh

The economy of Bangladesh is dependent on agriculture — rice, wheat and jute. About 84% of the population live in rural areas and are directly or indirectly engaged in a wide range of agricultural activities. The agriculture sector is the single largest contributor to income and employment generation. It accounted for 32% of total GDP in 2002 and is responsible for 63% of total national employment. In 2002, agricultural exports of primary products constituted 10% of total exports. Agriculture is a vital element in the country's struggle to achieve self-sufficiency in food production, reduce rural poverty and foster sustainable economic development.

Opportunities and constraints

The opportunities are that:

- the agricultural sector is the single largest contributor to GDP
- the crop production system is highly labour intensive and there is an abundance of labour in the country
- agriculture is the largest source of employment for skilled and unskilled labour
- a favourable natural environment exists throughout the year for crop production
- different crops and agricultural commodities are the main sources of nutrition

The constraints are that:

- agriculture is dependent on the vagaries of nature and is risky
- the availability of land for farming is decreasing
- there is widespread poverty among the population engaged in agriculture
- there is a lack of required capital for agricultural activities
- there is insufficient appropriate technology
- there is no guarantee of fair prices for agricultural commodities because of the underdeveloped marketing system
- agricultural commodities are perishable and post-harvest losses are high
- there is limited knowledge about the nutritional value of agricultural commodities, including vegetables and fruits

The objectives of the Ministry of Agriculture for the future are to:

- establish policies, regulations and projects that will ensure sustainable food production
- achieve self-sufficiency in food-grain production through sustainable growth in rice and wheat production
- increase rural employment through the adoption of modern agricultural practices
- achieve low and stable food prices for consumers

and improve the nutritional status of the population

- establish policies that enable farmers to be responsive to domestic and world market opportunities
- provide high-quality infrastructure and government services that will enable farmers to grow and market products at low cost
- provide incentives to establish labour-intensive production and agro-based processing industries
- work with organisations such as Grameen to achieve greater self-determination for rural areas

Grameen

Grameen Bank was set up by Muhammad Yunus, an economics professor in Bangladesh, to allow poor men and women to have access to banking facilities. Its micro-credit schemes offer loans to groups of villagers which do not exploit them but help to develop their communities.

Grameen Telecom is a more recent development of the organisation which gives poor rural people access to telephone services. There is no adequate terrestrial phone system in rural Bangladesh and mobile phones are expensive. However, Grameen Telecom gives loans to individuals who are supported by a local group to buy a mobile phone. This individual then provides a commercial service to other villagers who pay for the calls they make. This village phone (VP) system works well and loans are quickly paid off by the profits made.

In addition Grameen has provided 'village computing kiosks' that allow local people to access computers and the internet. Thousands of educated young people in rural areas (mainly young women who would otherwise remain unemployed or have to move to squalid urban slums) have become computer-literate by taking courses at these kiosks.

Neil Cooper/Still Pictures

Photograph 11.4 Planting spinach in Bangladesh

They are then able to secure rural-based employment by working as subcontractors for national and international companies, doing data-entry and transcription work as well as writing simple computer software.

The kiosks have also enabled unemployed and underemployed labourers (both skilled and unskilled) in the rural areas of Bangladesh to search for jobs through the internet. In addition farmers can find the price of their produce anywhere in the country, or anywhere in the world, thus ensuring them a fair price.

Grameen already has kiosks in 37,000 Bangladeshi villages. On its website, Grameen is not reluctant to state its success: 'In short, it is our belief that Grameen is in a position to really make something happen — rather than simply talk'.

Case study Sugar cane production in Brazil

Sugar cane production in Brazil is once more showing signs of growth potential because:

- Trade in sugar cane is being eased. The subsidies that maintain sugar beet production and exports in the EU are being gradually reduced as a result of the Uruguay Round of GATT. In addition, there has been a reduction of tariff barriers on the entry of sugar into countries such as the USA and Japan.

- Environmental pressure in the MEDW for fuels from renewable and non-polluting sources to replace fossil fuels has created a new consumer market for fuel alcohol from sugar cane, particularly in the USA.
- China, the country with the world's largest population and the highest economic growth rates in the last two decades, still has very low per capita consumption of sugar. In the USA and the EU each inhabitant consumes 30 kg sugar per year; the Chinese consume less than 6 kg. There is therefore great potential for growth in exports to China.

Brazil is in a privileged position to meet demands for sugar and fuel alcohol. The country has two producing regions, with alternating harvests, so it is able to maintain its presence in the world market throughout the year. It has advanced technology for alcohol production from sugar cane. It has the lowest production costs in the world and still has potential for expansion of both the planted area and its productivity.

The northeastern region of Brazil, the traditional sugar producer, has been losing its relative position to São Paulo state in the south. Better soils, areas suitable for mechanised farming, heavy investment in research and a more regular climate have given São Paulo state much higher productivity than the northeast, with an average harvest of almost 80 kg ha^{-1}, compared to 60 kg ha^{-1} in the northeast.

São Paulo state's share of production is therefore increasing. It accounts for 80% of fuel alcohol production, compared to 6% in the northeast. The factories in São Paulo state produce over 50% of total domestic sugar, compared with only 30% in the northeastern factories.

Prospects for the alcohol fuel sector in Brazil are directly related to the future of alcohol-powered cars. A new generation of such cars entered production in Brazil in 2003. These 'flex-fuel' cars are capable of using pure alcohol, pure petrol or any blend of the two. In 2004, the first full year that 'flex-fuel' cars were on sale, they accounted for 18% of the Brazilian market. Brazil will be in a key position when other countries, such as the USA, seek to use more crop-based motor fuel.

However, to meet this demand, growth must occur, mainly in the flat areas of São Paulo state and in the new sugar areas of the Cerrado region in central Brazil. The Mato Grosso and the Minas Triangle are suitable for growing sugar and the northeastern region may even have a reduction in its planted area in the next 5 years.

Rural poverty in the LEDW

The *Human Development Report* in 2003 provided some depressing statistics about rural poverty in the LEDW:

- More than 1 billion people still struggle to survive on less than 1 US$ a day. Most of them also lack access to basic health services and safe drinking water.
- Globally, one child in five does not complete primary school. In sub-Saharan Africa, a child has only a one in three chance of completing primary school. One in four school-aged children in south Asia is not being educated.
- In much of the developing world, the HIV/AIDS pandemic continues to spread unchecked. More than 14 million children lost one or both parents to the disease in 2001 and the number of AIDS orphans is expected to double by 2010.
- Nearly 800 million people (15% of the world's population) suffer from chronic hunger. Under the Millennium Development Goals, the world community is striving to halve that percentage by 2015. However, if current trends continue, south Asia and sub-Saharan Africa will not meet that target.

- Half a million women die in pregnancy or childbirth each year — one every minute of every day. A woman in sub-Saharan Africa is 100 times more likely to die during pregnancy or in childbirth than is a woman in western Europe.

Much of the poverty in the LEDW occurs in rural areas. Figure 11.16 summarises the main effects of the cycle of poverty in subsistence farming economies, which stem from the inability of people to provide themselves with adequate food. There are long-term problems of malnourishment made worse by shorter-term disasters. Floods, drought, plagues of locusts and wars take place in many countries, particularly in Africa, at different times and in different years. These add to the endemic problems arising from low economic development.

Considerable debate takes place between development experts as to how best to raise living standards in the LEDW, particularly in remote rural areas where environmental conditions are harsh and constraints are enormous. Much government and World Bank aid has funded large capital projects (for example, mega-dams that are intended to be multi-purpose catalysts to regional development). In theory, the wealth that is generated by such **top-down** projects trickles down to the poorer peripheral areas. In fact, many of these projects make the lives of the rural poor worse, rather than better, and they have been severely criticised. **Bottom-up**, small-scale projects tend to work better at raising living standards in poor areas. This is because the development is initiated in consultation with local people and is more targeted to local needs. Bottom-up schemes:

- grant greater self-determination to rural areas by using communal decision making
- are often small scale and tailored to local needs
- use limited funding effectively to make a difference
- give priority to projects that serve basic needs — for example health and education
- give land to the people by land reform
- use external physical resources only when local resources are inadequate
- improve rural–urban and internal village communications
- mobilise local indigenous human resources to create employment and increase labour intensive activities
- emphasise the need to work with local environments and culture on development projects that are sustainable

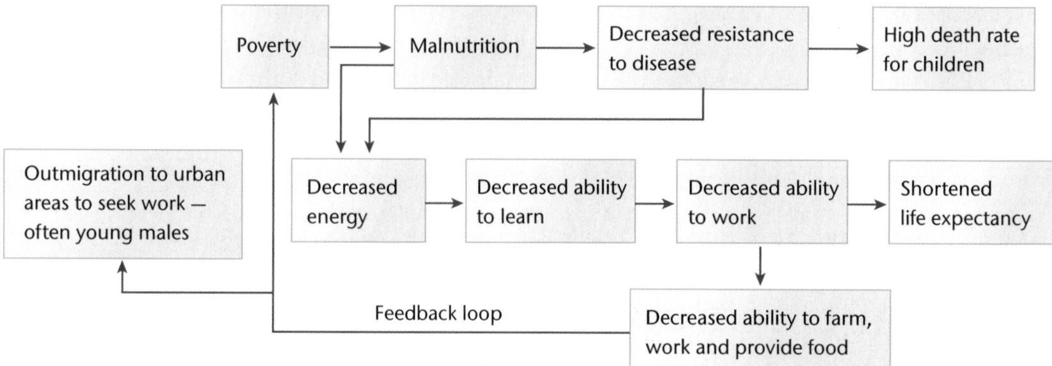

Figure 11.16 Effects of the cycle of poverty in subsistence farming economies

The emphasis of such schemes is on using **appropriate** or **intermediate technology**. The main features of appropriate technology are that:

- it is affordable for many villagers
- it involves local people in design
- it is constructed locally by local people
- it should be simple to build, small scale and appropriate to the needs of local communities
- it provides local employment
- it should be easy or cheap to repair and maintain
- it should cause limited damage to the environment
- it may use local materials
- it develops local skills
- it promotes self-sufficiency and self-reliance
- it often relies on renewable sources of energy — for example solar power or mini-hydro schemes
- it is low cost but is more efficient than traditional methods

Case study Appropriate technology

Each year, about 57 million women worldwide give birth without the help of a trained health worker. These births often take place at home, where the risk of infection is high. Some 1,600 women per day die from complications (usually infection) associated with pregnancy or childbirth. Around 2,600 newborns also die from infection each day. The clean-delivery kit is a simple approach to reducing these deaths. It helps women and newborns avoid life-threatening infections.

Over the past decade, the non-governmental organisation PATH has helped develop such kits in Bangladesh, Egypt and Nepal. Most kits contain a small bar of soap for washing hands, a plastic sheet to serve as the delivery surface, clean string for tying the umbilical cord, a new razor blade for cutting the cord and pictorial instructions that illustrate the sequence of delivery events and hand-washing.

Research and field-testing during development ensured the cultural acceptability of the kits and allowed PATH to customise them for local conditions. In Nepal, for example, it is traditional to cut the umbilical cord on a coin, for good luck. Out of respect for this custom, kits produced in Nepal contain a plastic rupee to serve as a clean cord-cutting surface.

Once the kits were in use in Nepal, PATH conducted interviews and role-plays to gauge the responses of women who had used them. Mothers and birth attendants generally appreciated the kits and found them affordable.

PATH recently quantified the positive impact of another delivery kit on the health of women and children in Tanzania. The study, conducted with funding from the US Agency for International Development, involved more than 3,200 participants. Results suggested that women who used the kit were substantially less likely to develop genital-tract infections and their infants were substantially less likely to develop cord infections.

With each delivery kit project, PATH's goal is to make sure the kits are available to the women who need them. It does this by building the capacity of local organisations and small businesses to produce and distribute or sell kits. In Egypt, PATH helped community health promoters develop a plan to use kits as an income-generating activity that would contribute to their health programmes. In Nepal, it gave a local, woman-owned business a head start. The campaign that it funded promoted the kit via wall paintings, advertisements, street dramas and training for community-health volunteers. Within a year, sales increased from 28,800 to 46,800 kits per year, contributing to the long-term stability of the company. Maternal and Child Health Products Ltd continues to make kits available to Nepali women at prices they can afford.

Famine

The Food and Agricultural Organization (FAO) of the UN insists that there is sufficient food for everyone in the world. Food is not in short supply — globally, we produce enough to feed everyone 2,700 calories per day. However, an estimated 30 million people die every year from starvation and a further 800 million suffer from chronic malnutrition. Some of these people live in countries that export food products to MEDCs.

Malnutrition is defined as a condition resulting from some form of dietary deficiency. This may be because the quantity of food, as measured in calories per day, is too low or because certain important food nutrients are absent. Malnutrition weakens immunity and makes people more vulnerable to diseases. It may also lead to deficiency diseases such as beriberi or anaemia. Some authorities refer to the condition that results from consuming too little food over a period of time as **undernourishment**.

The characteristics and causes of famine

- Most famines result from a combination of natural events and human mismanagement. Some authorities refer to famine as a decline in the access to food, rather than to there not being enough food.
- Famines are not always widespread. They can be very localised and can affect only one group or social class.
- In areas affected by famine it is not uncommon to see food available in markets and some agricultural produce being exported.

The decline of food availability is said to be the result of a deterioration in the entitlements of certain sectors of society. Poorer people have limited access to food as a consequence of weaker purchasing and bargaining powers. They have low status, menial occupations and limited land ownership.

Famines on a large scale occur as a result of one or more of the following factors.

- **Drought** — lack of rainfall causes soil and groundwater sources to decline, which ultimately leads to a reduction in the supply of water. The soil moisture will not meet the needs of particular plants and agricultural crops, creating serious problems for areas that depend on farming, both arable and pastoral.
- **A population increase greater than the rate of crop (food) production** — this often occurs in areas where there is a sudden influx of refugees, fleeing a war zone or an area of civil unrest. It can also occur as people migrate from one drought zone to another.
- **A rapid rise in the price of foodstuffs and/or animals** — this can occur when the quality of farmland and grazing land declines (often during a drought). It is further compounded by a breakdown in the local economy

Case study Drought in southern Ethiopia and Somalia, 2000

Ethiopia's worst drought of the twentieth century occurred in 1984–85. Dramatic pictures of starving refugees were brought to the television screens of richer Western countries and a massive aid appeal was launched, including Bob Geldof's Live Aid. Fifteen years later, in 2000, the rains failed again, leading to another severe drought that affected 43% of the population. The drought had the following effects:

- It led to unusual movements of people and livestock as herders moved in search of water and fresh pasture.
- As a result of these migrations, too much pressure was put on those areas that had sufficient water and pasture.
- The lack of food and water took a heavy toll on herders and thousands of cattle, sheep, camels and goats died.
- The death of livestock led to a deterioration in people's nutritional status.
- Milk, one of the main components of the diet (particularly that of women and children) became scarce.

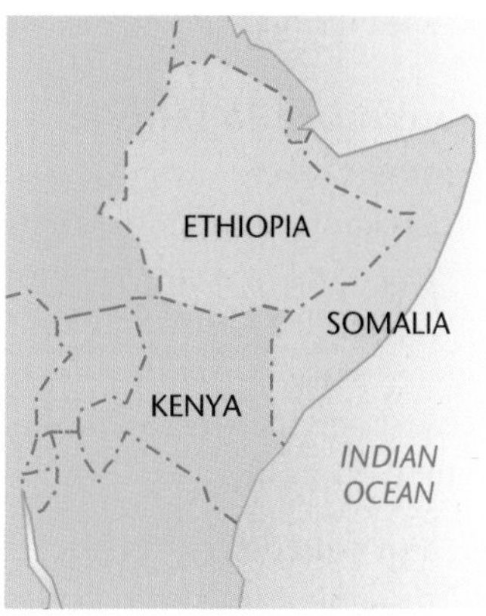

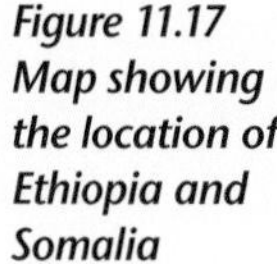

Figure 11.17 Map showing the location of Ethiopia and Somalia

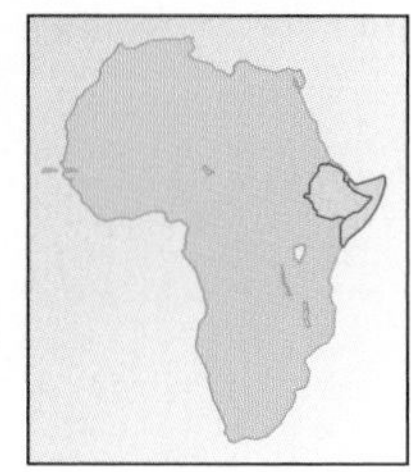

- Food prices began to rise.
- Thousands of families abandoned their lands and headed for the cities. Many camps for these internally displaced persons had to be set up. One camp, on the outskirts of the town of Denan, contained at least 13,000 people.
- Large amounts of foreign aid were required to run these camps; the rate of malnutrition was estimated at over 50%.

TopFoto

Photograph 11.5 Gada Wakoyo squats on land that was once pasture for his family's livestock, Ethiopia

and marketing systems. Control mechanisms react too slowly and inflationary price rises fuel panic buying, which rapidly leads to shortages of basic foodstuffs.

Solutions to famine

Famine relief

This short-term aid takes the form of distributing food. Famine relief is usually carried out by a combination of non-governmental aid organisations (NGOs, e.g. Oxfam, Red Cross and Save the Children) and government. Much of this aid is temporary in nature. It is usually given with caution because it could result in overdependence by the receiving country and might damage the local agricultural economy.

Long-term aid

The long-term response involves helping people develop a more productive system of farming, to prevent another famine. Such aid could involve:

- increased use of fertilisers and new technologies such as high-yielding varieties of seeds
- improvements to systems to ensure that produce gets to markets more efficiently
- easing international trade and cancelling national debts

Issues related to famine relief

Issues related to famine relief include:

- The **cost** of providing relief — all NGOs have overheads, the costs of which have to be met from the money raised through charitable donations. Donors to charities often question these internal costs, although they are generally very low.
- **Disaster fatigue** — modern communication systems publicise disasters quickly but can lead to a feeling of helplessness in donors as yet another famine occurs.
- The type of **food** provided — it must be available, non-perishable and easily transported. It must also be consumable, reflecting local tastes. The sending of powdered milk to the drought-stricken area of Ethiopia in the mid-1980s was a classic food-aid error because there was no clean water with which to make it up.
- **Infrastructure** to deliver aid — there should be international-standard entry facilities into an area (a port or an airport) as well as adequate roads for delivery by lorry.
- **Coordination** between aid agencies and national governments — this is essential when famine relief is necessary in an area of civil unrest.
- **Targeting aid** — how can those most in need be identified?

Rural futures in the LEDW

The key to the success of future rural development is sustainability. **Sustainable development** in a rural context can be defined as development that meets the needs of rural people in the present, without compromising their future needs. Thus rural living standards are improved, but not at the expense of the environment. Sustainable development implies equity and social justice, allowing the poorest rural communities to be empowered to shape their own futures.

In the LEDW the focus must be on sustainable agricultural development, because this is the backbone of the rural economy, employing up to 80% of households. Other forms of rural development projects, for example agroforestry and ecotourism, can also be sustainable. However, for these education and training are both necessary and fundamental. It is essential to raise basic literacy standards, as well as to improve skills if development is to work.

The main features of a rural aid project in Eritrea (east Africa) are shown in Figure 11.18.

Figure 11.18 The main features of a rural aid project in Eritrea, east Africa

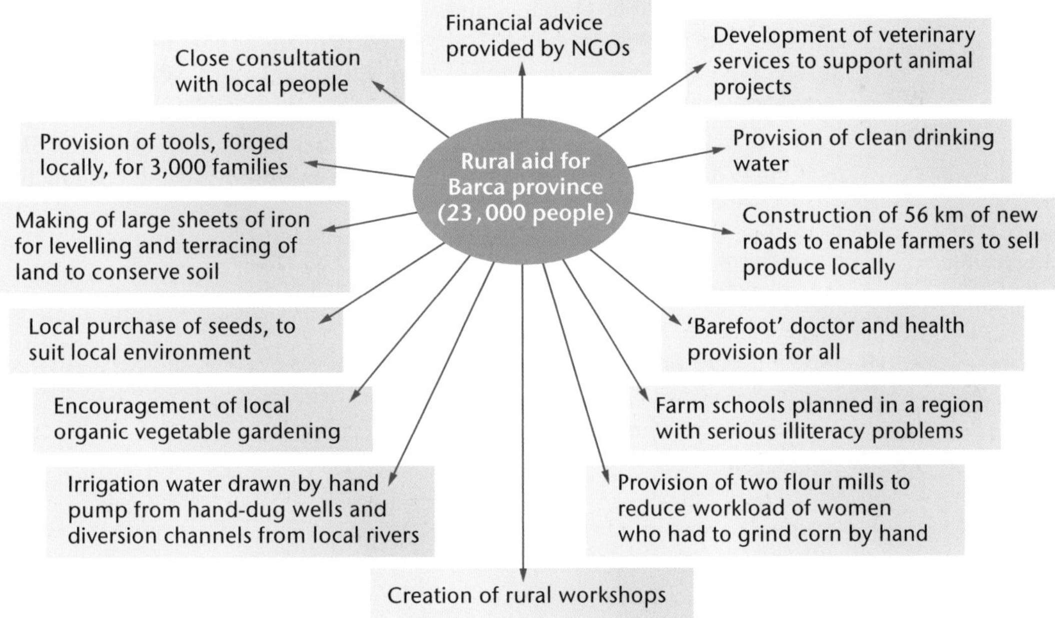

Chapter 12

Managing cities: challenges and issues

Central area changes

The central business district (CBD) of a city contains the principal commercial areas and major public buildings and is the centre for business and commercial activities. The CBD is accessible from all parts of the urban area and has the highest land values in a city. These occur at the peak land value intersection (PLVI). The CBD is not, however, static. It can grow outwards in some directions (**zones of assimilation**) and retreat in others (**zones of discard**). In some CBDs, retailing is declining because of competition from out-of-town developments.

Figure 12.1 The key features of the CBD

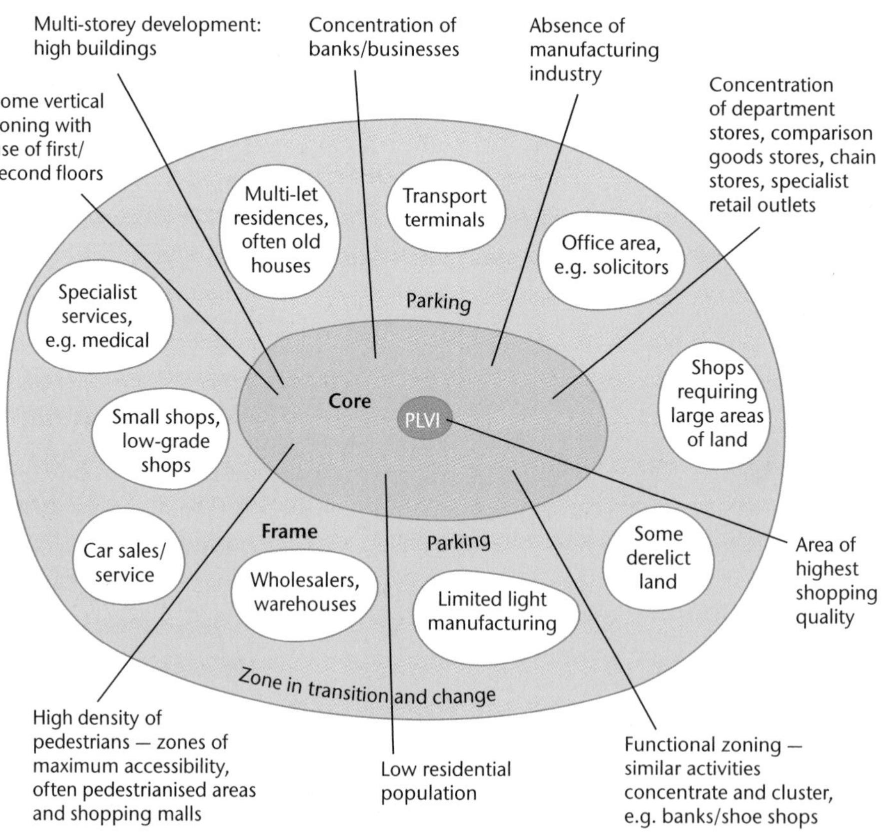

PLVI = Peak land value intersection: the highest rated, busiest, most accessible part of a CBD

This means there is a greater emphasis on offices and services. In a sizeable urban centre, there is often segregation of different types of businesses within the CBD, forming distinct quarters. Retailing tends to be separate from commercial and professional offices and forms a distinct inner core. The outer core is made up of offices and entertainment centres with some smaller shops. Beyond this, the outer part of the CBD (known as the **frame**) contains service industries, wholesalers and car parks, among other features (Figure 12.1).

The CBD has been affected by changes in retailing over the past 30 years in the UK. These are described in Chapter 6.

CBDs in decline

Most CBDs in cities in the MEDW are under threat. There are three main reasons for this:

- the loss of the retailing function (particularly food retailing, electrical goods and DIY) to out-of-town shopping centres. Evidence for this that was often quoted in the 1990s was the closure of branches of Marks and Spencer in some small towns
- the loss of offices to suburban or peripheral locations in prestige science parks
- the increasing costs of upkeep and development of the CBDs themselves. The CBD is becoming increasingly expensive, congested and inaccessible, especially as the bulk of a city's population lives in suburban areas

Most decision makers are worried that CBDs are in decline. A major concern is that run-down city centres can become dangerous places, particularly at night. Most people visiting a city arrive in the centre and a run-down CBD can discourage investment. Dereliction, vacant buildings, increased numbers of low-grade shops (e.g. charity shops and discount stores) and lack of investment all fuel decline. This situation is sometimes referred to as the 'dead heart' of a city (in the USA as an 'urban donut').

Figure 12.2 Factors influencing CBD decline

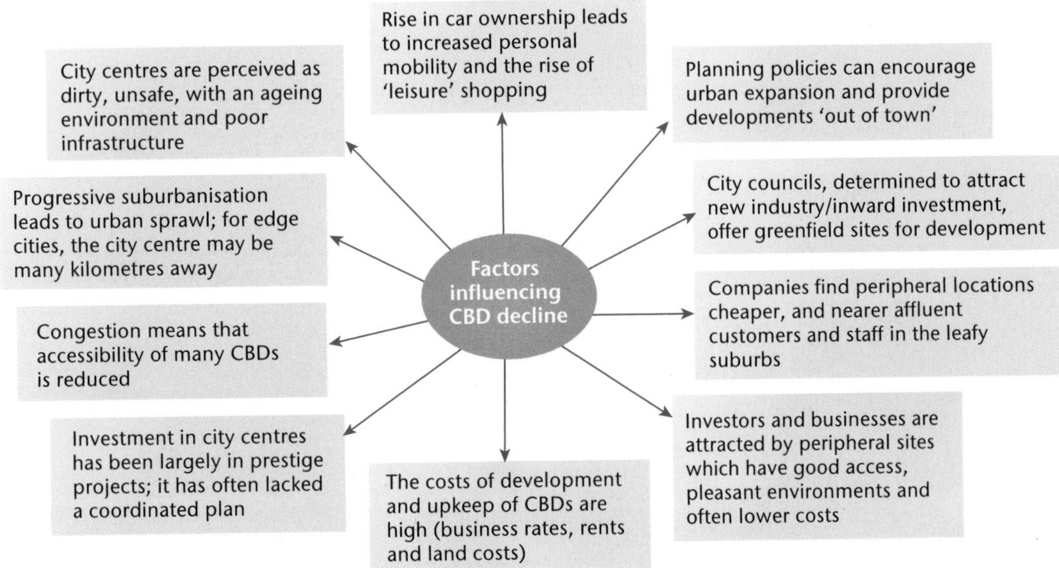

Planners see the CBD as an important social and cultural meeting point. A declining CBD will only accelerate the success of out-of-town shopping centres. However, the general public seems unconvinced about the worth of CBDs as they flock in thousands to shop in retail parks. Many companies have moved out to suburban offices in science parks.

Case study Glasgow city centre: shops and shopping

Glasgow is the largest retail centre in the UK, outside of London. The vibrant shopping district in the heart of the city is focused around the pedestrianised areas of Buchanan Street, Argyle Street, and Sauchiehall Street.

Within the city there are a number of **specialised shopping areas:**

- **Buchanan Galleries** is the newest, and some say the best, shopping centre in the heart of Glasgow. Positioned at the junction between the famous Sauchiehall Street and Buchanan Street, Buchanan Galleries is near rail, underground and bus stations. The shopping centre has its own award-winning 2,000 space car park, which is only minutes from the M8 and is easily accessible. There are 80 quality shops, including a John Lewis department store, H&M, Habitat, Mango and Next, giving customers a good choice for fashion, clothing, accessories and gifts.
- The **St Enoch Shopping Centre** is the largest glass structure in Europe. It has a wide variety of shops including department stores such as Debenhams, Boots, TK Maxx and Bhs. Children can enjoy the Kids Play Area, Kiddy Cabs and a two-man ride simulator. There is also Scotland's largest food court, with over 850 seats and outlets such as Sandwich Delight, Sea Fresh, Spuds'r'Us, Di Maggios and McDonald's.
- **Prince's Square** is a fashionable and elegant shopping centre housing a cosmopolitan selection of designer names, exclusive boutiques, cafés and bars under an art nouveau glass roof. It also houses the Scottish Craft Centre, which has an outstanding collection of work created by some of the nation's most talented craftspeople.
- **Argyll Arcade** is one of Britain's oldest covered shopping arcades. It was built in 1827. It is a covered street that has 32 jewellers' shops under one roof.

Mills Corporation

Photograph 12.1
St Enoch Shopping Centre, the largest glass structure in Europe

- The **Italian Centre** has a selection of Italian designer stores, including the UK's first Versace store. Pavement cafés complete the centre's contemporary theme.
- **Sauchiehall Street Shopping Centre** has been recently refurbished. Situated on the north side of the city centre, it houses a number of regular mall shops, for example Superdrug, WH Smith, and Primark.
- The **Barras Market** has an eclectic mix of covered and open stalls, selling a huge range of goods from antique furniture to computer games. The Barras has gained an unenviable reputation for selling counterfeit videos, CDs and DVDs of dubious quality, often available there before anywhere else in Europe. This is definitely at the lower end of the Glasgow shopping experience, in terms of quality of material services. However, it does have great character and the ever-present opportunity for a genuine bargain.

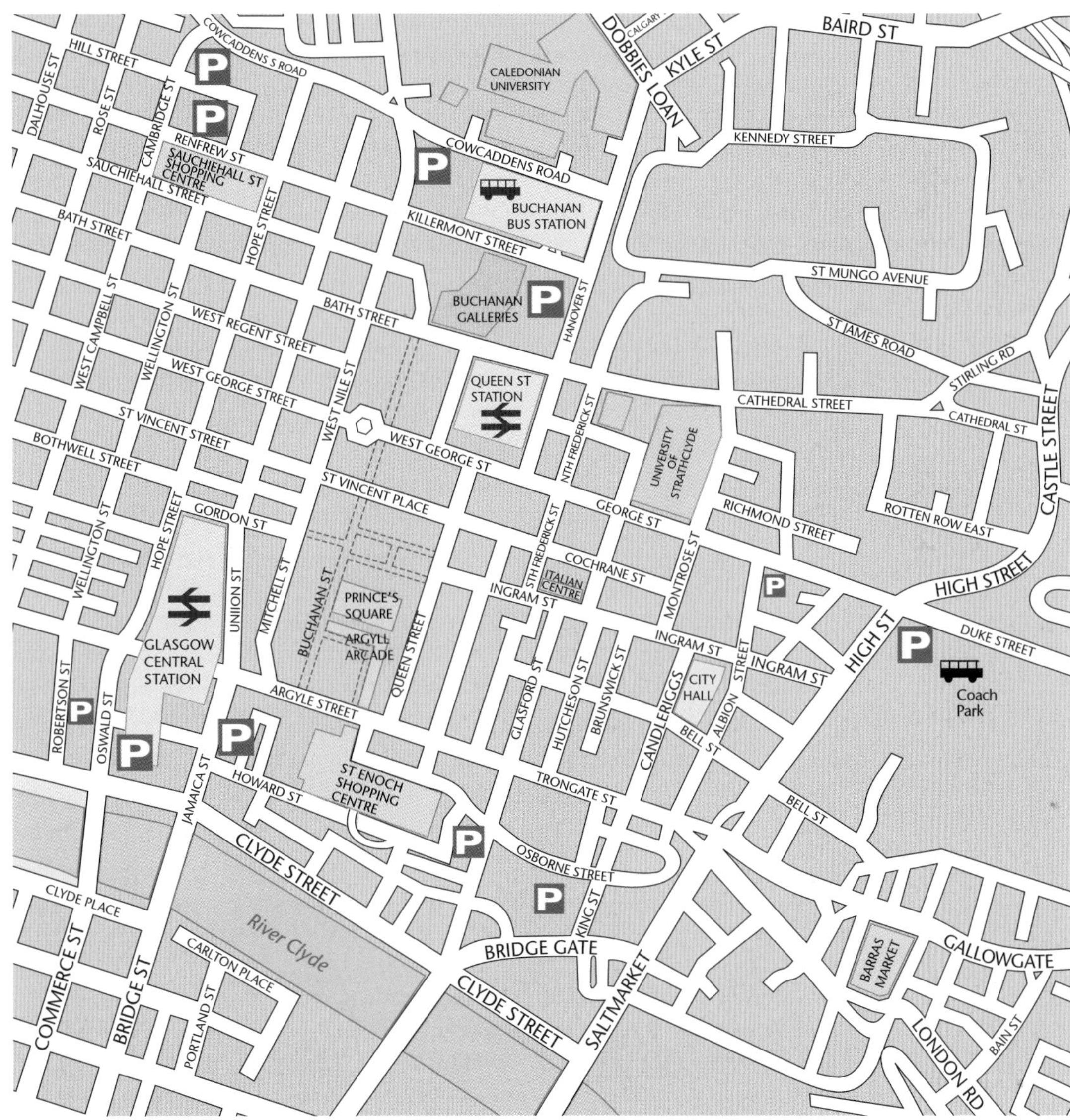

Figure 12.3 Map of Glasgow city centre showing the specialised shopping centres

Reversing the decline

Despite the negative predictions of the previous section, CBDs in the MEDW, like Glasgow (see case study, page 377), do continue to flourish alongside the new out-of-town locations. In some cases, the CBD has moved slightly in one or more directions; in other cases it has re-invented itself with new indoor shopping areas or malls.

A number of strategies are being devised to help reverse the decline of city centres, including:

- the establishment of business and marketing management teams to coordinate overall management of CBDs and run special events
- the provision of a more attractive shopping environment with pedestrianisation (which increases pedestrian safety), new street furniture, floral displays, paving and landscaping
- the construction of all-weather shopping malls that are air-conditioned in the summer and heated in the winter and which often have integral low-cost parking
- the encouragement of specialist areas, such as attractive open street markets, cultural quarters and arcades
- the improvement of public transport links to the heart of the CBD, including rapid transit systems, park-and-ride schemes and shopper buses
- the extensive use of CCTV and emergency alarm systems to reduce crime and calm the fears of the public, particularly women (see below)
- the organisation of special shopping events such as Christmas fairs, late-night shopping and Sunday shopping — sometimes referred to as 'the 24-hour city'
- conservation schemes, such as the refurbishment of historic buildings in heritage cities like Chester, York, Bath and Cambridge, to attract shoppers and tourists

Making CBDs safer for women

Perception has an important role to play in judging a place. Whether or not you feel safe in an area will influence whether or not you go there. CBDs have increasingly been perceived as threatening and unsafe environments. Individuals or groups in society whose movements and activities are constrained by fear can be classed as disadvantaged. They suffer from reduced accessibility and a poorer quality of life. It has been suggested that women perceive themselves to be restricted in this way. What can be done to alleviate these feelings and make women feel safer in CBDs?

One answer is segregated transport for women, for example:

- separate compartments on trains or night-buses
- priority taxis after 10 p.m. — in Manchester, this is known as the 'Lady Cab' service
- the formal licensing of mini-cabs in cities so that all private hire vehicles are registered and regulated

Improvements can be made to the street environment, including:

- CCTV, which is now widespread
- better maintenance of street lighting
- help points at key locations, for example subways, with emergency alarms connected to local police
- smoother pavements, few obstacles and better enforcement of on-kerb parking regulations to help women with prams (this is linked to required improvements for disability access)
- more seating in public places
- transparent bus shelters, to prevent people hiding behind them
- cutting hedges at the top and bottom, to increase light and safety

Multi-storey car parks are often seen as threatening environments. Here, suggested improvements include better lighting and the provision of ground-floor women-only sections.

Functions other than retailing

Many cities are encouraging the development of functions other than retailing to increase the attractions of a CBD, including:

- Encouraging a wider range of leisure facilities, including café bars, restaurants, music venues (such as the 'Arenas' in many city centres), cinemas and theatres that people visit in the evening. For example, Nottingham refurbished St Peter's Square, making the area more attractive by planting shrubs and other plants, giving permission for open-air cafés and employing staff to clean the area in the early morning.

ID:8 Photography

***Photograph 12.2* Workstation in Sheffield's Cultural Industries Quarter is a managed workspace for cultural businesses. It was originally a garage and car showroom**

- Promoting street entertainment, such as at Covent Garden in London.
- Developing nightlife, such as clubbing, for example in Manchester and Leeds. (There are negative issues associated with this, including the high level of policing that is necessary.)
- Establishing theme areas, such as the gay area in Manchester and the cultural quarters in Sheffield and Stoke (Photograph 12.2).
- Developing flagship attractions, for example the photographic museum in Bradford.
- Constructing new offices, apartments, hotels and conference centres to raise the status of the CBD for business and to encourages tourists to remain near the city centre.
- Encouraging residential activities to return to city centres, by providing flats to rent above shops, redeveloping old buildings (a form of **gentrification**) or building new up-market apartments (**reurbanisation**) (see pages 148–151).

Most CBD managers are trying a range of these strategies and shoppers are being attracted back to city centres. However, this can only happen in conjunction with planning controls to limit the number of suburban or out-of-town shopping centres. Indeed, some politicians believe that retail development in out-of-town locations has gone far enough. A number of these major shopping areas have sought permission to expand and, in most cases, this has been refused.

Some supermarket chains are turning their attention back to their existing and new CBD outlets. For example, Sainsbury's has developed new Sainsbury's Local stores in CBDs and Tesco has opened Tesco Direct stores. These CBD outlets do not sell the full range of goods found in the larger stores, but stock items targeted at local needs.

Case study Edinburgh

Many of the changes that have taken place in the CBD of Edinburgh are examples of the developments described above. For example:

- pedestrianisation of streets in the CBD (e.g. Rose Street)
- an altered road network to include a one-way system, bus/taxi lanes and cycle lanes (Charlotte Square, Queen Street and Princes Street)
- many modernised city-centre shops and new shopping malls (Harvey Nichols and the Waverley Centre)
- new offices, apartments, hotels and conference centres (the *Scotsman* newspaper offices, the Sheraton Hotel and the Edinburgh International Conference Centre)
- renovated tourist facilities and cultural attractions (the National Gallery of Scotland and the Dynamic Earth exhibition)
- refurbished or new civic buildings (the Scottish Parliament on Holyrood Road)
- several multistorey car parks adjacent to the major shopping malls (St James Centre)

In Edinburgh, the CBD is bisected by the castle and Princes Street Gardens. There are planning restrictions to ensure that the historic nature of the city is conserved. Related to this is the work that Edinburgh City Council has done to enhance Edinburgh's image as a 'global city'. It is a major international tourist attraction, and millions of people attend the Edinburgh festival each summer.

Case study The St Stephen's Development, Kingston-upon-Hull

The site of this development lies west of Ferensway and comprises 17 hectares. It includes major work on the existing Grade II listed railway station.

Site

The brownfield site currently comprises a mixture of ownerships, buildings and vacant lots. The general ambience of the area is one of neglect and decay. Various piecemeal redevelopment schemes over the years have come to nought. The development sponsors, Kingston-upon-Hull City Council and Yorkshire Forward, now own or have acquired all of the site.

Scheme

The scheme will provide:

- a flagship development that is intended to complement and reinforce city-centre activities by having a mixture of retail outlets, a 10,000 m^2 foodstore, a leisure complex, a hotel, a new home for the Hull Truck Theatre Company, a music centre, 1,550 car parking spaces and over 200 new residential units
- a new integrated transport interchange

The basic design concept is built around a diagonal pedestrian route across the site which curves gently at either end to form an 'S'. At the east end of this route there is a mix of retail, leisure, hotel and cultural uses, with associated parking and servicing. The route will be roofed over where it passes through the retail and leisure accommodation and this will form a covered street in the tradition of nineteenth-century arcade developments. At the west end of the pedestrian route there is an area of open space. New-build residential accommodation is proposed to the north and south of the open space.

Transport interchange

The aim of the £10 million transport interchange scheme is to transform the existing Paragon Rail Station and add a new bus station to provide an integrated transport interchange and new gateway to the city.

The interchange is promoted by a partnership between Kingston-upon-Hull City Council, Yorkshire Forward, Railtrack, Arriva Trains Northern Ltd, East Yorkshire Motor Services and Stagecoach Ltd.

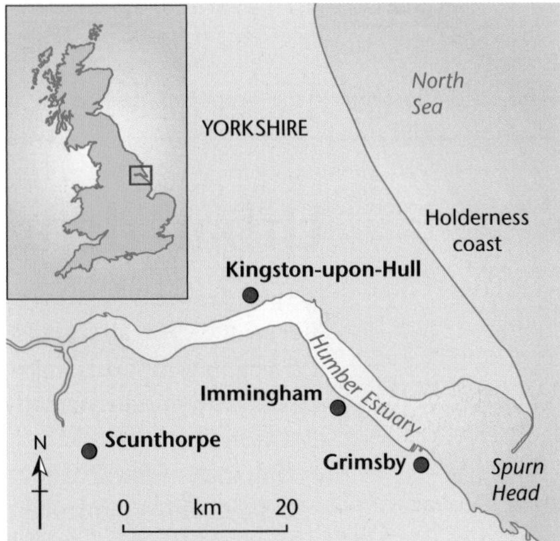

Figure 12.4 Map showing the location of Kingston-upon-Hull

Case study Regeneration in Reading, Berkshire

A number of steps have been taken to regenerate the town centre of Reading:

- In 1969 a new inner ring road was constructed, taking through traffic away from the centre of the town.
- During the following 20 years, pedestrianisation took place in Broad Street and Friar Street.
- In 1999, the Oracle Shopping Centre was opened.

This brownfield site covered a considerable section of the former CBD and land previously occupied by an old bus garage. The centre covers 9 hectares with a mix of retail, leisure and residential land use. There are over 90 shops indoors. The outdoor part of the centre, beside the River Kennet, has 22 restaurants, cafés and bars and a 10-screen Vue cinema. In 2004, the development

was awarded a Waterways Renaissance Award by the Waterways Trust.

- Reading's other major shopping area — the Broad Street Mall — has recently undergone a refurbishment that has extended its retail area.
- The development of the CBD has also included innovative housing projects, creating new affordable homes in empty spaces above shops and offices. These are located alongside high-price prestige apartments.

Reading City Centre Management (RCCM) is a public–private partnership concerned with the strategic development of central Reading. Along with a number of interested parties, RCCM has developed a 5-year plan entitled 'Reading City Centre, 2010'.

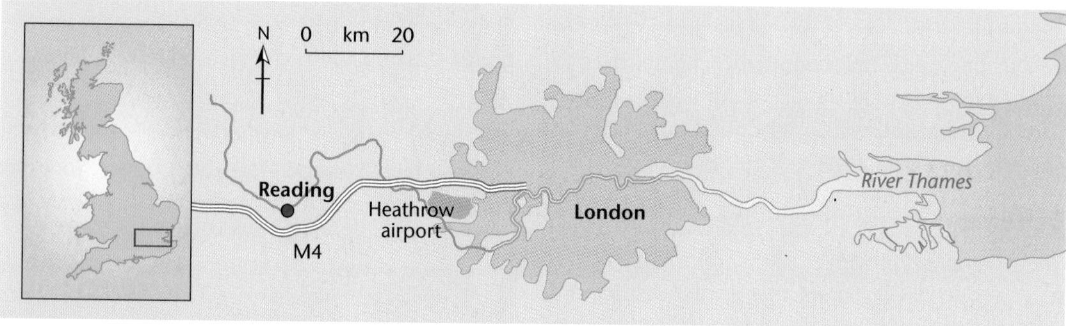

Figure 12.5 Map showing the location of Reading

Urban deprivation

Inequalities occur in all urban areas — enormous contrasts in wealth can be found over relatively small distances. When you do fieldwork in an area, you can sense if a neighbourhood is improving or deteriorating. The wealthy and the poor do seem to concentrate spatially — a form of social segregation. There are a number of reasons for this:

- **Housing** — developers, builders and planners tend to build housing on blocks of land with a particular market in mind. Wealthier groups can choose where they live, paying premium prices for houses well away from poor areas, with pleasing environments and services such as quality schools and parks. The poorer groups have no choice and have to live where they are placed in welfare housing, or where they can find a cheap place to rent.
- **Changing environments** — housing neighbourhoods change over time. Houses that were built for large families in Georgian and Victorian times are now too big for the average UK family. Many have been converted into multi-let apartments for private renting to people on low incomes. Conversely, former poor areas are being taken over by more wealthy people and upgraded (gentrification). The right to buy legislation of the 1980s transformed many council estates, as houses were bought by their occupants and improved.
- **The ethnic dimension** — ethnic groups originally come to the country as new immigrants. When they first arrive they often suffer discrimination in the job market and may be either unemployed or employed in low-paid jobs.

They are only able to afford to buy cheap housing (inner-city terraces) or they have to rent privately. Therefore, newly arrived migrants concentrate in poor areas in the city, often clustered into ghettos for cultural reasons. Such ethnic groupings tend to persist into later generations.

Measuring inequalities

It is possible to measure the **quality of life** in an area using primary data, such as the quality, density and condition of housing and the nature of the physical and social environment. It is also possible to use secondary data from a census to assess **deprivation** levels. This may include **poverty**, in terms of low income, or manifested by poor health or the lack of possessions, such as cars. It is common for the poorest parts of an urban area to suffer from **multiple deprivation** (a combination of social, environmental and economic deprivation).

Urban social exclusion is a recent term that refers to the problems faced by residents in areas of multiple deprivation. Essentially, these people are excluded from full participation in society by their social and physical circumstances. They cannot get access to a decent job because of poor education, or obtain decent housing because of poverty. They often suffer from poor health and from high levels of crime in an unattractive physical environment. In a city, inequality can have major consequences in terms of lack of social cohesion. In extreme cases it can lead to civil unrest. Governments have to address social injustices for a variety of social, economic and political reasons.

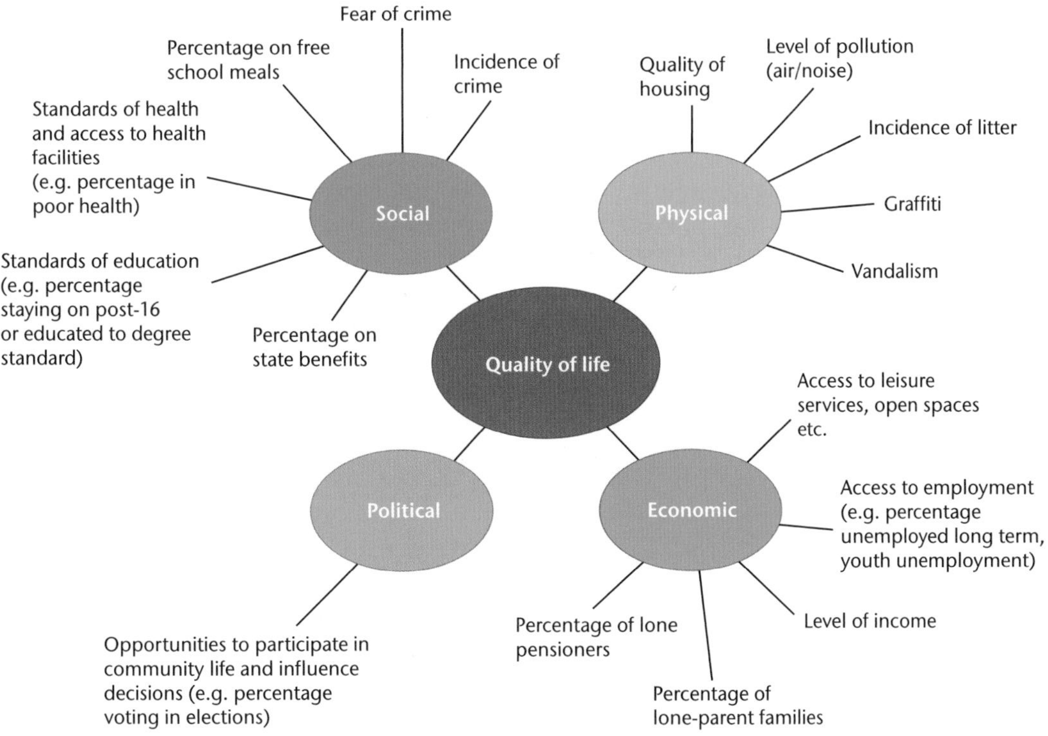

Figure 12.6 Measures of quality of life

The inner city

The characteristic features of inner-city areas are:

- high population out-migration figures
- many boarded-up shops
- many empty and derelict properties
- the closing of schools, particularly primary schools, and low levels of educational attainment and aspiration
- high levels of unemployment
- high incidence of crime, vandalism and graffiti
- low levels of participation in local democracy

The causes of inner-city decline

Over 4 million people live in the inner cities of the UK. These areas are typified by economic decline, personal poverty, social problems and environmental decay. They are also areas where political strength has waned, but where political discontent is often more visible.

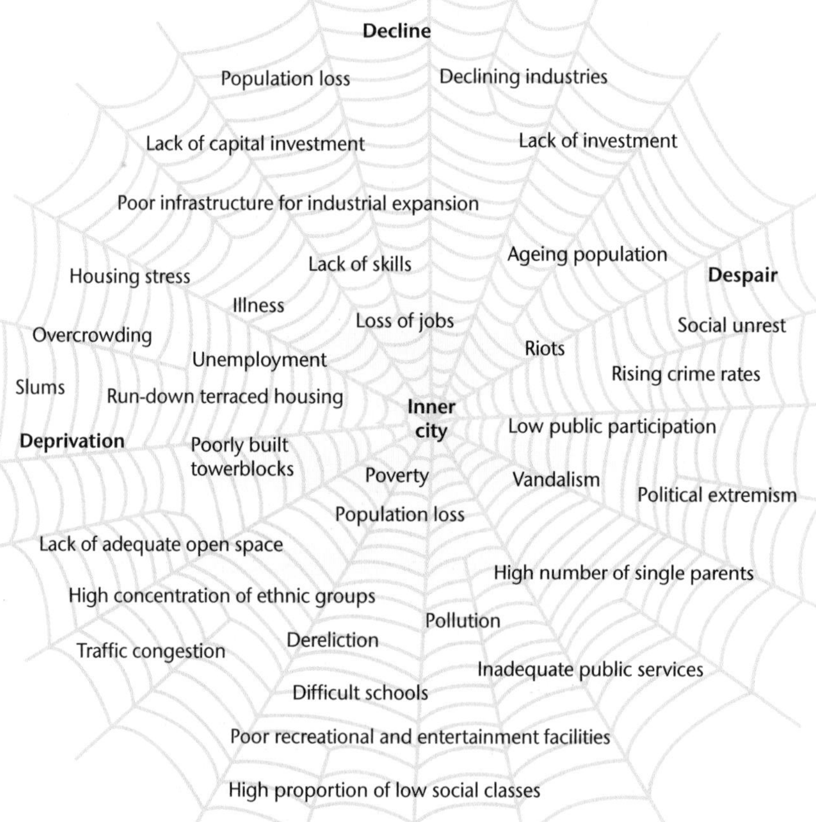

Figure 12.7 The web of inner-city decline, despair and deprivation

Economic decline

Since the 1950s, there has been a widespread movement of employment away from the large conurbations to smaller urban areas and to rural areas. This fall in employment has been largely in traditional manufacturing industries, formerly based on coal, steam power and railways. These industries were located in today's inner-city areas. Between 1960 and 1981, over 1.6 million manufacturing jobs were lost in the major urban areas. This accounted for 75% of job losses nationally.

This decline in manufacturing was accompanied by the growth of service industries. However, this growth did not compensate for the massive job losses in manufacturing. In addition, service industries did not require the same skills as manufacturing industries. Towards the end of the 1980s and in the early 1990s, the service industries in the inner cities also faced job losses. Employment in services in inner-city areas fell by 7%, compared with a national increase in such jobs of 11%.

Deindustrialisation in the inner cities was accompanied by the expansion of both manufacturing and service-sector employment in rural areas and small towns. This shift can be partly explained by:

- The changing levels of technology and space requirements of manufacturing industry, which resulted in a shortage of suitable land and premises in the inner cities. This had the effect of diverting investment and employment growth from urban to rural locations.
- The global economic change, which led to declining profits and increased competition. To remain competitive, companies were forced to restructure their production methods and labour requirements. This restructuring involved the acquisition of other companies, the introduction of new technology, and the geographical movement of investment to new locations in the UK and overseas.

The employment losses were skewed towards the inner cities because they contained many of the types of workplace most likely to be closed. These were old plants with the oldest production techniques, lowest productivity and most highly unionised workforces.

Unemployment thus became a major problem for the inner-city areas of the former industrial regions of Liverpool, Sheffield, Glasgow, Newcastle-upon-Tyne and Birmingham. The periods of unemployment for individuals became longer. Unemployment was particularly high among school leavers, the poorly qualified, the poorly skilled and ethnic minorities. In 1994, the inner cities of Britain had an unemployment rate 50% higher than that in the rest of the country.

Population loss and social decline

Between 1951 and 1981, the UK's largest conurbations lost 35% of their population and migration was the key cause. For example, in the 1970s, the out-migration of population from the inner areas of Liverpool and Manchester led to a population decline of over 25%. Many of these people were looking for better employment opportunities.

In the 1960s and 1970s the out-movement of people led to a growth in small towns around the large conurbations. In the 1980s, a significant proportion of the out-migration from cities involved people moving to rural areas, a process known as **counter-urbanisation** (see pages 142–148).

The key causes of population decline, therefore, are changing residential preferences, job growth and improvements in accessibility of suburban and rural areas, as well as the poor image of the inner city.

The people who have left the inner-city areas have tended to be the younger, the more affluent and the more skilled. This has meant that those left behind are the old, the less skilled and the poor. Therefore, economic decline of these areas has led to social decline.

The poor physical environment

The physical environment of the inner cities is usually poor, with low-quality housing, empty and derelict properties, vacant factories and unsightly, overgrown wasteland (Photograph 12.3). The physical deterioration of inner-city environments is characterised by high levels of vandalism, dereliction, graffiti and flyposting. These areas also have few amenities such as parks, open spaces and play areas. A more recent feature is the construction of urban motorways, with flyovers, underpasses and networks of pedestrian walkways that contribute further to the bleak concrete-dominated landscape.

Some of the dereliction is due to the continued existence of areas of nineteenth-century terraced housing, now often of poor quality. In addition, slum clearance schemes of the 1960s and 1970s created unsightly estates of poorly constructed houses and high-rise flats. Many of these have been demolished. Those that remain are unpopular and difficult living environments.

Political problems

There has been increasing concern that the problems of inner-city residents have been marginalised politically. There have been political clashes between local inner-city government and central government. Inner cities have the lowest election turnouts in the UK, reflecting the degree to which the people feel rejected. It is no coincidence that these areas, in an effort to draw attention to their plight, have elected members of far-right parties such as the BNP to local councils.

Jane Buekett

Photograph 12.3 The physical environment of inner cities is often poor

In addition, left-wing political groups have used the inner cities to press home their attacks on the more conservative elements in politics. Political tension has been heightened by the limited impacts of urban regeneration policies, which have led to much physical redevelopment, while the long-standing levels of social and economic deprivation remain largely unchanged.

Ghettos

Cities are noted for their multicultural plurality, which can lead to a mixing of ethnicities, religions and cultures. More commonly it leads to a mosaic of ghettos. A **ghetto** is an area where the population is almost exclusively made up of a single ethnic or cultural minority. Ghettos are common in inner cities in the USA and are increasingly found in European cities. The word 'ghetto' tends not to be used in the UK, where people are more likely to refer to social segregation on the basis of ethnicity, or **ethnic segregation**.

Ghettos are frequently areas of concentrated deprivation. Many new immigrants arrive with limited resources and discrimination can result in high levels of unemployment and low incomes. As ethnic groups are forced to concentrate in areas of poor housing, this pushes out groups from other races.

Factors that encourage segregation

Internal factors (those within ethnic groups) that encourage segregation are that:

- new arrivals need mutual support from friends, relatives and community organisations
- immigrants require religious centres, ethnic shops and foods, and these tend to group together to serve them
- immigrants need support from people speaking their own language
- ethnic groups encourage friendship and marriages, and reduce contacts (except via schools) that might undermine their culture and traditions
- employment and accommodation can often be obtained via networking in an ethnic community
- a closely knit ethnic community provides security against abuse and racist attacks — safety in numbers
- ethnic groupings encourage political power and influence development

External factors (those within the country or area) that encourage segregation include:

- as immigrants move in, the remaining majority population moves out, in fear of, for example, falling house prices
- the majority population may be hostile or unfriendly to new arrivals
- racism, abuse or racially motivated violence, or fear of such actions
- discrimination in the job market — ethnic minorities who are unemployed or in low-paid jobs are forced by circumstances into areas with cheap housing and substandard services
- discrimination by house sellers, estate agents and housing agencies, which keeps ethnic minorities in their ghettos
- discrimination by financial institutions, which forces ethnic minorities to use their own networks for small business development

Ethnic minority groups

The largest ethnic minority group in the UK is the Indian population, which makes up 27% of the total ethnic minority population. The next largest is the Pakistani ethnic minority (17%), closely followed by the black Caribbean (15%). There are smaller, but still significant, ethnic minorities of Bangladeshi, black African and Chinese people.

Ethnic minorities are concentrated in the major urban areas, particularly London and the southeast, the west and east Midlands, Manchester, Lancashire and West Yorkshire. Over 50% of the ethnic minority population lives in the southeast, which has only 30% of the white population, so the concentration here is highest. A significant proportion of ethnic minorities consists of people born in the UK descended from migrants who arrived from the former Commonwealth countries in the 1960s and 1970s.

There are some slight variations in the geographical distribution of ethnic groups, which owe their origin to factors in the early days of immigration. For example, there are large concentrations of the Indian ethnic minority in the Midlands (e.g. Leicester, Wolverhampton and Sandwell), Greater Manchester and Lancashire (e.g. Blackburn). The Pakistani minority is concentrated in parts of Bradford, Leeds and Birmingham and there are large Bangladeshi communities in Luton, Oldham and Birmingham.

The 1991 census brought to light geographical variations between some ethnic minorities in urban areas. Bangladeshi and black Caribbean groups are concentrated in high-density inner-city areas that are characterised by low levels of owner occupancy and high levels of unemployment. In contrast, people of Chinese origin are distributed across a wide range of area types — from deprived inner-city areas to the more affluent suburbs. Some research suggests that ethnic segregation is more geographically pronounced in northern areas than in, say, London.

London has a high proportion and diversity of ethnic minorities. Sixty per cent of the UK's black Caribbean population and 52% of the Bangladeshi population lives here, but only 18% of the Pakistani population. Most of these ethnic minority populations live in inner-city areas. Some areas are dominated by certain ethnic groups (e.g. Bangladeshis in Tower Hamlets). There is wider diversity in other localities, such as Brent and Newham. There is a strong concentration of black Caribbean people south of the River Thames in Lambeth, Brixton and Southwark. Even within these areas, there are some pronounced variations. For example, in the Northcote ward of Ealing, nearly 70% of the population are Indian; over 90% of the population of this ward are non-white. The London Borough of Brent has the most diverse ethnic structure. Here, there are large concentrations of black Caribbean, black African and Indian people, and a large subsection of the white community that is Irish-born.

In the initial phases of immigration, multiple occupancy in rented accommodation in terraced houses in inner-city areas was widespread. Ethnic minorities have not been very successful in securing conventional mortgages, which has forced them into less conventional, more expensive forms of finance. This limits the housing they are able to afford. The prospect of an expensive mortgage on a substandard property in a deprived area contributed to the low rate of owner-occupancy among the ethnic minority population.

Ethnic minorities have also been discriminated against in allocation of local authority housing and their representation in this housing sector is disproportionately low. In a number of urban areas this has led to the development of internal networks for housing provision, in which landlords belonging to an ethnic group provide housing for members of that group. This process is known as the 'racialisation of residential space'.

More recently, there has been an increase in owner occupancy and some more wealthy individuals have moved out into suburban areas. In addition many individuals from ethnic minorities run a small business such as a shop and live in part of the same building.

Housing and housing shortages

The character, distribution and availability of housing stock are important elements of urban areas in the UK. There are two main providers — the private sector and the public sector, and individuals can now rent or buy within either of these sectors.

It has been government policy since the 1940s to improve the quality of housing for all groups in society. Until the late 1970s there were two main thrusts to this policy:

- The private sector was encouraged to provide dwellings for ownership by individuals or families. Private-sector rented accommodation was therefore progressively squeezed out. For example, between 1950 and 1980, private house ownership increased from 30% to 56%, and private rented housing decreased from 52% to 12% of all housing tenures.
- The public sector was encouraged to provide rented housing, mainly in the form of local authority council housing subsidised financially by central government. This resulted in the construction of large council estates on the outskirts of urban areas, and many council-owned high-rise flats in inner-city areas. Surprisingly, the proportion of council housing tenure did not increase greatly between 1950 and 1980 (from 18% to 32%). This can be accounted for by the fact that much of the existing council accommodation was demolished to make way for the new estates and flats.

After Margaret Thatcher's Conservative Party took power in 1979, four major changes in housing policy came into operation:

- a reduction in funding for local authority housing by central government
- restriction on using the money raised from council house sales to build new council dwellings or renovate existing housing stock
- the right to buy legislation of 1980 gave council tenants the opportunity to buy their homes at discounted prices
- Housing Associations were created — private bodies in receipt of government financial support for the building or renovation of dwellings for rent (for more detail see page 394).

Figure 12.8 Houses built in England, 1975–2000

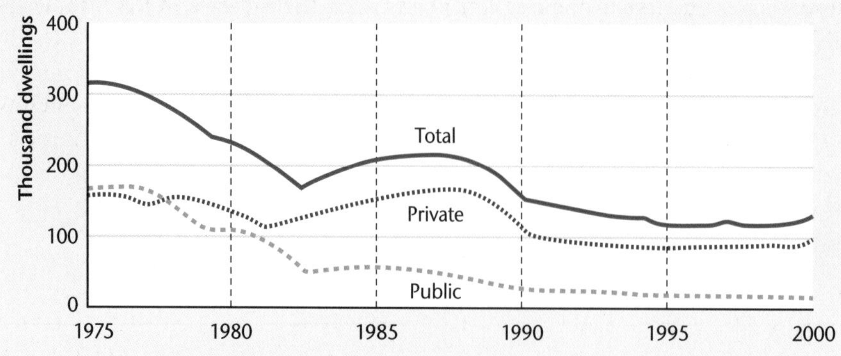

These four policies caused an increase of more than 50% in annual building rates by private developers, while completions by the public sector fell by 60% (Figure 12.8). The changes were not evenly distributed across the country. Demand for private housing rocketed in the economically prosperous areas of the southeast. Here, the price of houses rose more rapidly than inflation, fuelled partly by rising land costs. In 1987, for example, the price of the land constituted 53% of the value of the dwelling price in the southeast, whereas in Yorkshire and Humberside it was only 12%. Consequently, the difference in housing prices widened greatly between the regions. The north–south divide was increased, with the popular view that there were significant problems in providing enough housing in the southeast. The construction of new private properties increased greatly in the Greater London and southeast areas, and in parts of East Anglia and the east Midlands.

Changes in the supply of council housing

There are two ways in which a person can obtain a council house — either from the supply of newly-built houses or from existing properties which become vacant. During the 1980s the government steadily reduced the amount of money an authority could use to build new houses. In 1981, a local authority could use 50% of the funds raised by council house sales to build new homes, but by 1986 it had been reduced to 20%. In addition, by 1986 a further 650,000 council houses had been sold to their occupants, effectively removing them from the stock available.

Initially this did not cause too great a problem as many people who lived in council houses wanted to buy a house from the private sector. And an increasingly elderly population on the former council estates meant that deaths of tenants and movements into sheltered accommodation created sufficient vacancies for new tenants.

However, with the onset of the economic recession in the late 1980s demand for the falling numbers of council houses increased greatly. Applications for housing from homeless people in English local authorities increased from 220,000 in 1986 to 320,000 in 1996. This demand was not evenly spread: London was the area most severely affected.

The role of council housing then came under closer scrutiny. Was it increasingly to accommodate the vulnerable and the disadvantaged? New factors were coming into play — the rise in the number of divorces, the increase in the number of elderly people living alone, the growth of mortgage default, and the discharge of those with special needs from institutional care. As council house supply dwindled, local authorities increasingly concentrated on those they had a statutory duty to house, and those with greatest need. Council housing has become more and more 'welfare tenure'. It is often now called 'social housing'.

Waiting lists

All local authorities have more prospective tenants than vacant properties, which means there are waiting lists. Most waiting list schemes involve awarding points to establish priority based upon the urgency of the need for housing. Points schemes take into account a number of factors, each of which has a certain weight, and the points from each are added together to decide who should be housed first. Examples of these factors include whether or not children are involved; whether the existing dwelling is damp, or has no bathroom; whether a family is currently living with in-laws in an overcrowded house; and how long a name has been on the list. However, the weighting of factors varies between schemes — it would seem that the attitudes of local councillors and/or officials towards housing needs are more important than consistency and fairness.

Peripheral council housing estates

During the 1950s, 1960s and 1970s many local authorities built estates on the edges of their urban areas. These were to house overspill population and people who needed rehousing due to inner-city slum clearance. The estates consisted of typically designed council houses — semi-detached, uniform red brick with or without rendering, metal-framed windows, with gardens, limited garaging, and distinctive sequenced front door colours. Within these estates there were also system-built tower blocks and maisonettes made of prefabricated materials.

These types of housing were relatively inexpensive to build and were a cheap way for local authorities to meet housing demand. Planning controls were limited, and construction was done in great haste. Over time evidence has emerged of corruption by local authority leaders in issuing lucrative contracts for both the design and the construction of these properties.

It seemed a good idea at the time to build these estates, using greenfield sites to provide decent homes, with open space and public amenities, for the poorer elements of society. However, the result was that communities the size of small towns were created on the outskirts of cities without proper facilities and without affordable transport links to the city centre or to places of work.

During the 1980s and 1990s the physical fabric of these estates deteriorated markedly, and the environmental quality of the streets and open spaces became poor. Maintenance costs escalated to the point where, for many estates, demolition has been the best option. The houses and flats have not proved popular under the right-to-buy legislation, and so many have remained in rental tenure. This means that such estates contain above average proportions of the more vulnerable groups in society — low-income households, the unemployed, and the elderly living in poverty. They have become the centre of a whole range of social and economic problems.

Figure 12.9 Spiral of multiple deprivation on poor estates

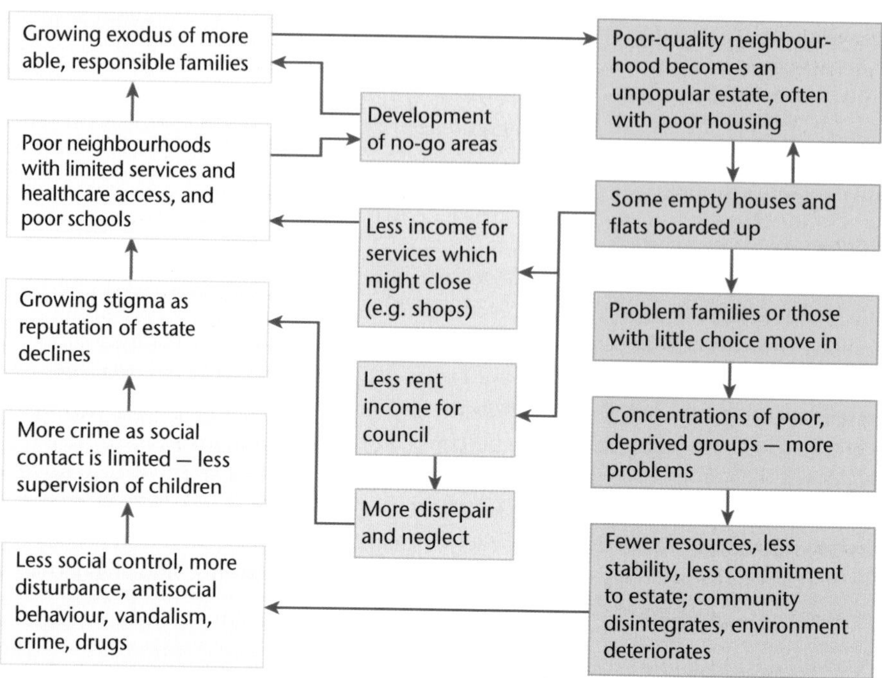

Case study Housing estates in east Middlesbrough

East Middlesbrough has 11 estates within an area of 5 km^2 containing over 10,000 homes, only 20% of which are privately owned. The housing is predominantly two-storey terraced and semi-detached with gardens. Some houses have had central heating and double-glazing installed. Most of the three- and four-storey maisonettes have been removed, but the high-rise flats remain. These have had some improvement but there are still problems with damp and security.

The problems of the area are not all visible, and have more to do with the people than the property. The biggest problem is unemployment — male unemployment is 30–40%, caused by the decline of the traditional local industries of shipbuilding, chemicals and engineering. Unemployment means low income and, as there are also a lot of retired people living in the area, 70% of the council tenants are in receipt of housing benefit.

Social problems such as marriage breakdown, low academic attainment, drug abuse and petty crime are endemic. An additional problem is that of isolation — many of the estates are 6–8 km from the city centre, and transport is an unaffordable luxury. Car ownership is low. Facilities are provided but they are restricted and choice is limited. Each estate tends to look inwards rather than outwards, and this means that its residents have low aspirations. Few people who do not live in these estates will have cause to visit them.

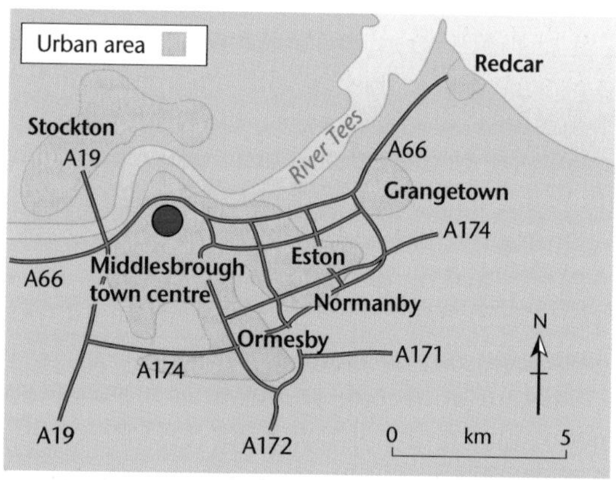

Figure 12.10 Housing estates in east Middlesbrough

Inner-city high-rise developments

High-rise flats were a common feature of both inner-city renewal and peripheral council estates in the 1960s and 1970s. Some were well built, but many were not. People hated living in them because:

- they lacked community feel
- they were poorly ventilated and suffered from damp
- they were expensive to heat
- the open spaces designed to develop a sense of community spirit actually belonged to no-one, so no-one cared for them and they were soon vandalised
- poor design led to many 'hidden' places where hooliganism and criminal activity took place

Many cities were, therefore, saddled with a nightmare combination of run-down old housing and unpopular new housing. Many councils have either already demolished these flats or are considering doing so.

Homelessness

In 2001, around 400,000 people in the UK were officially recognised by the government as being homeless. According to the charity Shelter, this is only the tip of the iceberg.

What does the word 'homeless' mean?

Many people think of a homeless person as someone sleeping rough in a doorway on a city street. Every night, there are about 600 people sleeping rough in London. Shelter estimates that there are 2,000 more in other towns and cities in the UK.

However, this is only the visible part of the problem. There are thousands of others who are also in need of a proper home. These people may be staying with relatives, sleeping on a friend's floor, living in a hostel or squatting.

Local authorities have a duty to house homeless people who are in priority need. This includes families with children, pregnant women, people considered to be vulnerable and those with a physical or mental disability. It does not include most single homeless people or couples without children.

Why do people become homeless?

Personal reasons for becoming homeless include:

- the breakdown of a relationship with a parent or partner
- being asked to leave by friends or relatives who can no longer provide a home
- fleeing domestic violence and abuse
- job or income loss which has led to a person falling behind with the rent or mortgage
- being an asylum seeker or refugee who has been allowed to stay in the UK

Political reasons include:

- a fall in the amount of new social (council) housing, as funding from central government has been reduced
- the closure of institutions aimed at the care of those with special needs and the discharge of their patients under the Care in the Community scheme
- the rapid inflation of house rents and prices in the 1980s and 1990s

Housing Associations

Housing Associations are one solution to the problems of housing shortages and lack of access to housing in many deprived urban areas. They are non-profit-making organisations set up to provide rented accommodation. Initially they were the third type of housing provider after the private sector and local authorities, but during the last 20 years their influence has increased. They use a system in which they borrow private capital either to build new houses or to buy existing housing stock (e.g. former council housing, NCB housing or even ex-military housing), and seek to make returns on their investments for further reinvestment. As they also receive government subsidy, they are able to provide housing for many people at lower rents.

They are also part of the strategy to encourage greater home ownership — people are initially offered housing for rent, but in the longer term may opt to buy the property. Some Housing Associations in inner cities use this system to initiate the process of home ownership in areas where this is not the norm. In some cases, Housing Associations may offer rental packages on furniture and other household items.

Case study The Stockbridge Village Trust Housing Association scheme

The Cantril Farm estate, on the eastern edge of Liverpool, is part of Knowsley Metropolitan Borough Council. The estate was built in the 1960s to rehouse people displaced by slum clearance in the city centre. In many ways the estate was a typical housing redevelopment of the time, including two-storey houses, maisonettes and high-rise flats.

Aims of the trust

In 1983 the estate was purchased by the Stockbridge Village Trust with loans from banks, building societies and Knowsley Council itself. The estate consisted of 3,000 homes in various states of deterioration, and there were signs of the population moving out. It was predicted that half the estate would be empty by the mid-1990s.

The trust was established as a non-profit-making association with four main aims:

- to demolish the most unpopular and unsafe buildings
- to refurbish the remaining housing stock
- to develop new private housing for sale and rent
- to redevelop the service provision of the estate, in particular shopping and leisure facilities

The trust was supported by the government of the time. The Merseyside Task Force had been established to coordinate the variety of initiatives in the Merseyside area and an allocation of urban programme funds was made available.

Problems

By 1985 the pace of change was not as fast as had been hoped. The costs of refurbishment of each house were more than double the original estimate (£6,700 rather than £3,000), the cost of redeveloping the shopping centre had risen from £2 million to £6 million, and only a small number of private houses had been built and sold.

There were two main difficulties. Rents were the main source of income, but these were subject to the fair rents legislation. In addition, incomes in the area were so low that few people could afford to buy houses under the right to buy scheme. The financial position of the trust gave cause for concern, and was made worse by the high interest rates at the time. It was clear that further support from local and national government was necessary or the scheme would collapse.

Progress

The Department for the Environment and Knowsley Council had to provide an extra £5 million between them. By 1987 most of the housing stock had been refurbished. Over 250 new houses had been built for rent, and a private developer had constructed over 125 houses, all of which had been sold. The trust built a new shopping centre, and Knowsley Council started work on a new leisure centre. The demolition of the high-rise flats also began.

During the 1990s the objective of the trust was to continue its housing programme. Housing repairs were to continue and there was a move to broaden the type of tenure. A further 250 new houses were built, some for rent and some for shared ownership. Private developers were also encouraged to add further properties to the area. The management role of the Housing Association is one of ensuring close collaboration between the public and private sectors to provide good-quality housing for all.

Inner-city initiatives

A number of governments since the Second World War have tried to regenerate declining urban areas. The main schemes that have taken place since 1980 are described below.

Property-led regeneration

Urban Development Corporations (UDCs) were set up in the 1980s and 1990s to take responsibility for the physical, economic and social regeneration of selected inner-city areas with large amounts of derelict and vacant land. They are an example of what is known as property-led regeneration. They were given planning approval powers over and above those of the local authority, and were encouraged to spend public money on the purchase of land, the building of infrastructure and on marketing to attract private investment. The intention was that private investment would be four to five times greater than the public money initially invested.

The appointed boards of UDCs, mostly made up of people from the local business community, had the power to acquire, reclaim and service land prior to private-sector involvement and to provide financial incentives to attract private investors. In 1981, two UDCs were established — the London Docklands Development Corporation (LDDC) and a Merseyside UDC. Eleven others followed, in areas such as the Lower Don Valley in Sheffield, Birmingham Heartlands, Trafford Park in Manchester and Cardiff Bay (Figure 12.11).

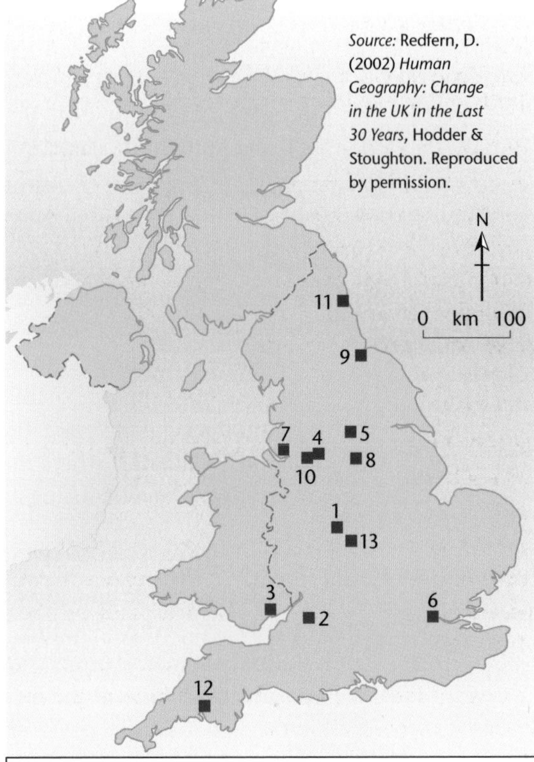

Figure 12.11 ***Urban Development Corporations***

Source: Redfern, D. (2002) *Human Geography: Change in the UK in the Last 30 Years*, Hodder & Stoughton. Reproduced by permission.

Location	Date started	Expenditure (£million) 1992/93	1995/96	Lifetime targets Land reclaimed	Housing (units)	Jobs
London Docklands	1981	293.9	88	846.5	24,036	75,458
Merseyside	1981	42.1	34	384.0	3,544	23,357
Trafford Park	1987	61.3	29.7	400.6	3,774	21,440
Black Country	1987	68.0	36.6	525.3	1,403	10,212
Teesside	1987	34.5	47.5	210.8	311	25,618
Tyne and Wear	1987	50.2	43.5	517.7	4,842	34,043
Central Manchester	1988	20.5	13.7	60.0	661	4,590
Cardiff Bay	1988	—	—	250.0	950	2,200
Leeds	1988	9.6	—	35.3	2,581	5,074
Sheffield	1988	15.9	11.6	68.0	561	8,369
Bristol	1989	20.4	8.7	259.6	0	17,616
Birmingham Heartlands	1992	5.0	11.7	129.1	878	5,983
Plymouth	1993	n/a	10.6	12.7	93	491

Table 12.1 Expenditure and targets of UDCs

By 1993, UDCs accounted for nearly 40% of all urban regeneration policy expenditure. Over £12 billion of private-sector investment had been attracted, along with £4 billion from the public sector. They had built or refurbished 35,000 housing units, and created 190,000 jobs (Table 12.1).

Criticisms of UDCs

Some people argued that this amount of new employment was inadequate. There were two more significant criticisms. First, the UDCs were too dependent on property speculation and they lost huge sums of money through the compulsory purchase of land which subsequently fell in value. Second, because they had greater powers than local authorities, democratic accountability was removed. Local people often complained that they had no involvement in the developments taking place. Indeed, there were some examples, particularly in the London Docklands, where the local people felt physically and socially excluded by prestigious new housing and high-technology office developments.

Partnerships between government and the private sector

City Challenge Partnerships represented a major switch of funding mechanisms towards competitive bidding. To gain funding a local authority had to come up with an imaginative project and form a partnership in its local inner-city area with the private sector and the local communities. The partnership then submitted a 5-year plan to central government in competition with other inner-city areas. The most successful schemes combined social aims with economic and environmental outcomes. By 1993, over 30 City Challenge Partnerships had been established and another 20 or more bids had been unsuccessful. By the end of that year partnerships accounted for over 20% of expenditure on inner-city regeneration.

Case study Central Manchester Development Corporation (CMDC)

CMDC is an example of a Development Corporation established after the LDDC, in 1988.

A partnership between the local authority and private developers was created. Its aim was to regenerate 200 ha of land and buildings in the southern sector of Manchester city centre. The area contained decaying warehouses, offices, former mills and contaminated land, unsightly railway viaducts and neglected waterways. It had been declared a conservation area in 1979.

Some of the buildings were refurbished into a range of uses including housing. For example, in the Whitworth Street district, warehouses were converted and redeveloped to create a village-like community of more than 1,000 household units, pubs, bars, restaurants and shops. The canals in the area were cleaned, and their banks were improved by the addition of lighting, seats and plants, all in an effort to improve the aesthetics of the area. This has now become a very popular entertainment-based area for young people.

The CMDC engaged in widespread consultation and formulated a development strategy that complemented the plans of Manchester City Council. For example, Castlefield, which was once an area of disused canals, wharves and warehouses, became a mixture of housing (including some luxury apartments), office developments and leisure facilities.

The area also developed its tourist potential and now attracts over 2 million visitors a year. Attractions include the world famous tour of Granada Studios, the Manchester Museum of Science and Technology, the GMEX Centre and the Bridgewater Concert Hall complex.The CMDC was disbanded in 1996, and planning powers have now reverted to Manchester City Council.

How City Challenge worked

The City Challenge initiative was designed to address some of the weaknesses of the earlier regeneration schemes. The participating organisations — the partners — were better coordinated and more involved. This particularly applied to the residents of the area and the local authority. Separate schemes and initiatives operating in the same area, as had happened before, were not allowed — the various strands of the projects had to work together. Many earlier initiatives had concentrated on improving buildings, whereas City Challenge gave equal importance to buildings, people and values. Cooperation between local authorities and private and public groups, some of which were voluntary, was prioritised.

All the City Challenge areas suffered from high youth and long-term unemployment, a low skills base, poor levels of educational attainment, environmental deterioration, increasing areas of derelict land and growing commercial property vacancy. Public-sector housing was deteriorating in almost all the City Challenge areas due to a combination of poor initial design and inadequate maintenance. The population of these areas usually had a higher than national average incidence of healthcare problems, high levels of personal crime and fear of crime, a high proportion of single-parent families and households dependent on social security.

Case study Hulme City Challenge Partnership

The Hulme area of Manchester was redeveloped as part of a slum clearance programme in the 1960s and a number of high-rise flats were built. Of the 5,500 dwellings, 98% were council owned. Over half of the dwellings were part of a deck access system, with many of the bad design features of prefabricated construction. The area had a low level of families with children, and a disproportionate number of single-person households. There was also a high number of single parents, and other people with social difficulties. There was some evidence that the local authority had used the area to 'dump' some of its more unfortunate residents.

Redevelopment

In 1992, under the Hulme City Challenge Partnership, plans were drawn up to build 3,000 new homes, with new shopping areas, roads and community facilities. A more traditional pattern of housing development was designed, with streets, squares, two-storey houses and low-rise flats. By 1995, 50 ha of land had been reclaimed, the majority of the former deck access flats had been demolished, 600 new homes for rent had been built, and over 400 homes had been improved and refurbished. The main shopping area was totally refurbished, including the addition of an ASDA supermarket. A new community centre, the Zion Centre, was also constructed. Crime in the area has been greatly reduced, and there is more of a social mix of people living in the area. The appearance of Hulme has altered radically.

The partners

A number of agencies and organisations were responsible for this transformation, including the Guinness Trust and Bellway Homes. These worked in close collaboration with each other and with Manchester City Council. The company responsible for Manchester airport also invested capital in the project. Hulme is a good example of how the public and private sectors can work together to improve a previously declining and socially challenging area.

The priorities of the different City Challenge areas varied. In Liverpool, priority was given to environmental improvement, while in Wolverhampton a science park formed the centrepiece of the project. In Hulme, Manchester, housing improvement was the main focus (see case study above).

Was the initiative successful?

Overall, the competition between areas for funding was believed to be successful — improving the quality of proposals and encouraging new and more imaginative ideas. The private sector, in particular, found the competitive principle attractive and argued that competition had encouraged local authorities to suggest solutions as well as identifying problems. However, the competitive nature of the scheme was criticised by others on the grounds that large sums of money should have been allocated according to need, not competitive advantage.

In some cases neighbouring authorities competed against each other when they could have worked together. It is rare for the limits of disadvantaged areas to coincide with an administrative boundary. The policy that all successful bidders should receive exactly the same sum of money, irrespective of need, was also criticised. Finally, competing authorities were not given clear information about the criteria on which their application was to be judged — for some it was a stab in the dark.

By 1997 the Conservative government was able to publish statistics pointing towards the success of City Challenge. Over 40,000 houses had been improved,

53,000 jobs had been created, nearly 2,000 ha of derelict land had been reclaimed, and over 3,000 new businesses had been established.

Schemes and strategies of the twenty-first century

In the early years of the twenty-first century, the Labour government moved in two main directions in its attempts to regenerate and redevelop urban environments in the UK.

- It created **prestige project developments** (also known as **flagship projects**), such as the waterfront developments in Cardiff Bay, the Convention Centre area of Birmingham (see case study below) and the St Stephen's Development in Kingston-upon-Hull (see case study, page 381).
- It began to develop **sustainable communities** in a variety of UK towns and cities (see case study below). In theoretical terms, urban **economic sustainability** should allow the individuals and communities who live in cities to have access to a home, a job and a reliable income. Urban **social sustainability** should provide a reasonable quality of life and opportunities to maximise personal potential through education and health provision, and through participation in local democracies.

Case study *The Convention Centre area, Birmingham*

Brindleyplace, just to the west of Birmingham city centre, was redeveloped during the 1990s. It covers an area of 6 ha alongside some of Birmingham's old canals. The development cost £250 million and has become a model for redevelopment of other parts of the city. At the heart of the redevelopment is the International Convention Centre (ICC), built in 1991, which is the largest such centre in the UK. Surrounding it are:

- 79,000 m^2 of office space
- 11,500 m^2 of shops
- 140 luxury flats
- the National Indoor Arena
- a sea-life centre
- the new regional headquarters of BT

The Brindleyplace redevelopment has made a dramatic improvement to the physical appearance of Birmingham. It has attracted many more people to the city for both business and pleasure.

However, there are mixed feelings about the development among the residents of Birmingham. Although many new jobs have been created, fewer than half have gone to local people. Many are low-paid, short-term jobs in the retail and tourism sectors. The development has provided no affordable housing for people living in the inner city. Indeed, it has forced up house prices in the surrounding area, making affordable housing harder to find.

Case study *Sustainable communities in London*

The Labour government has stated that the sustainable communities initiative has the following general aims:

> We will work closely with our key regional partners to identify practical steps to ensure that we have communities that:
>
> - are prosperous
> - have decent homes for sale or rent at a price people can afford
> - safeguard green and open space
> - enjoy a well-designed, accessible and pleasant living and working environment
> - are effectively and fairly governed with a strong sense of community

There is an urgent need for more affordable homes all over London to accommodate its growing population and to reduce homelessness. It is also essential that workers who are key to the delivery of the capital's public services are able to afford to live and work within its communities. The Government Office for London (GOL) is working with the Greater London Authority (GLA), local authorities and relevant agencies (the Housing Corporation, English Partnerships, the Commission for Architecture and the Built Environment [CABE] and English Heritage) to achieve these aims.

Photograph 12.4 Oxo Tower Wharf

TopFoto

Examples

The Holly Street estate redevelopment in Hackney has transformed a whole community. In addition to the newly created neighbourhood of small streets, small blocks of flats and brick-built houses with pitched roofs and gardens, a sports and community centre, an elderly persons' day centre and a health centre have also been provided. Alongside the aim of redeveloping the housing on the estate, the project sought to remove the fear of crime, improve security and improve the mental and physical health of residents, thus reducing the pressure on health services.

Greenwich Millennium Village is being developed on a brownfield site and is part of the larger Greenwich Peninsula development. Over a period of 5 years, 1,377 homes are being built, including homes for social rent or shared ownership. Sustainability, energy efficiency, waste management and quality in design and construction are key features of this project. The Millennium Primary School and Health Centre in the village is providing education, training, healthcare, crèche and other community facilities on one site.

Coin Street Community Builders (CSCB) is a social enterprise that has built social housing and commercial developments, including Oxo Tower Wharf, on London's South Bank. CSCB does not distribute profits from its commercial activities but uses them to cross-subsidise activities which otherwise would not be viable, including an arts and leisure programme. Its four housing developments are run by 'fully-mutual' cooperatives and provide 220 affordable homes for people in housing need.

Indicators of inequality within urban areas

In towns and cities, the quality of life varies from one area to another and produces patterns of inequality. These develop as a result of the decisions taken by individual families in the housing market. People with more money tend to move to areas with a better quality of life; people who are less well-off live in areas with a poorer quality of life. Typically, richer people move to the less crowded outer suburbs, leaving poorer people behind in the inner city. In recent years,

Ward	Population change 1981–2001 (%)	Under 16 years (%)	Over 65 years (%)	Those with long-term illness (%)	Home owners (%)	Renting from local authority (%)	No car (%)	Women in employment (%)
1	0.8	24	18	12	45	46	41	57
2	–7.4	18	21	8	70	22	27	69
3	–4.2	19	20	12	69	18	31	68
4	–4.9	24	10	6	92	3	13	67
5	–12.6	20	10	6	98	0	14	72
6	3.1	16	18	10	81	3	29	72
7	5.6	19	20	10	80	15	23	70
8	–10.2	18	18	10	67	19	25	66
9	12.4	22	23	11	59	38	30	63
10	68.7	25	7	6	88	6	12	73
11	197.0	24	7	5	85	9	11	72
12	–12.7	18	14	8	95	2	13	70
13	–9.6	17	21	11	64	30	30	67

Table 12.2 Population data for an area in southern England

inner-city redevelopment and suburbanisation have begun to change the established patterns. Some inner-city areas have become more desirable and some suburban estates have deteriorated.

Physical features such as rivers, relief and natural vegetation can affect the quality of life, as well as the location of major land users such as transport, industry and commerce. This is turn has an effect on the quality of life of those living nearby.

Government planning regulations in the UK have made an impact on urban patterns. The government designated certain areas of land around towns and cities as **green belt**. This has restricted urban growth in those areas but has encouraged it elsewhere, where the restrictions do not apply. In addition, local governments allowed council housing in certain areas of a town or city, but not in others. This impacted on the quality of life of those who lived on, or near, such estates.

The data in Table 12.2 were collected as part of a survey of the variations in social and economic conditions in an urban area in southern England. Similar data can be collected by means of the census for any urban area in the UK.

Using the data in Table 12.2 you could:

- discuss how each of the indicators might reflect quality of life
- choose which four indicators would be the most useful for this purpose
- conduct a correlation test and/or construct a scattergraph for pairs of indicators to assess the strength of the relationship between them
- calculate a socioeconomic index for each ward

To calculate a socioeconomic index, eight indicators are used to assess social and economic wellbeing or deprivation. The values for each indicator are ranked from 1 to 13 to produce an indicator score. Rank 1 represents high wellbeing; rank 13 represents high deprivation. For example, consider the indicator 'the percentage with no car'. The ward with the lowest percentage of people that do not have a car is ward 11. It is ranked 1. The ward with the highest percentage of people with no car, ward 1, is ranked 13.

The rank scores for each indicator are added together to produce a total score — a social and economic index. The maximum score (most deprivation) for the index is 104, if one ward is ranked 13 for each of the eight indicators.

This is a complicated task. You have to:

- think carefully about what would be an indicator of wellbeing or deprivation and rank accordingly
- be careful of tied ranks

The LEDW case

The growth, location and characteristics of shanty towns

In Chapter 5, the shanty towns (favelas) and housing improvement schemes of São Paulo were examined as an example of the impact of urbanisation in the LEDW. Here, shanty towns are considered as global phenomena of urban deprivation.

Most newcomers to a city in the LEDW would like to rent a proper house. However, they have little money. Even if they could afford to rent, there are usually not enough houses available. Instead:

- Many new arrivals move in with friends or relatives.
- Some people sleep on the streets. In some cities, thousands of people live rough. Most railway stations in India have a well-established resident population. People know who 'owns' each patch of pavement and the street people protect each other from outsiders. Street dwellers can include families in which three generations live together. There are also gangs of orphaned or abandoned children.
- Many people squat. They build a makeshift house on unused land, in an area of similar houses. This creates a squatter settlement or shanty town.

People squat on three main types of land:

- land that is not really suitable for building because it is too steep, too marshy or too polluted
- land close to the city centre that has not been built on because no-one knows who owns it, or the owner has left it empty, hoping it will increase in value
- land on the edge of the city that was once farmland but was abandoned as the city spread

It is not uncommon for local authorities to help people in such settlements by providing them with water and electricity, while leaving them to do most of the building work. Around the world, squatter settlements (shanty towns) have a variety of local names:

- in Spanish-speaking Latin American cities — barrios
- in Portuguese speaking Brazil — favelas
- in Mumbai, India — zopadpattis
- in Calcutta, India — bustees

Slums of hope or slums of despair?

Squatter settlements are often seen as places of deprivation — slums of despair. It is true that in many cases the physical, economic and social conditions are very poor. However, it is all a matter of perception. Other people see them as

Slums of despair	Slums of hope
High unemployment and underemployment	Some formal employment and much informal employment
Weak family and friendship structures	Strong family and friendship structures
Poorly built housing and little on-going improvement	Housing improvement through individual and group action
Poor water supply and sewerage	Water supply being improved with help from authorities; sewage usually stored in septic tanks and removed by tanker
Easy spread of infections and disease	Infections and disease under control
Illegal hook-ups to the electricity mains, or no supply at all	Illegal hook-ups to the electricity mains, which are gradually being replaced by legal connections
Widespread crime, prostitution, drug-dealing and other social problems due to poverty and lack of police control	Crime, prostitution and drug dealing not widespread because of strong social structures and cooperation between the community and the police
Settlement appears untidy and poorly organised; much litter, rubbish and piles of junk around houses	Settlement appears tidy and fairly well organised; piles of junk around houses are the raw materials of earning a living (recycling activities); much evidence of informal economy
City authorities opposed to settlement; threats to bulldoze houses make squatters insecure and cause the settlement to deteriorate	Cooperation between the settlement and the authorities, which do their best to provide an infrastructure of roads, bus services, education, healthcare, electricity and water

Table 12.3 Slums of hope or slums of despair?

'slums of hope' (Table 12.3). In reality, most settlements have some features of both hope and despair.

Urban regeneration in the LEDW

City authorities in the LEDW are aware of the problems of large squatter settlements, but rarely have enough resources to tackle them.

- In some cities, such as Lagos in Nigeria and Caracas in Venezuela, the authorities have built **high-rise apartment blocks** to re-house people. However, in most places this is not a practical solution because there is not enough money available.
- In some countries, the authorities have tried to help migrants to the city by allowing them to build houses according to certain guidelines in **site and service schemes**. An area of land is found which is not too far from workplaces in the city. It is divided into individual plots by the authorities. Roads, water and sanitation may be provided. Newcomers can rent a plot of land and build their own house, following the guidelines. As time goes by, and they have more money, they can improve their house.
- Once people have built a house, no matter how basic it is, they are likely to improve it. However, they will only do this if they are confident they will not be evicted from the land. If people are to improve their homes they must be given legal ownership of the land. **Self-help schemes** are important in almost all big cities in the LEDW. People improve their houses slowly, for example by replacing mud walls with bricks or breeze blocks and fitting proper windows

and doors. Houses may gradually be enlarged by building more rooms and then by adding upper floors. City authorities usually provide clean water from standpipes in the street and, later, help with sanitation and waste collection. Commercial bus operators will start services to the settlement and the local community may build health centres. In this way, people work together to improve the area. Over time it changes from a poor, illegal settlement to a legal, medium-quality housing area.

The brown agenda

Cities in the LEDW are affected by the **brown agenda**, a mix of social and environmental problems brought about by rapid growth and industrialisation, associated with economic development. It has two distinct components:

- traditional issues associated with environmental health, caused by the limited availability of good-quality land, shelter and services such as clean water
- problems resulting from rapid industrialisation, such as toxic or hazardous waste, water, air and noise pollution, and industrial accidents owing to poor standards of health and safety

In all cases it is the low-income groups in the cities that suffer most.

In many LEDW cities, water is contaminated by sewage and untreated industrial waste. City managers have to tackle these pollution issues without sufficient resources. However, environmental problems are not always solved by technology and capital. The empowerment of low-income communities to bring about their own improvements is equally important.

International bodies (such as the UN) have proposed city-specific solutions to the brown agenda. A suggested management framework to enable these solutions to be carried out is as follows:

1. A basic urban environmental profile should be undertaken. There should be public consultation over what the main issues are, and a political commitment to improve.
2. The risks, impacts and purposes of improvement strategies should be assessed. A cost–benefit analysis of all the available options should be undertaken.
3. Action plans should be put into place. Specific task forces aimed at specific districts and/or citywide problems should be created.
4. Local support groups should be established, with training for community leaders. Further consultation and involvement at a local level are priorities.

These broad principles will now be examined in specific case studies of Calcutta and Cairo. You should assess the extent to which the above principles are being followed in these cities.

Case study Calcutta, India

Calcutta lies in the Ganges delta, at the centre of an area that has a dense, overcrowded rural population. The soils of the delta are fertile, but the area suffers many natural disasters. It is often flooded by monsoon rains or by cyclones. In the late twentieth century, the area suffered from wars and civil conflicts. Each new war or flood brings refugees flocking to Calcutta.

Issues

The land is low-lying, so many of the squatter settlements (bustees) flood easily. The floods not only destroy homes, they also bring disease in the polluted floodwater. Until recently, Calcutta had a reputation for some of the worst slums in the world. It was here that Mother Theresa cared for thousands of street people.

Solutions

The Calcutta Metropolitan Development Authority (CMDA) has tried to improve the infrastructure by:

- reinforcing the banks of the River Hooghly and attempting to stop people from squatting on the lowest-lying land near the river
- improving sewage disposal — in the 1960s there were about 1,000 sewage-related deaths a year from cholera, but in recent years there have been very few
- improving the water supply — there is now at least one tap for every 25 bustee houses
- replacing mud tracks between the shacks with concrete roads
- installing street lighting in many bustees, to improve safety and to give some light to people with no electricity in their homes
- widening roads and improving public transport from the bustees into the city centre

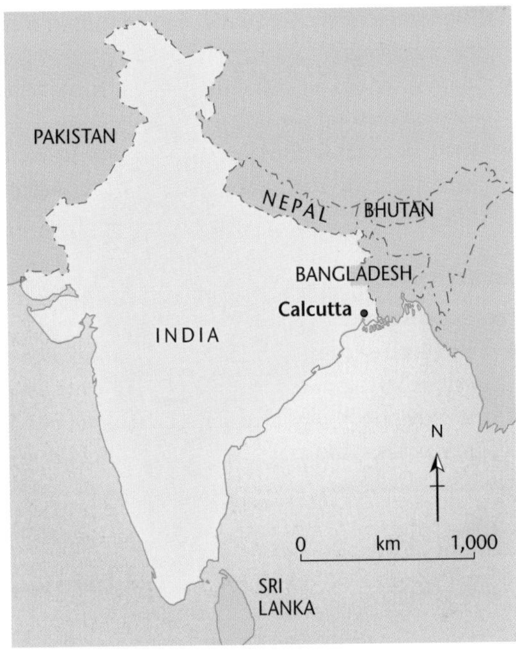

Figure 12.12 Map showing the location of Calcutta

The CMDA does not work on the bustee houses. The occupiers must improve their homes themselves.

Case study Cairo, Egypt

Cairo is built on raised land (the Magattam Hills), close to the River Nile. It is located between the fertile farmlands of the Nile Delta to the north and the irrigated land alongside the Nile to the south. Cairo has a very high population density (over 32,000 km^{-2}) and infant mortality rate (105 per 1,000 live births).

Issues

The main issues in Cairo are that:

- 30% of the city has no public sewage system; 55% of waste water is untreated as it travels through open canals and rivers to the sea.
- Although the city does not have extensive areas of squatter settlements (examples include Bulaq and Chobra), many people live in inappropriate locations — for example in the Cities of the Dead

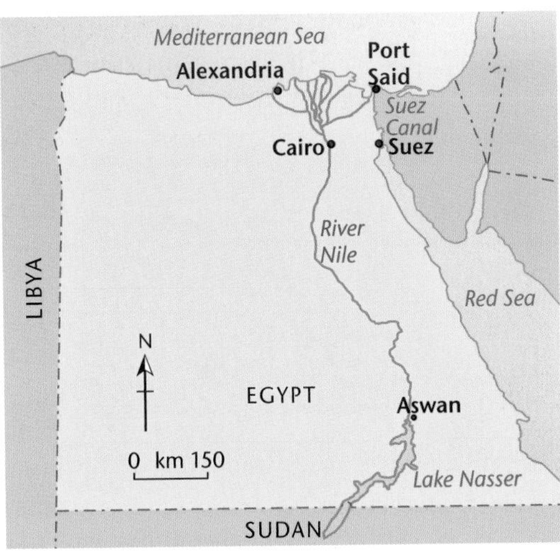

Figure 12.13 Map showing the location of Cairo

(the tombs of old Cairo) and on rooftops in make-shift dwellings.

- There is serious air pollution, caused by traffic and open-air cooking stoves.
- Waste disposal is disorganised. In some areas, it is carried out by the zabbaleen (waste collectors) using donkey carts.

Solutions

Possible solutions to these issues are:

- a project to repair existing sewers and to extend the system to those parts of the city currently not served
- the provision of pipes carrying clean water into the Cities of the Dead and to the roof-top homes
- the provision of low-cost accommodation in high-rise flats in new satellite towns in the desert such as 'Ramadan 10' and '15 May'
- schemes to reduce the numbers of vehicles on the road, in particular by extending the underground metro system
- the organisation of a subsidised waste collection system across the city
- giving the zabbaleen funds to purchase additional carts. These people already collect much of the city's rubbish and recycle it. They could be enabled to cover the entire city and thereby increase the rates of recycling of paper, plastic and metal

Environmental issues

Pollution

Air pollution in urban areas of MEDCs is covered in Chapter 2.

Pollution problems in the LEDW

Most mega cities in the LEDW have enormous environmental problems and can be regarded as unsustainable. Examples that are frequently quoted are Mexico City, Bangkok, Manila and Calcutta. The problems are further compounded in that most development and industrial activity is concentrated in these dominant or primate cities (see Table 12.4).

Waste disposal

The average person in the UK produces 350 kg of household waste every year. Waste disposal in the UK is efficient, so people are not generally aware of the problems that waste is creating. In recycling, reusing and managing household waste, the UK has lagged behind many other countries, particularly some in the EU. Many people feel that we need to change our attitude to household waste — to see it as a resource to be managed rather than as a nuisance to be disposed of.

Waste disposal measures

Landfill

Waste is dumped in old quarries or hollows, which is convenient and cheap. However, it is unsightly and is a serious threat to groundwater and river quality because toxic chemicals can leach out and contaminate the water. Decaying matter at landfill sites also produces methane gas. This is not only explosive; it is also a potent greenhouse gas. To discourage use of landfill sites, a landfill tax could be imposed.

Problem	Example	Causes
Air pollution	Air in cities such as Cairo is so poor that breathing it is the equivalent of smoking 60 cigarettes a day; major chemical and gas explosions, e.g. Bhopal, India	Traffic, factories, waste incineration plants and power plants, particularly where they are old and badly maintained Accidental spillages and explosions; poor health-and-safety standards
Water pollution	Untreated sewage in the River Ganges (from Varanasi and Kanpur)	Leaking sewers, landfill sites and industrial waste including oil and chemicals
Waste disposal	25% of all urban dwellers in the LEDW have no adequate sanitation and no means of sewage disposal, especially in squatter settlements	Volumes of liquid sewage and industrial waste have increased considerably Contamination and health hazards arise from poor systems of disposal, rat infestation and waterborne diseases More solid wastes (paper and packaging) are being created as general levels of affluence rise
Water supply	The overuse of groundwater supplies has led to subsidence and flooding, e.g. in Bangkok	Cities consume huge amounts of water, especially as incomes and living standards rise; aquifers become depleted
Transport-related issues	Traffic queues in Mexico City are over 90 km each day; private car ownership in Taipei has increased 100-fold over a period of 20 years	Rising vehicle ownership leads to congestion, noise pollution, accidents and health issues related to the release of carbon monoxide, nitrogen oxides, ozone and particulates Under certain conditions, photochemical smog can develop

Table 12.4 ***Pollution problems in the LEDW and their causes***

Energy recovery

Waste material can be converted into energy. The main method is incineration. In the past, many councils burnt their waste, but this adds to carbon dioxide emissions and releases pollutants into the atmosphere. Many old, polluting incinerators have therefore been closed down. Some modern incinerators generate electricity or power neighbourhood heating schemes and are considered to be a sustainable option for waste disposal.

Composting

On a small scale, organic waste (kitchen scraps and garden waste) can be used to make compost to fertilise gardens or farmland. On a much bigger scale, 'anaerobic' digestion is an advanced form of composting in an enclosed reactor. Biological treatment of organic waste speeds up the breakdown process. The biogases produced can be used to provide an energy supply and the solid residue can be used as a soil conditioner. Germany, Denmark and Italy all have such plants. However, they are expensive to set up.

Recycling

Waste products such as paper, glass, metal cans, plastics and clothes can be recycled if they can be collected economically. However, the initial start-up costs of recycling schemes can be high and the market value of the material may be low. Householders may also be unwilling to sort recyclables from their other household waste.

Photograph 12.5 A landfill site in Northern Ireland

TopFoto

Case study Waste disposal in Newcastle-upon Tyne

For many years, Newcastle-upon-Tyne has based most of its waste disposal at the Byker incineration plant.

- Waste is collected in lorries and taken to the separation plant. Giant magnets remove all the waste that contains iron or steel. This is sent for recycling.
- What remains is broken up and put into giant drums called centrifuges. These whirl round the waste to separate out material of different densities. Valuable metals like copper, lead and aluminium are then also sent for recycling.
- The residue is burnt in the incinerator.
- The heat from this incinerator heats water, which produces steam. This is used for central heating in the flats in the Byker Wall development and to heat the nearby swimming pool.
- The small amount of ash residue is either taken by barge and dumped at sea, or taken to be buried in landfill sites.

There are some environmental problems with this system. Much of the material burned in the incinerator is plastic. If the incinerator is not hot enough, fumes are produced that can cause health problems. In addition, ash dumped at sea makes the sea bed sterile, and has damaged some fishing grounds.

Case study Waste disposal in London

Landfill sites are used extensively in the London area. The main risk is that gases released from buried waste may contaminate the area in the long term. Current legislation states that new housing developments should not be within 250 m of a restored or currently operational landfill site.

One problem on landfill sites is the disposable nappy. It costs £40 million a year to dispose of an estimated 1 million tonnes of nappy waste, of which 75% is urine and faeces. Most nappy waste is taken to landfill sites where it adds to the build-up of methane gas. Once paper, glass and plastic have been removed, councils have found that nappies account for 15% of household waste. Nappies take an estimated 500 years to break down.

Case study Waste disposal in Kenya

In the LEDW, recycling is often an important part of the everyday economy. It is common for people to collect and make use of other people's rubbish.

Waste tips are scavenged for any recoverable or recyclable materials. For instance:

- old car tyres are cut up and used to make cheap sandals
- tin cans and old oil drums are used to make charcoal stoves, lamps, buckets and metal tips for ploughs
- glass bottles are collected and returned to stores for refilling
- food waste is collected and fed to animals or composted for use on vegetable plots

Waste is seen as an economic opportunity — it is often the easiest, and sometimes the only, way of making money.

Urban ecosystems

Urban areas contain a wide variety of habitats including:

- industrial sites and derelict land
- residential gardens and allotments
- parks and other open green areas
- transport routes such as canals, roadside verges and railway embankments
- urban forests and bodies of water

Each of these habitats contains a different mix of flora and fauna. Human impact also makes urban habitats somewhat unstable. Many of the plants and animals were introduced recently and there are relatively few indigenous (native) species. Cities are centres for the establishment and spread of foreign species; their vegetation contains a far higher proportion of exotic plants than that of rural areas. Such species include:

- Canadian goldenrod and aster from North America
- sycamore, laburnum, wormwood and goat's-rue from Europe
- buddleia and Japanese knotweed from China and Japan

They might be introduced to an area by escaping from neighbouring gardens, or from seed carried by the wind, birds and other animals, or forms of transport.

Urban areas are attractive for immigrant species because of the variety of habitats, the constant creation of new habitats and the reduced level of competition. Many of these habitats are specialised. On one site there can be a number of niches or microhabitats available for plants and animals to colonise. For example, on an abandoned and neglected urban site, available niches for plants could include:

- horizontal bare tarmac
- tops of walls
- vertical stone and brick walls
- rubble-strewn ground

Transport routes

Routeways are distinctive habitats because exotic species of plants and insects may be brought in by traffic or train. They also represent wildlife corridors comparable to rural hedgerows.

Railway lines enable animals to move around the city with little or no interference from traffic. During the days of steam, there were frequent fires on the lines which burnt off tall species and allowed light through, therefore encouraging light-demanding species, for example primrose, to become established. Windborne seeds can be sucked along by the trains, allowing the establishment of plants such as Oxford ragwort. A lack of human interference, because the track is fenced off, encourages wildlife such as badgers and urban foxes to live here. The many areas filled with brambles provide nesting sites for a variety of birds.

Roads act in a similar way, verges and embankments providing homes for kestrels and scavenging birds. The nitrogen-rich exhaust fumes boost the growth of some wildflowers and these in turn increase the presence of insects and animals further up the food chain. However, depending on when it is carried out, the number of wildflowers can be reduced by mowing. Some roadsides are managed; trees and shrubs are planted to act as noise screens and flowers are put in to brighten the landscape, as part of the Britain in Bloom competition or to provide advertising for local businesses.

Canals act like long ponds, providing a habitat for many aquatic plants (e.g. yellow flag iris), waterfowl (e.g. moorhen, duck, kingfisher) and water-loving insects (e.g. dragonflies, damselflies).

Urban conservation areas

Conservation areas are developed for a variety of reasons:

- encouraging wildlife back into cities
- making cheap use of an otherwise derelict area that would be more expensive to set up as a park
- reducing maintenance costs in an area
- maintaining a diverse species base and reintroducing locally extinct species

A great variety of work is done in such areas, including planting of trees and other species, planting of native species, dredging of ponds and other water bodies, and soil improvements. Groups and organisations behind such conservation include local authorities, national government, English Nature (Joint Nature Conservation Council), conservation volunteers, the Groundwork Trust, the National Urban Forestry Unit, the National Trust, English Heritage, potential users of the site and local inhabitants.

There is a range of **attitudes** to conservation of vegetated areas within urban environments. Different groups have different priorities, and these affect their view of conservation. For example, local authorities have planning needs, and have to balance the desire to make use of derelict land against the potential cost to local taxpayers. Conservation groups want to create environments where traditional species can re-establish. Local people often want a safe environment for leisure pursuits and may, through the National Playing Fields Association, wish to see sports fields. Urban wildlife groups prefer areas that provide cover for wildlife. Issues of conservation include the eventual management plan for an area, the resolution of ownership, cost and the satisfaction of the needs of various user groups.

Case study Dulwich Upper Wood conservation area

Dulwich Upper Wood is in southeast London, close to the site of the old Crystal Palace. It is a 2 hectare remnant of a much larger wooded area which once stretched some distance across south London. The park is open at all times and has a network of trails, some of which are suitable for wheelchairs.

Species in the wood

The wood developed from the abandoned gardens of old Victorian houses (now demolished) and a small core of ancient woodland. Trees on the site include sycamores, oak, ash, yew and chestnut, and there is also a magnificent line of lime trees. As most of the ground in the wood is deeply shaded, few of the garden plants remain, apart from shrubs, such as rhododendron and laurel. Plants from the ancient woodland have survived, including wood anemone, lords and ladies, bluebell and yellow pimpernel.

There are over 250 different types of fungi (mushrooms and toadstools) which are best seen in autumn. They live on dead wood or leaf litter, helping to break down these materials and return nutrients to the soil.

Many mammals, such as foxes, bats, mice and hedgehogs, live in the wood and over 40 species of birds nest here including woodpeckers and owls. There are also butterflies, moths and a great variety of other insects.

What makes the site interesting?

Figure 12.14 and the description above give some suggestions as to why the area is so interesting to ecologists and conservationists. Reasons include the following:

- conservation of both abandoned Victorian gardens and ancient woodland
- a number of both preserved and recreated habitats including coppiced areas, wet areas and a pond, herb garden and foxglove area
- the site is both managed and allowed to grow wild in different areas
- there is a range of different habitats
- there is plenty of wildlife on the site including mammals, over 40 species of birds and a wide variety of insects
- 'original' habitats have been preserved, enabling native species of plants and animals to survive
- it is a good example of how habitats can be preserved and created and yet still allow the public access through a network of trails
- the site has an educational value with a posted nature trail

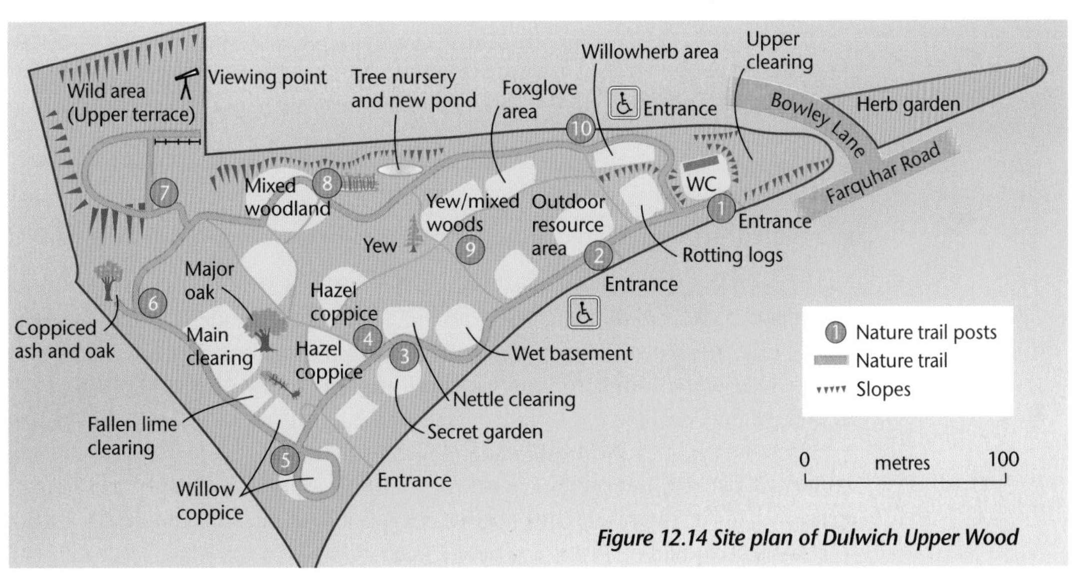

Figure 12.14 Site plan of Dulwich Upper Wood

Containing growth

Green belts

Green belts are an attempt to prevent urban sprawl. They are areas around the major cities in Britain in which planning restrictions were enforced, to curb building and to conserve areas for agriculture and recreation. The first green belt was created around London following the 1947 Town and Country Planning Act. Since then, green belts have been set around a number of other conurbations and cities. In some areas, they are not belts as such, but more like 'wedges'. In Scotland, they are referred to as **buffers**. Green belts serve the following purposes:

- limiting urban sprawl
- preventing neighbouring towns from merging
- preserving the special character of historically or architecturally important towns
- protecting farmland from urban development
- providing recreational areas for city dwellers

Since the establishment of green belts they have been leapfrogged by residential developments. Relatively little development has taken place within them. In the 1980s, they came under renewed pressure. This was particularly true of the green belt around London, as the demand grew for building land within southeast England. As a result, London's green belt was extended outwards.

Green belt restraint has not stopped landowners submitting planning applications for development in these areas. Success in obtaining planning permission is low, but the huge financial rewards for those who do succeed has encouraged land speculation in the rural–urban fringe.

The most spectacular breaching of London's green belt was the construction of the M25. Despite intense opposition from environmentalists and local people, the perceived need to reduce the traffic burden on London was given precedence.

The building of the M25 has put pressure on other parts of the green belt, particularly to the west of London. Anyone who wants to build on green belt land must demonstrate 'exceptional circumstances', such as:

- building science parks
- constructing housing estates in the extensive grounds of large mental hospitals that have been closed
- building on pieces of land cut off by new roads, that are too small to be farmed effectively

Green belts have received criticism from a number of quarters, including the same people who advocated their existence. The main areas of criticism are that:

- they restrict the supply of land for development, thus raising house prices
- they do not serve the recreational needs of urban areas as a whole, because they are used largely by local residents
- they are usually managed in an unimaginative way, and some areas are derelict
- they result in increased commuting distances and greater amounts of traffic-related pollution

Case study The Stepping Stones Project, Leicestershire

The Stepping Stones Project works with community groups, parish councils and landowners in the parishes around Leicester to help enhance the countryside for the benefit of people and wildlife.

The project aims to help protect the landscape and character of **green wedges**, which are open, relatively undeveloped areas of land that prevent the merging of settlements. They are identified in the Leicestershire County Council Structure Plan and the relevant Local Plans. The project is working with people who live in and around green wedges.

There are currently four Green Wedge Management Strategies for Scraptoft, Anstey and Sence, Soar Valley South, and Oadby and Wigston. These strategies offer recommendations for land management in these valuable oases, which can be used as guidance for future development.

The project aims to improve access to the green wedges for all by:

- initiating the development of new routes and circular paths around the project area
- facilitating improvements to access routes making them accessible to all sectors of the community
- promoting and encouraging development of new sites where there are increased opportunities for public enjoyment, appreciation and awareness of the countryside

The project aims to enhance the countryside by:

- promoting and providing advice, technical support and financial assistance on countryside management and environmental improvement issues
- supporting initiatives that encourage and promote sustainable agricultural practice within the project area
- increasing the area and quality of woodland cover, where appropriate
- supporting and promoting opportunities for community-based habitat creation and management schemes

The project aims to improve awareness of the countryside by:

- encouraging opportunities for training courses
- developing and supporting opportunities for environmental education
- promoting responsible use of the countryside

The project aims to encourage community action by:

- encouraging positive action to protect people's environments
- providing some of the resources to enable local people to plan, implement and manage projects on the ground
- facilitating links between the private sector and community groups
- supporting and encouraging nature-conservation volunteers

Source: Adapted from Leicestershire County Council website

Chapter 13

Recreation and tourism

The resource base

Tourism

Tourists can be classified according to the purpose of their visits:

- **leisure and recreation tourists** — holiday, sports and cultural tourism and visiting friends and relatives
- **business and professional tourists** — meetings, conferences and missions
- **other tourists** can include study and health tourists

Tourists can also be classified according to their behaviours and perceptions:

- the **mass-organised tourist** — low on adventurousness; typically purchases a ready-made package tour, is guided throughout by tour operators, hoteliers and guides and has little contact with local culture and people
- the **individual mass tourist** — similar to the above, but with more flexibility and scope for personal choice; the tour is still organised by the tourism industry
- the **explorer** — organises the trip independently and wants to get off the beaten track; comfortable accommodation and reliable transport are still sought
- the **drifter** — no connections with the tourism industry; the traveller has no fixed itinerary and attempts to get as far from home and familiarity as possible; the drifter lives with local people and becomes immersed in the local culture

Figure 13.1 The relationship between leisure, recreation and tourism

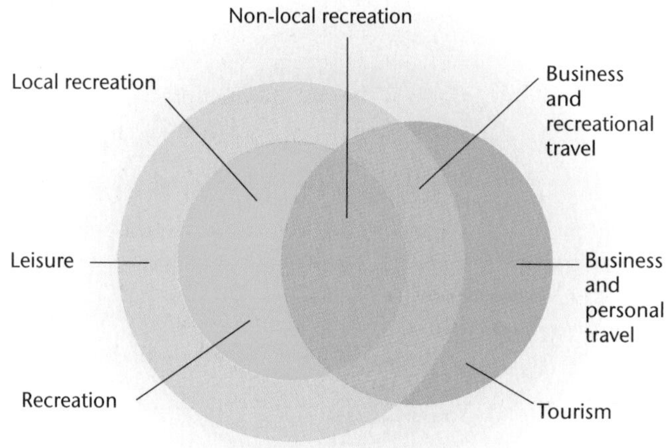

Resources

Like many economic activities, tourism involves the exploitation of resources. The resource base for this particular industry is immensely diverse. There is likely to be some potential for tourism almost anywhere in the world. However, some locations develop as tourist hotspots, whereas other equally well-endowed areas do not. In some cases, carefully planned artificial attractions have generated successful tourism in unlikely places.

Primary resources

Primary resources include the climate and other physical conditions such as scenery, as well as attractions like wildlife, history and heritage.

Climate

Climate is a major factor in the promotion of nearly all types of tourism. Sunlust tourism — the desire for the hot sun — has led to the growth of an enormous range of tourist areas, from winter-sun destinations such as The Gambia to the more traditional summer-sun destinations of the Mediterranean. The desire for a bronzed skin is very much a twentieth and twenty-first century phenomenon. Skin cancer scares may, however, eventually reduce the popularity of sunbathing.

Temperature can be significant for other reasons. Resorts such as Darjeeling in the foothills of the Himalayas developed because the administrators of the British Raj in India wished to escape the heat and humidity of the coasts and lowland areas of India during the monsoon season. Holidays in high-heat areas are now possible because of the widespread use of air-conditioning.

Precipitation is also an important factor. From a negative point of view, a wet British summer can be a disaster for domestic tourism and is the reason why modern resorts such as Blackpool and Center Parcs provide all-weather facilities. On the other hand, significant snowfalls are essential for ski resorts.

Extreme climatic events can have a major impact on tourism. Florida relies strongly on the British market during the hot and humid summer season, which is also the time for hurricanes. Tourists from the UK are attracted to Florida at this time of the year because the long-haul air fares are some of the cheapest in the world. However, hurricanes can greatly disrupt this trade — although to some they may be an additional attraction.

Physical factors

The nature of the tourist site is important. In seeking a new destination, resort-development companies combine their site assessments with evaluations of other key factors, such as access and land availability. For example, a new beach resort may require all or most of the following:

- a fine, clean, preferably white, sand beach, minimum 30 m wide and 200 m long
- warm water — 20°C minimum
- a good access slope — less than 15°
- a stable beach with little on-going erosion
- a gentle beach gradient (less than 8°) including a shallow entry zone for children to play and paddle
- no strong waves or currents, except at specific surfing beaches
- offshore features, for example coral reefs for water sports such as scuba diving

Key terms

Leisure All activities related to non-work time.

Recreation Any pursuit engaged upon during leisure (non-work) time. Recreation may be undertaken near to home or away from home. It may also include travelling from home to another location.

Tourism All activity undertaken by people staying away from home for at least 24 hours (i.e. overnight), on holiday, visiting friends or relatives, at business or other conferences, or any other purpose (e.g. health) other than semi-permanent employment. Tourism does not include any day-trip activity, such as visits to National Parks or cross-Channel shopping trips to France.

- silt-free clear water, ideally with a limestone sea floor
- an attractive backdrop, preferably not settled
- palm trees behind the beach to provide backland of shade
- safe and hospitable backland — no snakes or spiders
- low coliform count in the water
- water free from biological nuisances such as jellyfish and sharks

Many coastal authorities have to import sand for beach nourishment. Others use groynes to trap sand. However, this has consequences for other resorts down the coast.

Natural landscape can also be a great asset, for example an area of geysers (Iceland) or glaciers (Switzerland). Ideally, such landscapes should have good access and good-quality facilities. Surveys have shown that forests are viewed by many as being ideal for walking, driving and picnicking, especially in mountain areas. Forests have a high psychological carrying capacity, because people are screened from each other.

Ecological considerations are also important. The flora and fauna of a location may be a unique attraction, for example in the Galapagos Islands and the game parks of eastern and southern Africa. Wildlife tourism ranges from bird watching to trekking and safaris. The World Conservation Union has designated a range of protected areas:

- **Strict nature reserve** — an area of land or sea possessing outstanding or representative ecosystems, species or geological features which are available for scientific research and/or environmental monitoring.
- **Wilderness area** — a large area of unmodified land or sea, retaining its natural character without permanent or significant habitation and managed to preserve its natural condition.
- **National Park** — natural area of land or sea (Photograph 13.1) designated to:
  - protect the ecological integrity of one or more ecosystems for present and future generations
  - exclude exploitation or occupation that is inimical to the purposes of the designation
  - provide a foundation for educational and recreational opportunities
- **National monument** — an area containing one or more natural or cultural features of outstanding value because of their rarity or cultural significance.
- **Habitat/species management area** — an area of land or sea subject to active management intervention to ensure the maintenance of habitats and/or meet the needs of specific species [known as Sites of Special Scientific Interest (SSSIs) in the UK].
- **Protected landscape/seascape** — an area of land, coast or sea where the interaction of people and nature over time has produced a distinct character with significant aesthetic, ecological and/or cultural value.
- **Managed resource area** — an area containing predominantly unmodified natural systems, managed to ensure long-term protection and maintenance of biological diversity, while providing at the same time a sustainable flow of natural products and services to meet community needs.

Corel

Photograph 13.1 Zion National Park, USA, is a protected area

- **World Heritage Site** — an area of outstanding universal value, designated with the principal aim of fostering international cooperation in safeguarding such sites through the World Heritage Convention.
- **Biosphere reserve** — an area designated to meet a range of objectives, including research monitoring and training, as well as conservation roles through UNESCO's Man and Biosphere Programme.

Human factors

Historical, heritage and cultural factors often have the most difficult management problems. Some of the world's most popular sites present huge challenges, for example:

- access to Stonehenge at the solstices
- the erosion of the Acropolis in Athens
- the disintegration of the cave paintings of Lascaux in southern France, where a replica set has now been produced

Cultural attractions include the living expressions of existing cultures such as dress, artefacts, religious rites and customs, dance and music. Attractions of this nature are vulnerable to adaptation to fit perceived tourist taste and to contamination by mass tourism. For example, dances are staged throughout the year for tourists on the safari trail in Kenya, even though tradition states that these dances should only be performed under certain conditions or at certain times.

In the Western world, former industrial areas with their scarred landscapes, derelict factories and workshops, disused canals and railways are giving rise to a heritage tourist industry. Some abandoned coal mines, empty textile mills and deserted iron and steelworks are having a new lease of life. Examples include Ironbridge in Shropshire (see case study) and Beamish in County Durham.

Case study The Ironbridge Gorge World Heritage Site

The Ironbridge industrial heritage site has a range of facilities — educational, historical and entertainment:

- a visitor centre in a former warehouse
- the Coalbrookdale furnace and Museum of Iron which was the site of the original iron-smelting furnace of Abraham Darby
- the Coalbrookdale iron bridge (the first in the world) and its toll house
- the Bedlam furnaces — the first coke blast furnaces in the world on a large scale
- the Coalport China Museum
- the tar tunnel, where natural deposits of bitumen occur
- Blists Hill Victorian Town

Blists Hill Victorian Town

Blists Hill Victorian Town is one of the largest open-air museums in Britain. It has been created above 12 ha of woodland with walks on the banks of the Shropshire Canal. There are shops, offices and factories including a tile and brick works, a school house, a candle maker's workshop, a doctor's surgery, a pub and a slaughterhouse. Cottage gardens and smallholdings thrive. Refreshment is available at the New Inn Victorian pub and the Forest Glen Pavilion tearooms. Victorian souvenirs from cast-iron items to freshly baked buns are on sale.

Costumed staff provide information and portray various aspects of Victorian life. Visitors are able to watch the preparations and celebrations for a Victorian wedding, celebrate the arrival of spring, find out how Victorians spent their leisure time and join in hands-on activities.

Secondary resources

Facilities

Services and infrastructure are vital for the successful development of resort tourism. For instance, in Belize in Central America, tourism has been constrained by a lack of reliable water supplies and efficient sewage-disposal systems. This is frustrating for the tourist industry, as many hotels in the country could take more people.

In MEDCs, one of the main reasons for the development of urban tourism (short breaks in large towns and cities) has been the promotion of weekend breaks at discount prices. Hotels used by business people during the week wanted to fill rooms at the weekends too. Out of the main season (in the 'shoulder period' either side of the main season), conference tourism is a major earner in, for example, Blackpool and Bournemouth.

Access to resorts depends to a large degree on existing infrastructure. This includes roads, railways and airports, each of which is costly to provide. For example, when Sierra Leone ventured into long-haul tourism, largely from Germany and the UK, it had to depend on airlines from other countries because it had no suitable fleet of its own. To reach the only two quality hotels in the resort, Cape Sierra, tourists have a long and difficult journey from the one international airport. This involves a ferry crossing and a 3-hour bus journey. In the UK, fast road access from urban areas is the reason why the Peak District National Park is so heavily visited. It is surrounded by key motorways — the M1, M6 and M62. The M6 also provides access to the Lake District for people living in Liverpool and Manchester.

Isolation is only an advantage where 'hideaway' luxury tourism is planned and remoteness emphasises exclusivity, as in the Virgin Islands in the Caribbean.

Entertainment

Developers can create artificial attractions for tourists. These can fulfil the need for:

- thrills and risk-taking experiences — for example bungee jumping, white-knuckle rides in theme parks and gambling in casinos
- relaxation and social contact — for example carnivals, festivals, restaurants and entertainment complexes
- consumerism — facilities to purchase luxury goods, for example duty-free zones, factory outlets, antique fairs or leisure shopping at new out-of-town developments such as Bluewater
- education — galleries and museums; a major new museum can be an anchor attraction, for example the Lowry art gallery in Salford Quays

Well-designed resorts can more than compensate for indifferent natural resources. For example, Las Vegas was originally developed as a casino resort and for that reason was located in the desert away from the gambling laws of neighbouring states. It now benefits from being the closest major urban area to the Grand Canyon, and has become an all-round leisure and entertainment resort, with some of the most up-market hotels in the world (see case study).

Case study Las Vegas, Nevada, USA

Las Vegas is the largest gambling destination in the world. In 2000, it attracted over 33 million visitors and earned gambling revenues of over $6 billion. Las Vegas grew up as a stopover for travellers heading for southern California. It then became a service centre for local ranches and mines.

The gambling industry developed here because of:

- the state's liberal gambling regulations
- electricity generated from the Boulder Dam
- the attractive hot, dry climate and desert landscape of the region
- good accessibility — there are regular air services from all large cities in the USA and it is only 420 km from Los Angeles, along Interstate Highway 15
- large investors willing to back the entertainment potential of the city

Despite competition from other gambling locations in the country, notably Atlantic City on the east coast and new casinos on the riverboats of the Mississippi, Las Vegas has maintained its number one position because of its ability to reinvent itself:

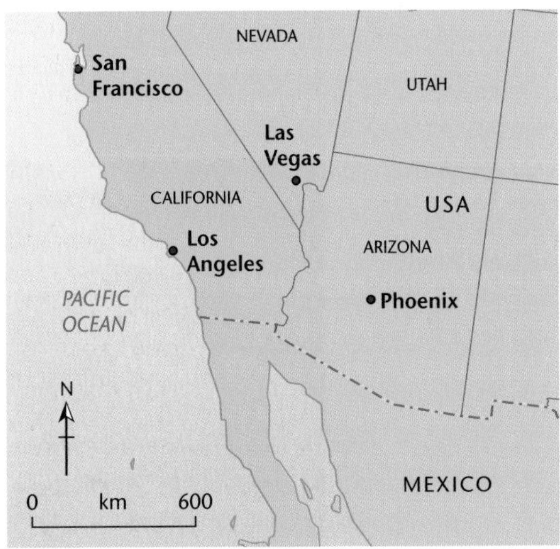

Figure 13.2 Map showing the location of Las Vegas

- Initially, the hotels were no more than two-storey dormitories for gamblers.

- In 1966, the huge Caesars Palace opened, with the theme of ancient Rome running through the whole complex. This hotel combined the attractions of gambling and stage shows on a large scale.
- In 1989, the Mirage hotel opened with 3,000 rooms, promising entertainment for gamblers and non-gamblers alike. Its lagoon and waterfalls are a major attraction.
- In 1991, the same developer opened Treasure Island, where the *Hispaniola* goes down twice a night to the blazing guns of HMS *Britannia* and the restaurants are in the style of pirates' taverns.
- Other developers followed with Excalibur (Arthurian pageantry), Luxor (an Egyptian pyramid) and New York-New York, where a roller coaster whips through a succession of famous skyscrapers.
- In 1996, the city became the USA's top convention centre, attracting over 3.5 million conference participants.
- By 1997, more than 10% of visitors were bringing their children with them. Attractions for younger visitors were provided along Sunset Strip and in the theme park complex in the MGM Grand.
- In 2005 the largest hotel in the world, the Wynn Las Vegas, opened at a cost of $2.7 billion.

Theme parks

A theme park can be defined as a self-contained family entertainment complex. Such resorts require a huge level of investment and are risky business ventures. They rely on a high threshold population with year-round throughput in order to achieve economic viability. Such complexes have a big impact on the local area, both positive in terms of job creation and negative in terms of traffic issues.

Theme parks create artificial destinations from scratch. The Disney theme parks are the world's biggest tourist draws. Attendance at the most popular theme park in the world, Tokyo Disneyland, topped 17 million in 2000. Over 4 million Britons travel to overseas Disney parks — in Florida and France — each year.

***Photograph 13.2* Alton Towers is the most popular charging tourist attraction in the UK**

Alton Towers

One of Disney's advantages is that the company started out in entertainment, the business that tourism is increasingly coming to resemble. It has also moved into retailing, selling vast quantities of souvenirs and branded goods. A vital element of the Disney empire is its research centre in Glendale, California where the latest technology is used to develop new experiences for visitors. It researches what audiences want and then strives to create it.

In the UK, Alton Towers in Staffordshire remains the most popular charging tourist attraction, with 3 million customers in 2000 (Photograph 13.2). Only one other theme park, Chessington World of Adventures, attracts more Britons than Disneyland Paris. In total, 13 million people visited the top 15 UK parks in 2000, spending over £250 million. At present, most of these are outdoors and are, therefore, only open from March to November. Almost all visitors are day-trippers — Alton Towers has only recently built an on-site hotel to encourage visits of 2 days or more.

Tourism in the LEDW

Many communities in the LEDW have suffered as the worst of Western values have been forced on them by tourism. Problems include:

- The **loss of locally owned land** — some resorts have been developed regardless of the wishes of local people, for example in Goa, India. In some cases, communal land is only made available for tourism provided the tribal chiefs are given shares in the development company. This has become common practice in Fiji.
- The **loss of traditional values and practices** — in India, the hunter-gatherer Adivasis tribe has had its access to the forest it has lived in for centuries severely curtailed because it forms part of the Nagarahole National Park. The people are no longer allowed to hunt or to cultivate land, keep livestock or collect forest produce, or visit sacred sites and burial grounds. In Hawaii, traditional burial grounds have been destroyed to make way for new resorts. In Bali, devout Hindus have been angered by large-scale tourist developments overshadowing their temples.
- **Displacement** — in Myanmar (Burma), according to the pressure group Tourism Concern, the military junta has forcibly moved millions of people from their homes to make room for tourist development. Thousands of people have been used as forced labour on tourism-related projects, such as clearing the moat around the Royal Palace at Mandalay. Similar forced movements have taken place in Lombok, Indonesia, where the government is accused of tearing down homes to make way for tourist developments.
- **Alcoholism and crime** — in some areas, the anti-social behaviour of foreign tourists has become a major issue. Problems of drunkenness and laddish behaviour have spread from European resorts to other parts of the world. Thailand has attracted a lot of attention because of its problems with child prostitution and pornography.

Case study The Kruger National Park

The Kruger National Park in South Africa is an example of many of the concerns that people have about tourism in the LEDW. The park's website states the following:

> In the heart of the Low Veld, stretching for 352 km from north to south along the Mozambique border, one of the world's foremost national parks can be found. This is the Kruger National Park, a wildlife sanctuary larger in area than Israel. Covering 19,624 km^2 and averaging 60 km in width, Kruger provides a refuge for 147 mammal species (including elephants, rhinos, buffalo and lions), 500 species of birds, 116 reptiles, 34 amphibians, 49 fishes, 457 types of trees and shrubs, 1,500 smaller plants, and countless insects.
>
> Each year approximately 950,000 people visit the Kruger Park, and half of them stay overnight in the 26 rest camps that range from the intimate 19-bed Malelane, bordering the Crocodile River in the extreme south, to historic Punda Maria in the far north. South Africans account for 80% of all visitors and for many a visit to Kruger has become a kind of spiritual pilgrimage.

However, for most of its existence, the park has been regarded by black South Africans as an Afrikaaner-dominated institution reserved for whites. Poverty-stricken tribesmen living on its borders would gaze resentfully as the relatively affluent drove around looking at the game that they craved for food, the trees they wanted for firewood and building material and the water they needed for survival. Worse, many of them had been dispossessed of ancestral land as the authorities expanded the boundaries of the reserve to create the vast wilderness the park now occupies.

There are now more than 2 million people living in villages, townships and squatter camps on the boundaries of the park, most of them on or below the poverty line. While some 500 water holes have been created for wild animals, women on the other side of the fence have to walk for many kilometres to find drinking water for their families.

South Africa is now a democracy and the government is considering a sharing arrangement which it hopes will balance local, national and international interests in the park. Several black communities have made legal claims for restitution of substantial portions of the park, stating that their people were forcibly removed during the apartheid years. Some of these claims have official backing. One, by the Makuleke community near the Zimbabwean border, has succeeded. Here, the community and the park authorities jointly manage the region as a tourist attraction, with wilderness trails and tented camps. The success of this process is being closely watched by a number of development and environmental agencies.

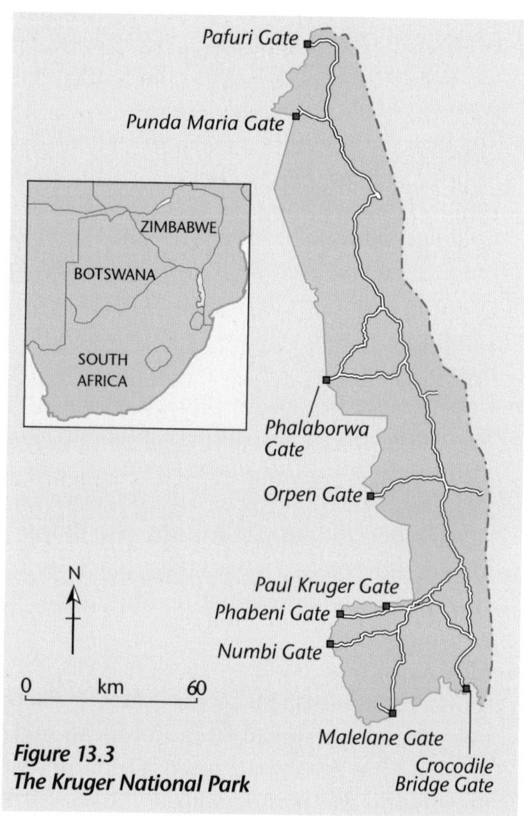

Figure 13.3 The Kruger National Park

The carrying capacity of tourist resources

An understanding of the concept of **carrying capacity** is vital for tourism studies. It can be defined individually for each destination as the level of tourist activity that can be sustained in the long term without creating serious or irreversible changes to the people's lives and environment. If the carrying capacity is exceeded, then the destination will be dominated by rapidly increasing negative effects and any positive benefits will be lost.

Optimum carrying capacity is the level of tourist activity or tourism that creates acceptable impacts on the host economy and environment, yet allows the tourists to enjoy themselves in a way that is sustainable for the future. The number of tourists, their length of stay, the degree of seasonality, the spatial concentration of the visitors, and the characteristics of the tourists and the destination are all important in defining this optimum level.

It follows, therefore, that there is a threshold limit beyond which further numbers will produce an unacceptable impact. This is the **saturation limit**. It may be easily reached when tourism is augmented by day visits, for example in the more accessible parts of National Parks such as the Peak District.

There is no single measure for determining the carrying capacity of an area. Furthermore, the ability to absorb tourists may increase over time, as the hosts become more willing to accept them and as building projects develop. However, there are four major aspects of carrying capacity:

- **Physical** — the amount of land suitable for facilities. It also includes the finite capacity of facilities, such as numbers of car-parking spaces, tables in restaurants and bedrooms. It is a straightforward measure of capacity that can be used in planning and management control. It is also referred to as **throughput capacity** — the maximum number of people that can be coped with at any one time.
- **Ecological** — the biological capacity is exceeded when environmental damage or disturbance is unacceptable. This can relate to flora or fauna but usually measures thresholds of vegetation at, for example, picnic sites, along paths and in coastal dune systems. It is important to look at the total ecosystem (such as the Norfolk Broads) rather than at individual elements.
- **Economic** — the concept of economic carrying capacity is derived from ideas of tourism planning and sustainability. It attempts to define levels of development that are acceptable to the residents and businesses of the host community.
- **Perceived** — the perceptual, or psychological, capacity of a site is exceeded when the experience of visitors is significantly impaired. Some people are tolerant of crowds and enjoy busy places; others shun them. This is, therefore, a very individual concept and difficult to influence by management and planning. Landscaping can be used to reduce the impression of crowding.

The tourism boom in the MEDW

Butler's model

Butler's model of the evolution of tourist areas (Figure 13.4) illustrates how tourism develops and changes over time. In the first stage, the location is explored independently by a small number of visitors. If visitor impressions are good and local people perceive that real benefits are to be gained, then the number of visitors will increase as the local community becomes actively involved in the promotion of tourism. In the development stage, holiday companies from the developed nations take control of organisation and management, with package holidays becoming the norm. Eventually, growth ceases as the location loses some of its former attraction. At this stage, local people have become all too aware of the problems created by tourism. Finally, decline sets in. However, because of the perceived economic importance of the industry, efforts will be made to re-package the location. If successful, this will either stabilise the situation or result in renewed growth (rejuvenation).

The shape of the curve varies according to the particular destination. It depends on factors such as ease of access, rate of development, market trends and tourism

Figure 13.4 Butler's model of tourist development

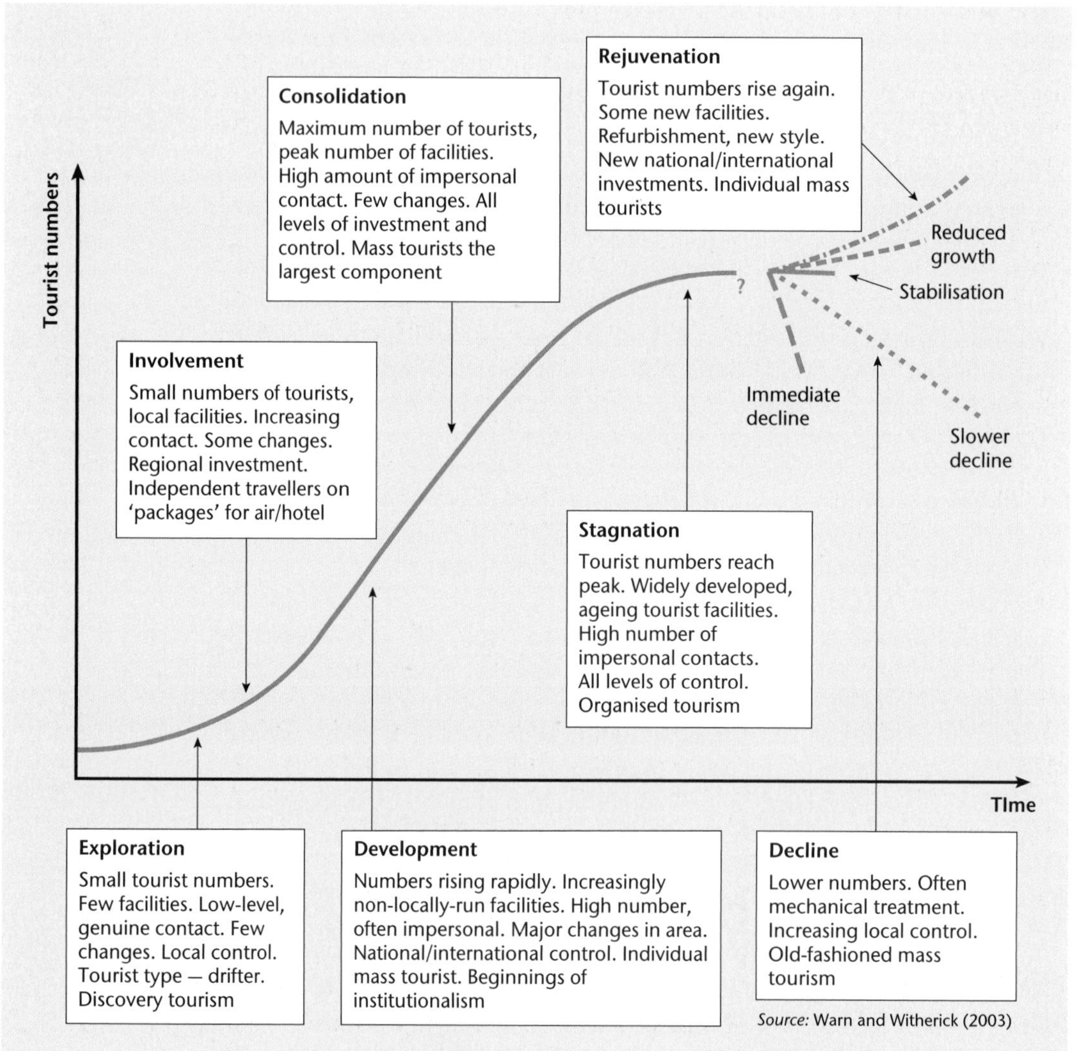

Source: Warn and Witherick (2003)

fashions, as well as the competitive strength of rival tourist areas. Planning and management at national, regional and local levels also determine the way an area develops.

Other key matters are:

- controlling the spread of mass tourism
- managing the destination after the stagnation phase
- how destinations can rejuvenate themselves to avoid 'boom and bust' periods
- how destinations can change direction and image in order to retain their industry — a switch to higher quality may compensate for a decrease in the number of tourists

As with many other models, Butler's model serves as a yardstick with which to assess reality.

The changing UK tourist industry

People have had a fascination for travel since the earliest historical periods. There has always been the urge to discover the unknown and to experience new environments. Travel to achieve these ends is not new. However, mass tourism is relatively modern in origin.

Resort tourism: its rise and fall

In the eighteenth century, it was fashionable to go to inland resorts to 'take the waters'. Doctors recommended the medicinal properties of mineral waters and, there was a boom in spa towns like Bath, Buxton, Tunbridge Wells and Harrogate. These were originally places for the sick, but gradually transformed themselves into resorts for the fashionable elite, who sought the social pleasure of theatre, dancing and walking. Spa towns became very elegant places.

Towards the end of the eighteenth century, sea bathing became fashionable — encouraged by the Prince Regent at Brighton. The coastal resorts along the Kent and Sussex coasts became popular with wealthy Londoners, many of whom moved to the south coast for the summer.

A number of factors made seaside resorts much more popular in the mid-to-late nineteenth century. The most important factor was the railway. This allowed mass transport from the industrial towns of the north and Midlands to seaside resorts on the west and east coasts. (The first package tours arranged by Thomas Cook took advantage of this transport system, taking people from Leicester to Loughborough to attend temperance meetings.) The second factor was that factory and mill workers were given holidays. In the Lancashire textile towns these were known as 'wakes weeks', during which time the mills were shut down. Acts of Parliament were passed to enable this to occur and Friendly Societies were established to help people save money for their holidays. However, it was not until 1938 that paid holidays were made compulsory.

From the late nineteenth to the mid-twentieth centuries, close links existed between certain seaside resorts and their feeder areas. Examples include Sheffield as a feeder area for Cleethorpes and Skegness; Leeds and other West Yorkshire towns with Scarborough and Bridlington; London with Clacton, Southend and

Margate; and Liverpool and Manchester with Blackpool, Southport and Llandudno. More remote resorts, such as those in Cornwall, tended to be smaller and received their clientele from a much wider catchment area. Although the railway was still important, more visitors came in coaches (charabancs) and motor cars. Over time, a whole range of cheap alternative accommodation developed, including holiday camps (Butlins' first camp opened in Skegness in 1935), holiday flats and chalets, as well as camping and caravan parks.

Following the Second World War, tourism continued to grow. There was substantial growth in personal leisure time, affluence and mobility. In the UK in 1950, 25 million people took a holiday. By 1970, this had risen to 35 million. An increasing number of people started taking their holidays abroad. This put pressure on British seaside resorts which had to face the stark alternatives posed by the Butler model: stagnate and die slowly or regenerate and rejuvenate. A number of strategies for survival have been adopted:

- attracting development grants for refurbishment (e.g. a private company takes over and improves a large hotel) or redevelopment (e.g. for building new shopping malls, leisure facilities, conference facilities and marinas)
- developing the short-break sector with spring, winter and autumn attractions (lights, festivals, targeted bargain breaks for pensioners) to ensure a more even flow of business through the year
- providing business and conference facilities
- moving into pseudo-resort functions, for example converting guest houses and hotels into retirement homes and flats or, more controversially, making arrangements with organisations that work with the homeless and with asylum seekers
- upgrading facilities including open-air swimming pools, entertainment, self-catering opportunities, restaurants, car access and parking, and ensuring that the top hotels in the resort have 4- or 5-star ratings

The main aim has been to achieve a critical mass of tourism based on year-round business. If revenues are to be maintained or even increased, both the quality and quantity of tourists are vital.

Modern development strands in UK tourism

Since 1970, there have been radical changes in the UK tourist industry, not least in its organisation and coordination. The Development of Tourism Act (1970) sought to strengthen the UK's tourist market overseas, by encouraging people to visit the country and by improving tourist amenities. These facilities could also be used by domestic tourists and day-trippers as car ownership increased.

A network of tourist boards was established to support and develop the industry regionally. These promote and coordinate an enormous range of commercial, public and voluntary provision. A network of tourist information offices has been established to link demand with supply, via displays, maps, brochures and booking facilities. The government has encouraged tourist initiatives with financial support, for example the Farm Diversification grant. Increasingly, funds are being made available through the National Lottery. Most local authorities now recognise the importance of tourism and have a tourism promotion unit as part of their economic development strategy.

By 2000, tourism was the UK's most important single industry. It employed nearly 2 million people in over 200,000 enterprises, earned over £30 billion (of which nearly £10 billion came from overseas visitors) and provided 30 million domestic short breaks (1–3 nights) and 18 million longer breaks.

Tourism in the UK now has a wide range of destinations and activities. Some major new development strands are covered below.

Rural tourism

In the nineteenth century, the Lake District, the Peak District and Scotland were popular destinations with wealthier tourists because of their landscape value. Gradually, during the twentieth century, trips to the countryside developed for other people, including 'mystery trips' by coach and organised outings from clubs and factories. Many people became interested in cycling, camping and youth hostelling.

The creation of the National Parks and the rise in car ownership led to more tourist pressure on rural areas. A growing number of rural attractions, such as country houses and their gardens, wildlife parks, working farms, craft centres and rural museums were developed. These were listed in guidebooks and leaflets produced by the regional tourist boards and by motoring organisations. Accommodation in country farmhouses, country inns, bed and breakfasts and self-catering cottages was made available and encouraged touring holidays. Marketing involved themes, such as 'Shakespeare country' and 'Bronte country' or links to popular television series such as *Emmerdale*, *All Creatures Great and Small* and *Heartbeat*. Rural tourism prospered at the expense of resort tourism. Only a small number of seaside resorts are suitable as touring centres for inland destinations — Scarborough, Whitby and Tenby are the best.

The National Parks could be said to be the victims of their own success. They were set up with a number of aims, which some commentators believe were conflicting:

- to conserve precious environments

Corel

Photograph 13.3 In the Lake District National Park

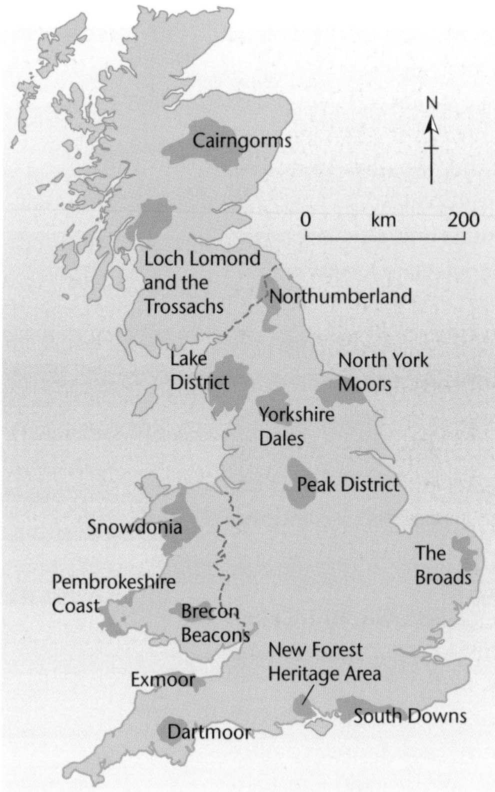

Figure 13.5 ***Britain's National Parks***

- to enable access and opportunity for a wide range of outdoor leisure pursuits
- to support jobs and the economy (especially farming)
- to protect the quality of life of local people

The number of visitors to the UK's National Parks has increased to more than 100 million per year. The nature of the visitors changed from rucksack carrying walkers in the 1950s through car-bound picnickers in the 1980s to all-action sports people in the 1990s. Commercial ventures, such as timeshare holiday centres, have grown alongside.

The most visited parks are those with the greatest access by fast road from urban communities. Problems can be severe:

- The police have sometimes closed the southern entrances to the Lake District National Park because of the long traffic queues waiting to enter.
- Visitor pressure has led to widespread footpath erosion in the Peak District, particularly on the Pennine Way. In addition, off-road vehicles have damaged many of the ancient tracks on the moors.
- In both parks, and in others, there are severe problems of congestion at honeypot sites on bank-holiday weekends or hot, sunny, summer Sundays.

Radical solutions to these problems have been put forward, including:

- imposing a visitor tax
- halving car parking provision
- closing honeypot sites except to permit holders
- creating areas that can only be reached by park-and-ride schemes

In 1997, the Countryside Commission report *Fit for the Future* made further recommendations. For the commission, the top priority is to conserve scenery and wildlife — the recreational role should be downgraded to quiet enjoyment. It recommended:

- allowing public access to all open land in the parks to reduce pressure on existing public areas. This 'right to roam' in many areas was achieved in 2005
- signposting and legally defining all the 19,000 km of public rights of way in the parks
- ending military training in over 40,000 ha of the parks, although some have argued that these no-go areas, as in the Northumberland National Park, actually conserve ecosystems
- stricter control over traffic, with experimental car-free zones to encourage people to walk

Center Parcs

Photograph 13.4 The pool at a Center Parcs village

- new systems of farm support to restore and extend wild areas by reducing overgrazing by sheep (a particular problem in the Peak District and the Yorkshire Dales)
- ending all major coniferous forestry planting

Holiday villages

Holiday villages are large-scale developments like Center Parcs, which some view as environmentally friendly. They are, in effect, inland resorts. Center Parcs locations include Sherwood Forest (Nottinghamshire), Elvedon (Suffolk) and Longleat Park (Wiltshire). Up to 600 villas are set in up to 200 ha of woodland with full village facilities, a subtropical leisure dome, restaurants and shops. They are popular, especially for short-break holidays, and frequently have occupancy rates close to 100%.

The villages generate about 800 jobs at each location but over half of these are domestic work and two-thirds are part-time. Local purchasing by the village is another direct benefit — 20% of supplies at the Sherwood site come from local sources. Indirect spending by visitors off-site is another perceived benefit. However, the reality is that visitors rarely leave the site during their stay. The main use of local services tends to occur during change-over days.

A major drawback to holiday villages is the effect on traffic volumes, particularly on change-over days — up to 3,000 extra traffic movements have been recorded on such days.

Urban tourism

Historic cities such as York, Chester and Bath (see case studies, pages 429, 430) and the capital cities London, Edinburgh and Cardiff with their galleries, museums and theatres, have long been popular with tourists. London and Edinburgh dominate the market with foreign tourists. However, in recent decades, a new type of urban tourism has emerged, associated with short breaks and day trips. It has encompassed leisure shopping at out-of-town shopping centres such as MetroCentre at Gateshead, as well as heritage and cultural tourism (for example Ironbridge Gorge World Heritage Site, see case study, page 418).

Heritage tourism is a key factor in the urban regeneration of cities like Liverpool, Manchester and Leeds. Towns such as Canterbury and Oxford, which have always had a tourism strategy, are being joined by a new generation of up-and-coming tourist towns, such as Stoke-on-Trent, Doncaster and Wigan. A number of reasons are cited for this rise, including industrial legacy and nostalgia. In an ageing society, many people are interested in looking back at the times of their childhood.

Cultural tourism is associated with heritage tourism. The conservation of cultural resources and their transformation into tourist products can be a real incentive to reviving traditional cultural identities, for example in Lancashire and Yorkshire. At the same time, it allows the celebration of contemporary multiethnic culture. An example of this is the gastronomic 'curry trails' in Bradford and in Rusholme, south Manchester.

Some declining city centres have been regenerated to provide leisure facilities for local people. For example, new leisure facilities have been built on former industrial sites in the Lower Don Valley in Sheffield (the Don Valley stadium and the Sheffield Arena) and at Festival Park in Stoke-on-Trent (including a multiplex cinema, waterworld and dry ski slope). In some places, additional provision for conference facilities has been made, as in the centre of Birmingham.

Case study Chester, a heritage city

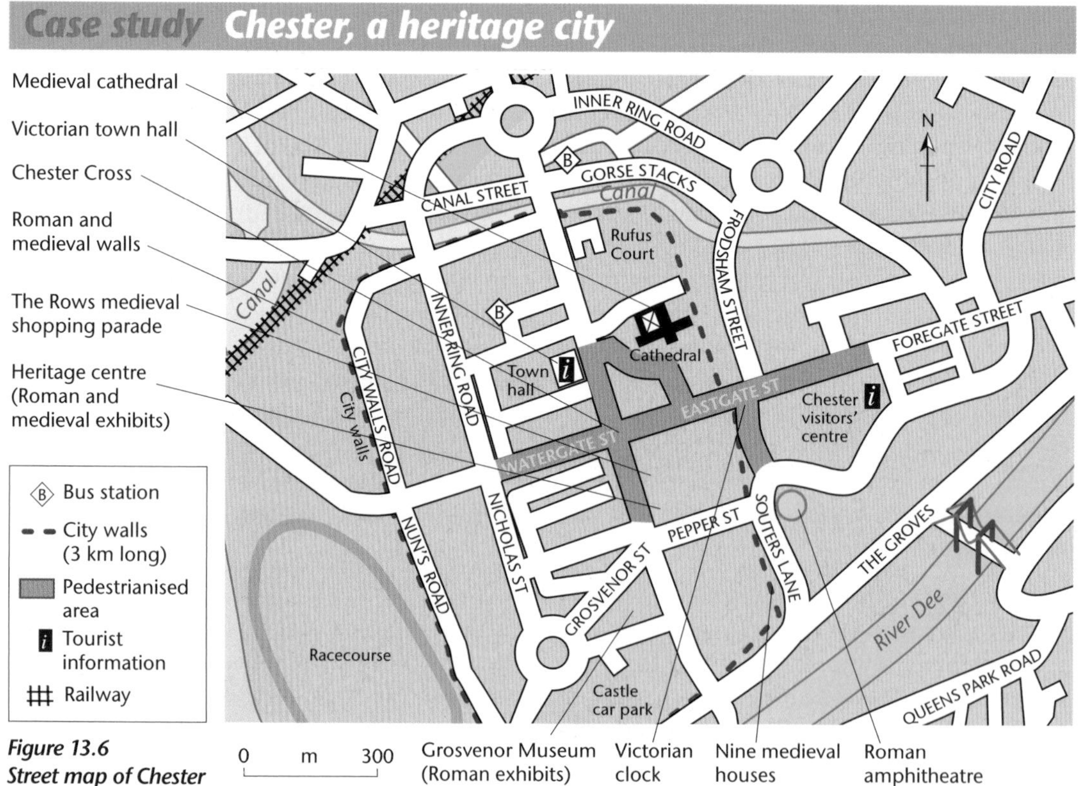

Figure 13.6 Street map of Chester

Chester has a range of buildings and features from a variety of historical periods, all within a small urban area. These include:

- a Roman amphitheatre and remnants of walls from this period
- several medieval buildings — the Rows (a medieval shopping arcade with shops on two levels, one of which has a raised walkway), the cathedral, the almost complete wall around the city and the well-preserved medieval core of streets
- Victorian landmarks— the Chester Cross (a street clock) and the large imposing town hall
- a number of museums that display exhibits from these periods

Case study Bath, a heritage city

Bath is based around a natural spring. In the 1700s, when mineral waters were thought to be a cure for rheumatic and other complaints, it became a fashionable resort for the well-off. Using local stone from the quarries at Combe Down, a series of Palladian mansions, terraces and townhouses were built. Architects such as John Wood (the Elder and the Younger) and Robert Adam designed and built prestigious streets, such as Queen Square, The Circus, the Royal Crescent, and Great Pulteney Street. The Royal Crescent is perhaps the most striking and well-known street in Bath. It has featured in a number of historical films. It consists of 30 houses in a sweeping curve above a sloping lawn.

Case study British tourism in Mallorca (Majorca)

Mallorca is the largest of the Balearic Islands, off the Mediterranean coast of Spain. Over the past 30 years, Spain has been the most popular country for British tourists to visit and Mallorca has been one of the main destinations. With a population of just over 500,000, the island attracts over 6 million visitors each year.

Thirty years ago, Spain was one of the poorer nations in western Europe and the Balearic Islands were among the poorest regions. Today, thanks to financial support from the EU and money earned from tourism, Spain has almost caught up with most of its European neighbours and the Balearic Islands are no longer poor.

Figure 13.7 Map of Mallorca

Something for everyone?

Mallorca has most of the attributes that allow travel agents to classify it as an ideal holiday island:

- beautiful scenery with historic and picturesque villages
- a variety of habitats, including wetlands, salt marshes, mountains and rocky cliffs, making it ideal for bird watching
- many secluded bays and harbours, ideal for marinas
- guaranteed summer sunshine
- safe beaches for swimming
- many types of accommodation

Effects of tourism

In the early 1990s, the government of the Balearic Islands became concerned about a fall in the number of tourists. It realised that people were deciding to go elsewhere because of a deterioration in the environment of the island. Tourism had changed parts of Mallorca almost beyond recognition. Aware that its image has been spoilt by cheap package holidays that attracted '*gamberos ingleses*' (English hooligans), the government has attempted to re-package the island as a tourist destination:

- Many hotels were built in the 1960s when the tourist boom began. Some are ugly and intrude on the natural landscape. They do not meet the high standards expected by tourists today. New hotels have to be built to higher standards and an old hotel must be demolished before a new one can be built.
- While in Mallorca, many tourists hire cars. This has led to a huge increase in traffic. New motorways have been built around Palma, but many smaller towns still suffer from congestion. Cycling is now being actively promoted as the best way to travel around the island.
- Large areas of the natural ecosystem and farmland have been lost, especially on the south coast. These areas are under pressure from tourist developments. Golf courses have taken over much of the land. To counter this some areas have been protected as nature reserves. The Isla Dragonera, which was once proposed as a new holiday resort, is now a protected area that tourists cannot visit.
- In the past, beaches were polluted by sewage discharged into the sea by hotels and boats. There is now tighter control of waste disposal. Some beaches have been improved by increasing the amount of natural vegetation around them. Almost half of the island's beaches have been awarded the EU Blue Flag for being clean, safe and well kept.
- In an effort to attract tourists to different parts of the island and at different times of the year, the types of holiday that the island offers are being broadened. A number of farms have been converted to agrotourism. Farmers provide villas and apartments on a small scale, where tourists can enjoy a quiet and relaxing holiday. Many farms have a swimming pool and tennis courts, yet still continue to grow vegetables.

The overall aim is to make tourism in Mallorca more sustainable, so that people will continue to go there.

Recent trends in holiday destinations

Cruising

When long-haul flights became possible passenger ships were made obsolete. Cruising developed as redundant liners were converted to offer entertainment, rather than just transport. In the early years, marketing was directed towards the rich elderly, who still make up a large proportion of the market. However, the appeal of this sector of the industry has now spread across the age and income spectrum.

North Americans take more cruises than any other nation, with over 5 million passengers in 2001. The growth of this sector has attracted companies such as

Malcolm Skinner

Photograph 13.5 Cruise ship in Agios Nikolaos, Crete

Disney, Thomson holidays and Airtours. Many established operators are also increasing the size of their fleets and the size of individual vessels. There are however, problems with increasing the size of cruise ships:

- The largest cruise liners are unable to pass through the Panama Canal.
- The number of destinations capable of providing shore facilities for thousands of passengers at any one time is limited.

Cosmetic surgery tourism

An increasing number of people from western Europe are going to the east of the continent and to parts of Asia for cosmetic surgery where it is much cheaper than in their own countries. They undergo surgery shortly after arrival and spend the rest of their stay on aftercare and conventional tourist activities, such as sightseeing.

Activity holidays

Activity holidays are aimed at people who are looking for something exciting and fun. There is a wide range of activities available in a variety of locations around the world. The holidays may involve physical activity, for example mountain biking, white-water rafting, surfing, canoeing, canyoning, horse riding, hiking or paragliding. Creative holidays are also available, for example cookery or painting holidays.

Expansion of tourism in the LEDW

Case study Tourism in Jamaica

Tourism is Jamaica's fastest-growing industry. It now earns almost half the country's income and employs a quarter of the population. However, tourism relies heavily on the involvement of foreign TNCs. Hotel chains such as Trust House Forte, Sheraton and Holiday Inn, well known in the UK, are found in

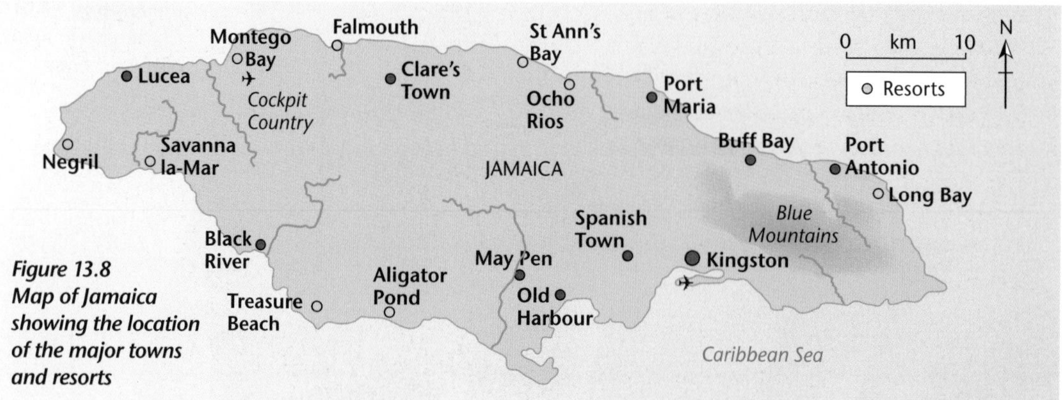

Figure 13.8 Map of Jamaica showing the location of the major towns and resorts

Jamaica too. TNC involvement does not end with hotels. Airlines carry tourists to Jamaica, construction companies build the hotels and travel companies organise the holidays. Many of these companies are based outside Jamaica, and drain profits from the country — a form of economic leakage.

However, not all TNCs operating in Jamaica are foreign-owned. Sandals is a Jamaican company that owns all-inclusive resorts in all the main tourist centres on the island, mostly concentrated on the north and west coasts.

The all-inclusive resort means tourists can have a luxury holiday in the Caribbean, without having to set foot outside the resort. Sandals was set up in 1981 and now has 12 resorts throughout the Caribbean, with a total of over 3,000 beds.

Why is Jamaica a popular tourist resort?

Jamaica's key resources are sun, sand and sea. The climate of the island is tropical so it is much warmer and sunnier than the major market areas of the USA and western Europe. It is also much wetter (Figure 13.10).

One Sandals resort is at Ocho Rios on the north coast. Tourists are attracted by the white sandy beach and the nearby Dunn's River Falls. The resort has the following features:

- There are 529 rooms. Most guests are foreign tourists from Europe or North America. Guests pay up to £2,000 per person per fortnight all-inclusive.
- Ninety per cent of the food and drink at the resort is produced in Jamaica. Many other resorts import all their food and drink.
- The resort provides a high level of service — two members of staff for every room. This is only possible because of the low wages on the island. Sandals employs 6,500 people in Jamaica.

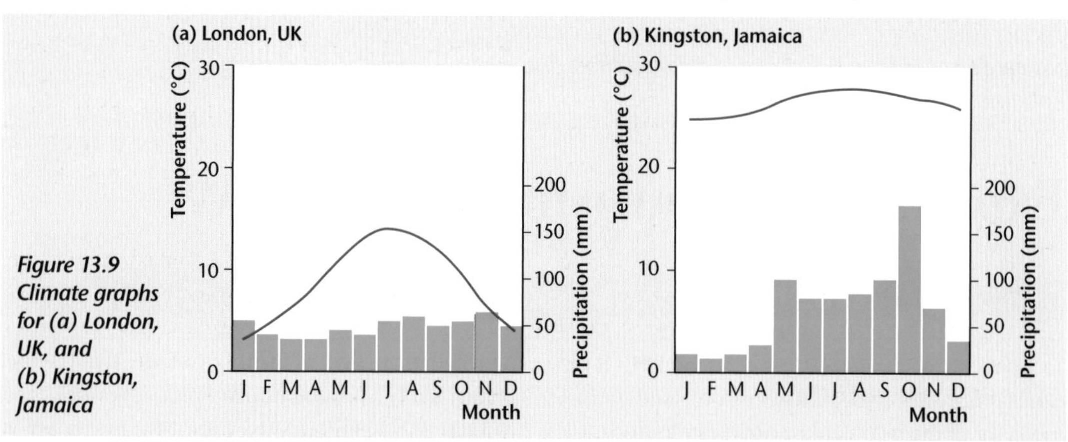

Figure 13.9 Climate graphs for (a) London, UK, and (b) Kingston, Jamaica

- Guests arrive by plane at Kingston or Montego Bay. The resort provides transport to and from the airport. Return flights from the UK cost around £600 per person.
- The resort has a private beach that is fenced off to prevent local vendors from harassing tourists. As a result, tourists may never come into contact with real Jamaican life.

Corel

Photograph 13.6 *Jamaica's key resources are sun, sand and sea*

Impacts of tourism

Tourists from countries with higher living standards than Jamaica consume more resources than local people. The average guest uses ten times as much water as a local person.

Inadequate sewage treatment and disposal by resorts pollute the sea and cause damage to coral reefs. Larger resorts like Sandals can afford to install their own sewage treatment facilities.

If tourist numbers continue to grow there will soon be as many tourists visiting Jamaica each year as its population (2.5 million). This puts huge pressure on all the island's resources.

Treasure Beach is a little-known resort on the south-west coast of Jamaica, far away from the tourist hotspots of the northern coast. It is a sleepy fishing village that has hardly changed within living memory. It is the sort of place that tourists dream of. But if tourism comes to Treasure Beach, will it ever be the same again? A website advertising the area states:

> Come to where the only footprints you are likely to see on the beach are your own, and where the residents treat you as guests, not tourists. Nicknamed 'desert coast' because of the ever-present sunshine, Treasure Beach is a scenic 100 km drive from Montego Bay. This area is still unspoilt and largely unaffected by tourism, yet it offers the best of Jamaica's natural beauty and charm; deserted sandy beaches, colourful coral reefs, beautiful sunsets, starlit nights and mountains that reach the sky.
>
> The natural beauty of Jamaica is only half of its magic. You will have the opportunity to learn about the rich culture and easy-paced lifestyle in which fishing and farming are done much as they were half a century ago. Relax and forget your worries — this is your holiday in paradise.

Jamaica's downside

Jamaica has a reputation for violent crime — images of poverty and problems between rival gangs are flashed around the world on television news. However, while the island's murder rate in undeniably high, its nightmare image is exaggerated. The tourist board stresses that you are more likely to be mugged in New York than in Montego Bay. At the same time, robberies, assaults and other crimes against tourists do occur. Tourists have to take the same precautions that they would take in any foreign city.

The chief irritation for tourists in Jamaica is unwanted and constant hard-selling by street-vendors. However, most of what is perceived as harassment is really nothing more than an attempt to make a living in an economically deprived country.

Case study Tourism in Iguaçu, Brazil

One of the most popular inland tourist destinations in Brazil is the Iguaçu region at the western edge of Parana state. The main attractions are:

- the Iguaçu Falls
- the flora and fauna of the Iguaçu National Park
- the Itaipu hydroelectric power station and reservoir
- the developing tourist facilities in the city of Foz do Iguaçu
- cheap shopping and casinos across the border in Cuidad del Este, Paraguay
- the local Indian population
- fishing in the Parana River

The Iguaçu Falls

The Iguaçu Falls are higher than Niagara Falls and wider than Victoria Falls. They are one of the world's most spectacular natural features. In 1986, the falls and the subtropical forest park surrounding them was designated a World Heritage Site. Although most of the falls lie in Argentina, the best views and most of the National Park are in Brazil.

The falls are formed by the Iguaçu River, 15 km west of its confluence with the Parana River. There are about 275 interlinking cataracts, over a distance of 3 km, and the main waterfall plunges over an 80 m high cliff. The volume of water is greatest in the wetter months of April to July. By the end of the dry season, the volume of water is reduced by about one-third. Only once in recorded history, in 1977, did the falls dry up completely.

Most visitors to the falls come from Argentina. However international tourists from the USA, Japan and Germany are increasing in number.

Iguaçu National Park

The Iguaçu National Park covers an area of dense tropical forest. In an effort to increase tourism in the area the price of a ticket to enter the park has been kept very low. There are a number of signposted trails with well-organised information centres at entry points. Visitors can walk or travel by jeep with a guide. A popular option is then to join a boat tour from the banks of the Iguaçu to the base of the larger falls. Due to the number of visitors and the noise of the helicopter rides viewing the falls, it is rare for visitors to see the full range of wildlife.

The forest contains over 2,000 plant varieties, 400 bird species including toucans, parakeets and hummingbirds, and many types of mammal, reptile and insect. There are 50 species of deer and 200 species of butterfly. Jaguars and mountain lions have occasionally been seen and tapirs are sometimes found around the water's edge. Much more common are coatimundi and capuchin monkeys. Expert guides are available to lead serious birdwatchers, botanists and photographers into the forest.

Adjacent to the National Park is the 16 ha Foz Tropicana, a bird park that doubles as a tourist attraction and a conservation and research centre. Only a quarter of the area is taken up with aviaries and other buildings. The rest is unspoilt subtropical forest, where birds live freely. Most of the birds are from Brazil, including some from the Pantanal and the Amazon. A successful breeding programme has been established.

The elegant regency style Hotel das Cataratas offers the only accommodation within the National Park.

Fishing

One of the greatest freshwater game fish, the dourado, inhabits the upper reaches of the Parana River. Known as 'golden salmon' because of their size and colouring, these powerful fish are popular with both South American and European anglers. The largest fish are most likely to be caught in the fast-flowing stretch of the Parana River around Iguaçu. The dourado season is from October to March, with the best fishing between November and January.

Other attractions

Foz do Iguaçu, about 20 km northwest of the entrance to the National Park, is a bustling city of over 250,000 people, boasting an international airport and a large convention centre. Foz is by far the largest urban settlement in the region. Part of its tourist strategy has been to host sporting events to draw in more visitors from Brazil, Argentina and Paraguay. Foztur, the city's tourist organisation, has initiated tours of the Itaipu dam, upgraded the facilities there and promoted a range of smaller attractions such as the Three Frontiers, where the Parana and Iguaçu rivers meet.

Ciudad del Este in Paraguay can be reached by the Amizade (Friendship) bridge across the Parana River. Taxes on imported goods are much lower in Paraguay than in Brazil. There are regular queues of traffic on the bridge as Brazilians cross the border to buy electrical goods, perfume, clothes, cigarettes and alcohol. Ciudad del Este also has a number of casinos that encourage cross-border movement.

People also cross the Tancredo Bridge to visit the town of Puerto Iguazu in Argentina. From here, there are daily flights to and from Buenos Aires, Cordoba and elsewhere in Argentina.

Tourism and the environment

There is a fundamental relationship between the environment and tourism. The environment attracts the tourist in the first place, be it scenery or historical heritage. In theory, the relationship should be mutually beneficial. Tourists enjoy beautiful environments, and revenue generated by tourists is used to maintain their quality.

A lot depends upon the nature of the tourists and the style of tourism. As tourist flow increases, tourism can cause major environmental problems. Unless successful management strategies are evolved, the costs of tourism can soon outweigh the benefits. This is especially true where there is overuse of relatively small areas of land or ocean that are vulnerable to damage. Pressures on coasts, mountains, National Parks, historic monuments and historic city centres are of particular concern.

Important factors

The nature of the tourism

Clearly, mass tourism tends to have a more intense and widespread impact on the environment. However, quite low-volume tourism can have a disproportionate effect. This is exemplified by the damaging effects of trekking in the Himalayas. Until recently, there has been a lack of management along the so-called 'Kleenex trails' in Nepal, where litter and waste disposal are major problems.

The nature of the destination

The spatial concentration of tourism plays a significant part in its impact. Urban areas can absorb high volumes of visitors and can plan for large flows. Small-scale historic sites like Stonehenge (Photograph 13.7), the Acropolis in Athens or the Lascaux caves in France (which had to be closed and substituted by a replica experience) are especially vulnerable to damage. Most grassland ecosystems are vulnerable to trampling. For this reason, flow management of visitors is a key feature of sand-dune and sloping grassland sites.

Photograph 13.7 Small historic sites like Stonehenge are vulnerable to damage

Corel

Types of activity

Some activities, such as motorcycle scrambling, mountain biking and skiing are more damaging to the environment than others.

Time of year

In theory, it is beneficial if tourism is seasonally concentrated so there is a recovery period during which, for example, paths can self-repair. Constant year-round activity in wet weather conditions is the most damaging of all.

Damaging impacts of tourism

Water

Tourist impacts include:

- discharge of rubbish and sewage into the sea, lakes and rivers
- release of oil from recreational boats, cruise ships and ferry boats
- bank erosion

Environmental consequences include:

- contamination and health hazards to local people and tourists
- change in, and destruction of, aquatic plant and animal life
- reduced aesthetic value
- increased toxicity in water bodies, which is detrimental to aquatic plants and may result in contaminated seafood
- problems for bathers
- problems with water supplies

These issues are particularly important around the Mediterranean and along the coral-reef coasts of the Caribbean and Florida.

Atmosphere

Tourist impacts include:

- air travel to tourist destinations
- the growing significance of recreational driving
- the operation of tour buses

Environmental consequences include:

- air and noise pollution, especially in peak season, which reduces the recreational value
- an adverse impact on plant and animal life
- global warming

There are problems of air pollution in historic tourist towns (e.g. Chiang Mai, Thailand) and in National Parks (e.g. Yosemite, USA).

Coasts and islands

Tourist impacts include:

- coastal development of resorts, campsites, golf courses and other facilities
- access roads, increased numbers of cars
- airport/heliport development
- marinas

Environmental consequences include:

- loss of coastal environments (e.g. mangrove swamps)
- the destruction of coral reefs
- loss of land for traditional uses
- beach erosion
- general loss of attraction

There are many examples of coastlines which have been developed for tourism, including the Thai coastline (e.g. Pattaya Beach and Phuket Island), Nandi in Fiji and Oahu, Honolulu.

Mountains

Tourist impacts include:

- trekking, mountaineering and skiing
- the construction of hotels, mechanical lifts, power lines and sewage systems

Environmental consequences include:

- deforestation, leading to soil erosion
- increased footpath erosion and litter
- loss of vegetation to create ski pistes
- increased landslides and avalanches
- the potential for visual pollution and increased water pollution

Trekking in Nepal and ski tourism in, for example, the French Alps and the North American Rockies have caused environmental problems.

Vegetation

Tourist impacts include:

- deforestation for resort construction and increased use of fuelwood
- trampling impacts at honeypot sites (cars and pedestrians)
- picking flowers, plants and fungi

Environmental consequences include:

- alteration of plant communities

- degradation of forests, leading to increased runoff and erosion
- risk of fire in high-value park areas
- the disappearance of fragile species due to constant trampling
- increased damage to plant habitats

These issues are evident, for example, in Nepal, along the coasts of Borneo and in tourist developments in National Parks in Thailand and in the Kakadu National Park, Queensland, Australia.

Wildlife

Tourist impacts include:

- hunting and fishing
- poaching wildlife for the souvenir industry
- chasing and harassing wildlife for photographs
- development of trails and highways through natural areas
- speeding vehicles

Environmental consequences include:

- a reduction in wildlife numbers, especially of endangered species
- disruption of feeding and breeding, and of predator–prey relationships
- relocation of feeding and breeding areas
- disruption of wildlife migrations
- drainage of wetlands

Photograph 13.8 The Sphinx in Egypt is being destroyed by air pollution

Corel

These issues are evident in the Coto Donana National Park in Spain and, as a result of safari tourism, in east Africa. Endangered species such as elephant and rhino are illegally hunted for tusks and horns respectively.

Archaeological, historic and religious monuments

Monuments are at risk from excessive use for recreational and tourist purposes.

Environmental consequences include:

- overcrowding, trampling, litter
- alteration of original function, commercialisation
- potential desecration
- vehicular access, which raises air pollution issues

Sites where there are particular problems include the Pont du Gard in France and Knossos in Crete. There are overcrowding issues at Stonehenge, the Taj Mahal (India) and the pyramids in Egypt. The Sphinx (Photograph 13.8) is being destroyed by air pollution.

Case study Tourism in Nepal

After foreign aid, tourism is Nepal's main source of income. Every year around 300,000 tourists visit Nepal. Of these, 25% visit National Parks and conservation areas such as Annapurna. They leave litter (known as the 'Kleenex trail'); they cause forest destruction by burning fuelwood to heat water and cook meals; the yaks they use to carry their supplies overgraze mountain pastures.

Park fees from tourism raise only one-fifth of the running costs. The trekking routes are lined with non-biodegradable litter, scattered in piles on the outskirts of villages or on riverbanks. In the absence of toilet facilities, pollution of water supplies has become a major problem. Along the trekking routes, large tourist lodges have been built in forest clearings. Rare species such as the red panda are threatened.

Historic towns

Tourist impacts include:

- expansion of hotels, restaurants, bars, entertainment facilities and souvenir shops
- increased car and coach traffic
- large numbers of visitors

Environmental consequences include:

- displacement of residents
- disruption and overcrowding through traffic congestion
- overloaded infrastructure
- increased pollution
- noise from late-night tourist activities
- unattractive architecture of new developments

Examples include overcrowding problems in Florence and Venice and the management of tourist traffic in Bath, Cambridge, Canterbury and Chester.

Beneficial impacts of tourism

Tourism does have some benefits for the environment. It provides the money to support conservation programmes and the preservation of endangered species, to rejuvenate old buildings and sites and to provide new facilities. High-quality interpretative features, such as submarine trails for snorkellers, can provide excellent environment-appreciation experiences and be educational.

Good planning and management can avoid (or reverse) some of the worst damage caused by tourism. Examples include the following:

- Pollution has a major environmental impact. However, in some places there are cleaning programmes to preserve the attractiveness of the location for tourists. An example is the Copacabana beach in Rio de Janeiro, which is made pristine every dawn.
- Tourism revenue can be used to finance repairs to areas damaged by trampling, for example using geotextiles on footpaths at Malham Cove and Goredale Scar in the Yorkshire Dales National Park.
- The revenue from tourism is being used to protect endangered species, such as the panda, and to establish new conservation areas and projects, such as the Annapurna scheme in Nepal.

- Infrastructure may be challenged by tourist overuse, but tourism can also conserve it. For example, tourist patronage has helped to save vulnerable branch railway lines such as the Heart of Wales line. Tourism can also lead to the building of new roads, the survival of village shops and services and the provision of much needed water and electricity supplies.
- Although tourism and the controversial 'right to roam' can encroach on farmland, they can also provide the revenue (via farm tourism) to keep marginal land in production.
- Tourist buildings can be eyesores. However, a tourism complex built on derelict land can enhance a site, as at Festival Park, Stoke-on-Trent.
- Tourism revenues can be recycled to plan and manage tourism more effectively. Revenue may come from pricing policies, exclusion controls, wilderness permits and vehicle admission controls, all of which require the collection of fees. The money can be spent on developing new sites with interpretative trails — to disperse tourist activity and take pressure off honeypot sites — and providing wardens to educate the public.

Case study Conservation in the Peak District National Park, UK

Conservation in the Peak District National Park involves a partnership between farmers, landowners, the National Park Authority and associated conservation bodies.

Villages and hamlets are the most obviously human part of the park landscape. Most buildings are made of local stone and reflect local building traditions. Settlements and buildings have changed with the changing economic and social conditions, but the traditional materials and scale of the buildings have been maintained. The National Park Authority is encouraging this by providing guidelines on the design of, and materials for, any new building or extension.

Conservation areas

There are conservation areas in many villages that have buildings of special historic or architectural interest. Normally, the conservation area is in the heart of the village. However, if the surrounding landscape has historic interest, such as the remains of medieval strip fields, the conservation area may extend into it. Trees in conservation areas cannot be cut down without permission from the National Park Authority. Enhancement projects in a conservation area might include paving, burying telephone wires and electricity cables, tree planting and restoring traditional features such as wells, pinfolds (small enclosures where stray animals were held) and lamp posts. Grants may also be provided for the repair and renovation of non-listed buildings.

Listed buildings

In the Peak District National Park there are over 2,700 listed buildings of special architectural or historic interest. Particular care is applied to their conservation. Grants are available from either the National Park Authority or English Heritage for their repair or restoration. Owners are encouraged to discuss any such proposals with the National Park Authority's specialist architects.

Historic landscape

Important areas of historic landscape can be found throughout the Peak District National Park. There are remains from the Neolithic Age (Arbor Low stone circle and the chambered tomb at Five Wells), Bronze Age (the stone circle and tomb on Stanton Moor), Iron Age (the hill fort at Mam Tor), Roman period (Navio fort at Brough and a Roman field system at Chee Tor) and many developments from the medieval period onwards (the Chelmorton field system). Lead mining has had a significant effect on the landscape with mines along rakes (veins of lead ore), soughs (drainage channels) and smelting sites.

Ancient monuments

There are about 200 scheduled ancient monuments in the park. Thousands of other monuments are listed in the Sites and Monuments Records, which grows longer whenever surveys are carried out.

Conservation of the landscape: the upper Derwent valley

The Derwent valley has been popular since the opening up of the old turnpike roads and the development of coach routes in the 1970s. In the mid-1980s over 1.25 million people visited the area each year and on summer Sundays there were up to 4,000 people and 600 parked cars in the valley. The roads were often congested on busy weekends, causing chaos and problems of access for local farmers, foresters and emergency services.

A management plan was drawn up to try to resolve these problems. Representatives on the management team were drawn from the National Park Authority, the water authority, the Forestry Commission, the National Trust, local councils and other interested parties. The joint action and funding of this management project has been a key point in its success.

Figure 13.10
Map of the Derwent valley

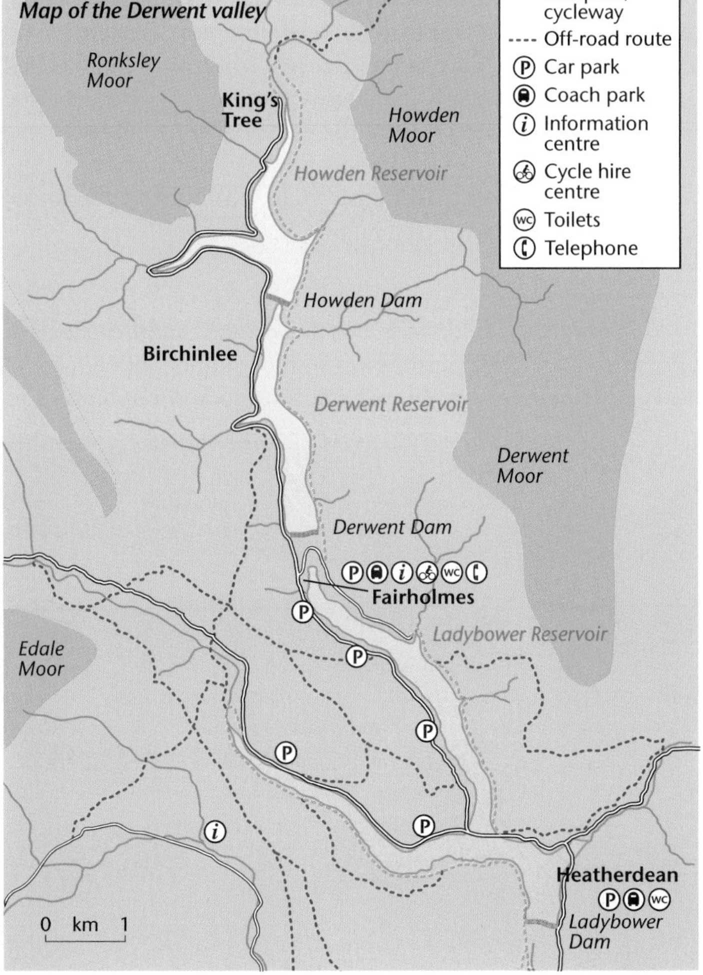

Achievements of the plan have been:

- **Reducing congestion** — roads north of Fairholmes are closed to motor traffic at peak times and to coaches at all times; a minibus is provided. The road east from Fairholmes is closed to non-local motor traffic. Six car parks for 450 cars and three coaches have been provided, including one at Fairholmes for 200 cars. Bus services from surrounding towns and cities have been improved.
- **Wildlife conservation** — a detailed ecological survey was carried out and recommendations for conservation are being implemented.
- **Conservation of the distinctive character of the area** — landscape improvement schemes have included the removal of concrete post and wire fencing. A tree-planting scheme has increased broadleaved plantations and improved the appearance of the landscape. Views across the reservoir have been opened up in the woodland.

- **Improving recreational facilities** — a new building at Fairholmes contains an enlarged visitor centre plus refreshments and toilets. Publications on local history and walks are sold at the visitor centre and a free illustrated visitors' guide is available on request. Cycle hire has been established and around 15,000 cycles are now hired each year. A full-time ranger, employed jointly by the National Park Authority and Severn Trent Water, has been appointed to liaise with local farmers, landowners and visitors. Footpaths have been constructed and waymarked from the car park at Fairholmes, including a section for wheelchairs. Nineteen kilometres of new concessionary walking routes have been agreed. Fishing from boats is allowed and there is a well-established and popular trout fishery. A platform for disabled anglers has been built at Ladybower Reservoir. Sub-aqua diving also takes place at Ladybower.
- Attractive **information boards** interpreting popular features and sites have been provided.

Wilderness areas

A wilderness is a wild and uncultivated area. Ideally, wilderness areas should never have been subject to human activity which might have resulted in manipulation, deliberate or accidental, of the area's ecology. In North America, large areas have been designated as wilderness and these are left wild and unmanaged (Photograph 13.9). Some people believe that there is a need for areas where those seeking 'spiritual refreshment' can experience the wildness of nature. There are strict controls within North American wilderness areas. Hunting and trapping, commercial development and motorised transport are prohibited or seriously restricted. Alaska has 35 such areas, which total over 300,000 km^2.

Antarctica

Antarctica is the world's last great wilderness. It is an unusual tourist destination in that it is not populated, except by scientists at a small number of permanent research stations. Polar scientists have always been concerned about tourism to

Corel

Photograph 13.9 North American wilderness areas are strictly controlled

the continent because they fear it will interfere with their scientific work and destroy the near-perfect environment. On the other hand, committed tourists can be supportive of such scientific work — publicising it and helping to raise funds.

In 1998, over 10,000 tourists visited the continent, 95% of them in cruise ships. Antarctic tourism is of three types:

- expensive camping trips for naturalists, photographers and journalists
- ship-board visits, largely by cruise ships but also by converted Russian ice breakers. Most start either in Ushuaia (Argentina), which is the nearest port, or in Port Stanley (the Falkland Islands)
- over-flights — these have restarted after an interval of nearly 20 years following the crash of an Air New Zealand DC10 on Mt Erebus, in which all passengers died

Tourists go to Antarctica to see the glacial landscapes and the wildlife, particularly seals, whales and penguins. They also go for the remoteness and isolation and the chance to test themselves in adverse weather conditions. Tourists may be interested in historic sites, as for example McMurdo Sound with its huts dating from the Scott and Shackleton expeditions. Tourism is concentrated in the short southern summer period, from mid-November to March.

Ship-borne tourism in Antarctica takes the form of 'expeditions'. This concept is reinforced by the issue of polar-style clothing. Most of the ships are comparatively small, with average capacity between 50 and 100 people. Therefore, the ship-based programme of educational lectures by Antarctic specialists creates a cohesive and motivated group. Tourists are carefully briefed on the requirements of the Antarctic Treaty and the Environmental Protocol. They are informed of the code of conduct in terms of behaviour ashore, adherence to health and safety requirements and rules about wildlife observation. When visiting any one of around 200 possible sites (tourists are free to land anywhere except at designated preservation areas or near active scientific research sites), the overall group is divided into boatloads of around 20, each led by an expert guide. Each site may only be visited every 2 or 3 days.

Impacts of tourism

Research on the impacts of tourism is being undertaken by the Scott Polar Research Institute in Cambridge, particularly at the high-pressure sites of King George Island and Elephant Island, and at all 200 approved landing places. Some findings have already been published and they show that the Antarctic environment has been little affected:

- Antarctic tourism is a well-run industry, living up to its sound record for environmental concern.
- Guidelines are widely accepted by operators and tourists alike, but they need updating to include the Environmental Protocol of the UN.
- Damage to vegetation (especially the fragile moss mat) is due to natural causes, such as breeding seals. Tourists are usually scrupulous in not walking on areas of fragile vegetation.
- No litter is attributed to tourists; they tend to be concerned about the waste they see around the scientific research stations.

Photograph 13.10 Fledgling emperor penguins and tourists in front of an icebreaker tour ship in Antarctica

Frank Todd/Bryan and Cherry Alexander

- Virtually no stress is caused to penguins by tourists visiting their breeding colonies. However, tern colonies seemed to suffer from disturbance.
- Seals are largely indifferent to the presence of humans. Tourists who follow wildlife guidelines cause no impact.
- Out of 200 landing sites surveyed, only 5% showed any wear and tear. These need to be rested, but at present there is no mechanism to implement this type of management.

Despite these encouraging signs, there are some concerns:

- The Antarctic ecosystem is extremely fragile — disturbances leave their imprint for a long time (footprints on moss can remain for decades).
- The summer tourist season coincides with peak wildlife breeding periods.
- The land-based installations and wildlife are clustered in the few ice-free locations on the continent.
- The demand for fresh water is difficult to meet.
- Visitor pressure is felt on cultural heritage sites such as old whaling and sealing stations and early exploration bases.
- There is some evidence that over-flying by light planes and helicopters is causing some stress to breeding colonies of penguins and other birds.
- The unique legal status of Antarctica makes enforcement of any code of behaviour difficult.

Ecotourism and sustainable tourism

The damaging effects of some forms of intensive tourism on the environment are well documented. There are many examples of successful and imaginative tourism that brings genuine economic benefits to a community without significant damage to the environment, but on the whole the impacts of mass tourism are depressing. Damage is becoming more common as the tourist industry grows.

Ecotourism is described as 'an economic process by which rare and beautiful ecosystems and cultural attractions are marketed internationally to attract tourists'. Therein lies a contradiction — once the flow of tourists increases, the potential damage becomes harder to manage and it escalates. Supporters state that ecotourism is sustainable tourism — conserving the environment for future generations — but many would argue with this.

The guiding principles of **sustainable tourism** are that:

- the environment has an intrinsic value which far outweighs its value as a tourism asset
- long-term survival must not be prejudiced by short-term considerations
- tourism should be recognised as a positive activity with the potential to benefit the destination and its community. A significant proportion of the profits should be retained locally
- a prime aim should be that the local community participates in the industry and its development, thereby developing local skills
- the relationship between tourism and the environment must be managed, with the ultimate sanction of the withdrawal of tourism to ensure that the environment is conserved
- tourist activities and developments should respect the scale, nature and character (including the traditions and culture) of their location
- in any location, harmony must be sought between the needs of the visitors, the place and the host community

In effect, sustainable tourism requires an up-grading of environmental and socio-cultural interests and a down-grading of purely economic aims. At its best, ecotourism is notable for the way it approaches the planning and management of tourism environments:

- It aims to build responsible tourism by developing tourism with dignity and by managing capacity.
- It encourages conservation, through the education of both local people and tourists.
- It develops a focus on the environment by solving environmental problems and exporting ecotourist ideas around the world.

Is ecotourism sustainable?

Many travel companies and countries have been quick to pick up on the public enthusiasm for exotic environments. They are keen to market small-group tours to faraway places as ecologically sound tourism, or ecotourism. These tours are designed to ensure that travellers get a worthwhile and unusual experience. Inevitably they are expensive, often based in luxury lodges and using small group transport. Environmentalists dismiss many of these tours as **egotourism**, claiming that it is ordinary tourism dressed up as politically correct. While some ecotours do fulfil the requirements of sustainable tourism, they are quite rare. If ecotourism is to work, it has to fulfil two conditions:

- The number of visitors must be limited to a level that the environment can sustain.
- It must be set up and run in cooperation and consultation with local inhabitants.

Ecotourism is one of the fastest growing sectors of the tourism industry. It has been developed largely by small, dedicated tour companies and still constitutes less than 5% of the market. Ecotourism is not a concept that blends well with the multinational companies that modern tourism has created. Many of the large companies, such as hotel groups, are making overt attempts to become more environmentally aware in terms of their management of waste, water and energy (see Aldemar Hotels case study). Companies such as British Airways have carried out a green audit of their business practices and reward green tourist initiatives. Cynics would claim that these strategies are designed to generate a good public relations image.

Case study Aldemar Hotels, Greece

Aldemar is a leading Greek hotel chain. It has worked with local communities on environmental issues for years. Its current environmental programme is called Mare Verde and aims to reduce the impact of the hotels on the environment.

What does the programme involve?

- The protection of water resources by using water sparingly and introducing biological cleaning systems.
- Using solar energy.
- Automatic deactivation of the electricity supply to hotel rooms when guests go out.
- The use of environmentally friendly materials in the construction of hotels.
- Reducing use of packaging materials and recycling waste paper.
- Sourcing fruit and vegetables from the company's own farm in Greece.
- Tree planting campaigns and involvement by staff in environmental activity.

Guests can contribute by:

- Not requesting clean sheets and towels each day.
- Turning off the supply of electricity to their rooms while they are out by removing the key card.
- Using Aldemar bags (made from a mixture of paper and fabric) instead of plastic bags.
- Turning off the taps while shaving or cleaning teeth and taking a quick shower rather than having a bath.
- Supporting local environmental groups.

Case study Small-scale ecotourism in the Napo region, Ecuador

The Napo region is in the rainforest of eastern Ecuador. In 1990, after a group of tourists came to stay with a local family who were paid for their hospitality, the indigenous population of Quicha Indians had the idea of developing ecotourism.

In 1991, Action Aid (a British charity) carried out a research project which recorded how the rainforest in the Napo region was being destroyed by a combination of oil exploitation and rainforest tourism, thus threatening the Quicha's traditional lifestyle. The ecotourism project was developed in an attempt to strengthen the community and to create a sustainable income for the indigenous people.

The Quicha people insist that all visitors must abide by certain rules and regulations:

- Exchanges of clothing or other personal items with community members are not allowed; nor are community members allowed to accept gifts.
- Visitors must not enter people's houses without being invited and are asked not to make promises they may not be able to keep (e.g. sending back photos after the visit).
- All rubbish (e.g. empty bottles and cans) must be taken away by visitors.
- When walking in the rainforest tourists are asked:
  - not to touch any branches without looking carefully first — they may have thorns or carry dangerous insects or even snakes
  - not to pull on branches or vines — they may fall down
  - if they need to go to the toilet and facilities are not immediately available, go to the side of the rainforest track, never in, or near, a stream or lake
- Visitors must avoid displays of affection, even with close friends. In this community it is considered rude to hold hands or kiss in public.
- Plants, insects or other animals must not be collected without permission to do so.
- Visitors must never go off for a walk alone. It is easy to get lost in the rainforest.

Visitors come from the USA and Canada and are usually committed environmentalists. They travel into the area by canoe, and have a 2-hour hike through the forest to their destination. Stays last for up to 6 days and include walks through the 'jungle', and visits to community projects such as the Garden of Medicinal Plants and to see pottery making. Tourists, in groups of up to 12, stay in buildings built by the local people.

The Quicha use their expert knowledge of the forest as the basis of the guided tours. They have trained their children, via an ecological training programme in the village school, to recognise plants and their uses. Money from tourism has led to major improvements to services in the villages.

In 1996, the Ecuador government banned the Quicha from running tours in the Napo region because it feared the local project was not benefiting the national economy. The government claimed that the Quicha were not registered as tour guides and did not pay taxes on their earnings. The government has since threatened to arrest local community leaders if they continue to run tours.

Converting this informal scheme to an official one and developing a booking and management structure for such a remote area, are key issues.

Tourism and development

Tourism is an industry, and the pattern of global tourism is little different from other parts of the global economy. Despite a growing number of visitors from the MEDW to the LEDW, most tourism is still concentrated in the richest countries. Eight of the top ten countries for tourist arrivals are in Europe and North America. Even where the pattern is changing, the role of TNCs ensures that the wealth generated from tourism finds its way back to the MEDW.

Tourism is seen by most nations as a way of helping to expand the economy. The generation of international tourism enables a country to earn foreign currency. Tourism is referred to as an invisible product, an export for the receiving country. Countries such as Spain, France, Italy and Greece show a surplus, whereas Germany, Japan and the UK show a deficit. However, in balance of payments terms, the apparent deficits are turned into surpluses because these countries control multinational companies, airlines and banking, all of which feed back capital.

Many countries in the LEDW have the potential to make money from tourism in that they have the resources to host it. However, as yet, their citizens do not have the wealth to be international tourists themselves. Although it is possible to identify many economic **benefits** from promoting tourism (income from taxation such as airport taxes, investment, employment and the payment of wages), in reality the balance between economic benefits and **costs** is not as favourable as it might seem. Profit margins are reduced by the **leakage** of profits to foreign developers and by having to import special goods for tourists.

Leakage may take a number of forms:

- Profits are taken out by foreign tour operators, airlines and owners of cruise lines.
- Governments and private investors repay loans and interest to international banks.
- If facilities are all-inclusive, even more profits go abroad, to the multinationals that own them.
- Imported goods and fittings are used to build foreign-owned hotels.
- Local entrepreneurs often reinvest their profits overseas.
- Foreign workers in hotels send their pay back to their home country.

Economic growth and development

Tourism is often seen by the LEDW as an alternative path to development — a way of breaking away from dependence on primary products and joining the global economy. Usually this involves foreign investment in mass tourism. However, this type of development has been criticised by some as being a new form of colonialism that is unlikely to bring benefits to most poor people in the LEDW. It is argued that it may even lead to underdevelopment, leaving poor countries vulnerable to changes in the world tourist industry. Others have a more optimistic viewpoint. They argue that tourism promotes the development of new economic links with the outside world — global interdependence. These ideas are summarised in Table 13.1.

Tourism is the world's largest employer. It creates an enormous range of jobs, both directly and indirectly. Tourism's labour demand is pyramidal in structure. At the top, there is a small, core labour force of full-time, highly paid and multiskilled managers. They are supported by a very large number of workers, often poorly paid, who are engaged in low-cost, labour-intensive functions such as cleaning. Often the better jobs in tourism do not go local people, but there are plenty of opportunities for local entrepreneurs to make a living.

Cumulative causation

The economist Myrdal put forward a theory to explain regional differences in economic growth. He stated that where a region has some form of initial advantage, for example a source of industrial growth, then this can start the process of **cumulative causation**. The establishment of the original industry may trigger

Tourism as a path to development	Tourism as a path to underdevelopment
Tourism enables the LEDW to develop in the same way that the MEDW has	Tourism helps the MEDW to develop more than the LEDW because profits go back to the MEDW — the LEDW becomes more dependent
Foreign investment, expertise and technology are brought to the LEDW by TNCs	TNCs control tourism in their own interests, not those of the local community
Mass tourism brings holidaymakers from the MEDW — they are attracted by advertisements showing idyllic resorts	Mass tourism may spoil the character of the resort and it could become a victim of its own success
Traditional local culture is an obstacle to tourism — it is replaced by modern Western culture, symbolised by McDonald's, Coca Cola etc.	The local community may be resentful if its culture is devalued — this can lead to crime and even terrorism
Tourism requires development of the local infra-structure (e.g. roads and airports), which may also benefit local people	Tourism can put too much pressure on local resources and reduce the quality of life for people through pollution
Tourism generates local employment and helps to increase wealth	Tourism exploits cheap local labour — the best-paid jobs often go to outsiders

Table 13.1 Tourism: a path to development or underdevelopment?

other developments — other industries, which supply the original industry with inputs, may be attracted to the region. Subsidiary firms, which use the products or outputs of the original industry, may also be attracted. This activity may lead to other **multiplier effects** caused by in-migration of labour and increased employment in construction, transport and services to supply the needs of the larger population. Infrastructure improvements take place that make the region more attractive to other industries. In this way, one development leads to the growth of others. The process is cumulative — a case of success breeding success.

Tourism generates its own multiplier effects. As a resort develops, so does the local economy. As profits from tourism increase and become more widespread, so profits begin to trickle down into the local economy. This often leads to the emergence of local suppliers of food, clothes and souvenirs, and a decrease in reliance on foreign imports. The multiplier effect also improves the quality of local services by encouraging a more buoyant economy.

However, there are some concerns about the economic aspects of tourism:

- tourism is a volatile industry on which to base economic growth
- tourism in the LEDW can increase dependence on foreign companies, which leads to extensive leakage
- tourism can be so effective in regenerating an area that it can lead to localised inflation, making basic foods and services too expensive for local people
- tourism can cause economic problems for other elements of an economy; for example an exodus of young people from a rural area may lead to a labour shortage in farming
- the overloading of infrastructure (e.g. water, sewerage and road systems) can lead to economic problems

Sociocultural development

The sociocultural impact of tourism depends on the type of tourism and the type of tourist. One classification of tourists and their impact has been devised by Smith (Table 13.2).

Table 13.2 Smith's classification of tourists

Type of tourist	Number of tourists	Adaptations to local norms
Explorer	Very limited	Accept fully
Elite	Rare	Adapt fully
Off-beat	Uncommon, but seen	Adapt well
Unusual	Occasional	Adapt somewhat
Incipient mass	Steady flow	Seek Western amenities
Mass	Continuous flow	Expect Western amenities
Charter	Massive arrivals	Demand Western amenities

In general, independent explorers fit in best with the local environment and community. This is because of their relatively small number, the slow rates of growth in their type of tourism activity and their potential for involvement in the community. On the other hand, package tourists usually arrive en masse to facilities that have been built rapidly, often with few links to the local economy. They usually only meet local people in bars, on the beach or as workers in shops and restaurants.

It is generally argued that the greater the difference in culture and living standards between the tourist and the host, the more likely it is that the relationship between them will be unsatisfactory. Doxey has suggested the following index of host irritation:

- **euphoria** — the initial phase of development; visitors and investors are welcome
- **apathy** — visitors are taken for granted; contacts between residents and outsiders are more formal
- **annoyance** — saturation point is approached; residents have misgivings about the tourist industry
- **antagonism** — irritations openly expressed; visitors seen as a cause of all problems

Spatial proximity is another key factor. In some all-inclusive hotels the beach is fenced off to keep out local people. Where tourism is dispersed throughout a community, relationships can be more effectively cultivated. Tourism in small 'hideaway' islands which have their own local communities can create particularly sensitive situations.

The marketing of culture

Tourists are attracted by elements of local culture such as handicrafts, local food, history, architecture, religion, art, music, traditional dress and ways of life. In many cases, indigenous cultures are used to promote and sustain tourism. However, these may lose authenticity as they are exploited. Traditional dance and music is often staged; for example, for visits by tourist safari buses to Masai villages in Kenya. Traditional village feasts can be excuses for heavy drinking, over-eating and poor behaviour by tourists, all of which bear no resemblance to indigenous cultural events. Traditional local craft industries are frequently overtaken by poor quality imports, often from the Far East.

The value systems and moral basis of traditional societies can be undermined by contact with tourists. The casual Western lifestyle can lead to local problems, including:

- the flouting of dress codes
- increased hooliganism, alcoholism, gambling, prostitution and crime
- the devaluing of religious customs and the lack of respect for conventions in religious buildings
- exploitation of women in sex tourism, with consequent health risks, such as AIDS
- erosion of local languages, with increased use of English, which is often Americanised
- increased tension between the generations of a society

A number of tourism-related human rights abuses can arise, for example:

- Tourism industries that thrive on sexual exploitation of women and children, as in India, Cambodia and Thailand. Poor families sell children to tourists; in some cases they may be kidnapped.
- The displacement of native people by the creation of nature reserves for wildlife tourism. In an extreme case, the Samburi pastoralists in Kenya have been denied access to the only water hole in the area, which is now part of a game viewing area for a luxury hotel.
- Local people are frequently forced from their lands and fishing areas by tourist developers who require the sites for luxury resorts and golf courses. Often pitiful levels of compensation are paid.

Case study Tourism in the Maldives

In the Maldive Islands in the Indian Ocean, tourists, although welcome for the money they bring, are almost always kept in isolation on atolls that have been specifically developed as resorts. There are now nearly 80 such island developments, and more are planned. Release of the islands for development is strictly controlled by the government.

Tourist numbers have grown rapidly in recent years. Apart from the island on which Malé International Airport is located, visitors are barred from the many inhabited islands unless they have a permit to visit a local family or are on an organised boat or helicopter visit. In this situation, local people queue up to sell to the tourists, of whom they see so little.

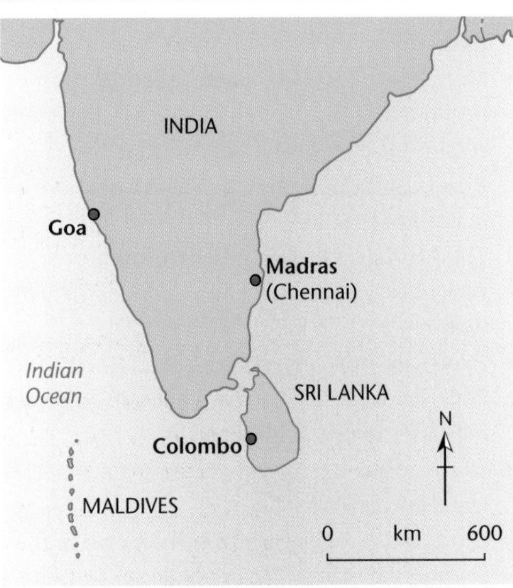

Figure 13.11 Map showing location of the Maldives

Careful security at the airport prevents the import of drugs, alcohol and pornographic literature. As is made clear in literature provided for tourists, the Maldives is Islamic, and the government wants to protect the 250,000 inhabitants from the worst of Western values. There is a strict behaviour code at the resorts. No nude or topless bathing (women) is permitted. If visitors are caught breaking this rule, both the tourists and their hotel have to pay a hefty fine.

The Maldives government argues that separation has happened by coincidence, rather than by design. It also states that the smallness of the islands (averaging 400 m across) makes separation necessary, if tourists want beaches to themselves, rather than sharing with local people. From the tourists' point of view, it probably does work. For a short time they can imagine themselves cast away on a tropical island paradise — albeit an air-conditioned one.

Case study Tourism in Nepal

The environmental impact of tourism in Nepal is covered on page 441. The socioeconomic impacts of trekking on village life are also of concern.

The Khumbu valley is a highland region in Nepal. Most of the Sherpas who are porters and guides for trekking expeditions come from this region. Traditionally the people of the Khumbu were subsistence farmers, growing staples such as potatoes and vegetables and rearing livestock on high pastures by means of transhumance. Surplus products were traded with Tibet. Fuelwood was the main source of energy.

The trekking industry has brought many changes to the area:

- Traditional village life has broken down — young men have severed links with their families and their villages.
- Many families now have second homes in Kathmandu, the capital. They leave the Khumbu region for part of the year so that they can run their businesses in the city. Some men have a wife in Kathmandu, as well as in the Khumbu.
- There is not enough labour in the region to do the agricultural work; this is now done largely by the women.
- There are now many more two-storey houses. Poor, landless men can earn enough as porters to rebuild or improve their houses.
- Fuelwood is becoming scarce because trekkers use it for cooking.
- Land and building prices have increased, especially in the main village of Namche Bazaar.
- Trekkers stay in commercial lodges, some of which have been set up by local businessmen. There is now an oversupply of beds.
- Yak breeding is no longer a central part of the economy, although there is a huge demand for yaks as pack animals.

Corel

Photograph 13.11 A boy at the village tap

- Villages look more prosperous (Photograph 13.11). Many young men working in businesses in Kathmandu send money back to their parents and wives.
- Electricity is supplied by a mini-hydroelectric scheme financed by trekking revenue.
- Sherpas buy rice and Western food when trekking. Diet is now more varied and health standards have improved.
- Many Sherpas suffer injuries and even death from carrying huge packs for tourist expeditions. They are poorly trained in health and safety and are not assured of compensation when injured.
- Traditional garments are no longer made. Western-style clothing and expedition kit are common.
- Encouraged by Sir Edmund Hillary, schools have been built, so education has improved.
- There is a surplus of young unmarried women in the villages. Population is declining in the villages as deaths outnumber births.

Stimulation of economic growth

Case study Tourism in Tunisia

The Tunisian National Tourism Office website states:

> Whatever the season, your first glimpse of Tunisia will be one of golden beaches and a deep blue sea. With over 1,200 km of coast, this sunny Mediterranean land is a paradise for the vacationer.
>
> Well-known seaside resort areas — Sousse, Monastir, Hammamet and Nabeul, and Djerba — offer their visitors the finest sandy beaches and crystalline water along with a dizzying choice of waterfront hotels featuring sun and sea sports. An hour's drive from these modern resorts will bring you to another Tunisia, one of ancient Roman, Arab, Berber or Phoenician sites. Reminders of this rich historical past abound.

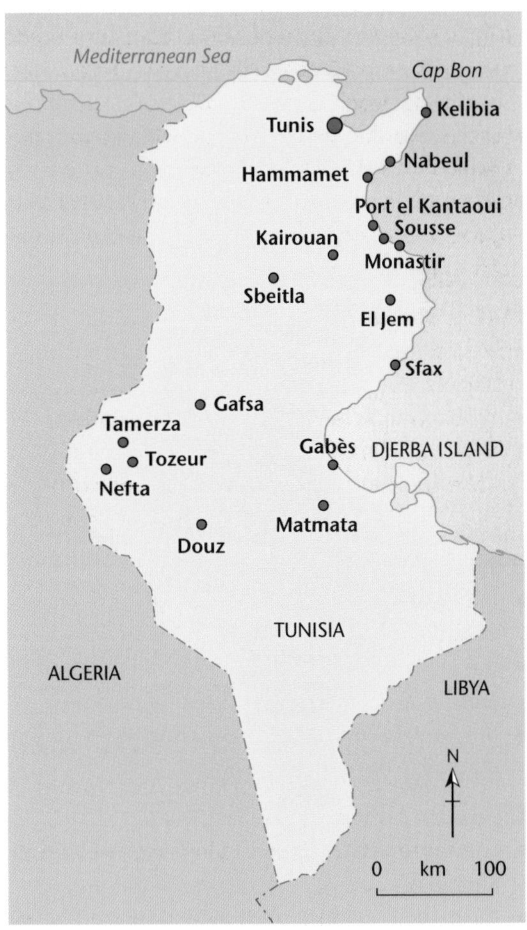

Figure 13.12 Map of Tunisia

The Tunisian economy relies heavily on tourism and remittances from nationals working abroad. In recent years the government has sought to exploit the tourist potential of the country and has actively encouraged growth in this area. A number of **tourist growth poles** now exist.

Tunis (the capital) possesses a number of attractions other than being the largest city:

- the Bardo Museum, with the world's finest collection of Roman mosaics
- colourful souqs and the Islamic architecture of the medina

Photograph 13.12 The landscape of Matmata was used in the **Star Wars** *films*

- views over the site of ancient Carthage from the top of Byrsa Hill
- the cobbled streets, whitewashed houses and blue-painted window-grills of the nearby coastal village of Sidi Bou Said

The Cap Bon peninsula has:

- a great expanse of sandy beaches at Hammamet and Nabeul
- Kelibia with its fort and spectacular ramparts
- the Punic ruins (dating from the third century BC) at Kerkouane

There are spectacular Roman remains in the interior of the country:

- the huge ancient city of Dougga with its remnants of houses, a theatre and 21 temples
- the almost perfectly preserved colosseum at El Jem
- the temple complex at Sufetula, said to be magical in the early morning light

The eastern seaboard and islands boast:

- coastal resorts at Sousse, Monastir and Port el Kantaoui
- the magnificent fort (ribat) at Monastir
- the ancient walled medina at Sfax
- the island of Djerba, with its idyllic beaches and distinctive architecture

The southern part of the country borders the northern Sahara desert. Here people can take part in more activity-based holidays such as camel trekking and off-road exploring across the desert dunes of the Grand Erg south of Douz, visiting the ancient Berber oasis towns and seeing the bizarre desert landscapes near Matmata.

One of the ways in which the Tunisian government has tried to broaden its appeal to tourists is to facilitate and heavily subsidise the use of Tunisian landscapes in Hollywood films. Some examples of Tunisian locations that have been used are:

- the ribat at Monastir — in *The Life of Christ* and *The Life of Brian*
- the medina at Sfax — in *The English Patient*
- the colosseum at El Jem — used as a model for the film *Gladiator*
- the landscape and troglodyte (cave dwelling) houses of Matmata — the home of Luke Skywalker in the *Star Wars* films

Tourism: the future

It is estimated that global tourism will, on average, grow by 4% per annum over the next 20 years. A number of trends are expected:

- Many more people will become tourists. This means that tourists will be drawn increasingly from the LEDW. Continued economic development of these countries will give people the time and the money to travel.
- In the MEDW, more people will go on holiday more frequently — perhaps as many as four or five times a year.
- Business tourism — currently 30% of the market — will increase greatly.
- People will travel further, and will extend the pleasure periphery. For example, travel to an exotic location with the express desire for relaxation will be a strong part of the market. Cruise-liner tourism and the number of all-inclusive resorts will continue to grow rapidly.
- Tourism will become more diversified. There is already a huge range of niche operators meeting the needs of specialist markets, some of which are highly specific.

An unregulated tourism industry can only lead to further environmental and social degradation, as well as new problems such as transmission of disease. The industry is controlled by big multinational companies that are concerned primarily with economic success. As with many global industries, a major issue is how their activities can be regulated and managed to be sustainable for future generations.

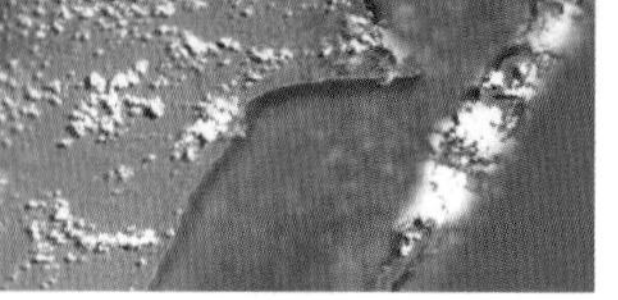

Assessment exercises

Population pressure and resource management

1 Study Figure A, which shows the trends in world use of selected energy resources and total population through the twentieth century.

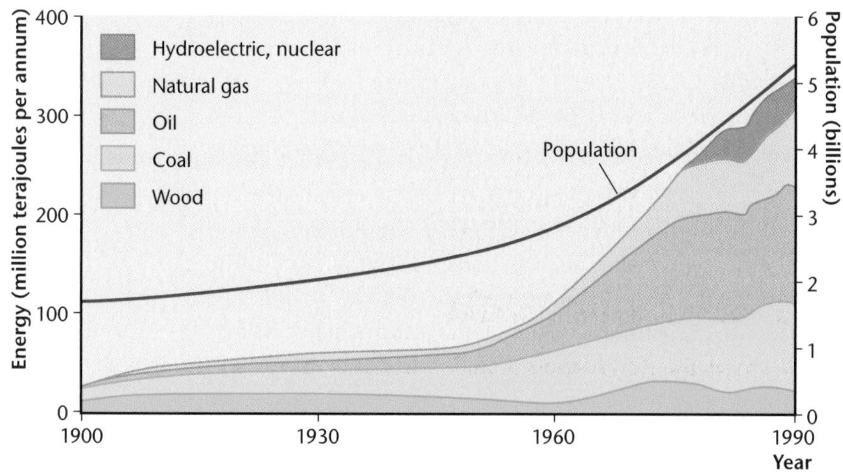

Figure A Twentieth century trends in world use of selected energy sources with total world population

a Comment on the trends in energy resource and population that are shown in Figure A. (4 marks)

b Outline the connections that exist between the use of energy resources and economic development. (4 marks)

c To what extent are the trends shown in Figure A compatible with sustainable development? (7 marks)

(15 marks)

Managing cities: challenges and issues

1 Study Figure B, which shows the location and date of origin of the shanty towns in Lima (Peru).

a Describe the pattern of growth of the shanty towns in Lima as shown in Figure B. (4 marks)

b Suggest reasons for the pattern that you have described in part (a). (4 marks)

c As the elected leader of the Lima City Council, what would you consider to be the most appropriate policies for shanty towns? Justify your views. (7 marks)

(15 marks)

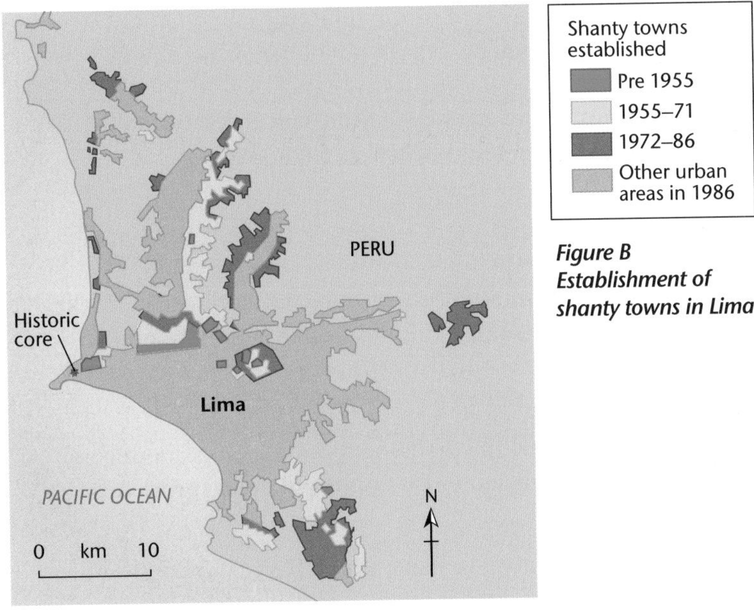

***Figure B* Establishment of shanty towns in Lima**

Recreation and tourism

1 Study Figure C, which shows the distribution of major tourist developments in Tunisia (north Africa) at the end of the twentieth century.

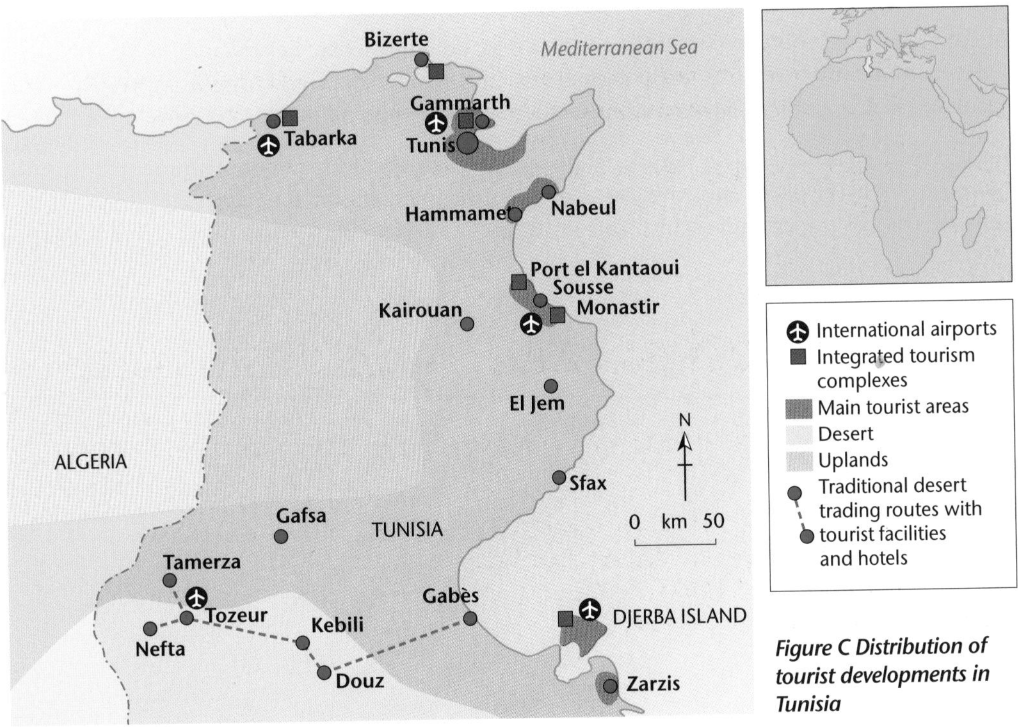

***Figure C* Distribution of tourist developments in Tunisia**

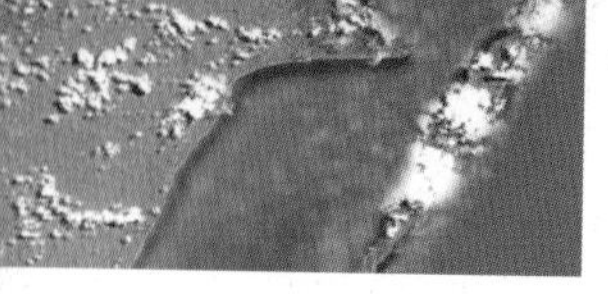

a Describe the pattern of tourist developments as shown on Figure C. (4 marks)

b What does the pattern of tourist developments suggest about the management of tourism by the Tunisian government? (4 marks)

c Suggest and comment on the possible reasons why the Tunisian government has decided to develop the tourist industry in recent years. (7 marks)

(15 marks)

Synoptic questions

The following questions are all **synoptic** in nature. This means that in your response you are required to show your knowledge and understanding of different aspects of geography, the connections between these different aspects and, where relevant, human perspectives upon geographical themes and issues.

1. **World population growth well into the twenty-first century will have both local and global effects on the natural environment and on human populations themselves. Discuss this statement.** *(30 marks)*

2. **Discuss the view that sustainability is a necessary and achievable goal for agriculture in both the developed and the developing worlds.** *(30 marks)*

3. **Urban problems are the same the world over and require the same solutions. To what extent do you agree with this view?** *(30 marks)*

4. **Environmental factors are just as important as social and economic factors in influencing the quality of life enjoyed by the inhabitants of large urban areas. How far do you agree with this view?** *(30 marks)*

5. **Successfully developing and maintaining an area of natural scenic beauty and amenity as a tourist resource, so as to maximise the benefits obtained from it, involves resolving many conflicts. How far do you agree with this statement?** *(30 marks)*

6. **Even if the beaches are idyllic and the climate perfect all year, it is not enough for countries in the LEDW to rely only on tourism as the main engine for economic growth. Discuss the extent to which this represents a valid view.** *(30 marks)*

A2

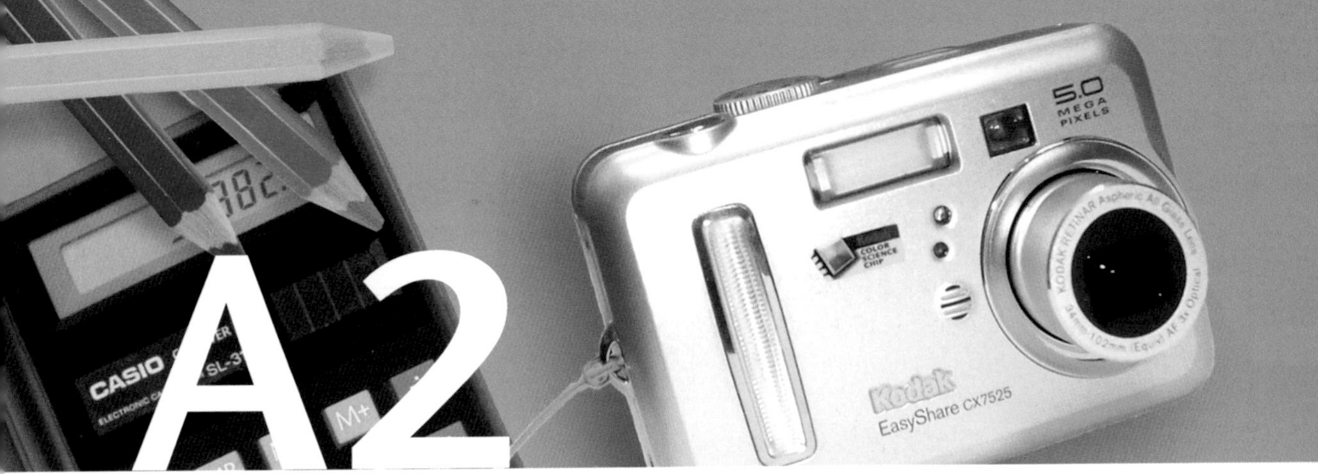

Module 6

Fieldwork investigation: coursework

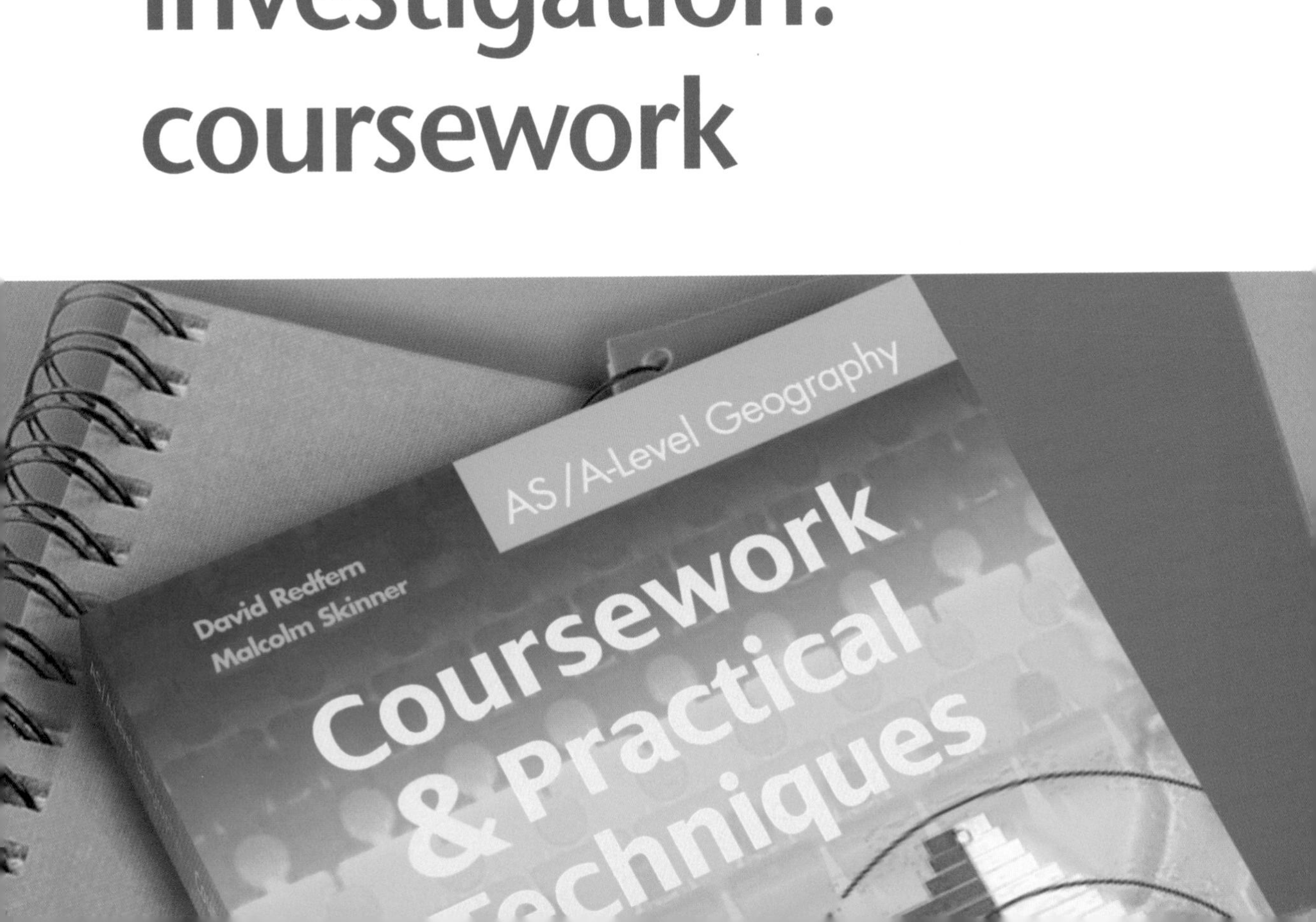

Chapter 14

Coursework

At A2, you are required to undertake investigative work in the field. This allows you to develop skills associated with planning investigations, collection of primary and secondary data, and presentation, interpretation and evaluation of results. You are required to *either* complete a fieldwork investigation and submit a report (Module 6) *or* take a written assessment based on a pre-release topic (Module 7).

This chapter deals with the Module 6 option. If you choose this option, you are required to submit a written report of up to 4,000 words that is the result of a minimum of 2 days spent in the field. There are no restrictions on what you study as long as your investigation includes primary data collection and is based on a small area of study. Any geographical argument, assertion or problem may be investigated. The report will be submitted to AQA and assessed by an appointed examiner.

What is a geographical investigation?

Your investigative work must be based on evidence from primary sources, including fieldwork, and secondary sources — in most cases a combination of the two. In simple terms **primary data** are those collected by you in the field, or material from other sources which needs to be processed. **Secondary data** are derived from published documentary sources and have already been processed.

Primary research is essential — you must have some direct contact with the area of study and the subject of investigation. Your study could, for example, involve a specific economic activity, an identified group of people or a local issue. You need to visit the area concerned and talk to the people there, or record data there.

All geographical investigations should follow the same stages:

- identifying the aim of the enquiry, often in the form of testing a hypothesis or establishing research questions
- selecting and collecting data using a range of techniques, for example measuring, mapping, observations, questionnaires, interviews
- organising and presenting the data using cartographic, graphic or tabular forms, possibly with the help of ICT
- analysing and evaluating the data, noting any limitations
- drawing together the findings and formulating a conclusion

- suggesting further extension to the investigation, including additional research questions which may have been stimulated by the findings
- a statement of success or otherwise of the investigation, with some commentary on the significance of the investigation for others
- demonstrating an awareness of safety issues and risk assessment in geographical fieldwork

The geographical investigation therefore provides an opportunity for you to demonstrate what you can do beyond the examination room.

Establishing a title

Hypotheses and research questions

The best type of investigation involves testing a **hypothesis**, or setting out one or more **research questions** that can be investigated and evaluated.

A hypothesis is a statement based on a question. For example, the question 'do the characteristics of a soil change down a slope?' could form the basis for any of the following hypotheses:

(1) *The depth of a soil varies downslope*
(2) *The clarity of the soil horizons varies down the slope*
(3) *The texture of a soil varies according to the position on the slope*
(4) *The acidity of a soil varies downslope*

and so on.

Once established, the hypothesis can be tested by collecting data. Following evaluation of the data, the results of the enquiry can be used to state whether or not the hypothesis was correct, and thus to answer the original question. The hypothesis or research question therefore forms the title of the investigation.

- A poor project title would be *Changes in the retail geography of a town over the last 30 years*. Here there is no question or hypothesis.
- A better title would be *What have been the major changes in shopping patterns in the area around Norwich in the last 30 years?* This establishes a question to which an answer can be developed.
- An alternative title, in the form of a hypothesis, would be *The CBD of Norwich has seen major decline in activity within the last 30 years caused by the growth of out-of-town retail outlets*.

Either of the last two titles are acceptable ways in which to proceed.

Aims and objectives

The purpose of the hypothesis or research question is to enable you to clarify your aims and objectives.

Aims are statements of what you are hoping to achieve. In the above example you will want to identify areas of change — evidence of decline in some shopping areas and growth in others, with possibly some reasoning for these changes.

Objectives are statements of how you will achieve your aims. What data will be needed to identify areas of decline or growth? How can these data be collected, analysed and presented? How will you obtain evidence of reasons for the changes?

Do you need to write to anyone, interview anyone or devise a questionnaire? What precise form of fieldwork needs to be undertaken?

What is a null hypothesis?

Some investigations are best approached by establishing a **null hypothesis**. This is a negative assertion, which states that there is *no relationship* between two chosen sets of variables. For example, a null hypothesis could state that *there is no relationship between air temperatures and distance from a city centre*. An alternative hypothesis can then also be established, in this case that *air temperatures decrease with distance from a city centre*.

The null hypothesis assumes there is a high probability that any observed links between the two sets of data, in this case temperature and distance from a city centre, are due to unpredictable factors. If temperatures are seen to decrease with distance from the city centre in the chosen city, it is a result of chance. If the null hypothesis can be rejected statistically, then the alternative hypothesis can be accepted.

One benefit of this seemingly 'reverse' approach to an enquiry is that if the null hypothesis *cannot* be rejected, it does not mean that a relationship does not exist — it may simply mean that not enough data have been collected to reject it. In short, the investigation was not worthless, but was too limited in scope. Another benefit of this approach is that it allows the use of statistical tests on the significance of the results.

The null hypothesis is a sophisticated way in which to approach an enquiry, and should only be used when fully understood.

Checking the feasibility of your investigation

Before embarking on this major piece of work which will, if properly undertaken, take a great deal of time to complete, you should check whether or not the tasks involved are achievable, and that an overall conclusion will be forthcoming.

Here are some questions you should ask yourself to see if your idea can really work:

Is the subject matter narrow enough?

In general it is better to study one aspect in detail than several aspects sketchily, for example to study one town rather than three. Many investigations are best suited to a local area of study — one that is large enough to give meaningful results, but not so large it becomes unmanageable. Can you easily visit the area of study — you may have to on more than one occasion? Again, seek guidance from your teacher on the scale of study for your chosen topic.

Table 14.1 Primary data sources

Quantitative	Qualitative
Land-use transects	Questionnaires
Housing surveys	Interviews
Environmental impact assessments	Field sketches
Traffic counts	Photographs (taken by you)
Climate surveys	
River measurements	
Soil surveys	

Will I be able to collect the data I need?

Remember, the use of primary data is paramount, and there is a whole range of sources of primary data, both quantitative and qualitative (Table 14.1). As the examination board places great emphasis on data collection, it is wise to use a variety of data sources for your investigation. Do not just use questionnaires.

Will I be able to complete the investigation within the time period allowed?
One type of investigation that needs to be carefully monitored is that which deals with changes over time — in other words, one that needs a 'before' and 'after' element. Examples of this include the impact of a new bypass around a settlement or the impact of a new retail park. Check whether or not you will have time to collect data before and after the development is built.

What equipment will I need?
The amount and type of equipment will obviously depend on the nature of the data to be collected. However, you do need to check whether the equipment is available and in working order.

What else do I need to do?
Here is a final checklist of some of the main requirements of any fieldwork or data collection:

- **Always ask for permission if it is needed**. Any investigation that involves you going on to someone else's land, or into a building, requires permission from the owner. In most cases a letter or telephone call explaining the purpose of your visit will suffice. However, it is often better to ask your teacher to write a short note on school or college headed paper in support of your work.
- **Check that you can get to your area, and get back**. Is there public transport to the area or will you need help? Note that much fieldwork is undertaken at weekends and Sunday timetables are often different.
- **Wear appropriate clothing**. If you are going into remote and difficult areas, then you must wear clothing that will keep you warm and dry. Wear comfortable, appropriate footwear, even in urban areas.
- **Be safety conscious**. Never work alone and always tell someone where you are working. If possible, give details of methods of travel and times of return. Be particularly careful in coastal areas. Check on tide levels, never work underneath crumbling cliffs, and stay on coastal paths.

Collecting primary data

Once you have established the aims and hypotheses of your investigation, work out what data you need to collect and what methods you will use. Investigations at this level are essentially based upon your own observations, which means using techniques such as questionnaires, interviews, river measurements, pedestrian surveys and urban transects. The whole of your investigation can be based upon such material but, depending on the scope of your work, it should be possible to include some secondary data from published sources.

Sampling

Sampling techniques are covered in Chapter 7.

Questionnaires

Many investigations at this level use questionnaires. Writing questionnnaires can be one of the most time-consuming and difficult aspects of individual investigations.

In designing a questionnaire it is important to have a balance between specific questions and open-ended questions. Examiners often criticise questionnaires for the use of too many open questions, because these produce results that are less quantifiable. However, they can provide additional information that is vital when trying to explain the behaviour revealed in the answers to the more direct questions.

Questionnaire surveys, for example supermarket studies, often involve a lot of effort but reveal little more than very basic information about the behaviour of shoppers. Oddities in the pattern of behaviour may not be accounted for unless open questions are included to help understand shoppers' motives.

Unless questionnaires concentrate on the spatial aspects of the sample being studied, they can become far too sociological and therefore of limited geographical value. Questionnaires that represent little more than a social survey should be avoided as they give little scope for mapping and analysis of patterns.

At GCSE, you may have undertaken a questionnaire survey in order to demonstrate your ability to complete it. At AS/A-level the aim is completely different — the quality, quantity and reliability of the data produced are as important as the means by which they were obtained.

Guidelines

The following list summarises the guidelines for conducting a questionnaire survey:

- keep it as simple as possible — busy people do not like answering a lot of questions
- try to write a mix of closed questions (yes/no answers or multiple response) and open questions (choice of answers or free statements)
- decide on an adequate sample size
- try to introduce your questionnaire in the same way to each person sampled (write a brief introduction)
- put the questions in a logical sequence
- ask questions that will produce data that can be analysed
- think carefully about sensitive questions and use tick boxes for such information if possible
- when asking for respondents' ages and other personal information it is often better to offer categories than to insist upon an exact figure
- try to ask questions about people's behaviour, not how they perceive their behaviour
- pilot your questionnaire by testing it out to see if it will produce the material you want
- always seek approval from your teacher or tutor before proceeding in order to avoid insensitive questions and also to prevent harassment of local people by swamping the area with too many questionnaires

- obtain a document from your school/college that states exactly what you are doing
- always be polite, look smart and smile, and do not get upset if people refuse to answer
- never work alone
- if you intend to stand outside a specific service or in a shopping centre it is a good idea to ask permission

Interviews

In the course of your work it may be necessary to conduct interviews to see how some people stand on an issue or how they would act in certain circumstances. In an investigation of rural land use, for example, it might be a good idea to interview farmers — they may give you information that helps explain some of the changes you have observed. If you are investigating a conflict as part of your work, it is essential that you try to obtain the views of the parties involved. This will certainly take you beyond the scope of a questionnaire, because you will need to put different questions to each respondent or group involved. It is not always possible to meet the people involved, so you might have to write to a person or group for their opinions.

Interviews give you the opportunity to explore more detailed areas and to follow up points that are raised. They can be time consuming, so think carefully before deciding upon such a course of action, and if you decide it is a good idea, use the technique sparingly.

Always send a well-written letter requesting the interview, and prepare for it properly — people do not like wasting time. Being prepared means you should have a list of direct questions you need to ask, making sure that the person you are interviewing has the information you require.

Do not ask questions when it is possible for you to obtain the information for yourself. Take notes at the interview or immediately afterwards. You may wish to record the interview, but always obtain permission before you start. Your final presentation can be very much enhanced by quotations from interviews, but always check accuracy and ask permission from the interviewee.

Sampling attitudes

Collecting information on people's attitudes is often difficult. You can ask about the attitude of an individual during the course of an interview, but if you are using a questionnaire survey to obtain a number of responses, you must phrase questions so that bias does not enter into your results. There are three main ways of collecting information on attitudes:

- **Bi-polar tests** involve establishing a rating scale based on two extremes of attitude (i.e. poles apart). For example, in a CBD survey you can ask shoppers if they find the shopping area attractive or ugly and offer them a sliding scale of response from (1) ugly to (7) attractive. You can put a number of such points to them and use the results to give the area an overall rating. This is useful when comparing shopping centres.

- A **point-score scale** is used to give respondents the chance to identify factors they consider to be important. You can ask respondents to place each factor on a scale from 0 to 4 in terms of importance, for example in attracting shoppers to a retailing centre.
- Using a **rating scale** allows respondents to agree or disagree with a statement. Statements can be put to them and they can be asked to place their responses in categories ranging from 'strongly agree' to 'strongly disagree'.

Types of survey

So far this chapter has mainly shown you how to collect information by asking people questions. There are other types of survey, not involving people, that you will find useful in obtaining information. Some of them are described below, with details, in many cases, of how to proceed.

Surveys in urban areas

A large and varied number of surveys can be carried out within the context of urban fieldwork.

Land-use surveys

These can be used in both rural and urban areas and must always be carried out with a clear purpose in mind. Divide land use into categories of similar types. Sub-groups within categories can be established, depending upon the detail required. Housing, for example, can be divided into terraces, detached, bungalows, semi-detached and flats.

Land-use transects

When the urban area is too large to survey as a whole, a sample has to be taken. The transect is essentially a slice through the urban area to see how land use varies. It usually starts in the middle of the urban area and runs along a radial road to the urban fringe. Such surveys are often used to show how the land use on one side of an urban area varies from another. They can also be used to show where CBD functions cease and others take over, and thus to delineate that central area.

As well as land use, other information collected on a transect can include building height, number of storeys, upper-floor use, building condition (using an index of decay) and age of buildings. It is also possible to collect information other than urban geography using this method. Such projects could include noise and pollution surveys, and temperature or humidity readings across an urban area.

Environmental surveys

These are a form of appraisal or assessment where the use of a point-score scale is recommended. Both positive and negative observations can be made. Environmental surveys can be carried out in urban areas, on beaches and within river channels and valleys. First-hand observations can be used, as well as interviews with local residents or, in the case of recreation and tourist areas, visitors. Noise, water and air pollution can also be studied.

Instruments and chemical testing kits can be used in such surveys, but simple tests or observations are also valid. Noise pollution can be estimated using a simple table, as long as the same person makes all the observations. Air pollution can be assessed using pieces of sticky tape to take samples from different surfaces in various parts of a town. Water pollution can be visually assessed (or assessed by smell!), but it is possible to use a chemical kit or a secchi disc. The latter is a black and white disc that can be lowered into the water. The depth is recorded at which it is no longer visible and at which it comes into view again when lifted.

Shop location/shopping quality surveys

Shop location studies usually take place in the central area with the aim of finding distinct patterns of land use in the CBD. Selected shop categories can then be analysed using the technique of nearest neighbour analysis which will indicate the degree to which the category is clustered. You can also calculate an index of dispersion. Surveys of service outlets and offices within the urban area can also be carried out. Shopping quality surveys can involve observational data or the use of a questionnaire.

Land value/house price surveys

These are often carried out to identify the peak land value point (PLVP) or peak value intersection (PVI) in an urban area. Taking the values of properties from estate agents and newspapers is much easier than trying to find the values used for local tax assessment (these can be obtained from the local authority's valuation office where records are open to inspection). Values should be converted into a unit per square metre of ground-floor space.

Traffic flow surveys

These involve measuring the traffic flow past several survey points within the urban area.

Pedestrian flow surveys

These are one of the recognised ways of indicating commercial activity within a CBD. There are a number of points to remember when contemplating such a survey:

- you will not be able to carry it out by yourself
- mornings and afternoons are best, avoiding the movement of office workers that takes place in the middle of the day
- do more than one survey in order to contrast different times of day or different days of the week
- at busy points use two counters, operating, if possible, back-to-back in the middle of the pedestrian thoroughway
- shopping centres are usually private property, so it is advisable to ask for permission

Surveys in physical geography

Some of the more popular types and areas of physical geography study are outlined below.

River surveys

Measurements can be taken and used to calculate fluvial features such as

discharge, load, friction and efficiency. The most popular — calculating the discharge of a river — involves finding the cross-sectional area at certain points and multiplying it by the speed of flow (usually obtained using a flow meter) to give a figure expressed in cumecs ($m^3 s^{-1}$). The calculation of the cross section will also identify the wetted perimeter. The stream gradient and bedload shape and size can be calculated too. A final measurement to consider is the extent to which the river meanders — its index of sinuosity.

Slope surveys

Surveys on slopes usually involve calculating the steepness by means of a clinometer, measuring tape and ranging poles. One feature of slopes that can be surveyed is the amount and type of vegetation present, information that can be displayed on a kite diagram.

Soil surveys

These can also be carried out on slopes, choosing sites in exactly the same way as one would for slope vegetation surveys. Various tests that can be carried out include those for soil acidity (using a chemical soil testing kit), soil texture (feeling the texture with your fingers to find the sand, silt and clay elements) and moisture and organic content (taking a sample, drying it overnight, burning off the organic matter to leave the inorganic matter, the mass of which can then be compared with that of the original sample).

Coastal surveys

These can involve measuring the direction and amount of longshore drift or examining the structure of sand dunes, including the environment for plants and animals.

Glaciation surveys

In the field, glaciation surveys usually involve a study of glacial deposits called **till fabric analysis**. This is based on the idea that stones within the ice become orientated in a direction that presents minimal resistance. This means they should be found in glacial deposits with their long axis parallel to the direction of ice movement. From this you should be able to establish the direction of ice movement and possibly its source.

Microclimate surveys

These can be carried out in your local area on a transect from rural to urban or across an urban area. Alternatively day and night conditions can be compared or, more ambitiously, seasons.

Field sketches and photographs

Sketches and photographs are both excellent ways of recording observations you have made as part of your investigation. Field sketches enable you to pick out those features within the landscape you consider important. Investigations in physical geography lend themselves nicely to this technique, particularly those on coastlines and glaciation. It does not matter if you cannot draw particularly well; it is far more important to produce a clear sketch with useful annotations.

If you are not confident about drawing, try photography as an alternative, but remember that far too many photographs find their way into fieldwork reports in the belief that they will make the work 'look good'. Only photographs which convey relevant information should be included and you need to select them carefully. As with sketches, annotation is vital, pointing out the features you have observed. Photographs should be included at the relevant points in the text and not in a large block, which sometimes makes it difficult for the reader to see their purpose.

Collecting secondary data

Secondary data collection involves the gathering of data that have already been put into written, statistical or mapped form.

If you are involved in an investigation that has a temporal context it is almost certain that you will have to access data from previous surveys. Secondary material can also provide a context in the early stages of an investigation, and can be used when explaining and discussing primary material. You may find it useful to combine field data with figures obtained from newspapers, maps, census returns, local authority and other secondary sources. This should give you a much wider database for analysis and comparison.

It is important to check the accuracy of secondary data, particularly if the information could be biased. Details of sources, including author, title, publication and date, must be given in your report, either in a reference list or as footnotes.

Remember that there is a distinction between plagiarism and the acquisition of material by research. The distinction lies in the use made by you, the candidate, of the information you have obtained, and its acknowledgement. Copying out of material from other sources and using it as if it is your own is plagiarism. If you make a direct quotation from secondary material, you must use quotation marks, and you should also ensure that it is properly referenced. This is why the examination board insists that you sign a declaration of authenticity.

Before you start an investigation, check that the sources you are intending to access include the information you need in a form you can use. It will make life very difficult if, at an advanced stage of your enquiry, you find your secondary sources do not match up with your primary research. One good example of this occurs in crime surveys. You may have carried out your primary research on an individual *street* basis, but when you come to access the secondary data, in this case urban crime figures, you will find that they are only available for *districts* within the urban area. It will therefore be impossible to match them up with your more detailed figures.

Sources of secondary material

National government material covers a wide range of data on the economy, employment, population and crime. Material is published by the Office of National Statistics and is available through Her Majesty's Stationery Office (HMSO), but

can be expensive to buy and is best accessed through your local library or the internet (**www.statistics.gov.uk**). The most helpful publications are:

- *Annual Abstract of Statistics* covering a wide range of data and with material available for previous years
- *Population Trends*
- *Social Trends*
- *Economic Trends*
- *Monthly Digest of Statistics*, the best source of up-to-date information

You can also contact government agencies for information.

Other national sources include:

- the media (newspapers, magazines and television/radio programmes)
- charities
- national organisations and action groups such as Shelter, English Heritage, National Trust, Countryside Commission
- environmental pressure groups such as Greenpeace and Friends of the Earth
- national company publications
- the Meteorological Office

Local data can be obtained from sources such as:

- your local authority
- the electoral register
- your local library, which will have population statistics for areas as small as electoral wards (small area statistics), census data going back into the nineteenth century, and back copies of local newspapers, as well as photographic archives and photocopying facilities
- the local chamber of commerce
- estate agents
- local newspapers
- *Yellow Pages/Thomson Local Directory*
- the local health authority (information on births, deaths, mortality rates and living conditions such as persons per room in households)
- local action groups

Geographical material comes from traditional sources including:

- geographical magazines and journals such as *Geography/Teaching Geography*, *Geographical*, *Geofile* and *Geography Review*
- maps from Ordnance Survey, the Geological Survey, local authorities and Charles Goad, whose maps show the ownership of CBD property

The internet offers an increasing number of helpful sites but it is important that you do not waste your time searching in the hope of finding something useful. Have a definite purpose in mind before accessing this source.

Presenting your results

Selecting the right technique

When you come to present your results, there is a wide range of graphical, cartographic and tabular techniques available to you. It is important that you select techniques appropriate to the purpose of your investigation. They should be applied to the data to enable you to describe any changes that are present, establish any differences and identify relationships. You should never be tempted to use all the techniques available — this can lead to data being presented in several different ways for no other reason than to show that you know how to construct a variety of maps and diagrams.

At AS/A-level, mark schemes award credit to those candidates who use a suitable range of techniques to provide the potential for analysis. Most investigations require techniques that fulfil the following functions (Table 14.2):

- identifying or describing differences
- describing spatial patterns
- identifying relationships
- classifying data according to characteristics

Whatever technique you choose, make sure that it is easy to understand, that it is as simple as possible and that it helps you convey information to the person reading your report.

Table 14.2 Main methods of presentation

Use	Graphical	Cartographic
A Identifying differences	Line graphs (arithmetic and logarithmic) Pie graphs and bar graphs Proportional symbols Histograms Long sections and cross sections	Pie graphs, bar graphs and proportional symbols can be placed on a base map to show spatial variations
B Describing spatial patterns		Isopleths Choropleths Flow diagrams and desire lines
C Identifying relationships	Scattergraphs	
D Classifying data	Triangular graphs	

Most of the methods listed in Table 14.2 are covered in Chapter 7 in the AS section of this book. At A2, the following additional skills are required:

- knowledge of maps with proportional symbols, such as squares, circles and bars
- knowledge of maps showing movement, such as flow lines and desire lines

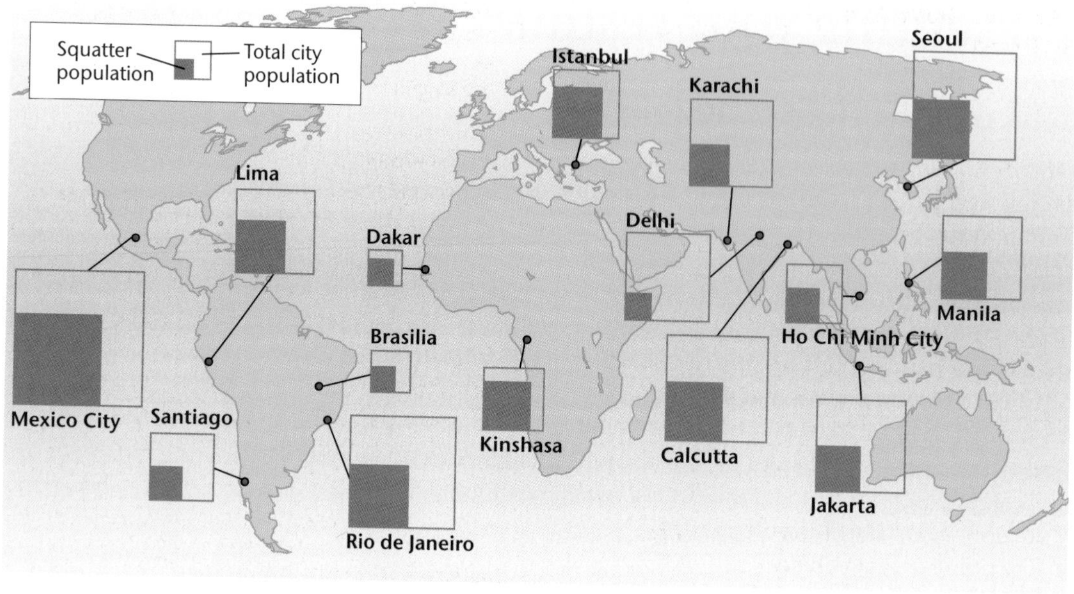

Figure 14.1 The size of the squatter population in selected world cities

Proportional symbols

These are symbols which are proportional in area or volume to the value they represent. Chapter 7 shows how the essential element in the construction of a bar graph is that the length of the column is proportional to the value it represents. This idea can be extended to pie graphs, drawing circles proportional to the total value of the data included in each graph.

Other symbols which can be used include squares, cubes and spheres. They can be drawn independently or placed on a map to show spatial differences (Figure 14.1). If you are using symbols on a map it is important that you take great care in placing them. It is essential to avoid too much overlap, but it must also be clear which area or place the symbol represents.

Flow lines and desire lines

These two forms of presentation are similar in that they both represent the volume of movement from place to place. They are useful to show such features as:

- traffic movements along particular routes (e.g. roads, railways and waterways)
- migration of populations
- movement of goods or commodities between different regions
- movements of shoppers

In both methods the width of the line is proportional to the quantity of movement. Using flow lines, it is possible to construct a map based upon one line per person. A flow line represents the quantity of movement along an actual route, such as a train or bus route (Figure 14.2). A desire line is drawn directly from the point of origin to the destination and takes no account of a specific route. Desire lines can be drawn for example to show where people shop; lines could be drawn from a village to nearby towns (Figure 14.3).

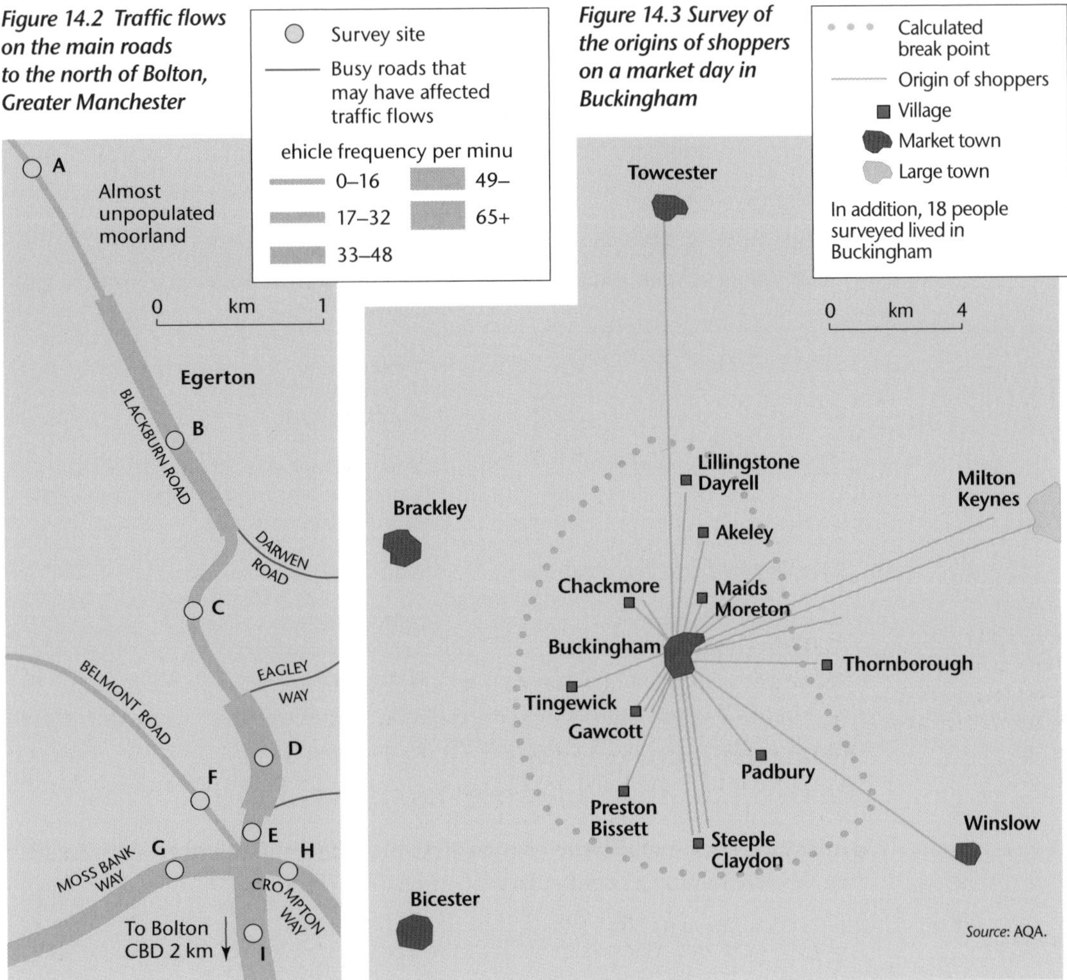

Figure 14.2 Traffic flows on the main roads to the north of Bolton, Greater Manchester

Figure 14.3 Survey of the origins of shoppers on a market day in Buckingham

Analysing and interpreting your data

Statistical analysis is used in geographical investigations because it is objective and can be used to support the conclusions suggested by a subjective view of the results. It should not be used just for show. It should form an integral part of the coursework report. You should think carefully about the most effective form of statistical analysis, and why that technique is appropriate. The best statistical analysis will help in evaluating the significance of the results.

It is obvious that any statistical technique should be used correctly, and that all calculations should be performed accurately. It is perhaps less obvious that the result of any calculation should be supported by statements explaining what it means. Many calculator and computer functions will complete the mathematical process for you, so it is essential that you understand the relevance of the values produced by them. In short, never use a statistical technique you do not understand or in which you are not confident.

Table 14.3 summarises some of the major statistical techniques. Several of these techniques are covered in Chapter 7. The remainder are described below.

Table 14.3 Statistical techniques

Reason for using statistics	Statistical technique(s)
Summarising and comparing data	Measures of central tendency: mean, mode, median
The dispersion and variability of data	Range Inter-quartile range Standard deviation
Correlating two sets of data	Spearman rank correlation coefficient, Pearson product moment coefficient and tests of significance
Measuring patterns in a distribution	Nearest neighbour statistic
Comparison of sets of data	Chi-squared test Mann–Whitney U test Student's *t* test

Measuring correlation: Pearson product moment coefficient

Unlike the Spearman coefficient, the Pearson product moment coefficient does not take the rank of a number into account. The formula is:

$$r_{xy} = \frac{1/n \, \Sigma(x-\bar{x})(y-\bar{y})}{s_x s_y}$$

where:
n is the sample size for the paired measurements
x represents individual measurements of the first variable, x
y represents individual measurements of the second variable, y
$\bar{x}$ is the mean of the first variable
$\bar{y}$ is the mean of the second variable
s_x is the standard deviation of the values of x
s_y is the standard deviation of the values of y

The procedure for calculation is:

- set out the data in pairs
- calculate the mean and standard deviation of each set
- calculate the coefficient using the formula

As with the Spearman method, the resulting coefficient should be between +1.0 and −1.0. A coefficient near to +1.0 indicates a strong positive correlation; a coefficient near to −1.0 indicates a strong negative correlation.

Pearson's method is also different from the Spearman method in that it assumes that:

- both variables are distributed normally
- the relationship between the variables is linear and consistent in direction

As with all correlation tests, there is always the possibility that the relationship shown has occurred by chance. Therefore, it is necessary to assess the statistical significance of the result (Table 14.4).

Degrees of freedom	Significance level 0.05	0.01
1	0.988	0.995
2	0.900	0.980
3	0.805	0.934
4	0.729	0.882
5	0.669	0.833
6	0.622	0.789
7	0.582	0.750
8	0.549	0.716
9	0.521	0.685
10	0.497	0.658
11	0.476	0.634
12	0.458	0.612
13	0.441	0.592
14	0.426	0.574
15	0.412	0.558
16	0.400	0.543
17	0.389	0.529
18	0.378	0.516
19	0.369	0.503
20	0.360	0.492
25	0.323	0.445
30	0.296	0.409
35	0.275	0.381
40	0.257	0.358
45	0.243	0.338
50	0.231	0.322
60	0.211	0.295
70	0.195	0.274
80	0.183	0.257
90	0.173	0.242
100	0.164	0.230

Note: Degrees of freedom = $N - 1$, where N is the number of paired observations.

Table 14.4 Critical values of the Pearson product moment coefficient

Comparative tests: chi-squared test

This technique is used to assess the degree to which there are differences between a set of collected (or observed) data and a theoretical (or expected) set of data, and the statistical significance of the differences.

The observed data are those that have been collected either in the field or from secondary sources. The expected data are those that would be expected according to the theoretical hypothesis being tested.

Normally, before the test is applied it is necessary to formulate a null hypothesis. In the example given here, the null hypothesis would be that there is no significant difference between the observed and expected data distribution. The alternative to this would be that there *is* a difference between the observed and expected data, and that there is some factor responsible for this.

The method of calculating chi-squared is shown below. The letters A–D in Table 14.5 refer to map areas A–D in Figure 14.4 (page 478). In the column headed O are listed the numbers of points in each of the areas A–D on Figure 14.4 (the *observed* frequencies). The total number of points in this case is 40. Column E contains the list of *expected* frequencies in each of the areas A–D, assuming that the points are evenly spaced. In the column $O - E$, each of the expected frequencies is subtracted from the observed frequencies, and in the last column the result is squared. The relevant values are then inserted into the expression for chi-squared, and the result is 4.0.

Map	Observed (O)	Expected (E)	($O - E$)	$(O - E)^2$
A	8	10	–2	4
B	14	10	4	16
C	6	10	–4	16
D	12	10	2	4
Sum	40	40	0	40

Table 14.5

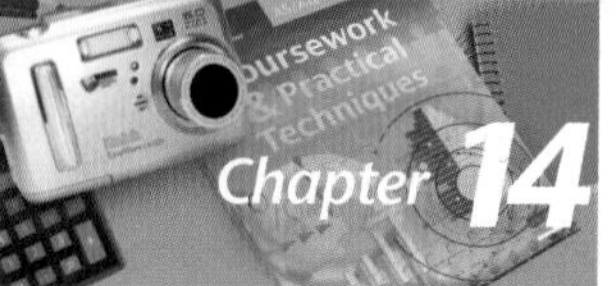

Figure 14.4

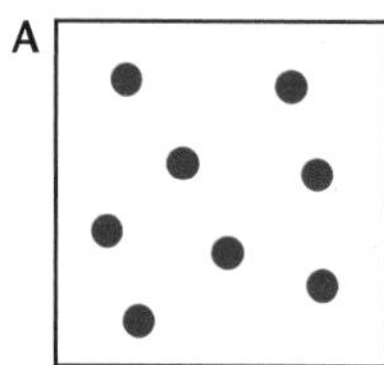

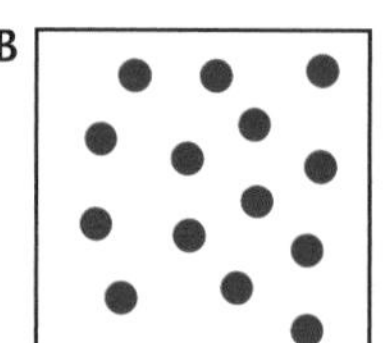

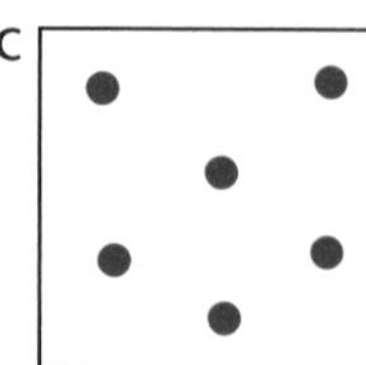

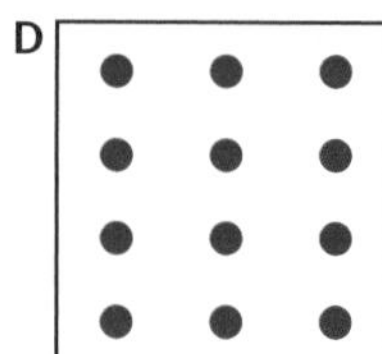

Table 14.6 Critical values of chi-squared

Degrees of freedom	Significance level 0.05	0.01
1	3.84	6.64
2	5.99	9.21
3	7.82	11.34
4	9.49	13.28
5	11.07	15.09
6	12.59	16.81
7	14.07	18.48
8	15.51	20.09
9	16.92	21.67
10	18.31	23.21
11	19.68	24.72
12	21.03	26.22
13	22.36	27.69
14	23.68	29.14
15	25.00	30.58
16	26.30	32.00
17	27.59	33.41
18	28.87	34.80
19	30.14	36.19
20	31.41	37.57
21	32.67	38.93
22	33.92	40.29
23	35.17	41.64
24	36.42	42.98
25	37.65	44.31
26	38.88	45.64
27	40.11	46.96
28	41.34	48.28
29	42.56	49.59
30	43.77	50.89
40	55.76	63.69
50	67.51	76.15
60	79.08	88.38
70	90.53	100.43
80	101.88	112.33
90	113.15	124.12
100	124.34	135.81

Note: When there are *A* rows and *B* columns respectively, degrees of freedom = $(A-1)\times(B-1)$. If there is only one row, then there are $(B-1)$ degrees of freedom.

$$\chi^2 = \frac{\Sigma(O-E)^2}{E}$$

$$= \frac{40}{10}$$

$$= 4.0$$

The aim of a chi-squared test, therefore, is to find out whether the observed pattern agrees with or differs from the theoretical (expected) pattern. This can be measured by comparing the calculated result of the test with its level of significance.

To do this the number of degrees of freedom must be determined using the formula $(n - 1)$, where n is the number of observations, in this case the number of cells which contain observed data (4). So, 4 – 1 = 3. Table 14.6 gives the distribution of chi-squared values for these degrees of freedom.

Then there are the levels of significance. There are two levels of significance: 95% and 99% (0.05 and 0.01 in Table 14.6). At 95% there is a 1 in 20 probability that the pattern being considered occurred by chance, and at 99% there is only a 1 in 100 probability that the pattern is chance. The levels of significance can be found in a book of statistical tables. They are also known as confidence levels.

If the calculated value is the same or greater than the values given in the table, then the null hypothesis can be rejected and the alternative hypothesis accepted.

In the case of our example, however, the value of chi-squared is very low (4.0), showing that there is little difference between the observed and the expected pattern. The null hypothesis cannot therefore be rejected.

Some further points on this technique

- The numbers of both observed and expected values must be large enough to ensure that the test is valid. Most experts state that there should be a minimum of five.

- The number produced by the calculation is itself meaningless. It is only of value for use in consulting statistical tables.
- As in Spearman rank test, only significance (or confidence) levels of 95% and 99% should be considered when rejecting the null hypothesis. Levels of confidence greater than these simply allow the null hypothesis to be rejected with even greater confidence.
- It is strongly recommended that you do not apply the test to more than one set of observed data because the mathematics become too complex.

Comparative tests: Mann–Whitney U test

To carry out the Mann–Whitney U test:

- set out the data in two columns
- rank each item of data in terms of its position within the sample as a whole; start with the lowest value first
- add the ranks for each column
- calculate the value of U by using the formula:

$$U = n_1 n_2 + \frac{n_1(n_1 + 1)}{2} - \Sigma r_1$$

where:
n_1 and n_2 are the two sample sizes
Σr_1 is the sum of the ranks for sample 1
- using a table of critical values, interpret the answer that you have calculated.

If the calculated value of U is less than or equal to the critical value at the chosen significance level, then the null hypothesis must be rejected. The null hypothesis is that there is no significant difference between the two data sets. Therefore, if the null hypothesis is rejected, there is a difference.

Worked example: Mann–Whitney U test

An investigation was carried out into the effect of the sea on a beach in the west of England at different times of year. Two samples of pebbles were taken, one in April and the other in October. The hypothesis is that the mean size of the beach material will be larger in October than in April. Therefore, the null hypothesis is that there will be no difference.

The size categories (phi categories) that were used in the survey are shown in Table 14.7.

Table 14.7 Size categories of beach material

Phi (Φ)	Particle diameter (mm)	Size category (Wentworth grade)	
–6.0	64.0	Cobbles	
			60.0 mm
–5.5	44.8	Coarse gravel	
–5.0	32.0		
–4.5	22.4		
			20.0 mm
–4.0	16.0	Medium gravel	
–3.5	11.2		
–3.0	8.0		
			6.0 mm
–2.5	5.6	Fine gravel	
–2.0	4.0		
–1.5	2.8		
–1.0	2.0		
			2.0 mm
–0.5	1.4	Coarse sand	
0.0	1.0		
0.5	0.71		
			0.6 mm
1.0	0.50	Medium sand	
1.5	0.355		
2.0	0.25		
			0.2 mm
2.5	0.18	Fine sand	
3.0	0.125		
3.5	0.090		
4.0	0.063		
			0.06 mm

Calculation of U

The mean particle sizes at six sites in October and April were calculated. After ranking, the data were recorded in a table (Table 14.8).

Site number	Mean particle size (using phi scale) in October (x)	Rank (r_x)	Mean particle size (using phi scale) in April (y)	Rank (r_y)
1	−2.506	5	−1.567	1
2	−2.483	4	−2.286	3
3	−2.612	7	−2.562	6
4	−2.726	8	−3.368	11
5	−3.281	10	−1.772	2
6	−3.394	12	−2.727	9
		$\Sigma r_x = 46$		$\Sigma r_y = 32$

Table 14.8 Mean particle size and rank at six sites, October and April

$$U_x = n_x n_y + \frac{n_x(n_x + 1)}{2} - \Sigma r_x$$

$$= 36 + \frac{42}{2} - 46$$

$$= 11$$

$$U_y = n_x n_y + \frac{n_y(n_y + 1)}{2} - \Sigma r_y$$

$$= 36 + \frac{42}{2} - 32$$

$$= 25$$

where:

n_x and n_y are sample sizes

Σr_x and Σr_y are the sum of the rank values of r_x and r_y respectively

Sample size		Significance level 0.05	0.01
n_x	n_y		
6	6	7	3

Table 14.9 Critical values for the interpretation of the value of U

Once the value of U_x is established as 11, it is necessary to interpret this value (Table 14.9).

The value obtained for U_x of 11 clearly exceeds the critical value of 3 or 7. This means that the null hypothesis must be accepted; the proposed hypothesis must be rejected.

Therefore, there is no significant difference in beach material size in April and October; the size in October is not larger than that in April.

Comparative tests: Student's *t* test

Sometimes in fieldwork it is not possible to collect this much data due to limitations in numbers of available individuals, or in time. In such cases it is still possible to compare two sample populations using Student's *t* test.

Student's *t* test is another way of comparing two samples to test a hypothesis. It should be used when there are no more than 30 individuals or sites in the sample. The *t* test uses the standard errors of the differences between the means. It uses a '*t*' distribution that is symmetrical and bell-shaped about a mean of zero (as is the normal distribution), but it is flatter and more dispersed. The fewer the individuals within the sample, the flatter the curve (Figure 14.5).

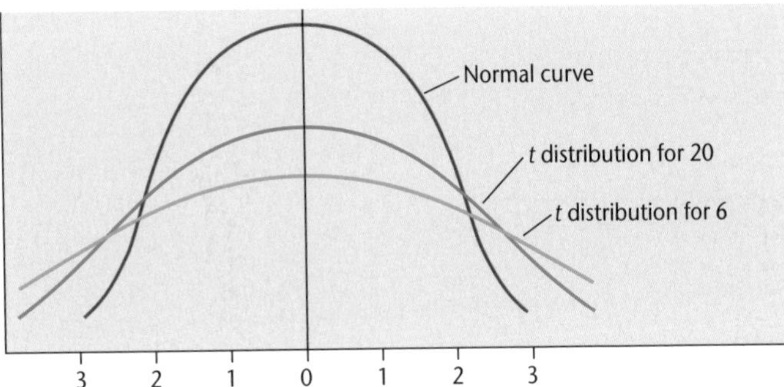

Figure 14.5 Distribution curves

The formula for the calculation of Student's t test is:

$$t = \frac{|\bar{x} - \bar{y}|^{*}}{\sqrt{\frac{\left(\sum x^2/n_x\right) - \bar{x}^2}{n_x - 1} + \frac{\left(\sum y^2/n_y\right) - \bar{y}^2}{n_y - 1}}}$$

where: $\bar{x}$ and $\bar{y}$ are each sample means

$\sum\bar{x}$ and $\sum\bar{y}$ are the sums of each sample

n_x and n_y are the number of individuals in each sample

$|\bar{x} - \bar{y}|$ * means that the absolute difference in sample means is taken,

i.e. the value must be positive

Degrees of freedom	Significance level 0.05	0.01
1	6.31	63.7
2	2.92	9.93
3	2.35	5.84
4	2.13	4.60
5	2.00	4.03
6	1.94	3.71
7	1.89	3.50
8	1.86	3.36
9	1.83	3.25
10	1.81	3.17
11	1.80	3.11
12	1.78	3.06
13	1.77	3.01
14	1.76	2.98
15	1.75	2.95
16	1.75	2.92
17	1.74	2.90
18	1.73	2.88
19	1.73	2.86
20	1.73	2.85
21	1.72	2.83
22	1.72	2.82
23	1.71	2.81
24	1.71	2.80
25	1.71	2.79
26	1.71	2.78
27	1.70	2.77
28	1.70	2.76
29	1.70	2.76
30	1.70	2.75

Note: Where the two sample sizes are A and B, degrees of freedom = $(A - 1) + (B - 1)$.

Table 14.10 Critical values for the Student's t test

Worked example: Student's *t* test

A vegetation survey was undertaken in an area of northwest England to see if there was a significant difference in the number of plant species supported by acid moorland and limestone upland. Using a quadrat, the researchers counted the number of species found within its frame at ten sites on an acid moorland and eight sites on limestone upland. The results are shown in Table 14.11.

Quadrat	Number of species on acid moorland (x)	Number of species on limestone upland (y)	x^2	y^2
1	6	14	36	196
2	8	12	64	144
3	9	6	81	36
4	4	11	16	121
5	7	15	49	225
6	11	14	121	196
7	7	17	49	289
8	6	8	36	64
9	8		64	
10	7		49	
	$\sum x = 73$ mean = 7.3 $n_x = 10$	$\sum y = 97$ mean = 12.13 $n_y = 8$	$\sum x^2 = 565$	$\sum y^2 = 1271$

Table 14.11 Plant species on acid moorland and limestone upland

$$t = \frac{|\bar{x} - \bar{y}|^*}{\sqrt{\frac{\left(\sum x^2/n_x\right) - \bar{x}^2}{n_x - 1} + \frac{\left(\sum y^2/n_y\right) - \bar{y}^2}{n_y - 1}}}$$

$$= \frac{4.83}{\sqrt{\frac{(565/10) - 53.29}{10 - 1} + \frac{(1{,}271/8) - 147.13}{8 - 1}}}$$

$$= \frac{4.83}{\sqrt{\frac{3.21}{9} + \frac{11.35}{7}}}$$

$$= \frac{4.83}{1.43}$$

$$= 3.38$$

The result is that $t = 3.38$ is greater than the critical value of t at both the 0.05 and 0.01 levels. Hence, the null hypothesis is rejected. Therefore, there is a significant difference in the number of plant species supported by acid moorland and by limestone upland.

Spatial distribution: the nearest neighbour index

Nearest neighbour is used to analyse the distribution of individual points in a pattern. It can be applied to the distribution of any data that can be plotted as point locations. Consequently, it is often used to analyse the distribution of shop types in a town centre, the distribution of various sizes of settlement in an area and the distribution of some public services, for example doctors' surgeries, in an urban area.

The basis of the statistic is the measurement of the distance between each point in a pattern and its nearest neighbour. This must be done for each point identified within the area studied. Once all measurements have been completed, the mean distance ($\bar{d}$) between each point is calculated.

The nearest neighbour statistic can then be calculated using:

$$R_n = 2\bar{d}\sqrt{\frac{N}{A}}$$

where:
N is the number of point locations in the area
A is the area of study

The statistic can be any value between 0 and 2.15.

- 0 represents a pattern that is perfectly clustered; in other words, there is no distance between nearest neighbours — all the points are at the same location. If this is the case, there is no pattern to analyse.
- 2.15 represents a pattern displaying perfect regularity — all points lie at the vertices of equilateral triangles. All distances between nearest neighbours are identical. Again this is highly unlikely in the real world.
- 1.0 is said to represent a random pattern, although this is difficult to prove.

In practice, the outcome of such a calculation will be on the continuum between 0 and 2.15. Proximity to one of these will indicate the degree of either clustering or regularity.

Requirements of the method

When carrying out a nearest neighbour statistic calculation, it is advisable to map the activity(ies) on a transparent overlay first. This removes any potential distraction in the measurement and calculation process. It is important that the units in which distance and area are measured correspond — in most cases they will be either metres and square metres, or kilometres and square kilometres.

A further complication is the delineation of the area to be studied. In the case of settlement-based work, you have to decide on the boundary of the area you are studying. You can then establish a 'buffer zone' around this study area. When measuring the distance between each point and its nearest neighbour, if the nearest neighbour is within this buffer zone then you should measure *to* this point. However, this point in the buffer zone should not be counted in the overall study as a point *from* which to measure to its nearest neighbour. In short, you should only measure *to* points in the buffer zone, not *from* them.

Writing up the report

The final report of your enquiry should be well structured, logically organised, and clearly and concisely written. There are three aspects of this process that you should consider: structure, language and presentation.

Structure

The structure of the report should help the reader to understand it, and should also assist you in organising it logically. The following checklist provides a generalised structure for your report:

- report approval sheet/cover sheet
- title page and contents page
- executive summary
- aims and objectives
- scene setting
- research questions/hypotheses/issues being examined
- sources of information used
- methods of data collection and commentary on their limitations
- data presentation, analysis and interpretation
- evaluation and conclusion
- bibliography and appendices

You need not write these in the order given. Indeed, it may be easier if you do not. For example, the executive summary is perhaps best written at the end of the whole process, as it is only at this stage that the whole picture can be described. The following is a suggested order of completion.

Data presentation, analysis and interpretation

This is the section where you present and analyse your findings. At this stage you will have collected the data, sorted them and selected the most useful pieces. You will know what you have found out and what it all means. Your results will be complete and they will be most fresh in your mind at this time. You should be able to interpret each separate section of your results and formulate conclusions for each one. The whole picture may begin to appear in your head.

Sources of information and methods of data collection

Now you can write about what information you collected and the methods you used. Do not forget to discuss any limitations of the methods of collection you used and of the data sources themselves.

Conclusion

This should include a summary and an evaluation of all the major findings of your enquiry. Do not present anything new to the reader at this stage. Towards the end of this section, try to draw together all the sub-conclusions from each section of the data analysis into one overall conclusion — the whole picture.

Aims, objectives and scene setting (introduction)

Having written up the bulk of the enquiry, you can now write the introduction, making sure it ties in with what follows. This section is intended to acquaint the reader with the purpose of the enquiry and the background to it.

Appendices and bibliography

The appendices contain additional pieces of evidence that may be of interest to the reader but are not essential to the main findings. The bibliography provides details of the secondary sources used in your research, either as guides or as sources of information. You should give the author, date of publication, title of the publication, publisher and page number. When quotes are used in the body of your report, you should provide the name of the author and the date of publication and cross-refer it back to the bibliography.

Contents page

All the sections of the report should be listed in sequence, with accurate page references.

Title page

This states the title of your report. Include also your name, candidate number, centre number and date of completion.

Executive summary

An executive summary should be a brief statement (no more than 250 words) covering all the main aspects of the enquiry. A good executive summary introduces the subject of the full report, refers to its aims and objectives, and provides a brief synopsis of the findings. A very good executive summary will tempt the reader into reading more by being comprehensible, interesting and stimulating. It should also make sense as a separate document from the full report.

Language

The quality of the language you use in writing up your enquiry is important. You are entirely in control of this aspect of the process, and your style of writing must be appropriate for this exercise. You should avoid poor or inaccurate use of English. In particular:

- your sentences should be grammatically correct and well punctuated
- your writing should be well-structured, with good use of paragraphs
- your spelling must be accurate (use a dictionary and your PC spellcheck)
- you must be clear in your use of specialist terminology and in the expression of your ideas
- you should be aware that the assessment of your work will take into account the above aspects of your writing

Proofreading is an important part of this process. Prior to submission, make sure you read through the draft from start to finish and mark any places where there are errors or inconsistencies. If possible, get someone to do this for you — parents may help. You need someone who is going to be highly critical of what you have written. A report littered with spelling mistakes or grammatical errors does not impress, and your PC spellcheck will miss many of these.

It is also essential to make sure that maps and diagrams are inserted in the correct place in the report — it is irritating to have to flick backwards and forwards when trying to read the document. Make sure all the references in the text are included in the bibliography.

Length

The examination board states the length of report it requires and will impose a penalty of some sort for overlong submissions. In such cases, it is the final parts of your report — dealing with the conclusions and evaluation — which are most under threat. These are important areas of your coursework and it is foolish to make the marks available for this section inaccessible.

Word limits are not designed to make life difficult — they should have the opposite effect. Reports written within the stated word limit tend to be better planned, structured and executed. No penalty is imposed for reports that are too short, but they are self-penalising because they contain inadequate material.

Presentation

It is a fact of life that most people are influenced by presentation, and that includes coursework examiners. Bear in mind the following:

- A neatly presented handwritten or word-processed report is going to create a favourable first impression, before its contents are read.
- Adequate heading and numbering of pages, with carefully produced illustrations, will make it easier for the reader to understand what is contained within the report.

- Layout is also important. Do not crowd the pages with dense text, which looks unattractive. Provide adequate margins, use either double or 1.5 line-spacing in word-processing, and make use of clear heading levels with short paragraphs.
- Make sure you allow enough time to add the finishing touches which give your work the 'final polish'. It goes without saying that this time will be available if you have not left completion too near to the final deadline.

You should now be in a position to submit your finished product confident in the belief that it is the best you could have done.

A2

Module 7

Fieldwork investigation: written assessment

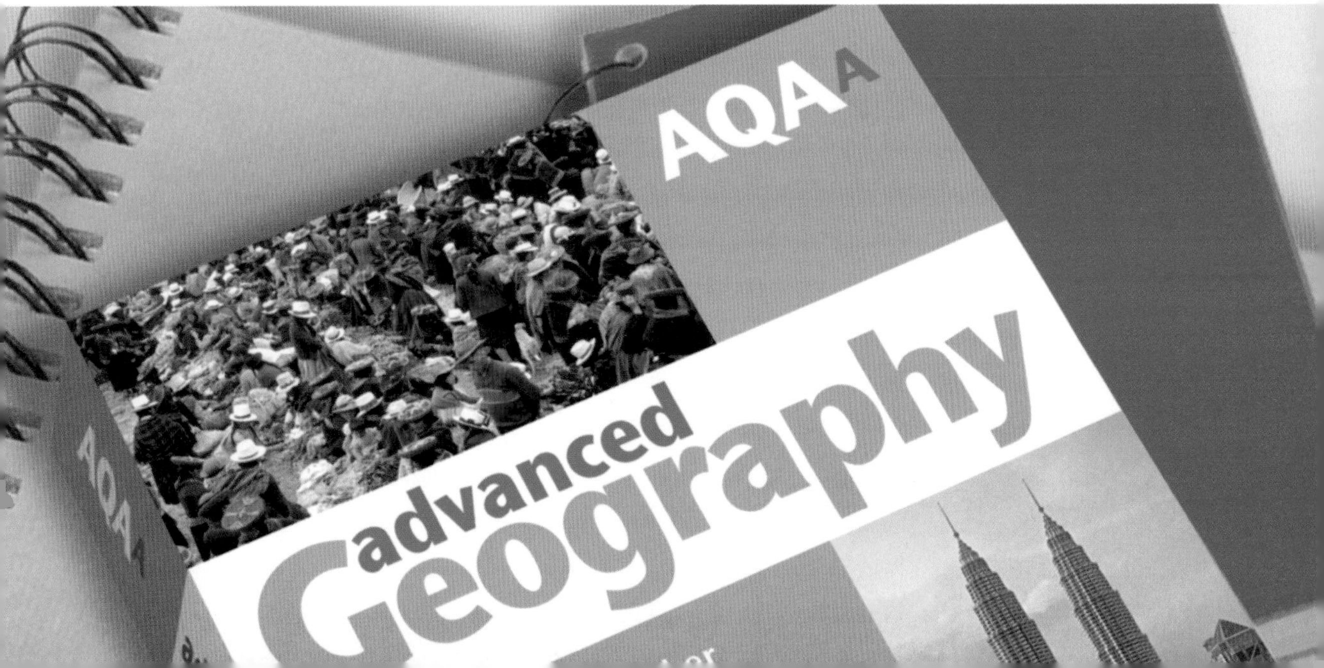

Chapter 15

Written assessment

At A2, you are required to undertake investigative work in the field. This allows you to develop skills associated with planning investigations, collection of primary and secondary data, and presentation, interpretation and evaluation of results. You are required to *either* complete a fieldwork investigation and submit a report (Module 6) *or* take a written assessment based on a pre-release topic (Module 7). A summary of the approaches to fieldwork investigation that applies to both Module 6 and Module 7 is given in Figure 15.1.

Figure 15.1 The approaches to fieldwork investigation

Module 6	Module 7
20% of marks Preparatory fieldwork Externally assessed	
Candidate selection of title Candidate collection of data 4,000 word limit recommended	Title provided Pre-release material 2 hour assessment unit
Understand aims and state theoretical concepts related to the location	
Understand and evalulate the methodology. Collect data — primary/secondary sources	
Consider the presentation of data. Should include relevant selection from cartographic, graphical and statistical techniques	
Candidate has free choice of statistical techniques	Statistical techniques restricted to those stated in specification
Consider the description, analysis and explanation of data. Interpretation should make reference to aims	
Draw conclusions referring to the results and evalulate in terms of the aims. Consider the further development of the study	
Additional data not specifically required	Consider how additional data might be collected
Use appropriate English and relevant geographical language	

This chapter deals with the Module 7 option. If you choose this option, you are required to take a written examination based on a topic set by AQA. The details of the topic area are published annually and are posted on the AQA website 2 years in advance of the examination. The theme is always based on a small area of study, which you are required to cover as part of your course.

Preparing for Module 7

To prepare for Module 7, it is essential that you undertake an appropriate programme of fieldwork. The topic area is known 2 years in advance of the examination, so appropriate work can be included in your programme of study.

Approximately 4 weeks before the examination, a **Pre-release Information Booklet** will be sent to your centre. This booklet will contain:

- an aim, hypothesis and question which will be explored, as an investigation, in the written assessment unit

- sufficient information to allow you to familiarise yourself with the data and analyse how they may be used before the exam
- some background information relating to the enquiry
- data (primary and probably secondary) in raw or part-processed form
- information on the method of data collection used

You should look at your own fieldwork investigations and identify investigative techniques that complement the hypothesis being assessed.

The key principle of Module 7 is that in the examination you only spend a limited amount of time on factual recall. This gives you the best opportunity to show your ability to apply the skills, knowledge and understanding gained in your personal investigative work and to demonstrate a broader understanding of the issues involved. You must be familiar with the pre-release material and know how to use it. To prepare for the examination you should ask yourself the following questions:

- What is the purpose of the enquiry?
- What is the relevant theoretical background to the enquiry?
- What/where is the study area and why might it have been selected for such an enquiry?
- What data are available and how were they collected?
- What are the advantages or problems with the data collection method?
- What are the alternative methods of data collection and what are the advantages or problems with these methods?
- How does the fieldwork I have carried out relate to the aims and objectives of the topic?
- How could the information in the pre-release document be processed or presented?
- What patterns emerge from the data?
- How does a description, analysis and explanation of the findings relate to the aims and objectives of the enquiry?
- What conclusions can be drawn?
- What will affect the reliability of the conclusions and how certain am I of the conclusions that have been reached?
- How could reliability be improved?
- How could the enquiry be extended?

In the examination, the investigation will be assessed under the following headings:

- aims
- methods
- skills, techniques and interpretation
- conclusion — you are usually asked to 'write a summary of your findings for this enquiry with specific reference to the aims and objectives given. Using your own experience of conducting an enquiry, you should, in addition, consider the reliability of these findings and suggest how this enquiry could be improved and extended'
- enquiry-related issues

Sample assessment exercise

This exercise provides a pre-release document, which you should study before attempting the question paper.

Pre-release document

Title

Is the vegetation succession on the sand dunes at Ainsdale typical of a normal psammosere?

Background information

A psammosere is a primary succession of plant communities that develops on sandy surfaces. In coastal locations, changes to the psammosere occur on sand dunes as distance from the sea increases. Figure 15.2 shows a model of a psammosere, indicating its expected characteristics.

Sand dunes occur where there is a large supply of sand, a gentle beach profile and a prevailing onshore wind. All these conditions are present to the north of Liverpool in an area known as the Sefton coast, which has the largest area of sand dunes in England. The location for this study is the Ainsdale Sandhills, which is one of the largest areas of dunes on the Sefton coast. Figure 15.3 shows the location of the Ainsdale Sandhills; Figure 15.4 shows the study area. At Formby Point, the current rate of erosion is up to 5 m yr^{-1}, but to the north the coastline is growing rapidly. The dunes have been growing for over 400 years and at present occupy a 1.5 km strip between the high water mark (HWM) and the Liverpool–Southport railway line.

Figure 15.2 A model psammosere

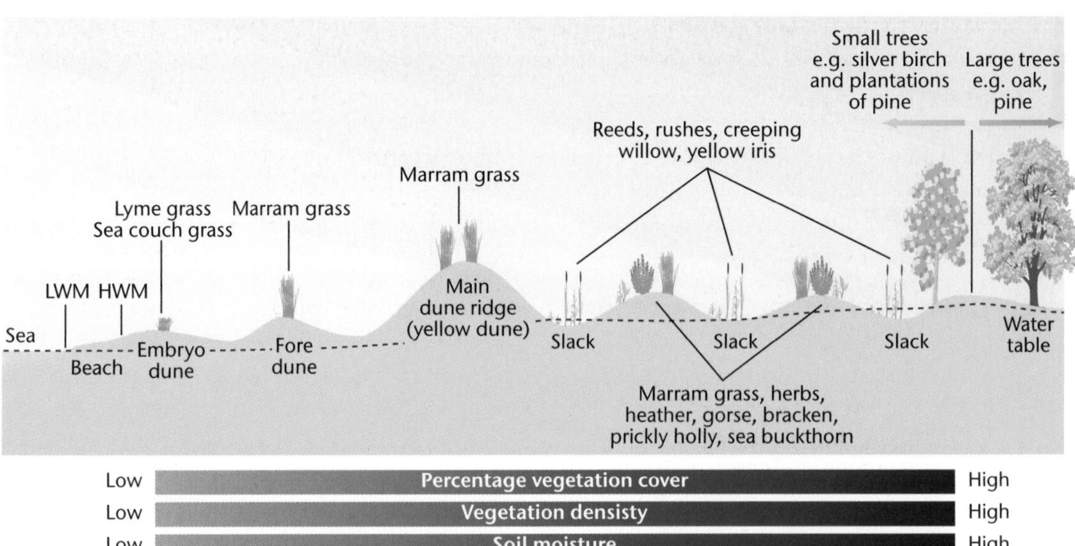

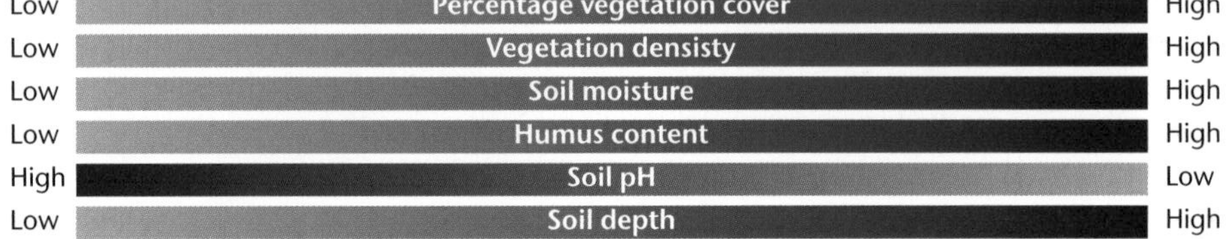

Aim

The aim of this enquiry is to determine the extent to which changes predicted by the psammosere model actually occur in the Ainsdale Sandhills. In order to complete the enquiry, a number of objectives can be identified:

- **Objective 1** To establish that the percentage vegetation cover increases with increasing distance from the HWM.
- **Objective 2** To establish that vegetation diversity increases with increasing distance from the HWM.
- **Objective 3** To determine whether soil moisture increases with increasing distance from the HWM and to note its impact on vegetation cover and diversity.

Data collection

A transect was drawn across the dunes from the HWM at right angles to the coast. Photograph 15.1 is a series of photographs taken along this transect to show the dune landscape. Photograph 15.2 gives an indication of the vegetation present along the transect line.

The transect was divided into segments based upon changes in slope angle; both the length and angle were measured and recorded. The results of this survey are shown in Table 15.1.

To collect the information, the following equipment was used:

- ranging poles
- tape measure
- compass
- clinometer
- quadrat
- dice (for selecting survey points)
- dune-plant recognition booklet
- soil-moisture meter

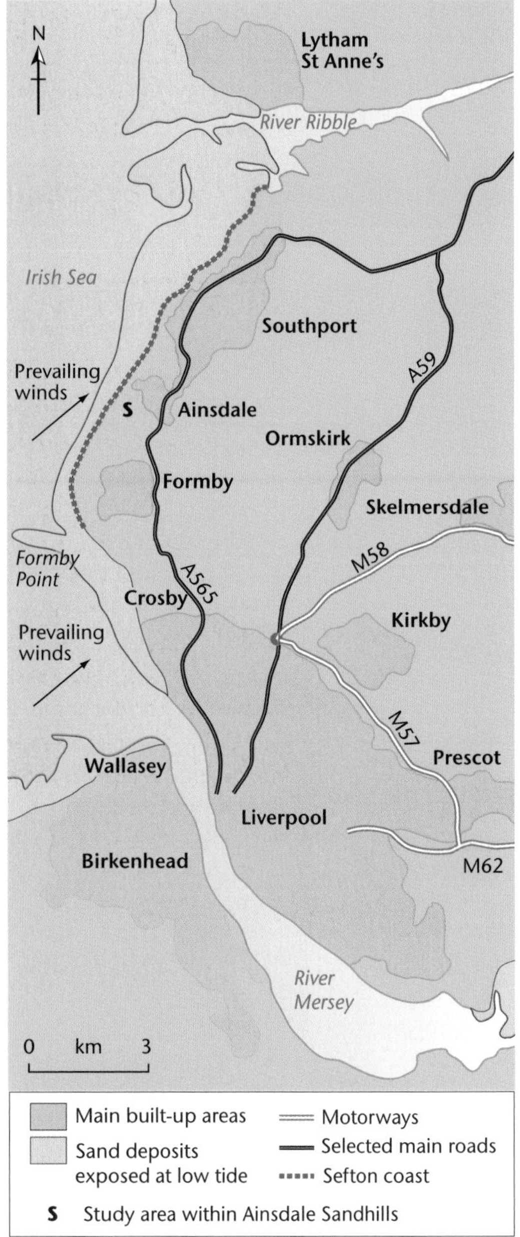

***Figure 15.3* Location of the study area**

The vegetation cover and its diversity were measured by means of quadrat analysis. To determine where to place the quadrat:

- Identify the middle of a segment.
- Roll a die:
  - if it is an even number, the quadrat is placed on the left (north) side of the transect
  - if it is an odd number, the quadrat is placed on the right (south) side of the transect

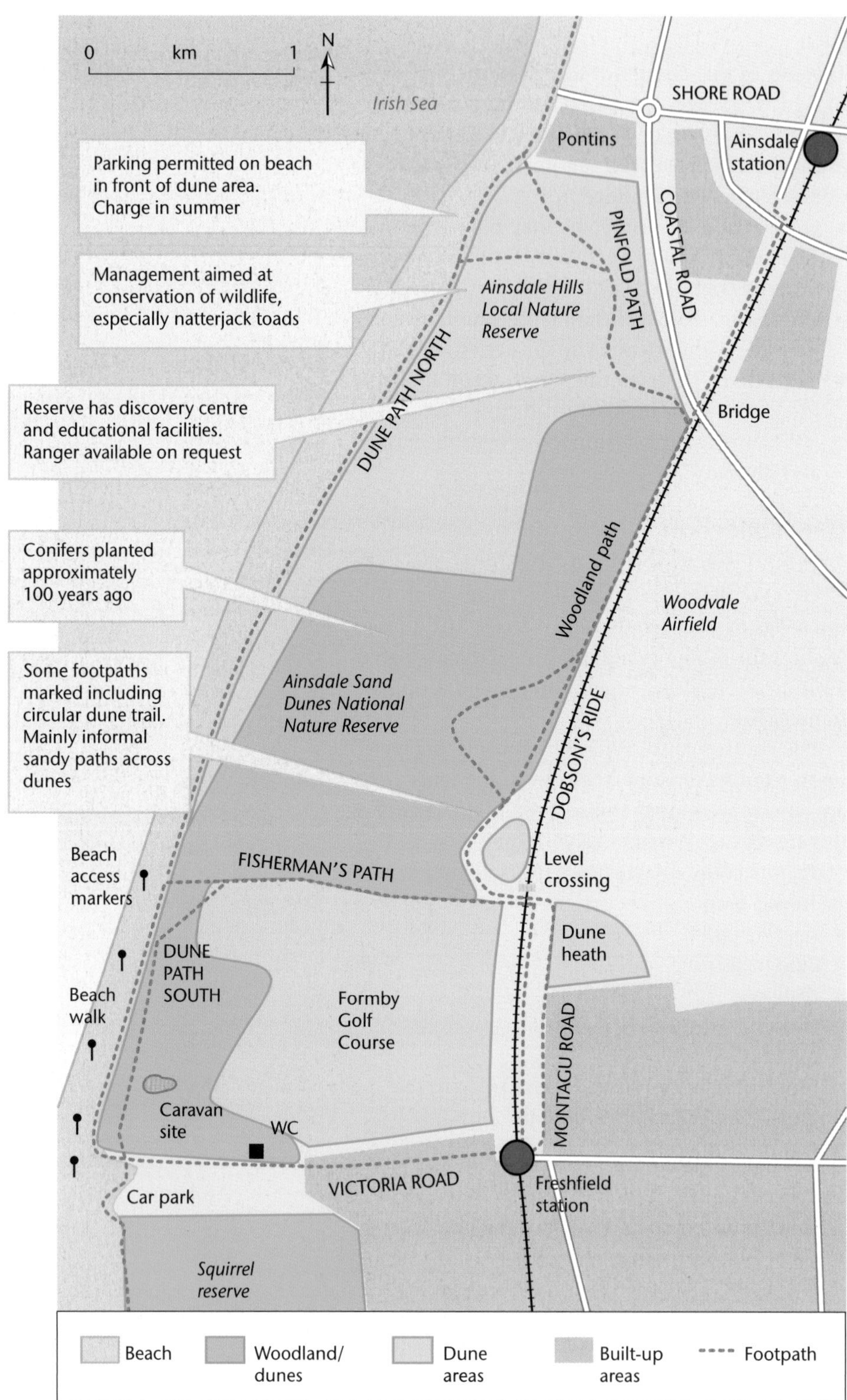

Figure 15.4 The study area

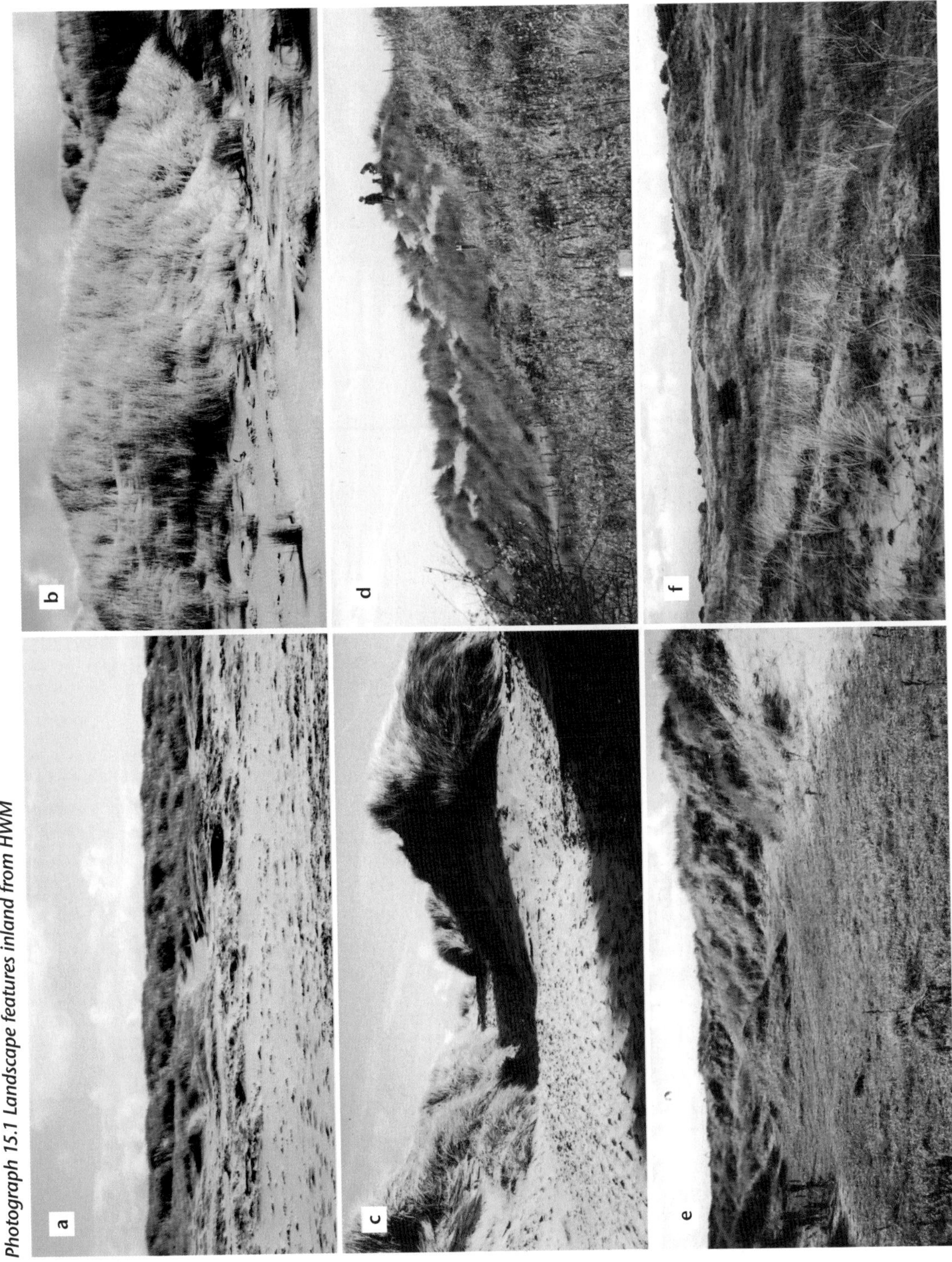

Photograph 15.1 Landscape features inland from HWM

Malcolm Skinner

Photograph 15.2 Vegetation at sites along the transect

Malcolm Skinner

Table 15.1 Dune-transect survey

Segment number	Segment length (m)	Distance of end of segment from HWM (m)	Mean slope angle (°)
1	29.4	29.4	3
2	8.7	38.1	15
3	3.5	41.6	–4
4	11.0	52.6	22
5	3.6	56.2	–38
6	5.2	61.4	4
7	17.7	79.1	10
8	17.4	96.5	18
9	22.0	118.5	–2
10	10.0	128.5	–39
11	10.0	138.5	–4
12	9.8	148.3	40
13	10.8	159.1	–34
14	9.8	168.9	9
15	28.4	197.3	18
16	19.5	216.8	–20
17	40.0	256.8	2
18	25.2	282.0	44
19	20.5	302.5	–38
20	40.0	342.5	39

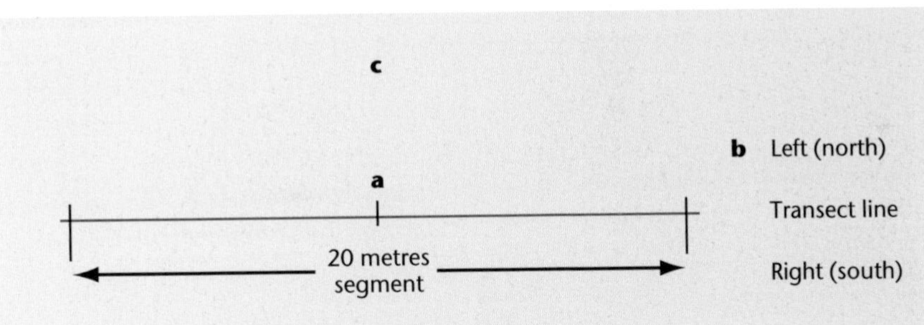

Figure 15.5

- Roll the die again. The number indicates how many metres away from the transect line to place the quadrat.

For example (see Figure 15.5):

- if the segment length is 20 m, the middle is 10 m (**a**)
- if the first roll of the dice is 2, the quadrat is placed north of the line (**b**)
- if the second roll of the dice is 4, the quadrat is placed 4 m away from the middle of the line (**c**)

The quadrat was placed at the determined location along the segment. The number of squares containing vegetation was counted and the percentage recorded. Using a recognition booklet, each square that contained vegetation was closely examined to determine the types of plant present. The results of this survey are shown in Table 15.2.

Table 15.2 Results of the survey. (a) Vegetation cover. (b) Vegetation diversity (% cover). (c) Soil moisture content

(a) Segment number	(a) Distance from HWM (centre of segment metres)	(a) Vegetation cover (%)	(b) Number of species	Lyme grass	Marram grass	Sea couch grass	Ragwort	Thistle	Sea spurge	Bramble	Sea rocket	Rest harrow	Dandelion	Creeping willow	Sea buckthorn	Moss rush	Other plant species	(c) Moisture content
1	14.6	0	0															8
2	33.7	65	2			5					14							6
3	39.8	84	2	64							20							2
4	46.9	95	2	43	52													1
5	54.3	76	2	28	48													1
6	58.8	0	0															1
7	70.3	88	3		52	24	12											1
8	87.8	40	7	8	11	7	6	3									EP 2%, H 3%	1
9	107.5	100	3		80		10	10										1
10	123.5	98	3	31	34	33												1
11	133.5	3	3			1									1		D 1%	9
12	143.4	58	2	25	33													1
13	153.7	10	2		9												EP 1%	1
14	164.0	40	3											32			D 3%, S 5%	10
15	183.1	100	10		21	29		9	7	8							H 8%, SH 2%, RBW 6%, 2 × U 10%	1
16	207.1	100	10		47			8	5				1	15	6	4	EP 5%, H 4%, O 5%	1
17	236.8	100	7		31		7							21		6	EP 10%, h 14%, O 11%	3
18	269.3	0	0															1
19	292.0	100	7		41					12		8		14			YFG 10%, FP 4%, KV 11%	1
20	322.2	100	11		36		22	6		5		6	1	11		3	FP 1%, TV 5%, KV 4%	1

EP – evening primrose, H – hawkbit, D – dock, S – sorrel, SH – sea holly, RBW – rose bay willowherb, U – unidentified plants, O – orchid, YFG – Yorkshire fog grass, FP – field pansy, TV – tufted vetch, KV – kidney vetch

The survey of soil moisture was conducted by using a soil-moisture meter at a point 1 m from the beginning of each segment (measuring from the seaward end). The meter was inserted at a depth of 5 cm for 10 seconds. The reading was noted on a scale from 1 (dry) to 10 (wet). The results of this survey are shown in Table 15.2(c).

Question paper

1 Aims

a With reference to your own experience of planning a fieldwork enquiry, show how Figure 15.2 could have provided the stimulus for this study. (4 marks)

b Why were the Ainsdale Sandhills an appropriate location for this study? (2 marks)

(6 marks)

2 Methods

a The results of the topological survey are given in Table 15.1. Which of the instruments listed in the pre-release document would you have used on this particular survey? What instruction would you give to students who had not previously collected such data? Make clear the role of each item of equipment. (8 marks)

b The method used in the vegetation survey is given in the pre-release document. With specific reference to *this* enquiry, suggest *one* strength and *one* weakness of this sampling method. (4 marks)

c The methodology for the soil-moisture survey is also given in the pre-release document. The results are shown in Table 15.2(c). Give an alternative method of obtaining this information and outline the relative merits of the method you have chosen. (4 marks)

(16 marks)

3 Skills, techniques and interpretation

a Draw and label a sketch of Photograph 15.1(a) to show the landforms and vegetation characteristics. (6 marks)

b Using Figure 15.2, Photograph 15.1 and Photograph 15.2 comment on the extent to which the photographs provide evidence of the vegetation changes predicted in Figure 15.2. (8 marks)

c The results of the topological survey are shown in Table 15.1. Information from the table for segments 1–17 is plotted in Figure A. Complete Figure A by adding the information for segments 18, 19 and 20. (4 marks)

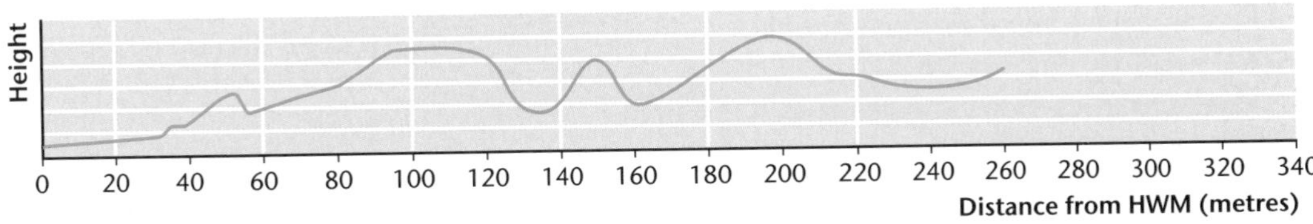

Figure A The topographical survey

d Table 15.2(a) shows the results of the vegetation cover survey. Some of these results are displayed in Figure B. Complete the figure by adding the information for segments 4 and 18. (4 marks)

e With specific reference to Objective 1, describe and suggest reasons for the relationship shown in Figure B. (6 marks)

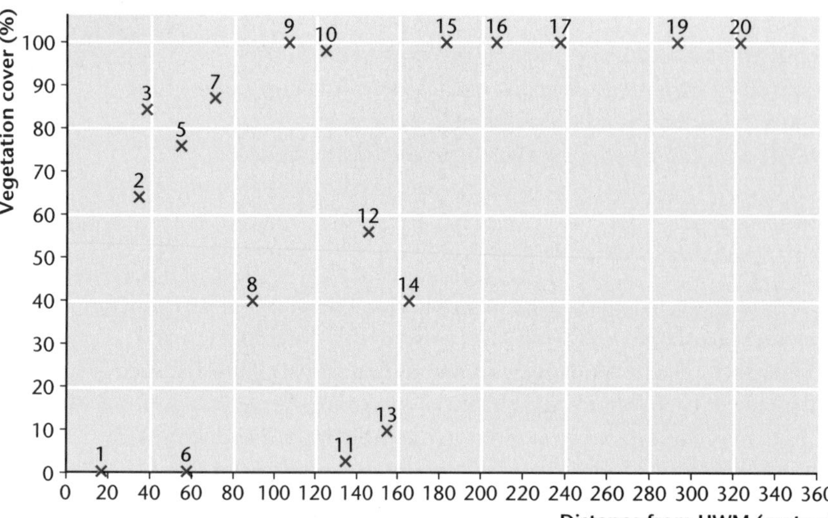

Figure B The vegetation survey

f Objective 1 can be further investigated by using Spearman rank correlation coefficient to see if 'as distance from the HWM increases, so the percentage of vegetation cover also increases'. The coefficient (R_S) was calculated using the information in Table 15.2 (a).
The correlation coefficient obtained was 0.39.
The significance data for R_S are given in Table 15.3.

Which significance level would you use? Give a reason why you would use it.
How many degrees of freedom would you use? Give a reason why.
To which critical value would you refer? (5 marks)

g Interpret the result of the Spearman test that you obtained from Table 15.3 with regard to Objective 1. (3 marks)

h The results of the vegetation diversity survey are shown in Table 15.2 (b). With the exception of segments 7 and 19, the results are plotted on Figure C. Complete Figure C by adding the information for segments 7 and 19. (3 marks)

Table 15.3 Critical values for R_s

Degrees of freedom	Significance level 0.05	0.01	0.005
4	1.000		
5	0.900	1.000	
6	0.829	0.943	1.000
7	0.714	0.893	0.929
8	0.643	0.833	0.881
9	0.600	0.783	0.833
10	0.564	0.745	0.794
11	0.523	0.736	0.818
12	0.497	0.703	0.780
13	0.475	0.673	0.745
14	0.457	0.646	0.716
15	0.441	0.623	0.689
16	0.425	0.601	0.666
17	0.412	0.582	0.645
18	0.399	0.564	0.625
19	0.388	0.549	0.608
20	0.377	0.534	0.591
21	0.368	0.521	0.576
22	0.359	0.508	0.562
23	0.351	0.496	0.549
24	0.343	0.485	0.537
25	0.336	0.475	0.526
26	0.329	0.465	0.515
27	0.323	0.456	0.505
28	0.317	0.448	0.496
29	0.322	0.440	0.487
30	0.305	0.432	0.478

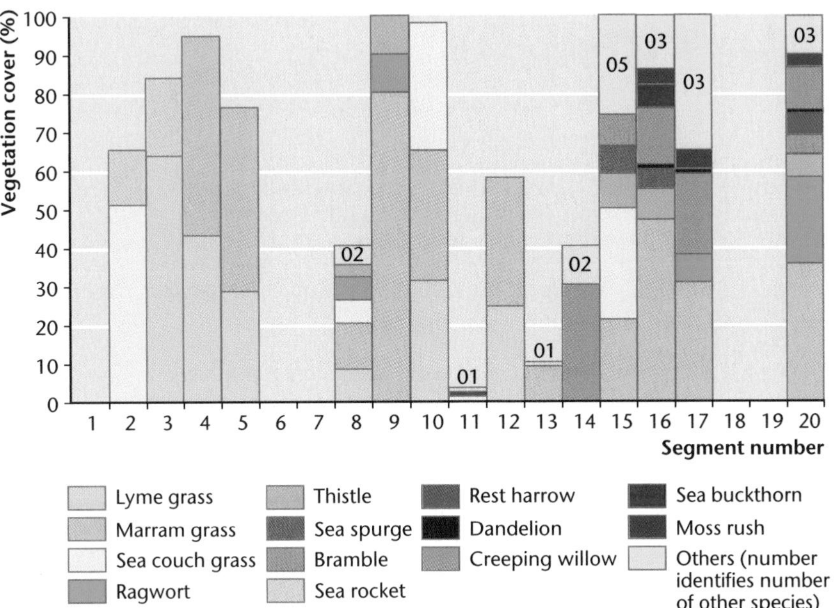

Figure C Data from the vegetation survey

j With specific reference to Objective 2, describe and explain the pattern shown by Figure C. (8 marks)

k The results of the soil-moisture survey are given in Table 15.2 (c). Assess the extent to which changes in moisture level are related to changes in vegetation cover and diversity. (8 marks)

(55 marks)

4 Conclusion

Write a conclusion to this enquiry with specific reference to the aims and objectives given in the pre-release document. Using your own experience of conducting an enquiry, you should, in addition, consider the reliability of the findings and suggest how the enquiry could be improved and extended. *(10 marks)*

5 Enquiry related issues

a Objective 3 is concerned with the impact of soil moisture on vegetation cover and diversity. Name *two* other soil characteristics that could be investigated. Justify their inclusion with reference to the aims of the enquiry. (5 marks)

b In Figure 15.4, there is the suggestion that the sand dunes of this area are used for recreation/tourism and that the area is managed. Suggest a hypothesis, question, problem or issue that could be investigated with reference to this. (2 marks)

c For the hypothesis, question, problem or issue that you have identified in part b, outline the collection of *one* item of primary data and *one* item of secondary data. (6 marks)

(13 marks)

Total: 100 marks

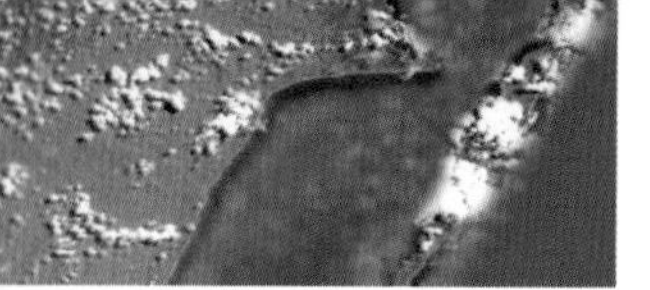

Bibliography

Anderson, D. (2004) *Glacial and Periglacial Environments,* Hodder and Stoughton.

Bishop, V. (1998) *Hazards and Responses,* Collins.

Cooper, S. (2001) *Student Unit Guide: AQA Specification A Module 1: Core Concepts in Physical Geography,* Philip Allan Updates.

Cooper, S. (2001) *Student Unit Guide: AQA Specification A Module 2: Core Concepts in Human Geography,* Philip Allan Updates.

Cooper, S. (2002) *Student Unit Guide: AQA Specification A Module 4: Challenge and Change in the Natural Environment,* Philip Allan Updates.

Dove, J. (2004) *Tourism and Recreation,* Hodder and Stoughton.

Frampton, S. et al. (2000) *Natural Hazards,* Hodder and Stoughton.

Gillett, M. (2005) *Ecosystems,* Hodder Murray.

Goudie, A. and Viles, H. (1997) *The Earth Transformed,* Blackwell.

Guinness, P. (2002) *Migration,* Hodder and Stoughton.

Guinness, P. (2003) *Globalisation,* Hodder and Stoughton.

Hill, M. (2004) *Coasts and Coastal Management,* Hodder and Stoughton.

Hill, M. (2005) *Urban Settlement and Land Use,* Hodder Murray.

Middleton, N. (1995) *The Global Casino,* Edward Arnold.

Nagle, G. (2002) *Climate and Society,* Hodder and Stoughton.

Nagle, G. (2003) *Rivers and Water Management,* Hodder and Stoughton.

Redfern, D. and Skinner, M. (2002) *AS/A-Level Geography Coursework and Practical Techniques,* Philip Allan Updates.

Sheppard, P. (2004) *Economic Activity and Change,* Hodder and Stoughton.

Skinner, M. (2003) *Hazards,* Hodder and Stoughton.

Skinner, M. et al. (2001) *The Complete A–Z Geography Handbook,* Hodder and Stoughton.

Skinner, M. et al. (2001) *A–Z Geography Coursework Handbook* (including Investigative Skills), Hodder and Stoughton.

Index

P

Q

R

S

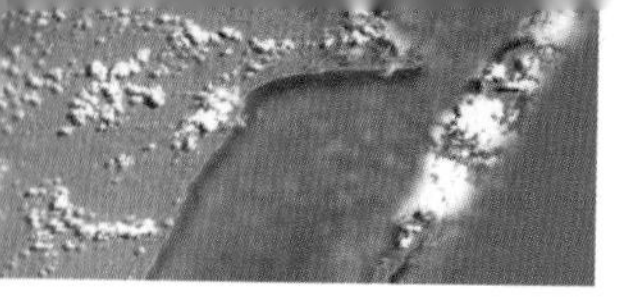